ENCYCLOPEDIA OF THE BIOSPHERE

BIOSPHERE

Humans in the World's Ecosystems

ENCYCLOPEDIA OF THE
BIOSPHERE

VOLUME 2: Tropical Rainforests

Project Director
Ramon Folch

Assistant Project Director
Josep M. Camarasa

Detroit
San Francisco
London
Boston
Woodbridge, CT

ENCYCLOPEDIA OF THE
BIOSPHERE

"Encyclopedia of the Biosphere" is an 11-volume work that treats the bioclimatic zones of the planet Earth and their corresponding biomes, and covers the settlement and use of these areas and systems by humans, as well as the problems that this has led to. This work has been planned in accordance with the principles of UNESCO's MAB (Man and Biosphere) Programme, under whose patronage it has been prepared.

ENCYCLOPEDIA OF THE
BIOSPHERE

Project Director

Ramon Folch
UNESCO/FLACAM Professor of Sustainable Development
Secretary-General of the Spanish Committee of the UNESCO/MAB

Assistant Project Director

Josep M. Camarasa
Member of the Spanish Committee of the UNESCO/MAB Programme

Editorial Advisory Committee

Francesco di Castri
Head of Research of the CNRS [Montpellier]
Former Assistant General Director of UNESCO's Environmental Coordination Programmes [Paris]

Mark Collins
Director at the World Conservation Monitoring Centre [Cambridge]

Ramon Margalef
Professor emeritus of Ecology of the University of Barcelona

Gonzalo Halffter
Director of the Institute of Ecology [Xalapa, Veracruz]

Pere Duran Farell
Founder member of the Club of Rome
President of the Spanish Chapter of the Club of Rome [Barcelona]

Alpha Oumar Konaré
Former President of the International Council of Museums [Bamako]

The original Catalan edition of this work was accomplished (1993-98) with the conceptual assistance and logistics
of the United Nations Educational, Scientific, and Cultural Organization (UNESCO).
The positions held by the Authors, the Project Director, the Assistant Project Director and the members of the Editorial Advisory Committee refer to the period
when the series was first prepared.

Catalan-language edition (volume 2): 1993
Biosfera. Els humans en els àmbits ecològics del món
Enciclopèdia Catalana

English-language edition (volume 2): **2000**

Editor: **ERF - Gestió i Comunicació Ambiental, SL** (Barcelona)
Director: **Ramon Folch**
Chief Editor: **Caterina López**
Editorial Team: **Josep M. Palau, Marina Molins**
Updating: **Josep M. Camarasa**

Publisher: **The Gale Group** (Farmington Hills, MI)
Art Directors: **Cynthia Baldwin, Martha Schiebold**
Editorial Coordinators: **Christine Jeryan, Pamela Proffitt**

Translation
Trevor Foskett
Graduate in Biology

Revision
Vernon Heywood
Ph. D., D. Sc., Professor emeritus, The University of Reading

English-language edition distributed to all markets worldwide by The Gale Group
27500 Drake Rd.
Farmington Hills, MI 48331-3535
U.S.A.

ISBN 0-7876-4506-0 (complete set)
ISBN 0-7876-4508-7 (volume 2)

2

Tropical Rainforests

Jonathan Adams
Julian Caldecott
Josep M. Camarasa
Graham Drucker
Xavier Ferrer
Ramon Folch
Domingo García-Espinoza
Albert Garriga
Montserrat Gispert
Robert Godshalk
Gonzalo Halffter
Caroline Harcourt
Cristina Junyent
Ariel E. Lugo
Arnald Marcer
Alessandro Minelli
Sara Oldfield
Rosa M. Poch
Jaume Porta
Kent Redford
Mario Rojas
Whendee L. Silver
Adolf de Sostoa
Carolus Sys
Víctor Manuel Toledo

coordinated by
Mark Collins

THE GALE GROUP

The authors and collaborators - volume 2

Jonathan Adams
School of Geography, University of Oxford [United Kingdom]

Julian Caldecott
Consultant on conservation and biodiversity
[Cambridge, United Kingdom]

Josep M. Camarasa
Codirector of the working group on the History of Science
of the Institut d'Estudis Catalans [Barcelona]

Graham Drucker
Collaborator at the World Conservation Monitoring Centre
[Cambridge, United Kingdom]

Xavier Ferrer
Professor of Zoogeography, Universitat de Barcelona

Ramon Folch
General Secretary of the International Academic Council
of the Latin-American Faculty of Environmental
Sciences / UNESCO Chair of Sustainable Development
[La Plata, Argentina]

Domingo Garca-Espinoza
La Amistad Conservation Area [San José, Costa Rica]

Albert Garriga
Graduate in Biology and Philology from the Universitat
de Barcelona

Montserrat Gispert
Professor of Ethnobotany at the National Autonomous
University of Mexico [Mexico, DF]

Robert Godshalk
Department of Wildlife and Range Sciences, University
of Florida [USA]

Gonzalo Halffter
National Researcher at the Institute of Ecology
[Xalapa, Veracruz, Mexico]

Caroline Harcourt
Collaborator with the World Conservation Monitoring Centre
[Cambridge, United Kingdom]

Cristina Junyent
Graduate in Biology from the Universitat de Barcelona

Ariel E. Lugo
Professor at the Institute of Tropical Forestry at Río Piedras
[Puerto Rico, USA]

Arnald Marcer
Technical collaborator of the Environment Department
of the Generalitat of Catalonia [Barcelona]

Alessandro Minelli
Professor of Zoology of the Università degli Studi di Padova [Italy]

Sara Oldfield
Researcher at the World Conservation Monitoring Centre
[Cambridge, United Kingdom]

Rosa M. Poch
Professor of Soil Science and Agricultural Chemistry at the
Universitat de Lleida

Jaume Porta
Professor of Soil Science and Agricultural Chemistry at the
Universitat de Lleida

Kent Redford
The Nature Conservancy [Arlington, Virginia, USA]

Mario Rojas
La Amistad Conservation Area [San José, Costa Rica]

Whendee L. Silver
Professor at the Institute of Tropical Forestry of Río Piedras
[Puerto Rico, USA]

Adolf de Sostoa
Professor of Zoology at the Universitat de Barcelona

Carolus Sys
Emeritus Professor of Soil Science at the Universiteit Gent
[Belgium]

Víctor Manuel Toledo
Professor at the Soil Science Centre of the National
Autonomous University of Mexico [Mexico, DF]

EDITORIAL TEAM

DIRECTOR: **Ramon Folch**, Doctor of Biology
ASSISTANT DIRECTOR: **Josep M. Camarasa**, Doctor of Biology
CHIEF EDITOR: **Montserrat Comelles**, Graduate in Biology
EDITOR: **Cristina Junyent**, Graduate in Biology
ART DIRECTION: **Rosa Carvajal**, Graduate in Geography, **Mikael Frölund**
SCIENTIFIC ASSESSMENT: **Jaume Bertranpetit**, **Mark Collins**, **Jaume Porta**
DESIGN AND PAGE-MAKING: **Toni Miserachs**
ADMINISTRATIVE SECRETARIES: **Maria Miró**, **Mònica Díaz**

EDITORIAL DIRECTOR: **Jesús Giralt**
PUBLICATION MANAGER FOR MAJOR PROJECTS: **Josep M. Ferrer**
HEAD OF PRODUCTION: **Francesc Villaubí**

Presentation

"Sublime grandeur:" perhaps no other description is more fitting for the tropical forests of Africa, the Americas, Asia, and Oceania than Charles Darwin's simple but striking phrase. The phrase shows the great naturalist's admiration and the limitation of words. These forests are in fact the richest, most varied, complex, and grandiose expression of life on Earth.

In his 1898 book, *Pflanzengeographie auf physiologischer Grundlage* (published in English as "Plant-geography upon a Physiological Basis"), Andreas Franz Wilhelm Schimper (1856-1901), a botanist and physiologist from Alsace, was the first person to name and describe the tropical rainforest (*Tropische Regenwald*), which he defined as an evergreen formation of wet habitats, 98 ft (30 m) or taller, with many lianas and epiphytes. This essentially defines a typical jungle, but the widespread use of the term rainforest has introduced a certain amount of confusion into the initial clear and simple idea. This is because there are commonly used terms that, precisely because they are widely used every day, are understood by different people in different ways. For example, in the expressions "the State of Alabama" and the "Spanish State," the word "state" has a different meaning. The United States of America is a nation of states or administrative regions, whereas the Spanish State is a kingdom made up of historically distinct nations. That this should occur in the excessively subtle and diffuse language of politics is understandable, but its occurrence in science, and specifically the earth sciences, is more surprising. Yet there is confusion about the term "rainforest."

So, what is a rainforest? In terms of biomes, at least three very different types can be considered rainforest—the evergreen intertropical rainforest, the evergreen intertropical cloud forest, and the semideciduous monsoon forest. Yet the term "jungle" may be used for almost any thick, dense forest. Furthermore, intertropical forest is often simplified to tropical forest, extending its geographical area to the tropical area within 5-10° on either side of the tropics. The confusion about these terms has paradoxically increased when, as a result of wishing to be more precise, new terms are coined, such as the single word rainforest, as this is equally applicable to the intertropical evergreen rainforest, the cloud forest, and the monsoon forest. This confusion about terms also increases when, in order to avoid problems with the term tropical forest, people use the term equatorial forest, even if it is not on the equator. This confusion is compounded when the term rainforest is used to describe temperate forests growing in a rainy climate (volume 6 of this series), such as the Misiones forest in the basins of the rivers Paraná and Uruguay.

Throughout the work *Biosphere*, rainforest has been used to mean intertropical (or equatorial) "jungle." The criterion followed is that there are three main types of tropical rainforest. The first is the evergreen lowland rainforest, the archetypal jungle; the second is montane cloud forest, which is also evergreen, and sometimes shortened to cloud forest; the third is semideciduous monsoon forest, also known as monsoon forest. These criteria need to be defined right at the beginning. Of course, there are other equally legitimate criteria, and many others will be found in the literature. The criterion we have used is obviously a phytoclimatically based one.

While our criterion for classifying rainforests is a phytoclimatic one, the concept of biome is based on vegetation and climatic criteria. This raises problems, because one of this work's essential features is that it deals with anthropic (relating to humans) phenomena, and these often blur any apparent bioclimatic limits. In any event, this volume of *The Encyclopedia of the Biosphere* deals with the bioclimatic lifezone of the intertropical rainforests, the jungle, but occasionally extends beyond it so as to take into account the current agricultural or stockraising situation. The text is arranged in three blocks corresponding to the three great types of forest mentioned above, although the basic phenomena common to all three are dealt with in the first block, the typical rainforest, and some subjects are dealt with again in the other two sections. This volume is thus divided into three sections, but deals only with a single biome, not three different ones.

The rainforest is a single biome but an extraordinarily diverse one. More diverse than any other biome, it is thus ideal for discussion of the phenomenon of diversity. The ancient idea of diversity has recently been redefined more strictly as *biodiversity*. Since this volume is the first to deal with a specific biome, following the introductory volume dealing with the general features of the planet, it starts with a discussion of the concept of biodiversity that applies to all the other volumes of *The Encyclopedia of the Biosphere*. This diversity has stimulated research and has generated an immense and rich, although incomplete and fragmentary, literature, impossible to condense into a single volume. Deliberately but reluctantly, we have thus had to exclude much of the available information. Yet we have tried to retain all that is needed to understand the kaleidoscopic world of the rainforests, their uses by humans, and their current problems.

We would also like to state the anthropological and ethnographic criteria followed in this and the following volumes, as the distribution of human populations does not follow the planet's division into biomes by ecologists and botanists. Some morphological or physiological characteristics are undeniably shared by humans living in areas with similar climates, as they are the result of natural selection, but in reality they have nothing to do with the phylogenetic relationships between populations. These adaptations that have arisen by selection, or have been maintained in human groups living in some biomes but lost in others, are irrelevant to the history of human populations, and are thus not central to our argument.

Studies of the phylogenetic relationships between human groups now use neutral genetic variation, the variation that natural selection does not act on. Modern humans have spread over the planet in the last 100,000 years, leaving their genetic traces everywhere, and so their current distribution contains the key to understanding their past. Some groups have lived in an area long enough for local climatic features to shape their anatomy or physiology, while others have continued roaming. Unknowingly, humans have left traces that we can now study (see the section "Molecules and Human Evolution" in Volume 1).

Yet neutral genetic variation alone does not contain the key to the past, as language is an additional tool to investigate the relationships between populations. Every group of humans on the planet has had a language, each one has evolved, changing and adopting words from other groups (especially when adopting new technologies and tools). Broadly speaking, the genetic distribution of human groups has been accompanied by the spread of their linguistic families. Absolute dates can be provided by archaeology through dating of physical remains, and these archaeological remains also help to understand cultural changes in human groups. Thus, an overall interpretation of genetic, linguistic and archeological information is necessary in order to understand human history. This is the thesis underlying *History and Geography of Human Genes* (1994) by Luigi Luca Cavalli-Sforza, Paolo Menozzi, and Albert Piazza, which we have followed.

To sum up, when dividing the history of human populations between the different volumes in this series, we have sought to superimpose on the worlds biomes a map of the distribution of migrations, a further map of linguistic families, and a third map dealing with the earliest archaeological finds. From this superimposition we have extracted two levels of information: macrogeographical and microgeographical. The macrogeographical level will seek to explain the history of the population or settlement of a continent or a large part of a continent (as in the case of Asia). The attribution of each continent, or part, to one volume is naturally arbitrary and based on convention, as climate has not influenced human population distribution at this level: we have tried to make this correspond either to the biome occupying most of a subcontinent (as in the case of India and southeast Asia) or to the biome in which settlement of a continent began (the case of the Americas). The microgeographic level, in turn, is based on data on human ecology, on more detailed demographic data on human groups in a given area or at a given time, such as the specific cases of populations that are endangered or with an unusual history (genes and languages that are the result of different pathways), on adaptations to different climates (that is to say, the effects of natural selection) and on medical and ecological data (especially on diseases). In cases of human adaptations to a given climate as a result of natural selection (skin coloration, for example, or stature, which coincide with the distribution of biomes), in no way do we wish to follow the antiquated and genetically worthless division of human groups into phenotypic "races" which we shall treat as of minor or only anecdotal value.

And finally, our thanks. This especially complex volume of *The Encyclopedia of the Biosphere* would not have been possible without the special dedication of Mark Collins, director of the World Conservation Monitoring Centre in Cambridge (United Kingdom) and a member of the board of editorial consultants for the work as a whole. We have discussed the first version of the list of contents with him, and he has put us in contact with many of the authors, all leading specialists seeking to communicate their scientific expertise to the non-specialized public. He has also afforded us the support of his Center, critically read most of the original texts, and at all times has shown a strong, dedicated and friendly commitment to our shared desire to provide the general public with scientific knowledge of the biosphere.

We must also thank the other members of the advisory council of *The Encyclopedia of the Biosphere*, and especially Gonzalo Halffter, the author of the first section on biodiversity, and the entire array of authors and illustrators who have made their own contribution. We would especially like to mention the contributions made by Xavier Ferrer and Adolf de Sostoa, professors at the Universitat de Barcelona, for their valuable suggestions regarding the illustrations for the volume and for the valuable photographic material they have provided. Nor must we forget to thank the other persons and institutions that have helped us by supplying or loaning documentation, by reading or critically reviewing different parts of the volume. We would like to make a special mention of our appreciation of the anthropologist and primatologist Jordi Sabater Pi, who has ceded us some of his field sketches. Nor must we forget to mention other individuals and institutions who have provided us with documentation, such as Cristian R. Altaba (Institut d'Estudis Avançats de les Illes Balears); the Biblioteca de Catalunya; the Library of the Jardín Botánico de Madrid; the Lunwerg Publishing Company in Barcelona; Francesc Calafell (Anthropology Department, Universitat de Barcelona); Òscar García (Hospital del Mar, Barcelona); Xavier Llimona (Department of Botany, Universitat de Barcelona); and the Department of Pharmacology and the Museo de la Farmacia Hispana de la Cátedra de la Historia de la Farmacia, both in the Faculty of Pharmacy of the Universidad Complutense de Madrid; the Johnson Space Center (Houston); together with the Goddard Space Flight Center (Greenbelt); and also the John C. Stennis Space Center (Mississippi), all part of NASA. Finally we must mention the help given us by the critical readings or comments on some parts of this book by Albert Masó (Ecology Department, Universitat de Barcelona), Oriol Vall (Hospital del Mar, Barcelona) and Marta Vigo (Anthropology Department, Universitat de Barcelona).

Ramon Folch
Josep M. Camarasa
1995

Equatorial rainforest

Trees, trees, trees! A single sea of green on myriad columns carpeted in mosses, mangy with lichens, covered with parasites and creepers, plaited and choked by lianas as thick as tree trunks. Barriers of trees, walls of trees, massifs of trees. Centuries of perennialness from the roots to the crowns, exceptional in the apparent stillness, torrents of sap which slide in silence. Green, silent abysses… Tangle of lianas… Trees! Trees!

Rómulo Gallegos
Canaíma (1935)

1
The embodiment of diversity

1. More species than anywhere else

1.1 The concept of biodiversity

Diversity is a general property of living systems and many biomes are characterized by their high diversity, yet no other biome comes anywhere near the overwhelming diversity of the equatorial rainforest. This fact makes it appropriate to begin this volume with some general considerations of the concept of *biodiversity*, some of its general implications, and those for the rainforest biome.

Biological diversity

Diversity is a fundamental general characteristic of all biological systems at all levels of organization, from molecules to ecosystems. Briefly, it is the result of evolution leading to the existence of many ways of life. Ignoring environmental accidents leading to the prevalence of one form or another at any given moment, mutation and selection determine the size and characteristics of the diversity present in a given place at a given moment. Biological diversity is present over the entire scale of organization of living beings: There are differences in the genetic inheritance and in the morphological, physiological, and ethological responses of different phenotypes, and differences in growth form, in their population dynamics and life cycles. Nowadays when people speak about biodiversity, it is generally on the scale of a specific ecosystem or biome, and thus refers to the diversity of species, variation within species and within populations, and, ultimately, to genetic variation.

To understand the origin of biological diversity and what it represents, it is necessary to consider one of the major differences between living organisms and late 20th century human civilization: life has always tended to diversify, but industrial society has always tended to standardize uses and processes. Contemporary human societies (or so-called western ones) use energy derived from sunlight in search of the greatest output by means of short-term efficiency and simplifying ecosystems, yet if nature has a strategy it is exactly the opposite: increasing the diversity of organisms and their responses, increasing complexity, and increasing stability within the changes (homeostasis) in the ecosystems.

Life's long evolution has shown a progressive increase in the number and complexity of different species (and taxa of all types) over geological time, interrupted drastically from time to time by periods of crisis during which many species, or even whole groups, may disappear (see volume 1, page 120). In any case, diversity does not depend only on the different classes of organisms (or other biological units) that are present, but also on the frequency of each one, that is to say, it depends on the number of each one present, from the rarest to the commonest. Measured or estimated diversity may vary depending on the conceptual scale used: diversity is usually considered at the geographical, ecological, and genetic (or intraspecific) levels.

On a territorial scale, in a given geographical context, biodiversity is measured by quantifying the biological mixture (heterogeneity) of a given region and depends on the diversity of the ecosystems in the geographical area considered. This is known as γ *diversity*. On the ecological scale, two forms of biodiversity are clearly defined in the analysis of communities. The first is α *diversity* and is a function of the number of species present in a single habitat, and is the most important (and the most frequently quoted) component of rainforest diversity and of other equally species-rich ecosystems, such as coral reefs, or the Mediterranean areas of South Africa. The second form of biodiversity, β *diversity*, is a function of the extent to which an environment is subdivided into different habitats, and is a measure of the spatial heterogeneity or the proximity of habitats in space.

Finally, there is a genetic, or interspecific, component of biological heterogeneity. There may be high or low genetic variation within a single

1 The "green desert" of the equatorial forest, a complex matrix of plants, climbing plants, epiphytes, and herbaceous vegetation, hides an abundant fauna that is difficult to see, although its presence is revealed by the permanent uproar of croaks and warbles. The description "desert" results from the feeling of loneliness while being watched that overcomes the visitor on entering forests like the one in this photo, the Amazonian jungle in the basin of the Napó river in Ecuador.
[Photo: Jeff Foott / Auscape International]

2 The diversity of plant species and forms and their adaptation to deep shade, a characteristic of the vegetation of the undergrowth, are clearly shown by this photo. Taken in a rainforest in Costa Rica, it shows a carpet of leaves with large fleshy blades growing alongside finely divided fronds of ferns. Many of these plants are beautiful, and their ability to tolerate high temperatures and little light means they are grown all over the world as houseplants. The photo shows dumb canes (*Dieffenbachia*), philodendrons (*Philodendron*), and aphelandras (*Aphelandra*).
[Photo: Michael & Patricia Fogden / Bruce Coleman Limited]

species, both genotypic (the number of different alleles the species possesses) and phenotypic (the features of the different individuals of the species in which these alleles are expressed). Genetic diversity depends on the evolutionary history of the population, on its degree of endogamy (inbreeding), on its reproductive isolation, on natural selection for or against the maintenance of hybrids (heterosis), and on other factors. Genetic diversity, or variation, is an extremely important component of biodiversity. There is general awareness of its importance in cultivated plants and domesticated animals: for decades great efforts have been made to conserve the diversity of native germ plasm for genetic selection by breeders of plant and animal races and varieties. Genetic variation is essential for the transformation of species by selection. This component of biodiversity is very important in wild populations, whose survival and adaptation often depend on their ability to maintain the minimum population levels required for the maintenance of some degree of outbreeding and heterosis, and below which populations may be in danger of extinction, simply because they cannot adapt to environmental changes by means of natural selection.

The notion of rarity

Diversity depends not only on the number of species, but also on the relative abundance of each species. Every ecosystem and community has a hierarchy of species in terms of abundance, ranging from the rarest to the commonest. If some species are highly abundant and others are very rare, community diversity is low. This is very common, for

example in some types of vegetation in temperate latitudes, such as pine forests and beech forests, in which one or two species may account for up to 90% of the biomass in the ecosystem, whereas the other 10% of biomass is contributed by a relatively large number of uncommon species. A clear understanding of the concept of biodiversity thus implies discussing the problem of rarity, considering a *rare* species as one whose population levels are low enough for it to be in danger of extinction. The maintenance of biodiversity is above all a problem related to the ecological behavior of rare species.

From an ecological point of view there are several types of rarity. There is *biogeographical rarity*, the species that only grow in very specific regions and are restricted endemically. An example of biogeographical rarity is the composite *Heterotheca thiniicola*, a species endemic to the dunes of the Great Altar Desert in the State of Sonora (northwest Mexico) and found in an area of just 2 mi^2 (5 km^2). Even so, its populations may reach very high densities, and many species of animals that are restricted to life in caves, on islands or high in mountains, may in fact be abundant in these sites. There is also *habitat rarity*, that of species restricted to very specific habitats but not biogeographically endemic. The species that live in a restricted range of habitats are known as *stenoecious*, and those that live in a wide range of habitats are *euryecious*. The plants of desert oases are typical stenoecious species, as they may be geographically widespread, but they are restricted to a very specific habitat. The last type of rarity is *demographic rarity*, species whose population densities are very low throughout their entire area of distribution, even if this range is very large and is not limited to very specific habitats. A clear example of this type of demographic

3 The white uakari (*Cacajao calvus calvus*) is a good example of biogeographical rarity. It is a very rare subspecies of primate that only lives in a small area of the northwest Amazon, in the basin of the river Negro, whereas the red uakari (*C. calvus rubicundus*) has a vinous (wine-colored) brown coat and occurs over a much larger range in the Amazon. The third and last Amazonian uakari is, however, very abundant. Yet all three uakaris are threatened by the loss of their forest habitat, especially the white uakari.
[Photo: Adolf de Sostoa & Xavier Ferrer]

rarity is provided by *Setaria geniculata*, a grass found throughout the American continents from California to Patagonia that never exceeds very low population densities: its rarity is not the result of its geographical distribution (it grows almost throughout the Americas), nor its environmental preferences (it is not demanding), but is because its population density is always low and nowhere is it an important member of the plant community.

Without a doubt, the most critical cases of rarity are those species that combine all three types of rarity: ecologically stenoecious biogeographical endemics with very low population densities. One of the most

notable cases of this group is a saprophytic monocot plant lacking chlorophyll, *Lacandonia schismatica*, a member of the no-less-rare Triuridaceae family that was recently discovered in the Lacandon forest in Chiapas (southern Mexico). This species has the doubtful privilege of living in an area of approximately a single hectare (1 hectare=2.47 acres) (biogeographical rarity), being associated with peaty tropical soils (habitat rarity), and showing an extremely low level of genetic variation and very low population levels (demographic rarity). A new family, the Lacandoniaceae, has been proposed to accommodate this single species, as it is the only known species in which the pistils surround the sta-

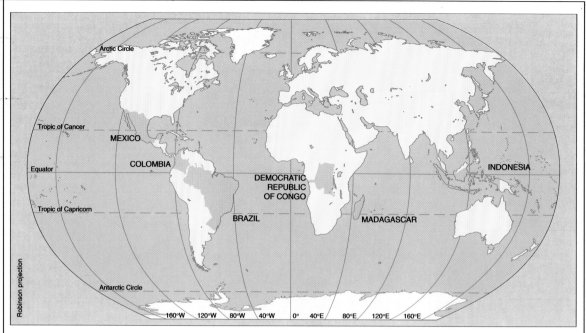

4 Megadiversity countries identified by the World Wide Fund for Nature (WWF). The map clearly shows the importance of Brazil: its 357 million hectares (1 hectare= 2.47 acres) of rainforest make it by far the most important country in the world with regard to this biome. Brazil contains 30% of the planets' tropical forest, three times more than the next highest country, Indonesia.
[Drawing: Editrònica]

mens and not the other way round, as in all other families with hermaphroditic flowers. It hardly needs to be stated that it is one of the worlds rarest plants. A comparably rare animal is the coleopteran *Liatongus monstrosus*, a scarabid beetle that is known to occur only in a small area near the western tip of Chapala lake near the village of Ajijic, in the Mexican state of Jalisco. This coprophagous (dung-feeding) beetle lives and nests only in the remains of the nests of the Mexican ant *Atta mexicana* (habitat rarity) and does not even occupy all of them, nor is it abundant, suggesting great demographic rarity. This taxonomically isolated insect has affinities to the tropical fauna of the Old World, and is in danger of extinction (if it is not already extinct) as a consequence of the growth of Ajijic and the disappearance of the traditional family vegetable plots where the ants nests were sited.

The erosion of diversity

Genetic biodiversity can be considered at three levels of organization: the set of different alleles for a single gene within a given species; the set of genetic differences that characterize the different populations of the species in question (or in other words, the group of alleles that tend to vary together); and the set of all the genetic information that characterizes each species (in other words, the complete genome).

The extinction of a species leads to the irreversible loss of its complete geneome. Loss of genetic diversity may, however, be more subtle, occurring in ways that are harder to assess, such as the loss of alleles by inbreeding and genetic drift: Any plant or animal population undergoing a period of low population levels will lose genetic variation in some of its alleles; and even if population levels recover later, the population will no longer be the same, it will have lost because some of the variation required for natural selection to act on as it did before the population decline.

Loss of genetic diversity can also lead to the extinction of local ecotypes and populations. Although the species does not run the risk of extinction, the loss of local ecotypes means that the species has lost part of its genetic variation. It will be less diverse, with less genetic variation. This problem is well-known and has been studied in relation to the genetic improvement of varieties of cultivated plants. Large germplasm banks that allow the development of new varieties aim to maintain under controlled conditions a part of the immense genetic variation that is found in the countless local varieties, often forming the traditional heritage of ethnic groups, of most cultivated plants.

1.2 Diversity in rainforests

The equatorial rainforests have more species than any other of the Earth's biomes. It is by far the richest in tree species, some of which reach enormous sizes. These large trees give the equatorial rainforest the "sublime grandeur" so impressive to Darwin and to all those seeing it for the first time.

The abundance of individuals and species

Yet large trees alone do not make a jungle. Growing with the trees, around them and on them, underneath them and within them, are the thousands of species of animals, plants, fungi, protoctists and bacteria making up the world's most diverse biota. It is estimated that half of all living species live in the equatorial rainforest, including many genera and families found nowhere else. Many are rare because they are restricted to a geographical area or to one of the many specific habitats in the equatorial rainforests. Yet even the most widespread species are much more numerous than in any other biome. This is shown by the trees: in temperate forests there is often only a single dominant species, or just a few (rarely are there more than about ten species of tree per hectare [1 hectare=2.47 acres]), but in rainforests there may easily be more than a hundred species with a trunk more than 4 in (10 cm) in diameter in a single hectare.

The reasons for the rainforests high diversity

The reason for this biodiversity is less obvious than it might appear to be. Is it due to climate, soils, habitat diversity, geological and evolutionary history, or all of them? In fact, this is one of the basic theoretical problems of evolutionary biology, and climate undeniably plays a major role. Brighter sunshine and heavier rainfall than in any other habitat type clearly make very high levels of biomass production possible.

Furthermore, production depends on the surface area, both for the interception of sunlight and the use of rainfall, but the accumulated production (for example, tree trunks) is not limited in this way, allowing growth upwards and the use of the third dimension. The high production and the persistence of necron (the organic material that is not strictly alive that has accumulated in the ecosystem) create possible new ways of exploiting greater resources for the consumers, and constitute new habitats for new lifeforms: lianas (woody vines) and epiphytes (plants that grow on other plants) that use the trees as a support, animals that depend on the dead materials deposited on the soil, on the branches, in inflorescences or in holes in trunks; arboreal, gliding, and flying animals, etc. (see volume 1, page 227).

Although reduction of the *production/biomass* ratio is inherent to the process of biological succession, high species diversity is not just due to high biomass production and persistence, as it is also closely related to environmental persistence or variability and to past and present evolutionary conditions. An unstable environment or one subject to disturbances is not compatible with the biomass accumulation required for forest formation. Rainforests undeniably show high stability and low turnover, but they also have a history. This history has not been without disturbances, but in geologically recent times has been relatively stable, at least in some refugia, and the only major disturbance now facing the rainforest is its rapid destruction by humans in many areas. The relative absence of disturbances in the last few tens of thousands of years, at least in large areas of the biome, may also explain the high level of diversity in the rainforests.

LOCATION	AVERAGE ANNUAL RAINFALL (mm)	ALTITUDE (m)	AREA (km²)	NUMBER OF SPECIES			
				Mammals[1]	Birds[2]	Reptiles	Amphibians
Barro Colorado Island (Panama)	2,600	164	14.8	97 (46)	366 (83)	68	32
Kartabo (Guyana)	2,500	10	0.6	73 (12)	464 (21)	93	37
Pasoh Forest (western Malaysia)	1,900	75-150	7.8	>90 (40)	212 (21)	>20	25
Burkit Langan forest (western Malaysia)	2,300	40	6.4	119 (30)	>119	50	23
Makokou forest (Gabon)	1,730	500	2,000	342 (59)	342 (59)	63	38
Gogol forest (Papua-New Guinea)	3,800	40-60	10.0	162	162	34	23
Analamazoatra forest (western Madagascar)	1,708	900	8.0	73	73	>47	54

[1] number of bat species in brackets
[2] number of small-scale migratory species in brackets

5 **Numbers of vertebrate species** (except fish) in seven regions of the worlds lowland rainforest where there is continuity of research, together with rainfall and altitude data for each.
[Information: From several sources]

2. Hot and humid

2.1 A very wet climate

The geographical space occupied by intertropical rainforests has a climate that is consistently hot, has a high rainfall distributed regularly over the year, and lacks any dry period, that is to say, a month with rainfall less than 2.4 in (60 mm). Relative humidity is also high, although it varies during the course of the day and between areas within the forest, and is rarely less than 80%, except among the treetops, high up in the forest canopy or above it, and in the largest clearings.

The intertropical convergence zone and the convection regime

Near the equator, in what is known as the *intertropical convergence zone* (ITCZ), the atmospheric circulation cells of the northern and southern hemispheres converge. Low in the atmosphere, the trade winds in both hemispheres blow towards the equator (from the northeast in the northern hemisphere and from the southeast in the southern hemisphere), and when they reach this low pressure area, they raise hot air that is moisture laden due to the intense evaporation from seas, rivers,

lakes, and forests. Hot, moisture-laden air masses are intrinsically unstable, and so at equatorial latitudes this rising moist air easily condenses, leading to heavy rainfall and often storms. These tropical storms may reach peak rainfall intensities of 4 in (100 mm) per hour.

The intertropical convergence zone is not stationary but moves from one hemisphere to the other, depending on the strength of the respective trade winds, which blow strongest in the hemisphere during its cold season. Thus the ITCZ is between 5 and 10°S in the southern hemisphere during the northern winter from December to March, but it moves to the northern hemisphere from June to September, reaching its northernmost position in August (20-25°N). On the edge of the convergence, on the side of the strongest trade winds and thus in the hemisphere undergoing its cold season, what is known as the *intertropical front* forms. This blows strong storms from east to west and these bring rainfall to the eastern sides of the continents (northeast Australia, the Mata Atlântica of Brazil, and Madagascar) or the sea-facing slopes of some of the higher inland ranges, such as the southern slopes of the Himalayas and some mountain ranges in southern China, the

6 **Humidity and sultriness, rain, and gentle breezes through the undergrowth** are constant features of tropical rainforests; the organisms that inhabit them spend much time in the rain, or at least in an atmosphere saturated with humidity. The humidity can almost be felt in this photo of Daintree National Park on the York Peninsula (Queensland, Australia).
[Photo: Jean-Paul Ferrero & Jean-Michel Labat / Auscape International]

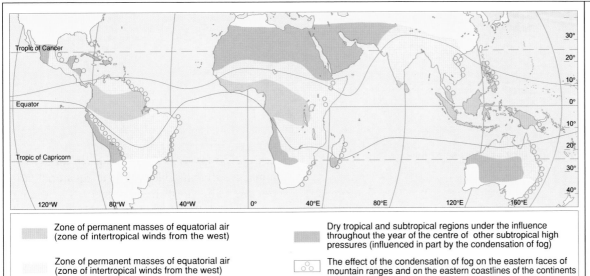

Zone of permanent masses of equatorial air
(zone of intertropical winds from the west)

Zone of permanent masses of equatorial air
(zone of intertropical winds from the west)

Intertropical convergence in January

Dry tropical and subtropical regions under the influence
throughout the year of the centre of other subtropical high
pressures (influenced in part by the condensation of fog)

The effect of the condensation of fog on the eastern faces of
mountain ranges and on the eastern coastlines of the continents

Intertropical convergence in July

7 **The circulation of the wind has a decisive effect on climate**, as shown by the diagram of the variation of the winds at three different times of year in the *intertropical convergence zone (ITCZ)* (lower diagram), the belt of low pressure where the trade winds blowing from the northeast and the southeast converge, and the ITCZ's position on the world map in January and in June (upper diagram). At low altitudes the winds tend to circulate from the tropics to the equator, while at high altitudes the circulation is from the equator to the tropics. In both hemispheres the resulting winds blow from the east, and are known as the trade winds. This circulation pattern shows clear seasonal changes: in the winter the dominant winds blow from the east, over both the sea and the land; in the summer, winds blow only consistently from the east over the oceans, while over the land, the formation of depressions means the circulation is more diverse—winds blow from the east on the flanks facing the poles, and from the west on the flanks facing the equator. This seasonal rhythm shows high regularity, broken only by the frequent appearance of disturbances, mainly of dynamic origin, such as cyclones and typhoons, and especially monsoons, whose periodicity is much greater. *[Drawing: Editrònica, from several sources]*

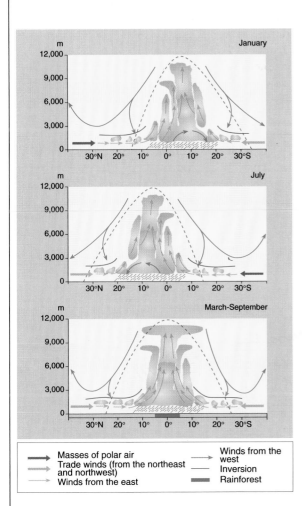

Masses of polar air
Trade winds (from the northeast and northwest)
Winds from the east
Winds from the west
Inversion
Rainforest

water vapor it releases. It is high rainfall that allows equatorial rainforests to exist, but the rainforest also supplies part of this rainfall. Data on the proportions of oxygen and hydrogen isotopes in river water collected at 17 sites in the Amazon basin show that more than half the rainfall in the basin comes directly from the evapotranspiration of the forests trees. The trees, not the ocean, are the main source of the moisture that later falls as rain on the forest and farther inland. The water vapor derived from evapotranspiration produces cloud masses 62-621 mi (100-1,000 km) in diameter and up to 9 mi (14 km) high, over the enormous areas of tropical forest occupying much of the basins of the Amazon and the Zaire rivers.

Rainfall distribution

Total annual rainfall values are usually between 79 and 157.5 in (2,000 and 4,000 mm), but even higher values are not unusual. In Andagoya, Colombia, a weather station at a latitude of 5°N and an altitude of 197 ft (60 m) recorded average annual rainfall of a little over 275.5 in (7,000 mm) over a period of 8 years, and in Débundscha, at the base of Mount Cameroon in the Cameroon, over 394 in (10,000 mm) have been recorded in a single year. As an example of extremely high rainfall, in one year the Ensenada de Utria National Park, on the Pacific coast of the Colombian department of Chocó, recorded nearly 630 in (16,000 mm) of rain.

The rainfall regime is not totally uniform over the year. It usually has two peaks, one at each equinox, with 12 in (300 mm) or more of rain in

Pacific coast of Colombia, and Mount Cameroon. The convective nature of most tropical rainfall means that peak rainfall is generally not at sea level but at altitudes of between 2,625 and 4,921 ft (800 and 1,500 m).

Evapotranspiration plays an essential role in convective rainfall because of the large quantity of

8 Distribution of the different climatic types of tropical rainforest, relating the range of annual and daily temperature variations, the temperature limits, and the average temperature of the coldest months. The diagram has been adapted to the types of rainforest that are dealt with in this work.
[Drawing: Jordi Corbera, from several sources]

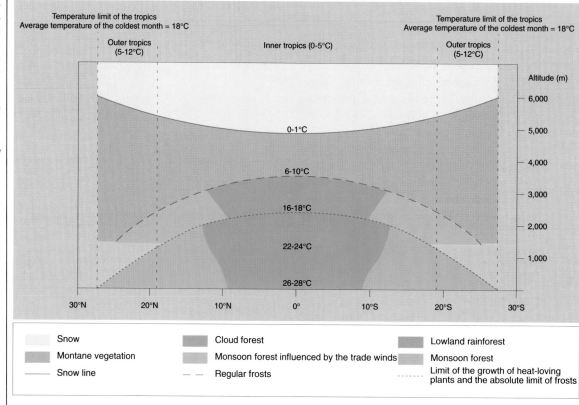

Temperature limit of the tropics
Average temperature of the coldest month = 18°C

Temperature limit of the tropics
Average temperature of the coldest month = 18°C

Outer tropics (5-12°C)   Inner tropics (0-5°C)   Outer tropics (5-12°C)

Altitude (m)

0-1°C

6-10°C

16-18°C

22-24°C

26-28°C

- 6,000
- 5,000
- 4,000
- 3,000
- 2,000
- 1,000

30°N   20°N   10°N   0°   10°S   20°S   30°S

	Snow		Cloud forest		Lowland rainforest
	Montane vegetation		Monsoon forest influenced by the trade winds		Monsoon forest
	Snow line		Regular frosts		Limit of the growth of heat-loving plants and the absolute limit of frosts

March and in September, and with rainfall peaks and troughs that vary in extent depending on the distance from the equator, the general geography and the local topography. Even the most strictly equatorial regions of the central or western Amazon, the Zaire Basin and southeast Asia show some seasonal variations in rainfall. Dry periods of 30 days or more may occur in the heart of the rainforest in the Democratic Republic of Congo about every 12 years. As long as the periods of relative drought do not exceed three months, the rainforest can flourish, even on relatively low rainfall. If the dry period exceeds three months, equatorial rainforest will not become established even in areas with much higher annual rainfall. Western Africa is a good example of this: Conakry, the capital of the Republic of Guinea, has an annual rainfall of about 157.5 in (4,000 mm), but the four month dry season from December to March means the rainforest cannot develop here. In contrast, Ibadan in southwest Nigeria is in the area of the equatorial rainforest, even though total annual rainfall does not exceed 48 in (1,230 mm), because the dry season is not so prolonged and the relative humidity remains constant throughout the year.

Rainfall oscillations over the course of the day may be even more important than the oscillations over the course of the year. Rain falls almost every day, although there may a few dry days in a row, rainfall follows a regular cycle over the course of the day, with few variations. In most cases rainfall is concentrated in the early afternoon, that is to say in the period following the conditions of maximum convective heating, although in coastal areas rain tends to fall at night. A typical day in the rainforest starts with bright sunshine, cloud over at noon and building up to a brief storm, and then the afternoon is sunny again, with temperatures of 86°F (30°C) or more.

2.2 High, stable temperatures

Sunshine is strongest at the equator. Throughout the year sunlight falls almost perpendicularly on the surface, and the heat energy per unit surface area reaching the equator every day is around 780-900 langleys, or in other words 780-900 gram calories per square centimeter.

Heat absorption

Estimates suggest that only 1% of the sunlight reaching the canopy of an equatorial rainforest reaches the soil, and only about 0.4% of the photosynthetically active radiation (PAR) reaching the canopy reaches the soil. Forest soils of northern Sumatra receive only 0.2-0.7% of the total light, and similar results have been obtained in forests in the west of the Malacca Peninsula, the interior of Guyana and the south of the Ivory Coast. The harsh tropical sunshine is thus highly attenuated within the forest as a consequence of the forests own structure: measurements taken at different heights above ground level in a forest in the Ivory Coast gave values for light intensity at 151 ft (46 m), above the forest canopy, of about 100,000 lux, while at 108 ft (33 m) it was only 25,000 lux, and at about 3 ft (1 m) above the ground it was a mere 800 lux, only 0.8% of the light reaching the crowns of the emergent trees.

Not only does the light diminish in intensity, but it also changes in quality, as the light is refracted and reflected by the surfaces and other parts of the plants. Thus, the lights spectrographic composition varies with height and situation, partly determining which plants can grow in each layer of the forest. Leaves are opaque to most visible light, except for a narrow band of green light around 550 nm. Leaves are, however, transparent to infrared, and thus a high proportion of the radiation within the forest is infrared light. It seems that the balance of red and infrared light, which plants measure using the pigment called phytochrome, is much more important for the germination of the seeds of some plants than the actual intensity of the light.

The distribution of temperatures

In the rainforest, because the duration of the day and night varies little over the course of the year (not at all on the equator itself, half an hour at 5° latitude, two hours at 10° and three hours at the latitude of the Tropic of Cancer or Capricorn), the variation in the incoming light over the course of the yearly cycle is very small, which explains why the average monthly temperatures—which are never below 68°F (20°C) in the coldest month—are almost constant throughout the year. The average annual temperature in most regions of equatorial rainforest is between 79 and 82°F (26 and 28°C), and average monthly temperatures vary between 75 and 82°F (24 and 28°C). Yet at the edges of the tropics where rainforest grows as a result of favorable atmospheric circulation patterns, such as eastern Australia and the Philippines, or in tropical montane areas, average monthly temperatures may be less than 64°F (18°C), and there may be days when minimum temperatures are below 50°F (10°C). Maximum temperatures rarely exceed 100°F (38°C), well below the peaks that may occur in the continental regions of North America or Europe.

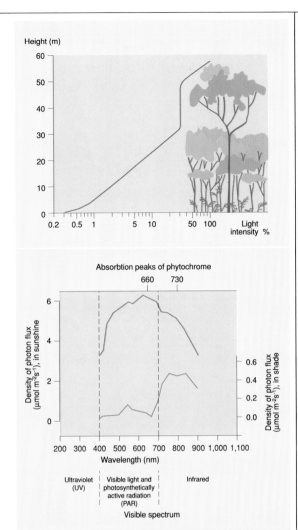

9 The light penetrating the forest canopy loses intensity as it passes each layer and also changes in quality. The upper graph shows how the light intensity diminishes as it filters through the leaves at different heights. The lower graph shows the difference between the spectrographic composition of the light in open areas, dominated by visible light (red line), and in shaded areas under the tree canopy, dominated by infrared light (blue line). Plants distinguish these different light regimes by means of phytochrome, which exists in two forms, one of which absorbs red light and the other absorbs infrared light. The absorption of light causes one form to change into the other.
[Drawing: Jordi Corbera, from several sources]

Temperature differences between day and night and those between the interior and the exterior of the plant cover are more determining factors than the average annual temperatures and the annual temperature variations. The daily temperature range may be as much as 13-18°C in areas lacking plant cover or in the upper canopy, but this daily range is only 6-9°C inside the rainforest, yet another example of this highly complex ecosystems self-regulatory abilities. Observations in December in Ivory Coast (between 5 and 10°N) at 151 ft (46 m) above ground level, in the upper canopy gave a daily temperature range of 10.8°C, but this was only 4.4°C at a height of 3 ft (1 m) above ground level in the forest. Measurements in June show a daily range of 4°C in the canopy and 1.7°C at 3 ft (1 m) above ground level. At Bogor, on the island of Java (between 5 and 10°S), the difference between the average temperature of the hottest and coldest months is only 34°F (1°C) (75.7°F [24.3°C] in February and 77.5°F [25.3°C] in October), but any sunny day in November may show variations of nearly 9°C (between 75.7°F [24.3°C] at 6 a.m. and 90.3°F [32.4°C] at 2 p.m.).

10 Map showing distribution of lowland rainforest (in dark green) and the rest of the rainforest (light green), together with heat and temperature diagrams of different cities representing different areas of the biome. Each diagram shows altitude and latitude (in black), the average temperature (in red) and the average annual rainfall (in blue). The average annual temperatures are between 75 and 81°F (24°C and 27°C), while the total annual rainfall lies between 79 and 157.5 in (2,000 and 4,000 mm). In all the diagrams the temperature curve is always above the rainfall curve, so that there is no dry period. Nor is there any period of frost.

[Drawing: Editrònica, from several sources]

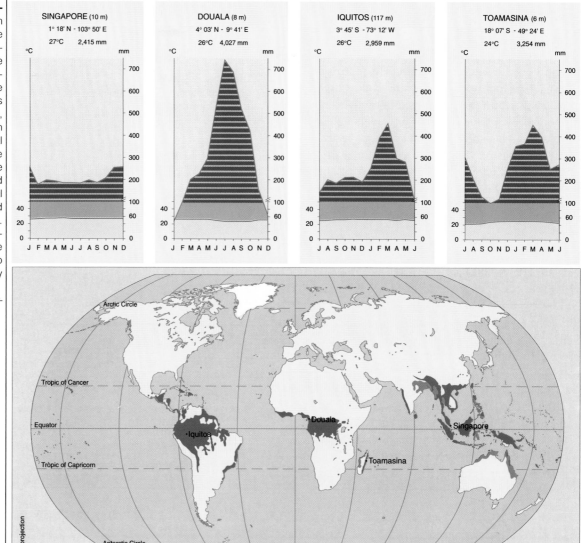

2.3 A universe of microclimates

As will be explained later, the equatorial rainforest has a complex layered structure and a high density of biomass, so there are differences in many climatic factors, such as temperature, humidity, rainfall, and wind strength, between the conditions inside the forest and those in clearings, and there are even differences between the distinct layers of the forest.

In particular, the *leaf area* per unit of crown volume greatly affects microclimatic conditions, not only because it directly affects interception of sunlight and rainwater but also because it may affect air circulation within the forest. Tropical forests have a high *leaf area index* (*LAI*), but the forest's height means that the average leaf area per unit volume is relatively low. The wind's main effect in the micro-climate is to accelerate air turbulence, which in turn controls the vertical transport of heat, humidity, carbon dioxide, etc., and so forests with a medium-to-low leaf area per unit volume have microclimates showing greater uniformity along a vertical transect, because the lower resistance to air flow gives rise to sufficient turbulence to make the microclimate uniform.

Thermal stratification

As already stated, the temperature conditions inside the forest are clearly different from those above the canopy or those in a clearing. Above the canopy, temperatures may reach 90°F (32°C) in the early afternoon and drop to 68°F (20°C) or less at sunrise, but within the forest, temperatures are usually between 75 and 82°F (24 and 28°C), with a small rise shortly after the canopy's peak.

11 **The elongation of the leaf blade to form a drip tip** so water drips off is a morphological feature shown by many leaves in the rainforest, such as this *Philodendron* leaf in Costa Rica. The advantage of the drip tip is that the leaf rids itself of rainwater more quickly, reducing the risk of the growth of leaf epiphytes (see figure 222) that would reduce its ability to catch the sunlight that is so scarce in the forest understory.
[Photo: Michael & Patricia Fogden]

I. THE EMBODIMENT OF DIVERSITY

Forests in the Ivory Coast show a variation of 4.1°C between the average maximum of temperatures over a week in February at 151 ft (46 m) above the ground in the upper canopy (90.1°F [32.3°C]) and that measured on the same days 3 ft (1 m) above the ground (82.7°F [28.2°C]). Minimum temperatures, however, are relatively constant, as the difference is only 0.3°C (73.6°F [23.1°C] in the canopy and 74.1°F [23.4°C] near the ground).

The stratification of humidity

Humidity follows quite a different pattern to temperature. Humidity is lowest above the canopy in the early afternoon and peaks in the early morning. Above the forest canopy in Pasoh (Malaysia), values for relative humidity as low as 50-60% have been recorded in the early afternoon, whereas values at the soil surface remained between 96 and 100% throughout the day. At night the air may be saturated with water vapor, which is transferred from the inside of the forest to the outside of the canopy.

Although rainforests are usually highly humid, there are also periods of relatively dry conditions. Rain may not fall for many days in a row, leading to the replacement of the normal humidity by dry conditions. In forests in Malaysia, where there are many dipterocarp trees, it has been shown that many of these trees may actually require this type of dry period for flowering and fruiting to occur, and they are so well-adapted to a regime including dry periods that they dominate these forests. The leaves in the crowns of the emergent trees undergo water stress even if dry periods do not occur: They experience a few hours of dry conditions every day, due to the high temperatures caused by the intense sunlight.

Rainfall affects each layer of the rainforest differently. The forest's structure largely determines the amount of the water that simply evaporates, that which is intercepted and then runs down the trunks, and that which falls directly on to the ground. This balance is also affected by the distribution of epiphytes, lianas, and aerial roots; the density of trees, branches and leaves, the morphology of the leaves (especially their bases and tips); and the characteristics of the different barks. Between a quarter and a half of all rainfall simply evaporates, accounting for most of the forest's high humidity.

Very little rain runs down the trunks, as the almost continuous canopy and the shapes of most of the leaves mean that the water either drips off the leaftips or collects in the small reservoirs formed by the leafbases of many epiphytes and some trees and lianas. Most of the rain is intercepted by the leaves in the upper layers and drips from leaf to leaf in smaller and smaller drops, and this helps to reduce the risk of soil erosion that is so high in areas lacking tree cover because of the intensity of tropical rainfall.

Cyclones, typhoons and hurricanes

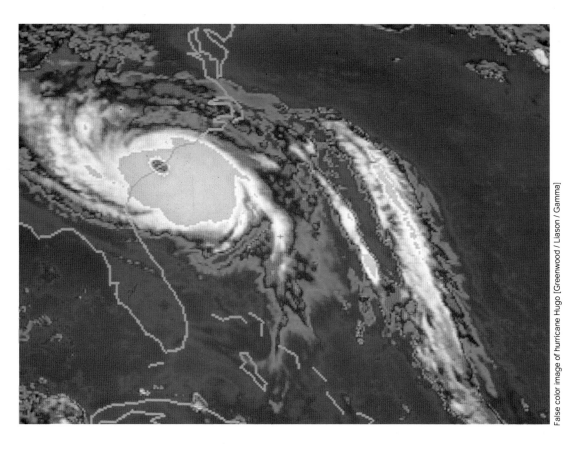

In 1900 the Australian meteorologist Clement Wragge decided to give each tropical storm the name of a person. Wragge gave anticyclones, which bring good weather, the names of people he liked and he named the depressions that bring bad weather after politicians he disliked. The idea caught on among American meteorologists, but they gave names only to the devastating depressions and these began to receive girls names: Carol, Tracy, Edna, etc. Obviously likes and dislikes betray the unconscious, and this discriminatory treatment did not show a scientific spirit of impartiality; therefore, since 1970, a devastating tropical depression can be given a boy's name (such as Hurricane Hugo, which hit Puerto Rico in 1989). It cannot be just any name: It will be the next name in strict alphabetical order on a previously agreed list which includes a range of names (in English). Thus, one of the more energetic tropical storms of the next few years might receive a name like George or Betty.

A tropical cyclone is a spiral weather system that rotates at high speed and causes heavy rains. The fact that it spirals and moves quickly (8-20 knots, 9-22 mph [15-35 kmph]) means that it behaves like a whirling whip that passes quickly, leaving a trail of downpours and wind damage in its wake. It is an ascending spiral system of rising air (the reason why there is a depression in the center) and as the air rises it cools, leading to heavy rainfall. The depressions are exceptionally well defined and violent: 311-435 mi (500-700 km) in diameter, with a relatively calm central "eye" of 3-9 mi (5-15 km) (or more), an atmospheric pressure of only 930-950 millibars (normally 1,013 over the sea), spinning at speeds greater than 108-115 ft (33-35 m) per second (72 mph [115-125 kmph]), sometimes as high as 50-60 m/s (180-215 kmph) and releasing heavy rainfall (100-200 liters per square meter, or more, in a few minutes).

These violent tropical depressions, or cyclones, are also called typhoons and hurricanes*. Although these three terms describe the same thing, they are used in different areas. Cyclone is used in the southern Indian and Pacific Oceans (it is the preferred academic name), typhoon is used in the Bay of Bengal and the China Sea (derived from the Chinese, *tai fung*), and hurricane is used in the Pacific coast of the Americas, the Caribbean and the Gulf of Mexico (the term is derived from a Caribbean language). The cyclones that drift west and towards the pole, the typical route of a Caribbean hurricane, form south of the Antilles, devastate Florida and the neighboring states, and then die out in northern Virginia. They always arrive with very strong winds and intense rain caused by the arriving front, then there is a strange lull when the eye of the storm is passing, with a clear sky surrounded by a cylindrical wall of clouds, followed by the repeat devastation of the leaving front.

Hurricane Fefa over the Pacific [Age Fotostock]

* *Tornadoes* are sometimes also called cyclones, but it is better to use this term for the much smaller spiral storms that occur at middle latitudes, a few dozen or hundreds of feet in diameter, although the wind intensity may be the same or greater.

The quantity of energy released is enormous, in the order of billions of kWh in a day. The record is held by typhoon "Tip," which hit Guam in October, 1979. It was estimated that about 10 billion kWh were released in a single day. This cyclone was 1,367 mi (2,200 km) in diameter, with an incredible barometric depression at the center of only 870 millibars and winds of up to 279 ft (85 m) per second (more than 186 mph [300 kmph]). They can cause record rainfall such as the 317 gal/m² (1,200 l/m²) that fell in only four days in a cyclone in Mauritius, or the 180 recorded in a single day in a hurricane in Puerto Rico in 1928 (more than 2.5 billion liters of water fell, i.e., 2,500 million tons of water!).

Devastation after hurricane Hugo in Guadalupe [Marcel Astruc / Gamma]

Certain conditions have to be fulfilled for a tropical cyclone to form. The first is that the storm should arise between 5-6° and 15-20° in latitude, whether north or south; this is the band within which the strength of the Coriolis force allows the formation of the typical circular movement of the cyclone. The second condition is that the surface temperature of the sea must be 81°F (27°C) or more over a large area so that the energy used in the evaporation of water is as small as possible. Third, and finally, the column of air above the ocean must be unstable and without vertical friction. Only when all these conditions are fulfilled, obviously restricted to the tropics, can a cyclone form.

The life of a tropical cyclone can be divided into several phases. In the first stage, formation, the structure begins to appear. Then it is possible to talk of an immature phase, as the wind is beginning to gather speed and starts to form a vortex, spiralling inwards and upwards. The next phase is the mature cyclone; that is, it forms a cyclone with winds of more than 108-115 ft (33-35 m) per second. The final phase is decay, and the cyclone turns into a weather front. Many Atlantic cyclones finally arrive at the European coastline after turning into low pressure or storm centers with an associated rain front.

Cyclones inflict great damage on human settlements. The combination of very high wind speed, and the sudden, violent lowering of pressure and heavy rain, as well as uprooting trees and toppling buildings, also causes giant waves and storms, sudden high tides, flooding and landslides. The rivers of mud produced by the combination of flooding, landslides and rivers and dams overflowing are particularly destructive. The dead may be counted in hundreds (300,000 people died in Calcutta as the result of a typhoon in 1737).

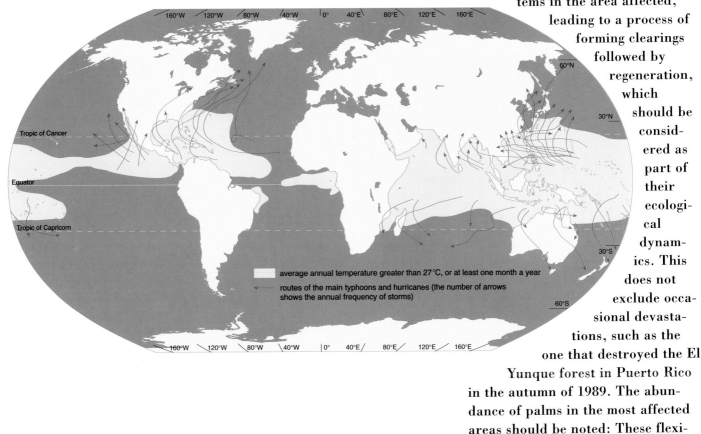

160°W 120°W 80°W 40°W 0° 40°E 80°E 120°E 160°E

60°N

30°N

Tropic of Cancer

Equator

Tropic of Capricorn

30°S

60°S

160°W 120°W 80°W 40°W 0° 40°E 80°E 120°E 160°E

average annual temperature greater than 27°C, or at least one month a year

routes of the main typhoons and hurricanes (the number of arrows shows the annual frequency of storms)

In spite of their destructive capacity, cyclones represent an environmental factor in the evolution of forest systems in the area affected, leading to a process of forming clearings followed by regeneration, which should be considered as part of their ecological dynamics. This does not exclude occasional devastations, such as the one that destroyed the El Yunque forest in Puerto Rico in the autumn of 1989. The abundance of palms in the most affected areas should be noted: These flexible plants have stems capable of bending in the wind without breaking.

Even though research is being carried out into ways of reducing the strength of cyclones, the most prudent thing to do is to take precautions, such as detecting the cyclone in time to take measures to minimize damage. This is the aim of the hurricane research project of the American National Oceans and Atmosphere Administration (NOAA). To do this they have a well equipped scientific staff (using radars, satellites, etc.) and airplanes that can fly into the eye of the hurricane to get readings: a somewhat terrifying job…

3. Rich lands, poor soils

3.1 Substrate diversity and soil diversity

Climate is responsible for the presence of rainforests around the equator and largely controls their distribution and composition, but the role of soils is no less important. Soils are always the result of interaction between the geological substrate, the climate and the living organisms, and in rainforests the organisms' role is especially important. Rainforest soils are often thought to show few variations, but this is far from correct: their soils show the enormous diversity that is so typical of all aspects of the rainforest.

Geological diversity

In the first place, the soils of tropical forests are formed on a wide range of geological formations, from sedimentary rocks to highly altered metamorphic rocks and intrusive and extrusive igneous rocks. Geologically, the African continent can be considered as an immense mass of ancient pre-Cambrian rock, two-thirds of which is covered by sedimentary deposits, with only two areas affected by folding at the northern and southern tips, far from the tropical area under discussion. The parent materials of the soils of most central and western African rainforests are thus saprolites (chemically rotted rocks) of Pleistocene deposits derived from the complex forming the African platform.

12 *Tepuis* **are remains of the former sandstone plateau that covered the granitic Guyana Shield** and now rise above the lowland forest of the Orinoco. They are surprisingly tall geomorphological formations, up to 9,842 ft (3,000 m) high and are totally isolated from each other, making them biogeographical islands with high levels of endemism: as many as 50% of the species found in each tepui are exclusive to it. (See "The colors of frogs," pages 356-359.) Tepuis have highly acidic soils, with a pH of 3.5, and extremely high levels of aluminium. These factors make plant growth difficult, favoring the presence of carnivorous plants, such as those of the genus *Heliamphora*. The tepuis are rocky islands in an ocean of rainforest and are highly typical of the Venezuelan areas of Duida and Canaima (see also figure 252).
[Photo: Mark Edwards / Still Pictures]

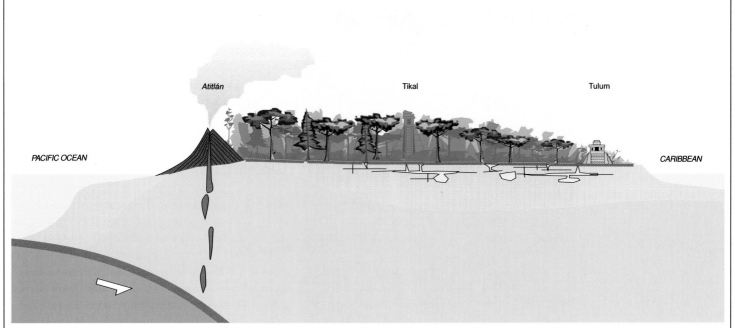

Atitlán Tikal Tulum

PACIFIC OCEAN CARIBBEAN

Unlike the African continent, the geological features of the American tropics show great complexity. In the west, the extremely high Andes range is formed by Palaeozoic and Mesozoic sedimentary rocks and by volcanic materials; to the north lies the Guyana, and to the east the Brazilian, crystalline pre-Cambrian granitic shields, formed by granitoids, gneiss and mica-schists, and between them are large sedimentary basins of the Amazon, Orinoco and Paraná rivers. Rainforest occupies most of the Amazon's drainage basin, part of the Orinocos, the drainage basins of the pre-Cambrian shields, and the lower slopes of the Andes in tropical latitudes. Other tropical areas, such as the Caribbean or southeast Asian islands and India, are mainly formed of volcanic materials.

Soil diversity

The combination of these materials with the intense processes of peneplanation (the lowering of land surface to form a peneplain) and weathering have formed deep saprolitic soils that now occupy most of the peneplains formed at the end of the Tertiary period. These saprolites are characterized by different levels of mineral weathering, with such heavy washing of the basic cations and silicates that it may lead to their almost total loss, and the neoformation of kaolinitic clay and of iron and aluminium oxides (hematites, goethite, hydrargillite).

The geomorphological and soil evolution of the peneplains has been greatly influenced by the climatic variations in the Quaternary. Pleistocene

stratigraphy of rainforest areas in central and western Africa shows a series of pluvial and interpluvial periods that led to successive periods of erosion that profoundly changed the relief. The relief formed by this erosion of deep saprolites consists basically of raised residual platforms surrounded by areas with very abrupt relief, where the geological profile is characterized by bundles of surface deposits (saprolitic materials reworked by erosion) covering the saprolite previously formed *in situ*. This superimposition of materials is clearly shown by the frequent presence of "stone-lines."

13 The arrangement of substrate and vegetation in an idealized cross section of the Yucután Peninsula (not to scale). The zone of volcanic activity along the Pacific front reveals itself in the exposure of acid igneous materials and the formation of a recent steep relief, in contrast to the calcareous sedimentary plain that dominates the rest of the area. A process of karstification that increases from west to east leads to the formation of underground caverns, or *cenotes*, lying symbolically between the constructions of Tikal and Tulum. As a result, effective water availability decreases from west to east, meaning that the rainforest formations are less and less striking and by the Gulf of Mexico they are reduced to a tropical vegetation that is not exactly rainforest.
[Drawing: Albert Martínez, from several sources]

14 The soil's red color and homogeneity at depth are characteristics of some tropical soils, such as this ferralsol in Madagascar, showing an A horizon enriched with organic material and an underlying oxic B_{OX} horizon that is red and very deep.
[Photo: Carlos Roquero]

15 When soil forms on volcanic materials, as in this andosol in a high mountain area of Ruanda (above), there is a good incorporation of organic material in the volcanic materials, giving rise to dark and deep accumulation horizons. Volcanic materials derived from recent eruptions show almost no soil development, although they are often colonized by plants that have few soil requirements, such as in this lava flow in Virunga, in the Democratic Republic of Congo (below).
[Photo: Carolus Sys and Adolf de Sostoa & Xavier Ferrer]

Quaternary ferralsols and acrisols

The resulting soils are in most cases *ferralsols*; they have horizons rich in hydrated iron oxides, or else they are *acrisols* with a clay accumulation horizon and low base saturation (less than 50%). Ferralsols and acrisols are most frequent in seasonal climates (see the corresponding sections in volume 3, Savannahs), but totally dominate the intertropical rainforests of America and Africa, with ferralsols found on the oldest rocks, and acrisols, especially in Africa, on eroded Pleistocene surfaces.

In southeastern Asia and especially in Insulindia (the islands between Asia and Australia), ferralsols are rarer. For example, in Malaysia at altitudes of up to 1,968 ft (600 m), the characteristic association of soils is a combination of *orthic* ferralsols and ochric *acrisols*; orthic ferralsols have a subsurface horizon of accumulated organic carbon, iron and aluminium, but are not dominated by any one mineral in particular, and ochric acrisols have a surface horizon (*epipedon*) that is light in color and poor in organic material. At higher altitudes, the surface horizons (epipedons) have more organic material and form humic acrisols. At greater altitudes (above 4,593-4,921 ft [1,400-1,500 m]) and on mineral-poor rocks, podzols (called spodosols in the Soil Taxonomy nomenclature) develop as a result of the migration of organic material and iron oxides in quartzitic sands lacking basic cations. Some of these podzols form under a layer of acidic peat (*dystric histosols*), as happens in the soils known as *beris* of the eastern coast of mainland Malaysia.

Stone-lines

The soils of central Africa frequently show layers of stones or ferruginous gravel that are parallel to the soil surface. When digging or examining a soil section, this layer of stones appears to form a line, and this is why they are called stone-lines in English. Stone-lines vary greatly as does their position in the landscape. This has led to several theories to explain their formation, morphology, the stone's origin, and the fact that they accumulate in an intermediate layer of the soil profile that shows a greater concentration of large elements than the layers immediately above or below it.

Some theories consider that stone-lines are the result of erosion gradually washing away the fine particles, thus causing a relative increase in the mass of stones. This stone-covered erosion surface, the equivalent of desert pavement in more arid environments, was later buried by colluvion. The presence of stone-lines in lateritic materials has been used to identify lithological discontinuities in the sequence of materials with depth. Other researchers consider that this abundance of stones may often be due to the weathering of veins of quartz or other resistant rocks within the soil's parental materials. When these parent materials were weathered to a saprolite and soil formation took place, the original layout of these more resistant lodes was maintained. Finally, other theories suggest the material forming the stone-lines comes from elsewhere, derived from ancient lateritic crusts on residual surfaces that, as they eroded, formed colluvial layers of crust fragments that moved downwards.

Pleistocene gleysols, ferralsols, and andosols

Weathering products have also been deposited in the large sedimentary Pleistocene basins. These structural basins are covered by concentric deposits of sediments, with the most recent in the center and the oldest at the periphery. The best examples are found in the Amazon and Zaire river basins, crisscrossed by complex river networks, and have a dissected relief largely covered by sandy sediments.

As in Africa, the climatic changes during the Pleistocene had a great influence on the formation of the Tertiary deposits in the Amazon, which consist of kaolinitic clays and relatively unconsolidated quartzitic sands. The Amazon river network arose in the lower Pleistocene between the materials of the Plio-Pleistocene Amazon plateau, giving rise to a complex system of terraces. The ferralsols and acrisols of the *terra firme* are replaced by gleysols in the *varzea*, which is occasionally flooded, and in the *igapo*, which is permanently flooded.

Volcanic materials occupy large areas of India, and of the Ethiopian and Kenyan plateaux as well as large areas of southeast Asia and the Pacific islands, but they are also found wherever there has been volcanic activity, such as the Andes and the Gulf of Guinea. The abrupt relief in these regions consists of horizontal platforms with steep escarpments at the edges. The soils that form on these materials are basically ferralsols (on lava) or andosols (on ash). These andosols on ashes typically show the presence of allophane, the term used for unstructured, or amorphous, hydrated aluminium silicates with a large active surface, and this gives the soil a high cation exchange capacity.

Allophane forms microaggregates of spherical particles, the reason for its high porosity and water retention capacity. The upper horizons are very dark due to the organic materials' close bonding to the allophane and its resulting slow breakdown.

Alluvial soils

Areas of recent sedimentation include coastal plains, deltas, and alluvial plains. Coastal plains occupy larger areas in the tropics than in the temperate zones, and they are typically low energy environments (lacking cliffs), where there is a combination of marine and alluvial sandy deposits. It is precisely in these environments and in the deltas of the large rivers such as the Niger, Indus, Ganges and Mekong that marshy mangrove swamps develop, interspersed with raised sandbanks or levees. Alluvial plains are also humid areas that have undergone complex successions of sedimentation/erosion episodes in the form of the meandering and anastomosing of watercourses that have given rise to the current distribution of materials. They are dominated by gleysols, which are soils in which water occupies most of the empty spaces between the solids, meaning that they are dominated by anaerobic processes, leading to a pattern of green and gray mottling as a result of the reduction of iron.

3.2 Fertility and sterility

The lush rainforest vegetation grows on infertile soils that are highly dependent on the recycling of the organic material produced by the vegetation. The aggressive climate's abundant rainfall and high temperatures cause intense washing of basic cations and nutrients, leading to heavy chemical weathering, and this is why the soils are infertile. This deficiency is even greater in soils formed on certain substrates, and when exchangeable aluminium exerts toxic effects on the vegetation.

The problem of laterite or plinthite formation

When tropical soils were first studied in the 1920s by soil scientists from temperate or cold countries, mainly Russians, Americans, French, British, and Portuguese, the term *laterite* came into general use for all tropical red and yellow soils. This idea led to the association of laterite and tropical soils but is a generalization derived from insufficient knowledge of the soils of these

16 Plinthite, or laterite, hardens irreversibly on drying. For this reason it has long been used as a material for bricks, like these in Tsiroano-mandidy (Madagascar). The term laterite, the former term for plinthite, comes from the Latin word *later*, which means "a brick."
[Photo: Carlos Roquero]

areas. More recent soil data have now confirmed that tropical soils are far from uniform and that laterites represent less than 7% of the land surface of the tropics, and even then they are often below the surface.

The concept of laterite
In fact, the term *laterite* (from the Latin, *later*, a brick) was introduced by the British geographer Francis H. Buchanan (1762-1829) who described his voyage to India in his book *A Journey from Madras through the countries of Mysore, Canara and Malabar* published in 1807 by the British East India Company. The term laterite, widely used throughout the 19th century and the first half of the 20th century, was given to a construction material used on the Malabar coast, in the south of India. The term later spread throughout India and the world, to designate the surface formations this material is obtained from. It contains many red patches, concretions of iron oxide, in a slightly grayish kaolinitic matrix. While it is still moist it can be cut with a spade, but on exposure to air it dries out rapidly and hardens irreversibly, becoming as hard as brick, the reason for its name.

The term laterite is now widely and commonly used—but not in modern soil classification systems—to designate a material consisting of weathering products, formed mainly of oxides, oxyhydroxides, and hydroxides of iron, aluminium and, to a lesser extent, titanium and manganese. Ferruginous laterite consists basically of hematites (Fe_2O_3) and goethite ($FeOOH$), and is mined for iron and nickel in Cuba and New Caledonia. Aluminic laterite consists of gibbsite ($Al(OH)_3$) and boehmite ($AlOOH$) and is the main ore of aluminium. It has a characteristic appearance with reticulate polygonal dark red patches.

The question of names: from laterite to plinthite
The imprecise nature of the term laterite has led to confusion in its use. This is why the Soil Conservation Service of the U.S. Department of Agriculture (SCS-USDA) preferred to abandon the generic term laterite and replace it with plinthite (from the Greek *plinthos*, a brick), the term now used in soil classification systems, such as the Soil Taxonomy Classification and the FAO-UNESCO Soil Classification.

Plinthite, once it has irreversibly cemented as a result of cycles of humidity and dryness, is known as *petroplinthite* (comparable to the terms "ferruginous crusts" used by French soil scientists and "duricrusts" used by Australian ones). This hardening does not involve changes in the composition of the plinthite (or laterite), only the development of a crystalline continuity in the iron oxides. Cemented laterites are a resistant element of the landscape and the fact that they are now at the top of platforms means that there has been a reversal of the relief, as in southwest Nigeria and Australia, where they appear in relict Tertiary formations formed under tropical conditions.

The formation of ferralsols
Knowledge about ferralsol formation has increased considerably as more soil data have become available, mainly from India, Uganda, the Democratic Republic of Congo, and Australia. Briefly, there are three main overlapping processes (ferralitic weathering, latosol formation, and laterization), although they are explained separately for the sake of clearness.

Ferralization, or *ferralitic weathering*, occurs in hot tropical environments (average yearly temperature around 77°F [25°C]) with high rainfall (79-98 in [2,000-2,500 mm] a year). It mainly affects mafic rocks, and these rocks rich in ferromagnesian minerals (pyroxenes, amphiboles, biotite and chlorite) may be the source of iron in these environments. Ferralitic weathering consists of intense hydrolysis, accompanied in well-drained conditions by strong leaching of silica and any basic cations that are released. The resulting low environmental levels of silica allow only the new formation of allitic kaolinite-type clay minerals that are aluminium-rich and contain oxides, oxyhydroxides, and hydroxides of iron, aluminium, and titanium. One of the essential characteristics of the dynamics of the process is the ratio SiO_2/Al_2O_3, which determines whether kaolinite or gibbsite dominates the clay fraction. The most important physical feature of the soils affected by ferralitic weathering is the presence of pseudosand, particles of clay minerals and fine loam cemented by iron oxides to form grains comparable in size to sand. This gives them a stable microstructure, and an open texture that makes them permeable and suitable for cultivation, yet reduces their water retention capacity. As a result, these soils, which basically correspond to ferralsols, are sensitive to dry conditions.

The terms *latosol formation* and *laterization* have been used to describe the formation of iron oxide-

17 **The main rainforest soils, in accordance with the soil units of the FAO Classification (1990)**, including lowland forests, cloud forests, and monsoon forests. The name of each soil unit is accompanied by its most important processes, its most distinctive characteristics and its geographical distribution. Those at the bottom of the table are only found locally, depending on the parent materials or position in the relief.
[Source: data compiled by the authors]

UNIT	PROCESSES	CHARACTERISTICS	GEOGRAPHICAL DISTRIBUTION
Lixisols	Intense weathering, washing of clay (argillic horizon)	Very rich in cations and average cation exchange capacity in the argillic horizon; not very developed structure	Flat areas or sites with gentle slopes, in alluvial or colluvial materials, mainly in monsoon or semiarid climates
Acrisols	Illuviation of low-activity clay (argillic horizon), intense weathering	Low levels of cations and average cation exchange capacity in the argillic horizon; high acidity	Areas with gentle relief, in wet and monsoon tropical climates
Allisols	Illuviation of clay (argillic horizon)	Low levels of cations and high cation exchange capacity in the argillic horizon; high levels of free aluminium; less weathered than acrisols; contain clays in proportion 2:1	Areas with moderate relief, in monsoon and wet climates
Nitosols	Nitllluviation of clay (very thick argillic horizon) osols	Argillic horizon containing at least 20% clay in the top 150 cm; strong structure due to the active iron oxides; good physical properties; high water storage capacity	Mainly in central Africa, formed on basic rocks
Ferralsols	Ferralitic weathering (ferric horizon)	Ferric horizon thicker than 30 cm; low cation exchange capacity (loading depends mainly on pH); good physical properties	Common in Africa and America on Pleistocene surfaces
Plinthosols	Plinthite formation	Presence of more than 25% plinthite in any subhorizon more than 15 cm thick; high cation levels and low cation exchange capacity; high apparent density that impedes drainage and root penetration	Western India, western Africa and part of South America, in hot wet climates with high rainfall
Vertisols	Expansion-retraction of expandable clays	More than 30% smectic (layered) clays in the top 50 cm; wide deep cracks during the dry season; shearage surfaces between aggregates	On parental materials rich in smectic clays, with alternating wet and dry seasons
Leptosols[1]	Erosion	Highly superficial soils (less than 30 cm thick) or very stony (less than 20% fine soil in the top 75 cm)	Areas with steep relief
Regosols[1]	Hardly shown	Young soils, little developed on non-consolidated rocks, such as lutites	Eroded areas on non-consolidated materials
Histosols[1]	Great accumulation of organic material	Soils with organic materials in at least the top 40 cm	Badly drained areas, bogs
Andosols[1]	Typical of volcanic materials	Amorphous clays, anion exchange capacity, thixotropy, possible immobilization of phosphorus; good physical and chemical fertility	Volcanic areas
Podzols[1]	Podzolisation; migration of organic material and iron oxides	Spodic surface horizon that may or may not be cemented by iron oxides; often sandy; low chemical fertility	On nutrient-poor parent materials and in a regime of percolating moisture
Gleysols[1]	Gleyzation; reduction-oxidation processes	Reddish and greenish grey patches, due to iron being reduced and dissolved in the top 50 cm; deficient drainage; low physical fertility	Areas with water table close to the surface
Fluvisols[1]	Periodic input of alluvial sediments	Deep soils, irregular distribution of organic carbon at depth or greater than 0.2% at 125 cm depth; often occupied by croplands	Alluvial plains

[1] locally restricted soils

rich soils or horizons in environments where ferralitic weathering takes place. Initially, the term latosol formation was used independently of the presence or absence of laterite, although it later became a synonym of laterization. The difference between the two processes lies in the behavior of the iron. In latosol formation, the formation of horizons rich in iron oxides is due to relative enrichment as a result of the leaching of silica and basic cations. Laterization, however, implies the input of iron as a result of its movement within the soil or the landscape in the form of dissolved ferrous (Fe^{2+}) ions, and its accumulation in the lower areas where it precipitates. This precipitation may occur in the lower levels of the soil, at the base of slopes, or on peneplains at the bottom of synclinal folds. The existence of variable redox (reduction-oxidation) conditions is considered to be very important, and this means fluctuations in the depth of the water table or temporary waterlogging is essential for iron segregation to occur. The result is the formation of plinthite (laterite) and petroplinthite, which may consist of up to 70-80% of iron oxides in the form of vesicles and nodules that give a characteristic lattice appearance, with red and gray colorations.

Studies of how these soil formations arose must establish where the iron has come from, how it was mobilized, transported, and precipitated, and the development of the landscapes in which they occur. The presence of a fluctuating water table, at variable depths, is considered essential in the formation of plinthites in the Amazon. The low iron content of the main sediments in the Amazon mean that the regions lateritic crusts—plinthites—are not continuous and rarely cover large areas, in contrast to what occurs in Africa. In the Amazon the presence of an active water table in the soil and the degree of plinthite cementation are the criteria used to determine whether iron accumulation is fossil or recent. In many places, when these materials harden they act as resistant features in the landscape and this may lead to the reversal of the relief when the drainage network manages to fit between them.

The limitations of plinthitic materials

The presence of laterites is not a general problem in the soils of tropical areas, but shallow plinthites obstruct good drainage. In areas of high rainfall, such as rainforests, bad drainage caused by the presence of plinthites leads to the formation of a water table right at the top of the soil, and the roots grow badly because of the oxygen shortage. Poor root development leads to poorly anchored trees that are easily blown over by strong winds, and, because the roots only exploit a small volume of soil, nutrient availability is low.

Loss of plant cover in forest areas on plinthites may trigger erosive processes that bring the plinthite to the surface, leading to its desiccation and irreversible hardening unless cultivated. In the Second World War some western Africa agricultural areas on plinthites were temporarily abandoned, but the soils dried out and irreversibly hardened, leaving them totally useless for agriculture.

The toxicity of aluminium and the occlusion of phosphorus

The composition of tropical soils—kaolinitic clays with low activity because of their low cation exchange capacity, almost totally lacking calcium and magnesium and dominated by iron and aluminium oxides—is one reason for their low fertility, and the other reason is the way aluminium and phosphorus behave in these soils.

The behavior of aluminium in wet tropical soils

The final products of the clay weathering are kaolinite and gibbsite, both with a low cation exchange capacity that leads to a limited capacity to retain nutrients, although in some cases the high clay content may compensate for this deficiency. The intense washing these soils have undergone is the reason for their low content in basic cations and their acidity (pH between 4.6 and 5.2), a fact clearly showing the presence of exchangeable aluminium in the soil, possibly accounting for up to 5% of the cation exchange capacity, enough to be toxic. All those studying tropical soils agree that exchangeable aluminium is only present in acid soils, and especially in very acid soils (pH below 5.5). Soil acidity is one of the main factors limiting intensive agriculture throughout the rainforest area. The precise reasons for these low yields include toxicity due to aluminium and manganese, deficiencies or imbalances of basic cations, and the low nutrient content. The lack of technology and economic resources to buy fertilizers and introduce improvements mean that agricultural systems in these areas are very poor. It is, therefore, vital that their low natural fertility should be conserved.

The behavior of phosphorus

In chemical terms, the high iron oxide content in these soils explains their high capacity to fix phosphorus, making it unavailable to plants. In these cases the phosphorus is said to be occluded by the hydroxides of aluminium, iron and manganese that are very important components of the soils of the forests of Colombia and the Brazilian Amazon. These phosphates are so insoluble that they are considered to be unavailable to the plants. As most phosphorus in the surface soil horizons of tropical forests is in organic form, agricultural practices speeding up humus decomposition lead to faster phosphorus release into the soil solution. Liming, the application of calcium carbonate, when combined with the neutralization of the exchangeable aluminium and reduction of the positive charges, supplies calcium and may significantly increase the quantity of available phosphorus and the soils productivity.

The input of organic material

The input of organic material into tropical forest soils, mainly in the form of leaf litter, is very large. This input may be 7-9 t per hectare (1 hectare=2.47 acres) per year in Colombia and 15-18 t in west Africa. This organic material is the most important product of the tropical forest, yet it should be borne in mind that the higher the temperature, the lower the soils content of organic material. Biomass production in the tropical zone is very high but the high temperatures mean it is broken down very quickly when it reaches the soil, and so the soil does not contain as much organic matter as might be expected.

The dry weight of organic material present in a forest varies between 150 and 300 t per hectare, containing between 1.5 and 2 t of mineral ions. An annual input to the soil surface of a dry weight of 15 t/ha represents about 441 lb (200 kg) of nitrogen, 551 lb (250 kg) of other mineral nutrients and 551 lb (250 kg) of silica. They are all released rapidly when the organic matter decomposes, supplying the plants with their basic supply of nutrients, forming an almost closed cycle.

The content of organic material of forest soils in central Africa is about 110 t/ha, more than seven times annual input. This means that on average all the organic material present in the soil turns over in seven years, although some components are recycled more quickly and others more slowly. Nitrogen, however, takes 35-40 years to turn over

18 Leaflitter is a very important element of the composition and functioning of rainforest soils. Dead leaves decompose rapidly, and act as a determining source of soil nutrients, as in this rainforest in Corcovada (Costa Rica). [Photo: Adolf de Sostoa & Xavier Ferrer]

(input of 441 lb [200 kg] N/year for a content of 4.5-8 t of nitrogen per hectare). Comparing these two turnover periods shows that the soil is more efficient at retaining nitrogen than organic matter.

The quantity of nutrients stored in forest soils is related mainly to the organic material present, its production by the vegetation, and its decomposition by microorganisms and the fauna. The system is kept in balance because decomposition occurs at about the same rate as production, reducing losses by leaching in an area of very high rainfall. There are, however, factors, that can throw nutrient supplies out of balance. *Acidification* is common in tropical soils and favors fungal growth rather than bacterial growth, and in these conditions organic matter tends to accumulate, increasing the length of time taken for nutrients to turn over. This negatively affects plant nutrition, as organic material is the only nutrient source in these poor and highly weathered soils. In these areas total phosphorus content appears to be linked to the content of organic material.

4. The world's rainforest

4.1 The distribution and range of the rainforest

The tropical rainforest is a discontinuous biome, occurring on three separate continents, another example of its tendency to diversification. This biome also assumes clearly distinct forms in relatively close sites. The world's rainforests are related by their common origin, but have evolved in different ways over geological time. In any case, the biome covers much of the land in the intertropical zone.

The geography of the rainforest

Nearly all equatorial rainforest lies within 20° of latitude of the equator, although most is within 10° north or south. Maps showing the rainforest's geographical limits tend to vary depending on the author concerned. In many areas there may be a clear edge to the forest, but in many other places there is a gradual change over hundreds of miles into vegetation typical of cooler and drier climates, so there is no point where one can objectively say that the equatorial forest ends and another vegetation type starts. Yet as a whole, the equatorial forest area clearly follows the zones with hot, wet climates that occur around the equator.

Rainforest occurs between the two tropics on all the three continents, America, Africa, and the southeast of Asia, with outposts on the large islands such New Guinea, northeastern Australia and several tropical Pacific islands, the eastern coast of Madagascar, the Malabar coast (southwest India) and southwestern Sri Lanka. The rainforest reaches beyond the tropics in a few places: southern Brazil (reaching beyond 29°S on the Atlantic-facing slopes of the Serra do Mar, at the limit between the states of Santa Catarina and Rio Grande do Sul); the southeastern tip of Madagascar, in the region of Tölanyaro (beyond 25°S), and in northeastern India and northern Myanmar (Burma) on the border between Bangladesh, Bhutan, and China (an area that also reaches 29°N in the valleys of the Dibang and the Dihang,

in the Arunachal Pradesh region of northeastern India). Rainforest covers a total of 5.4 million sq. mi (14 million km²), approximately 10% of the world's land surface, divided between more than 70 countries of greatly differing levels of development (ranging from Australia and Singapore, among the most developed countries in the world, to some of the lowest income countries in Africa, Asia, or the Pacific, including some that are still subject to colonial status).

Brazil, (because it is so large and covers the Amazon Basin), the Democratic Republic of Congo (because it includes most of the Zaire Basin), and Indonesia are the countries with the largest area of rainforest within their frontiers. The smaller, although by no means negligible, areas of tropical rainforest can be considered as appendages of the three large strictly equatorial areas: (1) the South American area of the Amazon and the Guyanas, (2) the African area of the Gulf of Guinea and the Zaire Basin, and (3) and the area formed by Insulindia and New Guinea and southeastern Asia.

A common evolutionary heritage: traces of Gondwana

Despite the large distances between the different areas, there are clear floristic similarities between the biome's different areas, reflecting their common evolutionary heritage. Many of the same families and even genera of plants occur in rainforests on different continents, separated by thousands of miles of seawater.

Some of the closest floristic similarities between rainforest regions on different continents are probably due to the exceptional dispersal ability of some plants, whose seeds have been carried great distances by birds or ocean currents in the last few million years. This might, for example, explain how a single species of the highly specialized genus of carnivorous pitcher plants *Nepenthes* reached the Madagascar rainforest, while the other 70 species are restricted to the Far East. Yet the main causes for these floristic links lie further back

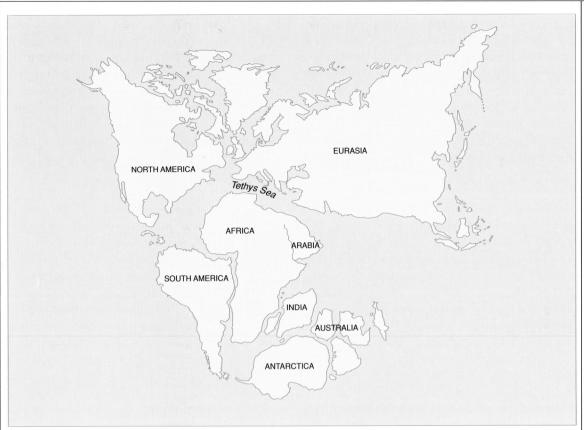

19 The distribution of dry land during the lower Cretaceous (120 million years ago), when the first angiosperms (flowering plants) were evolving. The map shows that the northern continents had already completely separated from the southern ones, South America had already separated from Africa, and India had separated from Madagascar. The expansion of the epicontinental seas separated northern Africa from Eurasia, and divided Australia-New Guinea into three parts. The circumtropical Sea of Tethys was already present. [Drawing: Jordi Corbera, based on J.C. Briggs, 1987]

in the distant geological past, when the world's different rainforest were in much closer contact.

The fossil record suggests many now distant regions of rainforest once formed continuous forest belts in periods when climates were warmer and moister. In the early Cenozoic, 55 million years ago, the equatorial forests seem to have formed an almost continuous belt from Africa, through Europe and southeast Asia, to Insulindia. Although this forest belt was intermittent due to the presence of narrow, shifting seaways, the floras of the African and southeast Asian rainforest regions would, presumably, have exchanged newly evolving plants rapidly and effectively. These links seem to have been interrupted about 30 million years ago, when the global climate became cooler and drier, yet the African and Asian rainforests' closer common heritage justifies their classification together as the Paleotropical realm (the Old World tropics), thus distinguishing them from the neotropical rainforest realm (the New World). The New World had separated from Africa long before, during the Cretaceous (140-65 million years ago), the period when the flowering plants (angiosperms) began to diversify and rise to dominance. The landmasses in the southern hemisphere were then still more-or-less joined in the former southern super continent of Gondwana; and although Africa and South America were already drifting apart, they remained relatively close to each other.

Many of the ancestors of the plant families of today's tropical rainforests would thus have been able to move between the two continents, either by land bridges or "island hopping" along the volcanic islands of the ocean ridges that were then forming. Members of the same plant families (such as the Euphorbiaceae, the Meliaceae, the Moraceae, and the Sapotaceae) still form major elements of the rainforest flora throughout the biome, although their subsequent evolution has given rise to separate subgroups in the Paleotropical and Neotropical realms. It is difficult to say how much exchange there has been between Africa and South America since they separated, but it seems reasonable to suppose that the chance of exchanging plants and animal species between the two continents was uninterrupted but decreased as they separated. The length and effectiveness of this separation means their common evolutionary heritage now consists of a single tree species (the *ehureke*, or hog plum, of the Ghanaian coast, *Symphonia globulifera*, Guttiferae).

The Australasian region (including Australia, New Guinea, and other smaller fragments) split from the southern part of Gondwana at about the same time as South America did, and the plants that had made it there then evolved into a distinctive flora. Wet tropical environments were absent from the Australasian region when it split off from the other continents but appeared later in the Tertiary, when the region moved north towards the equator. The region thus developed its distinctive rainforest flora from the plants that happened to be already present, giving an important role in the Australasian flora to some of the ancient groups of conifers that had dominated the forests of Gondwanaland before the evolution of the angiosperms. Even so, many of the families and even genera of angiosperms and conifers that evolved to occupy the Australian rainforest realm also occur on other continents, because of their ancient links through Gondwanaland.

The same general patterns are reflected in the fauna of the various regions of the forest but not always for the same reasons. Thus for example, the Asian and African monkeys form a closely related group (the *catarrhines*) distinct from those in the Americas (the *platyrrhines*). Monkeys are known to have evolved relatively recently, so they must have spread from the Old World by means of the forested land links that existed between Eurasia and North America in the mid-Tertiary; they then spread southwards across the Central American land bridge to South America. After the northern land bridge disappeared, these monkeys evolved into a distinct group. The bats of the Old and New World Bats show a similar pattern: the niche occupied in Asia and Africa by fruit bats and flying foxes (the Megachiroptera) is occupied in South America by a different, less specialized, group descended from the insect-eating bats (the Microchiroptera).

Advances and retreats over time

As the continuous zone of moist forest formerly linking African and Asian forests has long since disappeared, evolution has taken different paths in the two areas. Asiatic forests are now dominated by trees that are members of the Dipterocarpaceae, whereas the African members of this family are savannah and woodland trees and belong to a different subfamily.

Over the last 30 million years, the world's equatorial forests have continued to decline. In Africa and Australia increasing aridity has left only small remnants of their former extensive rainforests. Often these isolated pockets survive hundreds of miles apart, in coastal strips or on mountain slopes where the climate is still moist enough. During each of the cool, dry glacial periods that have occurred repeatedly over the last two and a half million years, the area of these rainforest pockets seems to have been even smaller and almost to have disappeared. With regard to the American rainforest regions, there is clear evidence of major arid periods in the last few million years.

A further complication is that two of the world's main rainforest realms are now merging. After the collision of the Eurasian and Indo-Australian continental plates starting about 20-30 million years ago, animal and plant dispersal across the relatively small straits separating these two continental masses has been gradual but continuous. Their distinct evolutionary histories have left a mark, known as *Wallace's Line* (named after Alfred R. Wallace, the great English naturalist and contemporary of Darwin who first described it in detail). The plants and animals on either side of this line are different: in other words it is a zone of floral and faunal discontinuity, closely following the line along which the edges of the two plates meet. So, after diverging since the dawn of the angiosperm era, these two regions of forest are now engaged in another major ecological and evolutionary experiment.

Similarities and differences

As a result of this complex history of climatic change and continental drift, the world's tropical rainforests show many regional structural and taxonomic differences that can be put down to evolutionary trials. These differences are, however, superimposed on such a striking background of evolutionary convergence and parallel evolution in the majority of the groups of plants that live there, thus giving tropical rainforests throughout the world a similar general appearance.

Thus, in Asia the role of the opportunist gap colonizer species in disturbed rainforest sites is filled by the large-leaved, fast-growing trees of the genus *Macaranga* (Euphorbiaceae), whereas in the Americas it is filled by species of *Cecropia* that are similar to them in appearance. Epiphytes grow in the crowns of canopy trees in all the rainforest regions, but they are far more abundant in the American tropics, where bromeliads (Bromeliaceae) have diversified with enormous

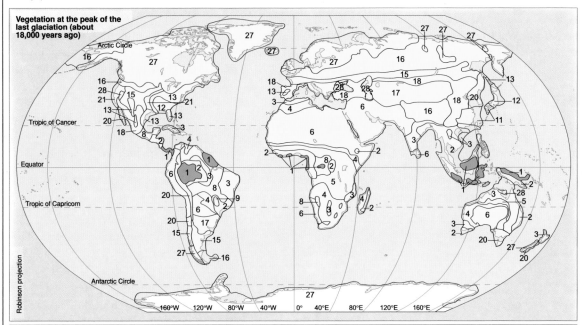

Vegetation at the peak of the last glaciation (about 18,000 years ago)

Robinson projection

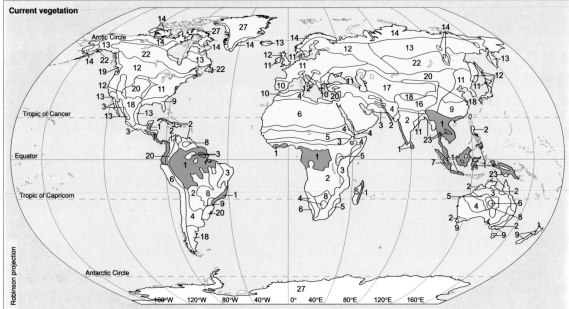

Current vegetation

Robinson projection

20 **Distribution of vegetation at the height of the last ice age (above) and today (below)**. Between about 10,000 and 20,000 years ago, ice covered much of the northern hemisphere and some mountainous regions in the south, and due to the large quantity of water trapped in the form of ice, the sea level was 394 ft (120 m) lower than it is now. The most important feature of the vegetation of the ice age is that it was scattered and open. The cold and aridity restricted many species of plant and animal to small refugia, where they found the conditions they needed to survive. About 14,000 years ago, the planet began to warm up and become wetter and the forests left their refuges and spread to altitudes as much as 3,281 ft (1,000 m) higher in the mountains, where they replaced the low alpine vegetation. Many of the species that were abundant during the glacial period were then confined to the refugia where they still persist. The last ice age is only the latest of a sequence of climatic fluctuations that have occurred over the last 2.5 million years. The repeated expansion and contraction of the distribution areas of species that took place during these climatic cycles has undeniably played an important role in the evolution and distribution of the plants and animals that now populate the planet. Vegetation distribution has been reconstructed from several sources, such as fossil pollen, animal bones, fossil soils, etc. The most reliable data are for the temperate and arctic areas of Europe and North America, while there are fewer data for wet tropical areas, as fossils are not easily preserved there. *[Drawing: Editrònica, from an original by Jonathan Adams]*

1. THE EMBODIMENT OF DIVERSITY

TROPICAL VEGETATION

1 Equatorial rainforest, evergreen or partially deciduous forests in wet tropics

2 Open tropical forest, relatively low, deciduous

3 Open tropical woody formations, with low woody vegetation, often spiny and generally deciduous

4 Tropical semidesert, with sparse herbaceous or low woody vegetation

5 Tropical herbaceous vegetation, with sparse trees

6 Extreme tropical desert, with very sparse vegetation or totally bare ground

7 Mountain tropical forest, evergreen, adapted to low temperatures

8 Savannah: herbaceous formations with sparse shrubs and trees

23 Monsoon forest, medium or high, deciduous or semideciduous

TEMPERATE AND HIGH LATITUDES

9 Broadleaf evergreen temperate forest

10 Mediterranean forest, with a mixture of sclerophyllous and deciduous shrubs and trees

11 Deciduous temperate broadleaf forest, including mixed forest

12 Conifer forest

13 Open temperate and boreal woody formations, with different types of woody vegetation, either coniferous or broadleaf

14 Typical tundra of herbaceous plants or low clumps

15 Southern steppe tundra (only in diagram of glacial vegetation)

16 Polar desert and northern steppe tundra

17 Temperate desert (cold winters), with very sparse vegetation

18 Temperate semidesert and sparse steppe, with open scrub and/or herbaceous vegetation

19 Dense coniferous rainforest (Pseudotsuga or Sequoia)

20 Temperate and montane meadows (cold winters), with herbaceous vegetation

21 Woody steppe or tundra, with shrubs or trees

22 Typical taiga: conifer forest with open canopy

27 Icecap and other permanent ice masses

28 Lakes

21 The similarities among the American species of ***Cecropia*** (such as *Cecropia peltata* in the upper photo), the African species of *Musanga* (such as *Musanga cecropioides* in the lower photo), and the Asian species of *Macaranga*, are a surprising case of morphological convergence and ecological vicariance. All three genera have palmately lobed leaves that are almost identical in appearance, and all three genera consist of opportunist species that colonize clearings in the rainforest (see the other *Cecropia* tree in photo 75).
[Photos: *François Gohier / Jacana and Jon & Alison Moran / Planet Earth Pictures*]

success to occupy this niche. Large emergents rise high above the main canopy in all the world's main rainforest regions, but different taxa dominate in different places: in southeast Asia large dipterocarp trees are particularly important emergents, but in other regions the emergents mainly belong to other families. Palms form part of the forest canopy in all rainforest regions, but they are far more abundant and play more diverse ecological roles in South American rainforests than elsewhere.

The list of similarities and differences could go on indefinitely. Looking broadly at the world's rainforests, it is obvious that common evolution-ary pressures must be responsible for the striking similarities between unrelated groups of plants growing in different parts of the world. Even so, there is also a certain degree of leeway that allows some types of plant with distinctive attributes and aptitudes to come to dominate the structure of the forest in a particular region.

The morphological convergences between plants from different families within and between rainforest regions are as striking as the results of recent studies on the number of species present in each region. It has long been known that the world's tropical rainforests are exceptionally rich in species of animals and plants and that some areas are even richer than others, and it is clear that within each region some plant groups have undergone explosive diversification as a result of the vagaries of history and opportunity; for example, there are 700 species of screw pines (*Pandanus*) in eastern Asia but far fewer in Africa.

Yet on a larger scale there may be a surprising amount of order in the world. Recent studies have shown that the number of tree species in each tropical rainforest region tends to follow the trend of mean annual rainfall. In the drier parts of rainforest regions (annual rainfall between 39 and 79 in [1,000 and 2,000 mm]) the number of tree species per 0.2 acre (0.1 ha) is 50-100, but rises to over 250 in areas of very high rainfall (around 236 in [6,000 mm]) and weak seasonality. In areas where more rain falls (354 in [9,000 mm] or more per year), the curve of rising tree species diversity tends to flatten out quite clearly.

It is surprising that, in spite of tens of millions of years of isolation and independent evolution, the number of tree species is roughly constant in different tropical regions with similar climates. Thus, present data suggests a hectare (1 hectare= 2.47 acres) of primary rainforest in Africa may have about the same number of species as an equivalent area of forest in Asia or South America growing in conditions of roughly similar rainfall (although its seasonality also needs to be taken into account). This model contradicts the previously accepted notion that African rainforests are relatively poor in species because their geological history included drier periods than those that occurred in southern Asia or the Americas. Furthermore, the large area of relatively dry, and thus species-poor, rainforest in the African region may account for the lower overall number of plant species in the region.

4.2 The African and Madagascar rainforests

By far the largest block of rainforest in Africa lies in and around the Zaire Basin, a large horseshoe-shaped catchment area, bounded to the east by the east African rift system; it includes the Equator, Upper Democratic Republic of Congo, Kivu and Eastern Kasai regions of the Democratic Republic of Congo, the northern half of the Republic of Congo, and much of the Central African Republic and of southeastern Cameroon. The substrate is Mesozoic rock overlying an older pre-Cambrian base. Most of the basin is below 3,281 ft (1,000 m) and has a flat or gently rolling relief with large swampy areas in the center. The river Zaire drains the valley towards the Gulf of Guinea through the Congolese coastal plain. The underlying rock here is mainly Mesozoic, but with more recent Tertiary rocks near to the coast.

Geologically, Madagascar is a micro-continent that split off from the eastern side of Africa at some time in the Jurassic (more than 140 million years ago). Its flora and fauna reflect its continuing geographical proximity to its African origin and its long isolation and independent evolution, but with the addition of a surprising number of Asian groups of plants and animals. Many of these links to the African and Asian mainlands must be due to chance dispersal across the oceans within the last few million years. However, some characteristic features of the Madagascar biota may be a testimony of the former distribution of the plants and animals of the long-vanished Tertiary forests of eastern Africa (or of the north-wards-moving Indian sub-continent) that managed to reach Madagascar but have since died out over their former range.

The African rainforest

The forest of the Zaire Basin grows mostly on soils with moderate to high nutrient levels (high, that is, for rainforest soils, which are notoriously nutrient poor). There are relatively few areas of the highly-leached, nutrient-poor, white sand that are frequent in parts of the Far East and the Americas. The center of the basin contains large areas of swamp forest and open reed swamp, some still uninhabited and unexplored.

To the northwest, a strip of forest continues to the Cameroon Highlands and along the north coast of the Gulf of Guinea, including the whole of Gabon and Equatorial Guinea (the mainland and the islands) and southern Nigeria. After a gap of several hundred miles in the climatically drier region between Cotonou (Benin) and Accra (Ghana), the forest reappears as a 124-186 mi (200-300 km) wide strip running along the Atlantic coast from Ghana to Sierra Leone. The drier climate to the east of the Zaire Basin restricts the rainforest to localized outposts on mountain slopes in the Rift valley region. To the south, the Zaire rainforest gradually changes into a mosaic of forest and savannah, and the components elements become less and less significant as the rainfall becomes more seasonal.

Relatively dry conditions

One characteristic feature of the African rainforests is that they are comparatively dry. Only the wettest areas of the Cameroon Highlands equal the rainfall of large areas of Amazonia and the Far East, and even they tend to have a definite dry season for part of the year. Indeed, most African rainforest seems to be close to its climatic limits. Dry seasons occur once or twice a year, and the canopy trees of much of the Zaire Basin show a strong tendency to be deciduous, although the understory trees tend to be evergreen.

This deciduous habit is most noticeable in well-drained sandy soils in which the effects of the dry season on the trees are likely to be more severe. Even so, leaf loss is not automatic but is a graded response that depends on the water economy of the individual tree. In wetter-than-average years many canopy trees tend to keep their leaves during the dry season, often replacing them with new ones when the new rainy season starts.

In the wettest climates of eastern Democratic Republic of Congo and of Cameroon, the trees of Caesalpinoid legumes are abundant and sometimes dominant. Palms are rare in the African rainforest and occur only in special situations, such as where the forest has been disturbed. In comparison with America and the Far East, there are very few epiphytic plants on the branches of trees in African rainforest. This may be partly due to Africa's drier climate but is also an evolutionary consequence of the fact that the major epiphytic family, the Bromeliaceae, has not managed to reach Africa, in contrast to the hundreds of species of bromeliad that occur in the Americas.

There has been much discussion on how far the contemporary African rainforest flora and fauna reflects a history of arid episodes that led to the wiping out of the forest death in some areas but allowed it to survive in others. These refugia may have preserved species that have failed to increase their populations fast enough to spread and recover all their potential range. There are clear signs that the forest cover shrank in the last Ice Age, between 25,000 and 12,000 years ago.

The forest is known to have survived in some areas, such as Cameroon, but further west it virtually disappeared.

There are signs that the forest was replaced by savannah and grasslands over much of the Zaire basin, although there may have been considerable areas of swamp and fringing forest. In general, the fossil and geological evidence suggests that the areas with greater contemporary species diversity (for example, Cameroon and eastern Democratic Republic of Congo) were glacial refugia; these are precisely the areas, however, that now have a more humid climate. It is very difficult to disentangle the effects of glacial history and of current climate, especially when the fossil data on forest distribution in the last Ice Age are sparse and ambiguous.

Human influence

The current distribution of rainforest is to some extent natural and to some extent a consequence of a long history of human influence. Modern humans go back further in Africa than anywhere else, but it is difficult to assess their effects on rainforests before the arrival of agriculture some 3,000 years ago. The savannah-forest mosaic to the south of Zaire rainforest, which in the western Congo extends like a finger almost to the equator, is generally thought to be a recent result of denser agricultural populations burning the savannah to keep the forest at bay. Yet fossil remains show that at least some parts of this mosaic have existed since the last glaciation, about 20,000 years ago. It seems that the relative proportions of forest and savannah have fluctuated in accordance with climatic changes, and maybe as a response to changes in human population density. Pre-agricultural humans might also have burned the savannah (to make hunting easier) often enough to have significantly affected the area of forest. Since the spread of agriculture, the influence of shifting cultivation has been so pervasive that it has led many authors to wonder if there was any truly untouched forest left in Africa. Ecological studies of apparently primary forest have found ancient traces of cultivation and habitation, such as charcoal, ceramic fragments, and hut foundations.

During the 20th century, some parts of Africa have suffered the same rapid loss of forest cover occurring in other parts of the wet tropics. West Africa has already lost most of its natural forest cover as a result of the expanding agricultural population, and Cameroon is beginning to suffer the same problem.

22 **Large trees, such as this 164 ft (50 m) tall sapele (*Entandrophragma cylindricum*)**, are still common in the Zaire Basin rainforest. They are generally colonized by epiphytes but have a clearer undergrowth than the American or Asian rainforests (see figure 135).
[Photo: Sylvain Cordier / Jacana]

In contrast, most of central Africa remains densely forested and sparsely inhabited. Satellite images show relatively few fires provoked by cultivators, unlike the situation of many other areas in the wet tropics. There are, however, signs of the formation of a grid of plantations and croplands, and its spread through the rainforest in Democratic Republic of Congo, corresponding to the main road network. There are also large areas of cultivated ground on the Gabon coast, and there is intense forestry activity in parts of eastern Democratic Republic of Congo, although its real extent has never been accurately mapped. With the pressure exerted by the growing population and increasing investment by foreign timber companies, all expectations are that the demands on the central African rainforests will increase in the coming decades.

The Madagascar rainforest

Madagascar is generally very arid but along its eastern coastline the climate is wet enough to support a long strip of forest. The high proportion of endemic species of plant and animal (around 85% of all Madagascar's plant species are endemic) reflects its high degree of isolation. Surprisingly, this rainforest has levels of species richness comparable with continental rainforest areas with similar climates, as if evolution had worked overtime on Madagascar to ensure it had its full quota of biodiversity.

Madagascar's plants are distinctive but not that different. Madagascar has only been isolated for a short period in comparison with the age of the angiosperms, so there has not been enough time for the process of evolutionary divergence to go far. In contrast to the large number of endemic species, Madagascar's rainforests contain only a single endemic angiosperm family, the Humbertiaceae. Many of Madagascar's plants belong to genera that are also found elsewhere in the Old World tropics, perhaps having reached the island by spreading from the African mainland, although some have since evolved into a considerable number of new species. As an example, five native species of coffee (*Coffea*) can be found in just 0.8 mi^2 (2 km^2) of rainforest; their resistance to the diseases affecting cultivated coffee varieties of African origin means they clearly have the potential to produce hybrids of great economic importance.

One group of plants that has diversified greatly in Madagascar is the palm family (Palmae). The island has 12 endemic genera of palms (compared with only three endemic genera in continental Africa), but they all show close affinities to the palms of Asia. The other seven nonendemic genera all occur in eastern Asia too, although they also have close relatives in Africa. Orchids also show high diversity on the island, with almost a thousand described species (more than on the entire African mainland), many of them confined to the rainforest. Perhaps the most remarkable of all Madagascar's orchids is the white-flowered *Angraecum sesquipedale* which has a spur 14 in

23 **The rainforest of the eastern coast of Madagascar**, where it has not been degraded, is dense and exuberant, as shown by this photo of the Hoaraka region. The members of the Musaceae, such as the traveler's tree (*Ravenala madagascariensis*), spread their highly characteristic large, frayed leaves in small clearings. [Photo: Langrand Olivier / Bios / Still Pictures]

24 **The prosimians of Madagascar are essentially typical of the eastern rainforest**, as shown by the table. Yet there are some species that also, or even exclusively, live in the dry forest and xerophytic scrub formations in the southwest of the island. Some of these species first became known to science as recently as the 1980s, such as *Propithecus tattersalli* or *Hapalemur aureus* (see "Overlooked mammals," pages 58-61). Many of them have an uncertain future due to the rapid destruction of their habitats. They are a singular group of organisms of great biological importance. In addition to the zoological groups and common names, the table shows the average length of the individuals of these species (body + tail) (see figures 83, 209, 210, and 277). [Source: data drawn up by the authors, based on Petter, Albignac, and Rumpler, 1977]

FAMILY AND SPECIES	AVERAGE LENGTH (body and tail, in cm)	GEOGRAPHICAL LOCATION rainforest	other biomes
CHEIROGALEIDAE			
Allocebus trichotis (allocebus or hairy-eared mouse lemur)	13+17	•	-
Cheirogaleus major (greater dwarf lemur)	27+25	•	-
Cheirogaleus medius (fat-tailed dwarf lemur)	19+17	-	•
Microcebus murinus (maki, or mouse lemur)	13+13	•	-
Microcebus rufus (microcebus, or mouse lemur)	12+13	•	•
Mirza coquereli (dwarf lemur)	23+32	•	•
Phaner furcifer (tanta)	24+37	•	•
LEMURIDAE			
Eulemur coronatus (gidre)	50+60	•	•
Eulemur macaco (komba)	50+60	•	-
Eulemur mongoz (gidre)	50+60	-	•
Eulemur rubriventer (bari)	50+60	•	-
Hapalemur aureus (golden gentle lemur)	30+45	-	•
Hapalemur griseus (grey gentle lemur)	30+45	•	•
Hapalemur simus (broad-nosed gentle lemur)	40+40	•	-
Lemur catta (ring-tailed lemur, or maqui)	50+60	-	•
Petterus fulvus (brown lemur, or varika)	50+60	•	•
Varecia variegata (ruffed lemur)	60+60	•	-
MEGALADAPIDAE			
Lepilemur dorsalis (midwife lemur)	25+25	•	-
Lepilemur edwardi (repaka)	30+30	-	•
Lepilemur leucopus (tranga)	25+25	-	•
Lepilemur microdon (fitiliki)	35+25	•	-
Lepilemur mustelinus (sportive lemur, or sonigika)	35+25	•	-
Lepilemur ruficaudatus (boengui)	30+30	-	•
Lepilemur septentrionalis (midwife lemur)	30+30	•	-
INDRIIDAE			
Avahi laniger (fotsi, or wooly indri)	30+40	•	-
Indri indri (indri)	70+ 3	•	-
Propithecus diadema (simpona)	45+55	•	-
Propithecus tattersalli (simpona)	45+55	•	-
Propithecus verreauxi (Verreaux's sifaka)	45+55	-	•
DAUBENTONIIDAE			
Daubentonia madagascariensis (aye-aye)	50+60	•	-

(35 cm) long. Alfred R. Wallace predicted that there had to be a butterfly with a proboscis long enough to reach the nectar at the base of the spur and drink it, as otherwise the orchid would not be visited by insects and could not be pollinated. Entomologists poured scorn on this hypothesis, but sure enough a butterfly was found 40 years later with a 14 in (35 cm) proboscis, long enough to reach the base of the spur, just as Wallace had predicted. This butterfly *Xanthopan morganii* forma *praedicta* only completely extends its proboscis when it approaches these flowers with their long spurs; it hovers above the flower while drinking its nectar and the orchid pollinia adhere to its proboscis, ready to be carried to pollinate the next flower. One feature of Madagascar's fauna that is very typical is the Lemuridae, a group of primitive primates that were formerly widespread throughout the world but are now restricted to the Madagascar forest. Their isolation on the island-continent has probably saved them from competition (and possible extinction) with more recently evolved groups of primates.

4.3 The American rainforests

Within the linked catchment basins of the Orinoco and Amazon rivers lies the world's largest contiguous area of equatorial forest. This area, together with the Brazilian Mata Atlântica, the rainforests of Colombia's Pacific coastline, the Caribbean rainforests, and the Mesoamerican rainforest makes up the world's most impressive display of rainforest diversity.

The Amazon and Orinoco rainforest

The western limit to the Amazon and Orinoco rainforest is formed by the Andes, where rainforest grows to an altitude of 5,249-5,905 ft (1,600-1,800 m) from a northern limit in the Cordillera Macarena in Colombia to a southern limit in the Bolivian province of Santa Cruz. From east to west the northern limit is formed by the Atlantic coasts of northern Brazil (starting in the north-east in the state of Maranhão), of French

Guyana, Surinam, and in Venezuela of the Orinoco delta. Further west, the limit with the Llanos region of Venezuela and Colombia follows the lowlands of the southern banks of the Orinoco and the watershed between the Vichada and the Guaviare rivers. To the southeast the forest is limited by the highlands of the west of the Brazilian state of Maranhão, the watershed between the rivers Tocantins and Araguaia (Serra das Cordilheiras and the Serra do Estrondo) to the southeastern tip of the state of Pará and to the northern outcrops of the Mato Grosso plateau, of the Serra dos Parecis, and of the Llanos region of northeastern Bolivia. Along the valleys of several rivers, such as the Guaporé, the frontier between Brazil and Bolivia, and the river Mamoré, the San Miguel, or the Blanco, the forest reaches even further south. It also extends beyond these limits in the lower parts of some interior valleys in the Andes, from Colombia to Bolivia, especially in the valley of the Napo in Peru, which shows exceptional biodiversity.

The climatic regime

Moist eastward-blowing air from the Pacific supplies most of the region's rainfall, so that the wettest climates are found to the west, near the Andes, where the air still contains much water vapor. As it moves east, the predominant airstream current collects much of the water vapor evaporated by the forest, and then deposits it further east in the form of rain. Nevertheless, there is also a constant loss of water from the system, as it flows down the rivers straight into the Atlantic Ocean. As a result, the climate becomes drier from west to east across the Amazon basin, although it becomes wetter when it approaches the Atlantic coast in the northeast.

Amazonian rainforests live in a much wetter climate than their African counterparts. There are areas of semievergreen forest on the southern and eastern edges of the Amazon region, but there is also a very large core area of evergreen forest. These wetter areas have annual rainfall greater than 79 in (2,000 mm) and lack any marked dry season, and so there are fewer motives or opportunities for biological processes to become synchronized, and plant and animal growth and reproduction occur more evenly over the course of the year.

Nonfloodable Amazonian rainforest

The large area of the Amazonian forests, together with the regional peculiarities of soil types and

25 The immense flat Amazon forest, at least in the middle and low parts of the basin, is a dense, continuous blanket that is interrupted only by the meandering—due to the extremely low gradient—and endlessly zigzagging watercourses. The photo shows a tributary of the Madre de Dios river in Peru.
[Photo: André Bärtschi / Pictures]

river systems within the basin, allows the existence of very distinctive forest types, each with its own specialized flora. By far the largest area is covered by the forest type called *terra firme* forest, the characteristic formation people usually have in mind when referring to the Amazon rainforest. The terra firme forest occupies all the well-drained soils that are relatively rich in available nutrients. This forest is tall (131 ft [40 m] or more) and is usually very rich in tree species, with a dense upper canopy and a relatively dark, open interior.

Other forest types occur under conditions that in one way or another are less ideal for the growth of forest vegetation. The Amazonian *caatinga* forest (also known as *campina* or *campinarana*) grows on nutrient-poor bleached white sands in regions with black waters, forming a low scrubby forest of trees with small hard leaves, that should not be confused with the spiny true *caatinga* of northeastern Brazil. *Caatinga* is a Tupi-Guaraní word that literally means "white forest" and refers to forest that is without a continuous canopy block sunlight. Caatinga is scattered throughout the Amazon region, especially in the River Negro catchment area, where the soils are formed on ancient sea beaches and other sandy deposits.

Liana forest, known in Brazil as *cipó* or *cipoal*, is a relatively open forest in terms of its tree cover; but it is almost smothered by the huge number of climbing plants (lianas) growing on, up, over and among the trees. It often seems to occur on highly weathered lateritic ferralsols (see 1.3, page 37), and to be associated with deposits of iron (as in the Serra dos Carajas region) or of aluminium, although may also occur on the more fertile soils known in Brazil as *terra roxa*. The cipoal tends to form a mosaic

among the other types of forest and is particularly abundant in the area between Maraba and Itaituba on the route of the Trans-Amazon Highway.

Another type of more open forest that is widespread in Amazonia is palm forest dominated by babassu palms (*Orbignya* spp.). The fire resistant babassu forests are partly the product of human interference, a consequence of frequent burning. In terms of the indigenous economy of the forest regions, this forest type is important for the Brazil nut trees (*Bertholletia excelsa*) that are present.

Floodable Amazon forest

Although there are some areas of permanent swamp forest, this is much scarcer than the seasonally flooded forests lining the banks and floodplains of the Amazon and its tributaries. The highly seasonal nature of the flooding is the result of the Amazon's huge catchment basin. As it stretches along the equator to the Andes in the west, it receives the seasonal rain falling far to the north and to the south of the equator, which then flows down as immense surges. The water levels of the rivers even in the relatively nonseasonal areas closest to the equator, may reflect the seasonality of the waters in the catchment areas upstream.

Along the river systems of the Amazon basin there are several types of seasonally or intermittently flooded forest. Where a river drains areas with clay soils, the suspended sediments in the water are deposited over the tops of the banks when flooding occurs. This builds up broad long ridges along either side of the river (levees), called *restingas*, that channel the flow of the river and limit the area of flooding. This area of levee-tops and floodplains is known as *varzea*, and is covered by a type of forest also

26 **The arrangement of the different types of Amazon forest** in a basin with blackwater and sandy substrates (on the left), and a whitewater area loaded with sediments that form *restingas* (on the right). [Drawing: Jordi Corbera, based on E. F. Morán, 1990]

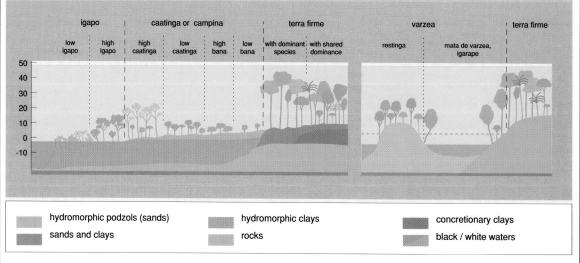

igapo | caatinga or campina | terra firme | varzea | terra firme

low igapo | high igapo | high caatinga | low caatinga | high bana | low bana | with dominant species | with shared dominance | restinga | mata de varzea, igarape

50
40
30
20
10
0
-10

hydromorphic podzols (sands)
sands and clays
hydromorphic clays
rocks
concretionary clays
black / white waters

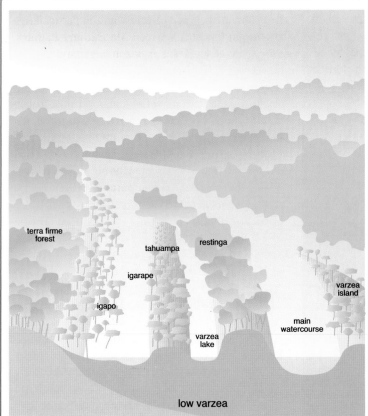

low varzea

high varzea

known as varzea, very similar in structure to the *terra firme* forest, although it is possible to distinguish three distinct types: the varzea lacking a dense herbaceous understory, typical of the upper Amazons (Solimões and Madeira); the more open varzea with large grasses, typical of the lower Amazon (between Manaus and the confluence with the Xingu), and the estuarine varzea, which has many species of palms. The trees tend to be strengthened by buttress roots (perhaps an adaptation to help anchorage in wet clay soils) and often have seeds with special flotation mechanisms that allow them to disperse when the river is in flood. The rubber tree (*Hevea brasiliensis*) is an example of a species that is clearly adapted to the varzea habitat, with seeds that can float for more than two months and form an important part of the diet of some fish. Possibly as a result of the regular supply of nutrient-rich sediments, the herbaceous understory layer is particularly rich in species of ferns and large members of the Marantaceae.

In clearwater and blackwater areas (i.e., where the water is dark and humic) where the underlying sediment consists of bleached podsolized sands, a very different type of flooded forest grows. This is the *igapo* of the regions of the Negro and Xingu River regions, a relatively low and species-poor forest that grows on nutrient-poor substrates that

are flooded, or at least waterlogged, more or less permanently. Many of the trees that have specialized in living in the igapo are members of the Myrtaceae, such as *Eugenia inundata*, and are zoned according to the differing degree of flooding. Partly due to the absence of levees, and partly because of the trees' relatively low height, the floods in the igapo forests are often high enough to reach the canopy.

Thus, at the height of the annual flood it is possible to experience the surreal sensation of canoeing through the rainforest canopy. The flood normally lasts a few weeks, or even months, and the trees need special biochemical adaptations to survive the lack of oxygen around their roots. During the flood season many trees release their fruit into the water, where they are eaten by fish. It seems that many of these trees are highly dependent on fish to spread their seeds, as their seeds have to pass through the gut of a fish before they can germinate.

Centers of diversity: real or imaginary

Within the Amazonian rainforest as a whole, there is undeniably a general gradient in diversity of tree species from west to east, mirroring the decline in annual rainfall. Yet many groups of animals and plants also show scattered centers of high diversity, with relatively large numbers of endemic species.

27 Idealized diagram of arrangement of the varzea zone in low and high waters (left and right, respectively). When the waters are high, both the igarapes or paranas, which are secondary arms of water—such as the tahuampas, which are swamps, and the lakes of varzea, which are lagoons, are covered by the water, leaving only the restingas standing above the water and the crowns of the trees on the islands of varzea. The igapo is always more-or-less flooded and the terra firme remains dry.
[Drawing: Jordi Corbera, from several sources]

28 The beautiful pendulous inflorescences of heliconias, such as this *Heliconia curtispatha* on the banks of the Palenque River (Ecuador), are a typical feature of the floodable areas of the Amazon forest.
[Photo: Adolf de Sostoa & Xavier Ferrer]

It has been suggested that these centers of diversity might have been refugia for rainforest species during the dry glacial periods, and that they have conserved many species that were too slow to disperse from these refugia when the forest expanded during the warmer interglacial periods. Recent studies, however, indicate that many of these centers of diversity may be no more than an illusion, resulting from the different quantities of field work done in the different areas. If more work has been performed collecting data in a given area, it is logical to expect that more species will have been discovered. It thus seems that further research will be necessary to establish if these centers of diversity really exist.

The Atlantic rainforest, the Mata Atlântica

Along the Atlantic coastal strip of southeastern Brazil, from Pernambuco to Rio Grande do Sul, the moist maritime air releases enough rainfall to support a long strip of rainforest. To the south, this forest blends imperceptibly into evergreen temperate forest, losing much of its species diversity as it does so. The small monkeys of the group of golden tamarins (*Leontopithecus*) are perhaps the most representative mammals of these rainforests (see insert "Overlooked mammals" on pages 58-61).

Separated from the main Amazon rainforest block by hundreds of miles of dry scrub and savannah, the Mata Atlântica has a high proportion of endemic species, although around half the tree species found in this forest (such as the conspicuous *Guarea guidonia*, Meliaceae) are also found in the Amazon forest or elsewhere in the Americas, reflecting some sort of common history in the recent past. Many of these nonendemic trees also occur scattered throughout the highly altered areas of tree savannah as small populations in strips of gallery forest along rivers. Thus, it is not difficult to see how they might have spread their seeds step by step across the small distances that separate one area of forest from another. Of course, former wetter periods might also have led to the spread of the gallery forest, thus making easier the gradual interchange of plants and animals.

The Caribbean forest

To the north of the central block of Amazon forest, many of the islands scattered throughout the

29 **The Brazilian Mata Atlântica and the Pacific coastal forest** are types of rainforest that are linked to the special climatic conditions that dominate the entire eastern Atlantic-facing front, from Pernambuco to Rio Grande do Sul and on the Pacific-facing front in Ecuador and Colombia. The "mata" is geographically separated from the Amazon rainforest, but has always been the area that people arriving in Brazil see first, helping to spread the incorrect idea that the entire country is an immense rainforest, as if the enormous areas of dry *cerrado*, arid *sertao* or swampy *pantanal* areas did not exist. The area of the mata also includes the large colonial or post-colonial cities, from Recife to São Salvador (Bahía) to São Paolo and Rio de Janeiro. The photos show the Mata Atlântica in the Carlos Botelho park in Brazil (left) and the Pacific coastal rainforest in the Ensenada de Utria park in Colombia (right).
[Photos: Adolf de Sostoa & Xavier Ferrer]

Caribbean are partially or totally covered by rainforest. Although much of this region has a seasonally quite dry climate, the steep relief of many of the islands means that the maritime air rises, cools, and releases its moisture in the forms of rain. Where this happens, annual rainfall may exceed 79 in (2,000 mm) and moist evergreen or semi-evergreen forest grows on lower mountain slopes and hills.

On Trinidad, mora (*Mora excelsa*) forms large stands in moist forests, but generally these forests are not dominated by any particular species. In the Windward Islands, at the southeastern tip of the Caribbean, typical trees of the forest canopy include *Sloanea caribea* (Elaeocarpaceae) and other species of the same genus, and *Canarium* spp. (Burseraceae). On the Greater Antilles (Cuba, Hispaniola, Jamaica, and Puerto Rico), species of figs (Moraceae) are particularly important, as are

species of *Psidium* (Myrtaceae), such as guava (*P. guajava*). These island forests are generally less species rich than those of the South American mainland, perhaps due partly to their current and past climate (dry with arid periods during the glaciations) and partly to their relative isolation from the larger sources of evolutionary innovation on the mainland. It is a general characteristic of islands that, when other factors such as climate are comparable, they tend to be poorer in species than mainland areas of the same size. The tree species that grow in the forests on the Caribbean islands show close affinities with those of Central and South America. Most genera are the same, and a large proportion of species are also shared with the mainland, (such as *Guarea guldonia* [Meliaceae], already mentioned, which grows in the Amazon forest, in Central America, and in the Mata Atlântica).

30 **The interwoven fabric of epiphytes and climbing plants** on the trees of the meso-American rainforest, in a photo taken in the Montes Azules National Park in Mexico. These formations are only 5° from the Tropic of Cancer and mark the northern limit of the rainforest.

[Photo: Adolf de Sostoa & Xavier Ferrer]

The Pacific coastal rainforest

On the western face of the Andes, in Colombia and in Ecuador, a narrow strip of forest runs parallel to the coast, in some inland valleys as far as the Peru-Ecuador frontier. Floristically and geographically, it is very close to the Amazonian forest on the other side of the Andes (only a few hundred miles away at the points of minimum separation), but they have probably been isolated from each other for millions of years, since the Andes arose between them. Thus, while many plants belong to the same genera as on the eastern face of the Andes, the species are different.

Annual rainfall is extremely high in the western foothills of the Andes (up to 9,000 mm in some places) and is distributed fairly evenly throughout the year. This perpetually moist climate has an excep-

tionally high number of species of trees, lianas, shrubs and herbaceous plants. The greatest diversity of forest trees ever recorded was found here—283 species of trees and lianas with stems 4 in (10 cm) or more in diameter in just 0.2 acres (0.1 ha) of forest. Furthermore, many plant species of these Andean foothill forests have extremely localized distributions, sometimes restricted to just one or two hilltops, while their place is occupied on the next hill by an equally localized species. On a broader scale this increases species richness even further, making these forests a truly remarkable reservoir of biodiversity.

The Mesoamerican rainforest

Further north, the forest of the western Andes connects with the Central American rainforest in Panama and then continues north to Mexico (where it reaches the Atlantic coast, in the south of the state of San Luis Potosí, and along the Pacific coastline to the Isthmus of Tehuantepec), except for areas with a more marked seasonal climate and a long dry season, such as the Pacific-facing regions of Nicaragua, El Salvador, and Guatemala or the northwest of the Yucatán Peninsula.

Although the Central American climate shows a certain tendency to be much more seasonal than the Colombian tropics, there is still a high number of species in the Central American forests. In Costa Rica a total of 233 species of plant were found in a single 1,076 sq. ft (100 m²) plot of forest! In general, the Central American forests are very similar in composition to those of the Amazonian and western Andes, with local endemic species mixed in with others that are more widespread throughout the region.

4.4 The Asiatic and Indo-Pacific rainforests

It has long been known that the rainforests of southern and southeastern Asia, Insulindia, New Guinea and Australia form a relatively coherent unit and share many floristic elements. The islands scattered between Indochina to the northwest, and Australia and New Guinea to the east, forms the floristic region known as Malesia, but it is too similar to the Indian region to be considered totally separate. The far eastern rainforests seem to be derived from separate and isolated floras that evolved on separate continental plates that later collided, allowing plants and animals to move between them. Each of these collisions has

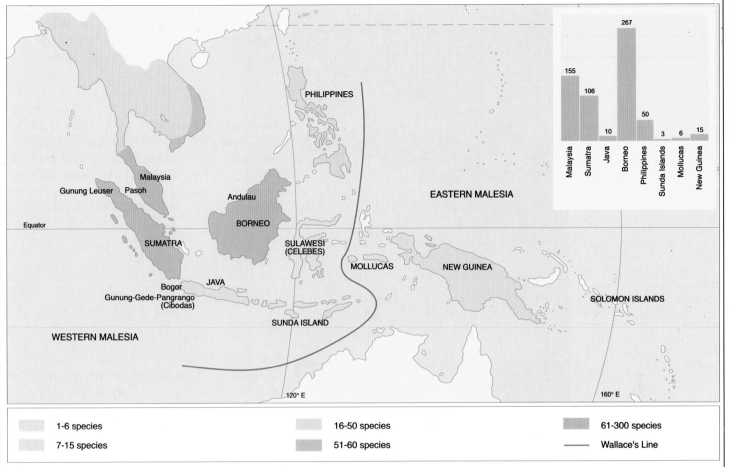

155	106	10	267	50	3	6	15
Malaysia	Sumatra	Java	Borneo	Philippines	Sunda Islands	Molluccas	New Guinea

Legend:
- 1-6 species
- 7-15 species
- 16-50 species
- 51-60 species
- 61-300 species
- Wallace's Line

left its mark on the biology of the forests and on the current distribution of plants and animals.

The flora of tropical Asia is clearly related to that of tropical Africa, a reflection of their remote common origin in the biota of the great northern continent of Laurasia, which was intermittently connected to Africa by a landbridge or separated from it by narrow stretches of sea. Further east there is also the floristic legacy of the long period of independent evolution of the Indo-Australian plate, which has now collided with the southeastern tip of the former Laurasian plate and received important contributions from its flora.

The Indian and Sri Lankan forest

Equatorial rainforest occurs in India in two widely separate areas: on the western maritime slopes of southern section of the western Ghats which run along the southwestern coast of the Indian Peninsula; and at the northeastern tip of India, near the frontiers with Myanmar (formerly Burma), China, and Bhutan. In both areas, semi-evergreen monsoon forest is more widespread than evergreen rainforest, probably due to the long history of human influence that has degraded the forest and soil structure, leading in turn to a more precarious water balance.

Dipterocarps are typical of the Asian forests and are important in both the southwest and in the northeast rainforest areas in India, but no species is common to both areas. In the Assam Valley in northwest India, isolated specimens of *Dipterocarpus macrocarpus* and *Shorea assamica* emerge above the canopy, reaching heights of up to 164 ft (50 m) with trunks more than 7 ft (2 m) in diameter. In the western Ghats, huge buttressed specimens of other species of *Dipterocarpus* rise straight up for more than 98 ft (30 m) before their first branch.

In general, the forests of the western Ghats are more diverse than those of Assam; this relatively small area of mountain contains more than 4,000 plant species, of which about 1,800 are endemic, mostly confined to the rainforest rather than to the other drier types of vegetation that also develop. As might be expected, the greatest species diversity is found in the humid southernmost forests of the Western Ghats where the dry season is shortest.

Sri Lanka's lowland rainforest would naturally occupy most of the southwestern half of the island, where annual rainfall is between 138 and

31 The distribution of dipterocarps in Malesia, showing Wallace's Line separating the two main centers of distribution. It is considered that Malesia (a floristic region with 25,000 species of higher plants, four endemic families and almost 400 endemic genera) consists of two major centers of origin and dispersal. One center is formed by Borneo, Java, Sumatra and the part of the Malaysian Peninsula that formed part of the former Sunda, from where most of these groups of plants and animals spread to the Asian continent and the Philippines. The other center consists of part of New Guinea that formed part of the ancient Papualand, from where they spread northwards by way of Gilolo, Molluccas and Celebes, towards the Philippines and eastern Australia and to Polynesia. It is now thought that the Malesian flora contains the key to many of the unknown details of the biogeographical history of the higher plants, as a result of its strategic position (see diagram 102). *[Drawing: Editrònica, from several sources]*

32 Swamp forest is a very distinctive form of rainforest, typical of some areas of western Malesia, such as the area shown in the photo, in the basin of the Seyonker River in the National Park of Tanjung Puting (Borneo). These forests may accumulate a layer of peat up to 66 ft (20 m) thick, and are covered in the flood period by a layer of water up to a 5 ft (1.5 m) deep. Their root systems obviously have to deal with an extreme abundance of humic acids, clearly shown by the color of the water, which lower the soil pH to less than five. Yet species diversity in this flora is very high and is dominated by species of *Shorea*; also some well known primates, such as the orangutan (*Pongo pygmaeus*) are relatively abundant in the forest.

[Photo: Wayne Lawler / Auscape International]

197 in (3,500 and 5,000 mm), but over the last few decades it has been sharply reduced in area. Many plant genera show affinities with those from southeast Asia, such as *Mesua* (Guttiferae), and *Vitex* (Verbenaceae). Dipterocarps are also locally important, with species such as *Dipterocarpus hispidus* and *Shorea* spp. occurring on the fertile wet soils of flood plains.

The western Malesian forest

The equatorial rainforests of west Malesia (Indochina and Insulindia) were first described in the last century, and they were not well mapped until satellite data became available. These rainforests cover the entire surface of the large islands of Sumatra, Java, and Borneo, the Molucca Islands, most of the island of Celebes, and much of the Philippines (except for the western part of the archipelago). To the north, the forest blends into deciduous monsoon forest, but bands with wet climates allow the forest to continue to its northernmost point in southern China.

The flora and fauna
Surprisingly, the scattered rainforest-covered islands of western Malesia have very similar floras and faunas. Many of these islands are separated from each other by hundreds of kilometers of seawater, and this might lead one to expect evolution to have followed different paths, due to the islands' relative isolation. Yet, as is generally true in the tropics, this great similarity between islands is a legacy of former landbridges. These links were last present in western Malesia about 10,000 years ago, after the last glaciation but before sea level had risen to its current level. Yet many local endemic species and local races remain restricted to a single island, or parts of it, although these differences may have more to do with variations in climate and soil type than with their recent isolation due to the rise in sea level.

Climatic fluctuations
Studies on the behavior of rainforest trees in Malaysia show that even the slight dip in rainfall that occurs twice a year is enough to stimulate leaf renewal and flowering in many species. The cue that the trees are detecting might be increased drought stress or a small change of temperature in the canopy. Some trees, especially members of the Dipterocarpaceae, do not reproduce every year, but show "mast fruiting," that is, they only flower every few years, when all the members of a population flower together over a large area. Mast fruiting appears to be synchronized with the occasional dry periods that may occur in even the wettest regions. These occasional droughts tend to be associated with El Niño (the El Niño Southern Oscillation event, ENSO, see volume 10, pages 40-43). The 1982 El Niño led to a long drought in Borneo and the destruction by fire of large areas of rainforest. The fires were made worse by a previous increase in forestry activity that had left inflammable debris scattered throughout the forest. Apparently, many of these fires were deliberately lit by shifting cultivators to clear small patches of forest but quickly went out of control.

Western Malesian forest types
The canopy of the western Malesian forest is normally 98-131 ft (30-40 m) high, with some large emergents reaching 197-230 ft (60-70 m). Most forests in the region live under conditions showing little seasonality and over 79 in (2,000 mm) of annual rainfall evenly distributed over the year. The wettest of all these climates is in northeast Borneo, where tree species diversity also reaches its highest levels. On special soil conditions, caused by variations in geology or drainage, different types of forest occur, each with its own characteristic assemblage of tree species, together with more widespread species.

Keranga is ecologically very similar to the Amazonian *caatinga*. It is lower than other lowland rainforest types, and the dominant species resemble heath; their clusters of small leaves on erect branches explain why the term *heath forest* is used for this forest type found in some zones of Malaysia. Like the Amazonian caatinga this forest grows on nutrient-poor podzolized soils. The abundant phenolic derivatives in the leaves, such as tannins, are thought to be a defense mechanism against herbivorous insects, so the plant does not lose its valuable nutrients. The phenolic derivatives seem to be responsible for the black coloration of the rivers in these areas, which are similar in color to strong black tea.

The spectacular karstic landscapes of Borneo and the Malayan Peninsula have their specific forest type, *limestone forest*, with calcicolous species. These areas have a very rich flora and many endemic trees and herbaceous plants that cling to the limestone rock faces. As limestone is so well-drained, the forests growing on it suffer relative

Overlooked mammals

Tri excitedly pointed to a group of plants, though not because they were particularly extraordinary or because they revealed anything of botanical interest. It was just that most of the highest shoots had been nibbled. Judging by the damage—a clear and still fresh wound—it was obvious that they had been chewed fairly recently, perhaps even only the day before. Tri and I both realized the significance of the discovery at once for this type of knowledge is basic in the jungle. "Son duong!" he cried. And then he added in simple Vietnamese for my benefit: "The wild goat has eaten here."

Stuffed head of son duong (*Pseudoryx nghetinhensis*) [Michael Gunther / Bios / Still Pictures]

Stuffed specimen of son duong (*Pseudoryx nghetinhensis*) [Michael Gunther / Bios / Still Pictures]

This fragment is from the camp diary of the World Wide Fund for Nature (WWF) expedition that in May 1992 penetrated the Vu Quang jungle in the north of Vietnam. They went there because of a rumor and returned with evidence that at the end of the 20th century a medium-sized mammal unknown to science was living in this corner of the Vietnamese rain forest. Quite a surprise! Even more of a surprise if you consider the fact that the locals, like the expedition's guide, Nguyen Van Tri, were very familiar with the *son duong* (wild goat), or *sao la* (long horns), also known as *vu quang*

and had long hunted it for its meat and horns and skin and bones, and had used whatever was not eaten for medicines or for magic potions.

A specimen, if this is the correct word to describe a set of horns and a skin, was finally obtained by the WWF expedition from a more proficient local hunter who had already skinned the animal by the time the WWF scientists were shaking with emotion at the sight of chewed plants and fresh footprints in the jungle. From these remains, and others from 20 different individuals, zoologists and molecular biologists in Copenhagen and Cambridge were able to piece together the son duong and give it a formal scientific name, *Pseudoryx nghetinhensis*. Two years after, in 1994, a living specimen was finally captured, a female with very short horns, that actually lives in the Vu Quang (Vietnam) reserve.

Okapi (*Okapia johnstoni*) [Alain Rainon / Jacana]

Engraving of okapis (*Okapia johnstoni*) [Dominique Halleux / Bios / Still Pictures]

It is a primitive bovid which weighs in at around 220.5 lb (100 kg), resembling equally a small antelope and a goat, with horns like an oryx. In short, it is evidence that many things are still hidden in the obscure depths of the fascinating diversity of the rainforest. After all, as we now know, it is not only insects or minute organisms that have been overlooked until now, but an ox, complete with horns! This is not an isolated case, as the relatively recent scientific discovery in 1937 of the so-called Kouprey ox (*Bos sauveli*), also in the Indo Chinese rain forest, illustrates. And indeed more recently, in 1994, also in Vu Quang, a new muntjak of great size, the *Megamuntiacus vuquangensis* was discovered. And then there is the famous case of the okapi (*Okapia johnstoni*), a zebra like member of the giraffe family, discovered in the Zaire rainforest in 1901, which must have provided many generations of pygmies with fresh and smoked meat.

Several similar events have occurred in the rainforests of Madagascar where the discovery of new species of lemur has become commonplace. In 1970, *Lepilemur septentrionalis* was described scientifically and in 1987 *Hapalemur aureus* was discovered. The story of these two finds are quite distinct from each other and illustrate modern research into mammals.

Golden tamarin (Leontopithecus chrysomelas) [Rod Williams / Bruce Coleman Limited]

Lepilemur septentrionalis was not discovered in the wild but in the laboratory. Examples of the species had been known for some time, but had always been confused with a close relative and eventually they were distinguished by chromosome analysis. On the other hand, *Hapalemur aureus* had never been seen until it was spotted by chance in 1985 by an expedition to the Kianjavato jungle, ostensibly in search of a third lemur, *H. simus*, which had been seen again in 1972 after having been presumed extinct since 1900. In 1985 they caught glimpses of a previously unknown species and two years later the first specimens were caught in Ranomafana, near Kinjavato, of *H. aureus*, thereby adding another species to the list of Madagascar's prosimians.

Unlike the son duong, this new lemur was unknown to the inhabitants of the area although its relatives, the relatively common *H. griseus*, and the now famous *H. simus*, were familiar and were both referred to as *bokombolo*, or "bamboo eater," a fitting name given the species' habitat and alimentary habits. In light of recent studies which estimate that the total population of *H. aureus* consists of barely a couple of hundred individuals, it is perhaps not surprising that it was unknown to the locals—further evidence of the fragility of the great biodiversity of the rain forest.

One final recently discovered primate is the golden black-faced tamarin (*Leontopithecus caissera*). This small, Mephistophelian-looking simian was first seen in 1991 and scientifically described the following year. Small and nervous like all tamarins, this monkey barely measures the width of a person's hand (tail apart). Aside from the face and the front part of the head which are dark, it is a reddish color and is known as *leoncito*, or little lion. Tamarins live throughout the South American rainforest, although the golden tamarins (*Leontopithecus chrysomelas*, *L. chrysopygus*, *L. rosalia*) only occur in the forests of Brazil's Mata Atlântica. The golden black-faced tamarin is also present in the Mata but remarkably, it seems to be confined to the small island of Superagui in the Paranaguá Bay. In other words, a new species of primate was discovered in 1991 just outside Paranaguá, the port of Curitiba, a city of one and a half million people!

The biological richness of the rainforest undoubtedly still has many further surprises in store for us.

Golden gentle lemur *Hapalemur aureus* [Dominique Halleux / Bios / Still Pictures]

33 **The Australian rainforest shows very high levels of endemism**. A good example is the beautiful palm *Licuala ramsayi*, whose orbicular leaves are clearly visible in this photograph of a specimen in the Queensland rainforest.
[Photo: Gilles Martin / Bios / Still Pictures]

drought stress in the dry season, and often develop autumn colors before shedding their leaves.

Swamp forest of various sorts occupies large areas of western Malesia, especially in Borneo. *Peat swamp forest* has a layer of peat, varying in thickness from an inch to several feet, under the trees' shallow roots. Unlike dry land forests, dipterocarps rarely dominate, although species like *Shorea platycarpa* sometimes form dense stands. The peat swamp forest in eastern Borneo suffered especially badly from the drought and fires in early 1983. At the time, the water table fell so far that large areas of the peat dried out and then burned, killing the trees rooted in it.

The eastern Malesian and Polynesian rainforest

The eastern Malesian region (New Guinea and northeastern Australia) consists basically of the eastern part of the Indoaustralian plate, part of the former southern continent of Gondwanaland. Australia and New Guinea are now separated from each other only by a shallow continental sea and have repeatedly been joined by a landbridge in the past, especially in periods of low sea level during the last two million years. Equatorial or subequatorial rainforest climates were apparently present over much of the northern half of Australia in the mid-Tertiary, but the rainforest is now restricted to a few fragments on the Queensland coastline. New Guinea, however, is still largely covered by rainforest, together with a few areas of monsoon forest on its southern and eastern edges and cloud forest on the highest mountains inland. Further east, rainforests also occur on many islands of the tropical Pacific.

The rainforests of Australia and New Guinea are now dominated by western Malesian plant groups that have managed to spread across the Eurasian and the Indo-Australian plate collision boundary. Many are isolated species belonging to genera that are much more diverse in western Malesia. Even so, some endemic or almost endemic Australian and New Guinea rainforest genera, even canopy trees, are found, such as the genus *Doryphora* (Monimiaceae), and include a large element of indigenous plant groups of the ancient rainforest flora. One legacy from this past is that some conifer genera, such as *Araucaria*, *Dacrydium*, *Podocarpus* and *Agathis*, still occur in lowland rainforest, sometimes in extensive stands. The only rainforest eucalyptus, *Eucalyptus deglupta* forms pure stands in the New Guinea *keranga* heath forests, and is of great economic importance as a timber tree; it has been widely planted in reforestation in many tropical regions outside its area.

2
Life in the rainforests

1. The ecological functioning of rainforests

1.1 The materials cycle

The rainforest's physiology is as dynamic as its morphology is diverse. It acts as a vibrant metabolic machine and reveals its workings: Everything, or almost everything, is visible to the naked eye and little or nothing happens underground. Temperate forest soils store nutrients and govern forest physiology, with elaborate but nutritionally modest aerial parts, yet rainforest soils are mere supports for the ecosystem. Rainforest life is above ground, the reason why it is so difficult for it to regenerate after destruction.

The behavior of biomass

Competition for light in terrestrial systems leads to the vegetation growing upwards to raise the leaves towards the light. This increase in height implies the extension of the vertical transport systems for water and nutrients, and all in all, represents a delay in the system's cycling of nutrients, because the structures built have to be resistant. This means the increase in wood biomass parallels the increase in leaf area per unit surface area. The rainforest, rarely limited by light, water or temperature, reaches the greatest height of all terrestrial ecosystems and has the greatest accumulated biomass.

Clearly, the rainforest plants' lush, apparently evergreen, foliage must over time produce new leaves and accumulate a mass of old, photosynthetically useless ones. The varied but omnipresent green seen by visitors contains varied patches: trees whose leaves are withering and others that have shed their leaves grow next to trees in full leaf. In contrast to other biomes, the leaves on one branch of a single tree may be withering, while those on the next branch have fallen and a third branch is in active growth. The explanation for this lies in the uniformity of the climate. The absence of a clear dry period or cold season to serve as a cue for the plants means that every individual flowers and fruits according to an internal rhythm that is in some cases adapted to the slight variations in the equatorial climate. Some deciduous or semi-deciduous rainforest trees may lose all their leaves, but do so without following any seasonal pattern.

Leaves are always falling on the rainforest soil, though not as dramatically as the seasonal leaf-fall in deciduous forests. This endless rain consists of flowers, fruits, and twigs, and to a lesser extent, branches and trunks. All this now useless material (except the fruits) still contains a lot of energy in its chemical bonds. They form the stock of inorganic molecules and nutrients required by the forest organisms as a whole. Rainforest soil contains more than plant remains, as the fauna contributes its bones, skin, scales and, above all, excrement to the soil. Leaf litter is, however, by far the most important component.

Mineralization processes

The volume of remains falling on the soil is about the same from year to year (the greatest difference observed between years is less than 12%). This dead forest material would pile up without the hordes of organisms (collembola [springtails], termites, and other insects, millipedes, acarids, fungi, bacteria, etc.) that break them down to carbon dioxide and mineral salts.

Decomposition releases carbon dioxide into the atmosphere. A simple way of measuring total soil decomposition is to measure the quantity of carbon dioxide released. As temperature and humidity are highly constant, soil respiration should hardly fluctuate over the year. It is advisable to take frequent measurements. Lowland rainforest in Java shows respiration rates of 21 mg CO_2 per ft^2 (224 mg CO_2 per m^2) per hour, corresponding

34 The ecological diversity and complexity of the rainforest are legendary, and even clichés. This is especially true of the insects, as there are hundreds of thousands, if not millions, of rainforest species. The remarkable caterpillar in this photo is just one example; this caterpillar of the butterfly *Lexias dirtea* is hungrily gnawing at a leaf in the Malaysian jungle. *[Photo: Kevin Rushby / Bruce Coleman Limited]*

35 The lack of clear seasons in the intertropical area (top photo) means that flowering and even leaf-fall are performed by each species—and even by each individual, independently of the rest of its species—depending on their internal rhythms, totally asynchronous with respect to other species and nearby members of the same species. At any given moment, as shown by this photo of the crowns of Central American rainforest in Darién (Panama), there may be trees in flower, trees in leaf, and even trees whose leaves have been shed (showing the slightly monsoonal nature of the park's climate).
[Photo: Javier Andrada]

36 The decomposition and mineralization of the organic material reaching the soil of the rainforest involves, above all, termites (second from top), insatiable wood-eaters that play an extremely important role. Fungi (second from bottom) also play an important role. Earthworms (bottom) play an important role in later stages of the process. The first two photos were taken in Cuyabeno (Ecuador) and the third in a forest in Goma (Democratic Republic of Congo).
[Photos: Adolf de Sostoa & Xavier Ferrer and Xavier Ferrer]

to 10.7 t per hectare (1 hectare=2.47 acres) per year. As leaf-fall accumulation in these rainforests is around 10.9 t per hectare per year, the annual balance in this forest clearly shows a very slight increase in the soil organic material. Decomposition, however, is not always so fast, and a rate of 5 t per hectare per year was recorded in an Amazonian forest below the confluence of the Branco and Negro River. Other data suggest the annual rate of leaf litter decomposition in rainforests is about 80%. This rapid decomposition, together with the slow rate of polymerization and humus formation, explains these soils' low humus content.

Decomposer organisms are mainly invertebrates and saprophagous microorganisms. As they feed, they not only obtain energy but also progressively break down the organic molecules to their mineral forms. The process is generally started by invertebrates, especially acarid mites and collembola, which prepare the materials for the action of fungi and bacteria, which are highly versatile decomposers. Both fungi and bacteria can break down the cellulose of plant cell walls, the most abundant constituent of leaves. The species of fungi with enzymes to break down lignin for its energy play an important role in rainforests, as lignin is highly resistant and forms the bulk of wood.

Termites are major decomposers and may represent 70% of the weight of invertebrates in the leaf litter. In the rainforests of the Democratic Republic of Congo and the Ivory Coast there may be more than 870 termite colonies per hectare (a biomass of 16 t/ha), enough to consume a third of all organic remains. Termites have symbiotic microorganisms (normally protoctists, but bacteria in some groups) in their gut to digest cellulose; some termites also cultivate fungi (*Termitomyces*, *Xylaria*) on piles of chewed, swallowed and defecated wood pellets; the fungi grow on these piles and the termite nymphs are fed the apparently highly nutritious fungal conidiophores, filaments bearing the asexual spores that form part of the reproductive cycle.

Earthworms burrowing in the soil also play a role in the breakdown of organic remains, either directly as in the mineralization of nitrogen compounds, or indirectly, by favoring the oxygenation of the soil. The breakdown of organic material to the inorganic forms available to plants requires oxygen, and earthworm burrows aerate the soil, allowing oxygen to diffuse freely.

Most decomposition, however, depends on microorganisms (fungi and bacteria, together known as the microflora) and not on the invertebrates (microfauna). If the soil microfauna is removed, the rate of decomposition (measured as weight loss) remains high. Fungi act mainly in the early stages of decomposition, and play a more important role in tropical rainforests than in temperate forests.

Wood and leaf litter as control factors

The volume of leaf litter consumed by decomposers determines the reserves of elements and inorganic molecules remaining in the dry leaves, out of reach to the roots. In rainforest, where humidity and temperatures are high, the fraction of nutrients retained in the leaf litter is less than in the other components. There are, however, exceptions: in a Surinam rainforest with a 3 ft (1 m) thick accumulated layer of leaf litter, the largest fraction is clearly not in the vegetation! Apart from these exceptions, nutrients rarely remain in the rainforest leaf litter for more than a year (measurements for phosphorus, calcium, magnesium and potassium range from two and a half to 14 months). As we shall see, the obvious high fertility of the rainforest is made possible by this rapid cycling of nutrients.

Obviously, leaves break down more quickly than wood. Complete leaf breakdown takes 150-300 days in a primary forest in Guatemala, but several years are necessary for total breakdown of all the wood. The rate of breakdown depends on the size of the fragments, and the smaller particles are obviously the first to disappear. In the Ivory Coast, branches 0.4-0.8 in (1-2 cm) in diameter take half a year to lose a third of their dry weight (i.e., discounting the weight of water). In Nigeria, in slightly wetter rainforest, blocks of wood 10 in (25 cm) in diameter may take seven months to lose a quarter of their dry weight. Even so, in the Panama forest, a whole tree can decompose in less than 10 years.

The input of wood into the soil organic material is less than the leaf input but is still large. Almost 20 t of organic material per hectare per year enters the soil, and almost one third is dead wood. The decomposition of wood occurs mainly on the soil surface. In El Verde (Puerto Rico) about 56 g/ft^2 (600

37 Data for the amount of leaf litter falling on the soil, the average quantity in the soil and the rate of decomposition for the fine leaf litter in the rainforest from different research stations. These different areas include all the different types of forest, ranging from lowland rainforest to semideciduous forest, as well as the Indonesian swamp forest and cloud forest.
[Source: data drawn up by T.C. Whitmore in Ecosystems of the World]

TYPE OF FORMATION AND GEOGRAPHICAL LOCATION	LEAF LITTER DEPOSITION (t/ha/year) (a)	SOIL LEAF–LITTER (t/ha) (b)	DECOMPOSITION RATE (K= a/b)
Evergreen lowland rainforest			
Mulu (Sarawak, Malaysia): ridge	7.7	5.9	1.3
Mulu (Sarawak, Malaysia): alluvial valley	9.4	5.5	1.7
Pasoh (Malaysia)	10.6	3.2	3.3
Penang (Malaysia)	7.5	4.9	1.5
Manaus (Brazil)	7.6	7.2	1.1
Semideciduous rainforest			
Barro Colorado (Panama)	13.3	11.2	1.2
Kade (Ghana)	9.7	4.9	2.0
Keranga			
Mulu (Sarawak, Malaysia)			
Forest on calcareous soil			
Mulu (Sarawak, Malaysia)	10.4	7.1	1.5
Swamp forest			
Tasik Bera (Pahang, Malaysia)	9.2	4.8	1.9
Montane rainforest			
New Guinea (four sites at about 2,500 m)	6.2-6.6	4.2-6.6	1.0-1.5
Colombia (1,630 m)	10.1	16.5	0.6
Barva Volcano (Costa Rica, 1,000 m)	6.6	4.2	1.6
Barva Volcano (Costa Rica, 2,000 m)	5.8	5.2	1.1
Barva Volcano (Costa Rica, 2,600 m)	5.3	6.3	0.8

g/m^2) of woody remains are generated per year, of which 5 g are branches and trunks, 13 g are roots and 37 g are twigs. In the Pasoh forest in Malaysia every year about 31 g/ft^2 (330 g/m^2) of branches with a diameter greater than 4 in (10 cm) fall on the soil every year.

The rate of decomposition depends on a series of factors: in a single site, total leaf decomposition may take from two and a half to six months. It also varies from region to region and depends on the plant species in question; palm leaves, for example, are more resistant, taking approximately 20% longer to break down than those of other plants. In El Verde it has been observed that the rate of decomposition of the leaves of one species may be two and a half times fast as those of another species. Other factors affecting the rate of decomposition are leaf age (older leaves decomposing more slowly) and humidity, which accelerates decomposition if annual fluctuations occur. The balance between rainfall and the rate of decomposition might explain variations from year to year. Rainfall also indirectly affects the rate of decomposition through the fauna and microorganisms.

Nutrient supply

The final result of the decomposition of organic material is the return of mineral nutrients (phosphates, nitrates, potassium ions, etc.) to the soil in a form available to plant roots. In tropical soils, the clayey mineral fraction is dominated by kaolinite (which has a low cation absorption capacity), and rainfall is so frequent and so heavy that it is essential to recover nutrients as quickly as possible before they are lost by leaching.

Root nutrient uptake

The risk of nutrient loss through leaching explains the extraordinary abundance of very shallow roots (in a rainforest in Ivory Coast 20-50% of the roots are in the top 4 in [10 cm] of soil). These overlapping and interlocking roots compete for the scarce free nutrients. In rainforests growing on nutrient-poor soils, the ground surface is often covered by hundreds of winding and interlocking lignified roots, in a frantic search for nutrients in the almost exhausted soil.

Root nutrient uptake closes the nutrient cycles, which may show several variants. When plant materials decompose, the cycle is short, as their nutrients are released to the soil and rapidly taken up again by the root hairs. If the plant materials are consumed by herbivores (or their remains by organisms that eat decaying matter [saprophagous]), that are then eaten by other animals, a chain of nutrient transfer starts that may further delay their uptake by roots, resulting in a complex cycle. This complexity increases if parasites intervene.

Mycorrhiza are very common on tropical trees. As their name indicates, mycorrhiza support a symbiotic relationship between a fungus and the roots of a

38 Rainforest trees have highly superficial root systems, because the rapid breakdown and high demand by plants means that their roots need to capture the minerals as soon as they are available, without waiting for them to filter through the soil. This reduces their ability to anchor the plant, as they spread in a large but shallow horizontal network, as is shown by this fallen tree in the Costa Rica rainforest (above) and by the interlocking superficial roots of a tree in the Ujung Kulon National Park in Java (below). This is why buttresses are so common in rainforest trees. *[Photos: Michael & Patricia Fogden and J.C. Muñoz / Incafo]*

plant. The web of fungal hyphae helps the uptake of salts by the plant, while the roots supply the fungus with organic compounds. In some cases, nutrients may flow directly, without any intervening breakdown to mineral forms, from the leaf litter to the roots through a decomposer—the fungus of the mycorrhiza. This direct flow of nutrients is very important in those environments where soil nutrient reserves are so small.

Nutrient cycles

In the rainforest the organisms themselves are its nutrient reserve. They are not static reserves, but highly dynamic. Nutrients generally have a residence half-life of about 15 years in the vegetation and less than one year in the leaf litter. This, how-

ever, requires some further clarification. A study in a Panama rainforest to estimate the turnover of phosphorus, calcium, magnesium, and potassium gave residence times of three months for fruit, about 12 months for leaf litter, and 12-15 years for timber. Data from Puerto Rico and Ghana coincide closely with those from Panama. Trunks and branches are the main nutrient reserve, followed by roots, and then, at a distance, by leaves, flowers and fruit. The greatest nutrient accumulation is at the lower levels of the rainforest's structure.

Nitrogen's behavior and characteristics distinguish it from other nutrients. It is essential for plants, but other organisms can fix nitrogen from the atmosphere and supply it to their roots. The

39 **The forest nutrient cycle** can be summarized schematically in the upper diagram. The lower table shows the levels of the main nutrients (nitrogen, phosphorus, potassium, calcium and magnesium) corresponding to four sample stations in different places in different parts of the world, to show the distribution of the inorganic nutrients above and below the soil layer. It also shows the values for biomass (in brackets). Note that the widely-held idea that most of the forest's nutrients are in the biomass is not always correct. Also note that the soil is in all cases, a layer from 0-1 ft (0-0.3 m), except in Costa Rica where it is from 0-0.8 ft (0-0.25 m).
[Drawing: Jordi Corbera, based on several sources]

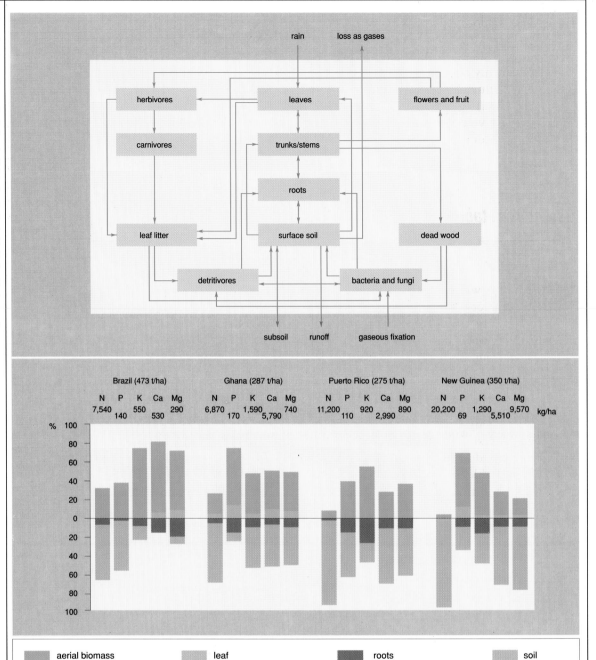

tropical members of the Leguminosae (many of them, but not all, of which are trees) may form a symbiosis with *Rhizobium* or other nitrogen-fixing bacteria.

Other tropical plants that are not members of the Leguminosae, such as species of *Dioscorea, Cycas* and some members of the Rubiaceae, have nitrogen-fixing nodules on their roots, stems or leaves. The free-living nitrogen-fixing bacteria are an important source of nitrogen for the ecosystem (0.4-2 g of N/ft^2/yr [4 and 24 g /m^2/year). Nitrogen is rapidly broken down to mineral forms in leaf decomposition and returns to the soil.

Loss of fertility
The effective cycling of elements in the rainforest means that watercourses, where the forest is still intact, are usually very poor in salts. The slight losses of nutrients detected may be replaced by the ions in rainwater. In the Mondo catchment basin in Java, the only soluble residue lost was silicic acid, and loss varied greatly with the flow of the river: about 0.4 t/ha/year.

In contrast, felling and burning the rainforest leads to great nutrient loss, either in the timber extracted or due to leaching of the ashes left in burned areas. A clearcut area repeatedly used for cultivation, becomes extremely poor after just a few cycles, supporting only herbaceous plants (the grass *Imperata*, [Poaceae] and the fern *Gleichenia* in Malaysia, and the fern *Pteridium* in Brazil). Thus, only areas with an external supply of nutrients (alluvial deposits, fertilization by new volcanic ash) or those with special characteristics (recent volcanic soils) are suitable for continued use after the forest has been cut.

1.2 Rapid metabolism, modest productivity

The rainforest is widely thought to show a great deal of growth every year. This impression is only half true and may well be due to observing the vegetation from watercourses, from paths through the jungle, or from clearings in the rainforest, i.e., from outside the rainforest, from a position where abundant light enters and where many pioneer heliophilous plants thrive and grow very rapidly. Yet the forest's large trees (40 years or older) do not grow very fast, hardly ever exceeding 3 mm growth in trunk diameter per year. The tropical forest is remarkable for its high accumulated biomass, not its high net production.

Yet the rainforest's highly complex structure shows that it is not immobile or static, as every 40-100 years the entire fabric dies and turns over.

Changes occur at the level of the species, the community or even the entire forest. On a shorter time-scale, there are also each individual's phenologically characteristic changes in production of leaves, flowers, and fruit.

Rainforest dynamics and productivity

Rainforest dynamics are thus more changeable than might at first appear. Nor are they homogenous in space, and they may show different physiognomies corresponding to different stages on the way to a hypothetical climax, the final mature stage. Schematically, there are three stages: the open phase, after tree fall or minor human intervention, where the trees have still not reached a height of 10 ft (3 m); the regeneration phase, when the trees grow in diameter and height; and finally the mature phase, when the trees stop growing in height while trunk diameter continues to increase, but declines almost to nothing. The duration of the mature phase means it occupies most of the rainforest. The open phase occupies only about a tenth of the forest.

Production and productivity
The production of organic material in the rainforest is very different depending on which stage the forest is in. Here we shall discuss the production of the mature stage of the rainforest. Plants catch sunlight (see volume 1, pages 186-192) and use it

40 The stratification of the different levels of vegetation is a very characteristic feature of rainforests, where species that are always present may never come into contact with each other, as they may be located in strata that are separated from each other. This occurs with the different tree species, which sometimes have crowns that barely reach halfway up the trunk of the tallest trees, and is especially true for the epiphytes, each growing at its own level, as shown by the photo of the Mata Atlântica in Brazil, with specimens at different heights of *Philodendron*, *Aechmea*, and *Vriesia*. [Photo: Tony Morrison / South American Pictures]

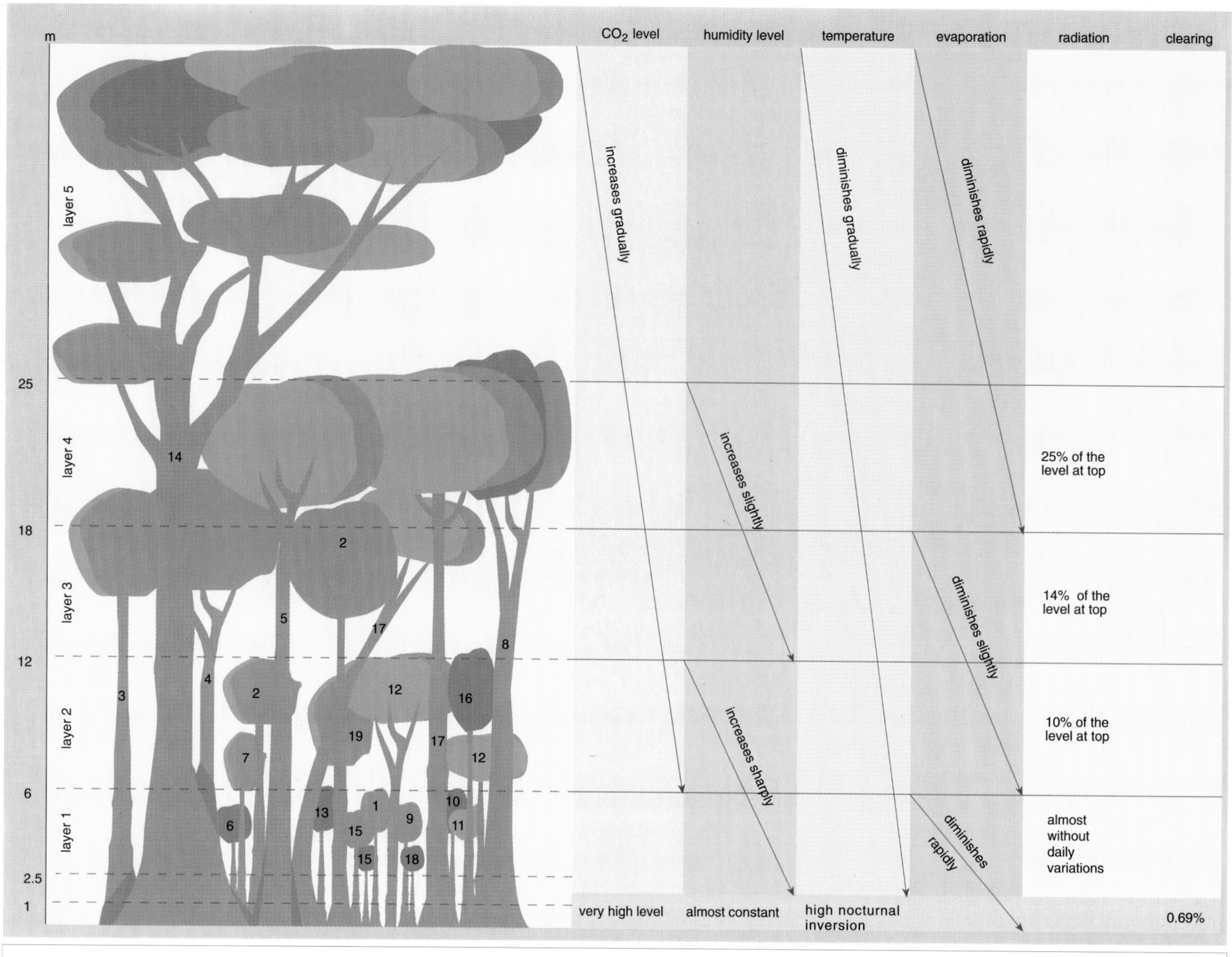

Diagram labels (top): CO₂ level | humidity level | temperature | evaporation | radiation | clearing

- increases gradually
- diminishes gradually
- diminishes rapidly
- increases slightly
- 25% of the level at top
- diminishes slightly
- 14% of the level at top
- increases sharply
- 10% of the level at top
- diminishes rapidly
- almost without daily variations
- very high level
- almost constant
- high nocturnal inversion
- 0.69%

Vertical scale (m): 25, 18, 12, 6, 2.5, 1

Layers: layer 5, layer 4, layer 3, layer 2, layer 1

1	Baphia nitida	5	Coula edulis	9	Drypetes gilgiana	13	Parinari aubrevillei	17	Strombosia glaucescens
2	Carapa procera	6	Diospyros mannii	10	Drypetes principum	14	Piptadeniastrum africanum	18	Trichoscypha oba
3	Cola nitida	7	Diospyros sanzaminika	11	Memecylon lateriflorum	15	Polyalthia oliveri	19	Xylopia quintasii
4	Corynanthe pachysceras	8	Diospyros soubreana	12	Microdesmis puberula	16	Scotellia coriacea		

41 **Variation in some ecological parameters in the different levels of the vegetation** in the tropical rainforest. The diagram represents an evergreen rainforest in the Tai Forest Reserve (Ivory Coast), and lists the main species dominating the structure at each level. The vegetation below 8.2 ft (2.5 m) has been left out.
[Drawing: Editrònica, from an original by Bourgeron and Guillumet, 1981]

to synthesize organic molecules for purposes of self-maintenance or to increase biomass (wood or reserves). *Gross primary production* is the term for the total organic material synthesized and *net primary production* is this total minus the part lost in respiration and corresponds to the increase in biomass.

Sunshine is strongest around the equator, which receives twice as much as areas at 60°N or S. One might thus expect biomass production per unit area to be at its greatest. Yet in a forest in Ivory Coast, net annual production is about 9 t per hectare (1 hectare=2.47 acres), not much greater than in a beech forest in Denmark. Measurements made in other tropical forest types give results that are little

higher than this. The explanation may lie in tropical vegetation's very high rate of respiration, and estimates suggest that in mature forests respiration may reach 70% of gross primary production! What is left over for the synthesis of cellulose and proteins is comparatively very small.

The few estimates of gross primary production available for tropical forests give average values of 86 t per hectare per year. Fewer estimates of net primary production are available, as many studies only deal with commercially exploitable trees. Even so, an average value of 20 t per hectare per year has been proposed, with values between 9 and 32 t per hectare per year (though other sources suggest average values of 25-30 t per hectare). The highest val-

42 Study of the rainforest canopy, the world of the tree-dwelling organisms that never leave this half-suspended habitat, is very difficult, due to the difficulty of access. Not only is it often difficult to reach some points within the jungle, but once you are there, the crowns of the trees are tens of yards above the ground, out of reach of all researchers who are not climbers. This is why so much is still unknown, and ingenious sampling methods have had to be developed, including earlier systems based on launching a projectile (arrows, lances, etc.) bearing nets or other collection devices. Since 1986 there has been a more sophisticated system: the canopy raft, a 102 x 72 ft (31 x 22 m) inflatable trapezoidal structure weighing only 1,653.5 lb (750 kg), that is deposited gently on the tree crowns by a balloon or a dirigible, together with a couple of operators to fasten it to the trees, who throw cables down to the ground to lift the scientists up so they can carry out their collecting, sampling, and recording of relevant measurements. The canopy raft, conceived by the Frenchmen Francis Hallé, Danny Cleyet Marrel and Gilles Ebersolt, began by studying the Guyana rainforest (shown in the photo) and then started research into Africa's rainforests.
[Photo: Raphael Gaillarde / Gamma]

ues are in the areas with the highest and most constant rainfall, and soil fertility must also be considered. Managed forests dominated by trees less than 20 years old may show even higher values.

To obtain more information on the dynamics of production, it is worth calculating the ratio of the forest's net production to its biomass. This gives an index of the efficiency of the system, its productivity. Like a rate of interest, it relates the yield to the capital producing it. A population of unicellular algae that divides every 24 hours shows daily productivity of 100%. Land vegetation makes a large investment in support and dispersal structures, and its productivity varies over a wide range, from 2-100% per year (turnover times of 50 years and one year, respectively), but is always less than in marine systems. Thus, rainforest has a very high rate of synthesis, but one of the lowest values for productivity.

On the other hand, the growth in diameter and height of the trees of the primary rainforest is less than that of some temperate trees (poplars, eucalyptus, some pines). In contrast, total production of organic material is twice or even three times that of temperate trees. The biomass of tropical forests, in dry weight, lies between 300 and 400 t per hectare (between 350 and 550 t per hectare according to some authors), 90% of which corresponds to branches and trunks, the most perennial structures. The leaf fraction, the most suitable material for insects and other herbivores, represents only a small part of the total, only 2%.

The distribution of productivity

A complete study of production would require measurement of the annual increase in the weight of leaves, wood, and roots as well as taking into account consumption by animals and the loss of dead structures. Only in the case of timber, for obvious reasons related to commercial forest management, are there techniques to measure growth; these require regular measurements of the diameter (and on occasions also of the girth) of the trunk at breast height, about 4.3 ft (1.3 m) above soil level, as well as the total height if possible. The biomass then has to be calculated using a different index for each species. These crude estimates are only useful for calculating the volume of wood. Many tropical trees have buttress roots rising 10-13 ft (3-4 m) up the stem, making measurement difficult. An individual tree's growth may be highly irregular, in both the short and long term, and they live long enough for possible climatic variations to have an influence.

The turnover time of renewable structures (leaves, fruit, etc.) is much shorter than that of permanent structures (trunks, branches, roots). Production of the different components also varies. Even in mature forest, the production of wood accounts for most of the net production. Leaf production accounts for 35%, while root production may be as low as 7%, although very few data are available. In

43 **Permanent research stations in the rainforest**, such as this one in Barro Colorado (Panama), make it easier to carry out studies of forest physiology over periods of months or even years. This is important because some phenomena can be understood only when observations taken over long periods of time are available.

large trees, one tenth of the wood decomposes before falling, and of the rest, more then 3 t/year of dead wood greater than 4 in (10 cm) in diameter falls to the soil.

It is simpler to assess what is called *dead cover*, everything on the rainforest floor. It only includes leaves, flowers, fruit, and twigs (excluding aerial and underground wood) but is still a good estimate of the production of the most dynamic component. Yearly variations in dead cover (around 10%) may partly be due to tree species suffering massive defoliation.

Factors conditioning primary production

Within the forest, production is conditioned by a set of factors. Light availability and the degree of

shading influence growth; thus shaded trees grow, on average, only a third as much as those in direct sunshine: trees less than 2 in (5 cm) in diameter in dense shade only grow 0.7 mm per year, and larger trees in the shade grow a little more than 1 mm per year. In open forest, however, growth may be much greater. Some species of *Flindersia* (Rutaceae) occurring in the rainforests of the Moluccas, New Guinea, Australia and New Caledonia, may show an increase in diameter of 2.5 mm per year in open sunny sites, while in shade it hardly grows at all. The trees suitable for wood production are the heliophilous species that grow in clearings: in the Philippines, for example, the mimosoid legume *Albizzia falcataria* reaches 7 ft (2 m) in two years, and is felled after eight years. Other species suitable for exploitation are pioneer species of secondary succession: limba (*Terminalia superba*) in Africa and teak (*Tectona grandis*) in the Far East.

The structure of the vegetation

The structure of the rainforest, with emergents (especially members of the Bombacaceae, Dipterocarpaceae, and Leguminosae) rising above the main canopy, favors heterogeneity. Their upper leaves receive direct sunlight and show little stomatal sensitivity, and so their intense transpiration turns them into enormous wicks. Many have sclerophyllous leaves with thickened cuticles and high reflectance. Thus, the canopy acts as a filter but allows a lot of light to reach the lower vegetation. The tall trees in the abundant sunshine contribute more to photosynthesis than those in the shady understory: In Cambodia, emergents account for more than half of the forest's production, but only a fifth of the leaf area. Species with a narrow crown show relatively high ratios of assimilatory surface to respiratory volume, and show higher productivity than trees with a wide crown (and thus a larger respiratory volume).

Water availability

If water availability is not limiting (ignoring extreme cases like waterlogging), the density of emergent trees increases, as does the density of lianas and epiphytes; the leaf area index of the canopy, and therefore the shade, increases. The rainforest biomass will increase while the productivity will hardly change. Plants, especially epiphytes, that suffer water shortage often use crassulacean acid metabolism (CAM), an even more efficient form of photosynthesis than C4 metabolism (see volume 1, page 185) in dry conditions. These members of the family Crassulaceae (such as *Sedum*), as well as bromeliads, cacti, and some ferns, open their stomata at night to absorb carbon dioxide (fixing it as malic acid) and close them in the day to avoid water loss; the malic acid accumulated in the vacuoles at night is decarboxylated to provide carbon dioxide to allow photosynthesis to continue during the day.

Light availability

Maximum photosynthetic capacity varies greatly from one species to another and is clearly related to habitat. Peak photosynthesis is very high in pioneer species (26 mg/dm^2/h), lower in the trees of the rainforest (6-24 mg/dm^2/h) and much less (2-4 mg/dm^2/h) in the shady understory plants that reach their maximum at low light levels. All rainforest plants can function with little light when young; the shady environment and their reduced biomass mean respiration is very low, so their net production shows a small but positive balance.

The effect of temperature

Temperature is also a relevant factor. The absence of a cold period prevents any interruption of the annual rhythm of production. This is perhaps the main difference between rainforests and temperate forests, and to an even greater extent between rainforests and the coniferous forests of the taiga. If there are no seasonal interruptions by relatively dry conditions, the wood of rainforest trees does not usually produce growth rings: evergreen species rarely make observable rings and there are even some deciduous trees that do not do so, either. Moreover, it has not yet been totally verified that high temperatures lead to increased respiration, but most authors accept that this is so. Cold nights may thus significantly reduce losses due to respiration.

Within the rainforest, there is a clear heat gradient: on a sunny day at noon the temperature in the upper canopy may be 90°F (32°C) and relative humidity is around 60%. In the still air and dense shade of the undergrowth, the temperature may be 79°F (26°C) and the relative humidity 90%—the famous stifling humidity of the rainforest.

Secondary production

Data on primary production is scarce and incomplete, but there is even less on secondary produc-

tion. Information on the systematics, distribution and even ecology of many animals is abundant, but there is as yet no complete study of the different species of heterotrophs in a single tropical forest. There are only estimates of production, by individuals and populations, made on the basis of the annual metabolic expenditure. Yet for a given trophic level, the rate of production varies between homeothermic animals (warm-blooded animals with greater metabolic expenditure), and poikilothermic (cold-blooded) ones. Even among consumers, the assimilation of ingested material is highly variable: some invertebrates assimilate between 80 and 90% of what they eat, but in detritivorous organisms (isopods, myriapods) assimilation is usually only 10-30%.

Assessing the overall increase in animal biomass is made difficult by the lack of data for animal biomass as such (which, together with the density, is required to establish the production of the fauna). Even so, some authors have given estimates (admittedly incomplete and preliminary) of the zoomass. Thus estimated values have been given of 187 lb/ac (210 kg/ha) in terra firme lowland rainforest in central Amazonia, and 105 lb/ac (118 kg/ha) for rainforest at the base of a mountain in Puerto Rico. These estimated animal biomass values are lower than those for vertebrate biomass in the savannah. Large savannah vertebrates would find little to eat in the rainforest, where the herbivores eat 98 ft (30 m) up in the trees and whose wood and leaves are more tougher to eat than the grass of savannahs or prairies.

The main herbivores in the forest are insects and small mammals. On the island of Barro Colorado (Panama) estimated nonflying zoomass is 47 lb per acre (53 kg/ha), of which 60% corresponds to sloths (*Bradypus*) and 12% to howler monkeys (*Alouatta*), both leafeaters well adapted to life in the trees. There is little information on the leaf biomass consumed by herbivores. In Costa Rica and Panama it is estimated to be 6-10% respectively, figures that seem low considering that this

GEOGRAPHICAL LOCATION	BIOMASS (tonnes dry weight/ha)		
	trunks and stems	leaves	roots
Banco (Ivory Coast)	504	9.0	49
Pasoh (Malaysia)	467	8.2	–
Brazil	370	10.0	≈40
Thailand	323	7.8	31
San Carlos (Venezuela)	317	8.2	56
Colombia	314	9.0	–

44 **Biomass values of different plant structures**, in tonnes dry weight per hectare, for sites in different tropical rainforest. Interpretation of currently available biomass data is difficult, as data obtained by different sampling methods are mixed together. Yet there are some general tendencies, such as greater values for trunks and branches than for roots, and greater values for roots than for leaves. Likewise, the nutrient content of the trunks and stems tends to be greater than that of other components of forest vegetation. [*Source: data drawn up by Frank G. Golley*]

45 Insects are very abundant in the rainforest and play an essential role in the food web. Colonial wasps, such as the ones in this photo taken in the Panama rainforest, are herbivores that nest collectively by the thousand under the leaves in an attempt to find shelter from the attacks of some species of carnivorous ant that eat their larvae and eggs.
[Photo: Xavier Ferrer & Adolf de Sostoa]

1.3 Ecological strategies and niches

The intertropical rainforest is the maximum expression of biodiversity. This is widely known, but the reason not as clear as often believed: It cannot simply be explained by greater energy availability, higher biomass production, and a stable climate over a long period of time, as this would then raise the question why a single or a few well-adapted rainforest species are not dominant as producers, primary consumers, secondary consumers, and decomposers over large areas with similar soils and climates. Why then have organisms diversified so much in the rainforest biome?

Diversity and history

Why have organisms diversified so much in this and in all other biomes? The world has few widespread and numerous species but many that are geographically restricted and scarce. Evolution is a process which feeds on itself and in a stable non-seasonal climate there is great potential for specialisation, thus avoiding competition with other species, but at the price of occupying a very restricted ecological niche. This leads to a large number of niches, many extremely limited and specialized, some of which are almost unbelievably extravagant or beautiful.

Some authors have considered this huge number of niches and species as a reflection of the system's hypothetical stability since the beginning of the Cenozoic, 65 million years ago, and that as a whole it has survived unaltered since then, undisturbed by the climatic variations that have affected other latitudes. Yet it is now known that this is not so. Rainforests covered the largest area in the early Eocene, apparently reaching 30° latitude, although the strictly equatorial regions were then drier and occupied by more open formations. By the mid-Eocene (50 million years ago), coinciding with planetary trend to a warmer drier climate, the rainforests shrank. In the early Oligocene, about 34 million years ago, further climate change restricted rainforests to the most equatorial latitudes, below 15°, smaller than the 20-25° they reach nowadays. Since then, changes in climate and in the area of rainforest have continued to occur.

is the main input of material and energy to the other trophic levels. Plants also have defensive mechanisms, such as latexes and toxins, produced to prevent their being consumed. Although its biomass is limited (and underestimated, according to many authors), the herbivore trophic level exercises some control over productive processes. Plant-eating insects, for example, might act to regulate production. Some plants have evolved together with an entire set of plant-eaters that, when they cause the death of the tree, improve water and light availability to the survivors and create a fertilized clearing for the seeds. Most of the biomass of heterotrophs is, however, in the soil, and is four or five times greater than that of herbivores and carnivores combined. It is 147 lb/ac (165 kg/ha) in the Amazon rainforest, where herbivore biomass is 27 lb/ac (30 kg/ha) and carnivore biomass is 13 lb/ac (15 kg/ha), and heterotroph biomass is 71 lb/ac (80 kg/ha) in a low forest where herbivore biomass is 22 lb/ac (25 kg/ha) and carnivore biomass is 9 lb/ac (10 kg/ha). The most important members of the soil fauna are the termites (which may be very important in some rainforests), oligochaetes, and microarthropods. The microarthropods, although their function is not well understood, are very abundant in the soil and the dead cover, where tens of thousands of individuals per acre have been counted.

It seems that at the coldest periods of the glaciations, the rainforests were reduced more than once to very limited areas, called "Pleistocene refugia," surrounded by seasonal tropical forest. The Pleistocene refugia hypothesis was first proposed for Amazonia, where some areas show high proportions of endemic species, and high species diversity of different animal groups (birds, reptiles and butterflies) and some plant families, whereas the surrounding areas have much lower levels of endemism and species diversity. Many centers of diversity have been identified in Central and South America, and may have been rainforest refugia during the most unfavorable periods of the Pleistocene; they include the centers in Yucatán, the Brazilian Mata Atlântica, the Chocó (on the Pacific coast of Colombia), the Guyanas, those in the eastern equatorial region, the Napó region of Peru and the southwest of Pará in Brazil. Three centers of diversity have been recognised in Africa, one in Upper Guinea, a second centerd on Cameroon and Gabon, and a third on the eastern rim of the Zaire Basin. The vagaries of history are the explanation for the rainforest's changes in species-richness, but it can only be argued that the rainforest has shown great stability in the case of these few Pleistocene refugia, and even then, for a period much shorter than the 65 million years since the beginning of the Cenozoic.

Nor can the rainforest's great diversity be explained just by the fact that equatorial regions receive the most sunlight and the highest rainfall, although it is undeniably important. Other factors, such as soil nutrients, being equal, these areas have the greatest potential production and growth in height (see page 227, volume 1). On the other hand, production depends on the surface area, both for availability of energy and rainwater, but accumulated biomass (and necromass) is not limited in this way and can also grow in the third dimension of space. Competition for light is the decisive selection pressure for trees, so they form the central axis of forest ecosystem organization, of which the rainforests are the best example.

The large trees dominating the rainforest do their best to optimize the formation of vertical structures for their leaves to catch the necessary sunlight, at the same time as shading their neighbors. They produce the largest vertical structures permitted by the limits placed by the water and nutri-

46 The enormous leaf size of some herbaceous plants is one of the most surprising features of the vegetation of the intertropical forest. Prominent examples are the members of the Musaceae, the banana family and some arums, whose growth form is often tree-like with immense leaves, like this arum in the basin of the Rio Palenque in Ecuador.
[Photo: Xavier Ferrer and Adolf de Sostoa]

47 **The diversity of tree species in the rainforest is very high**, and dozens of different species may be found in just a few hectares (1 hectare=2.47 acres) of rainforest. This is clearly seen in this photo of the forest canopy in the Central American rainforest.
[*Photo: Setsu / NASA Gamma*]

ent availability, the load-bearing capacity of their stem materials and structures (wood, in the case of forests), and the ability of their vessels to raise water and nutrients from the roots to the leaves.

The dominance of woody plants

Rainforest trees struggle for light and organise the three dimensions of an ecosystem to a great height, with a canopy at 115 ft (35 m) and the crowns of emergents at 164 ft (50 m). Trees are the main factor giving rise to a certain spatial heterogeneity and are thus responsible for the initial differentiation of environments and ecological niches, the source of increasing diversity.

The variety of tree forms
The diversity of the trees of the rainforests is enormous. Temperate forests are often dominated by one or a few species and usually contain less than 10 species per hectare (1 hectare=2.47 acres), but rainforests easily exceed 100 species, with trunk diameter of more than 4 in (10 cm) per hectare. This also implies a wide range of chemically diverse materials, variety in the substrate for epiphytes, and a stratification that, by forming microenvironments, stimulates speciation in the organisms living there. Light, temperature, and humidity conditions may vary enormously between the canopy and the soil level, as well as at different heights on the trunks and in the crowns, and even within every fork or hole in a trunk. On the other

hand, if the primary selective pressure for woody plants is competition for light, once the large trees' crowns have closed the canopy, the dominant selective pressures are different for all vascular plants (adaptations to growth in the dark understory or gaining access to the top of the canopy, to epiphytic life, to parasitism).

Abundant epiphytes and lianas
Among the most typical features of rainforests are *epiphytes*, plants that grow on other plants, such as trees, that provide support in the well-lit rainforest canopy, without doing any direct harm to the plant they grow on. Outside the tropics there are only microepiphytes (especially lichens and mosses, together with some ferns). Macroepiphytes are very abundant in rainforests, with 28,000 species belonging to 65 families. The orchid family (Orchidaceae), the largest of all families, has more epiphytic species than terrestrial ones, and the American rainforests contain numerous species of bromeliad.

Epiphytes can be separated by the layer they grow in. Canopy epiphytes are well adapted to absorbing and storing water and usually resemble plants of dry places (with hard, shiny leaves, or very thin ones) as they have to withstand intense sunshine, wind and occasional drought. Understory epiphytes live in humid dark conditions and have delicate leaves with drip tips to drain water and a wrinkled or velvet like surface to increase the light-catching area. Stout older branches are easier to colonize, and bear many epiphytes. Rough barks attract climbing roots and tendrils. Epiphytes have developed a range of mechanisms to survive in these unusual conditions. One way is to have stems or leaves that store water to buffer changes in water and nutrient availability. Another adaptation is the presence of two types of root, one set for attachment to the host, and sponge like roots that penetrate the humus or spread in the air to take up moisture. Symbiosis with other organisms is common: fungal mycorrhiza may provide nutrients, especially in the first stages of plant growth, and ants may bring soil fragments or leaf litter remains to build their nest. There is also a range of associated fauna (other insects and even small frogs) that find the shelter, humidity and food they need in this midair forest, and many animals complete their entire life cycle without ever leaving it.

Lianas (woody vines) are especially abundant in the tropics and contribute to the rainforest's dense and mysterious appearance. Like epiphytes and hemiepiphytes (those that do not spend their whole life as an epiphyte), lianas are evading the deep shade of the understory. Therefore, they invest in structures for rapid growth and in mechanisms to climb up the tall trees that dominate the rainforest. In lowland forests, around 8% of all plants have adopted this strategy and the proportion is even higher in secondary forest.

The behavior of the fauna

Plants as a whole provide many habitats and resources, so it is not surprising that the fauna occupies specialized niches unimaginable in other biomes, and shows high diversity, partly made possible by the rainforest's conditions of light and humidity. This diversity begins in the soil fauna, with a great variety of acarids and collembola that eat wood-inhabiting fungi. Earthworms, however, are not very well represented, while ants and termites are surprisingly abundant (they may account for three quarters of the soil biomass) and are consumed by anteaters and pangolins, as well as by tree lizards. Termites are essential for wood decomposition, whereas ants, especially army ants, are ferocious carnivores.

The advantages of high environmental humidity

The rainforest's high environmental humidity means that animals with thin, unprotected skins run little risk of desiccation and occupy habitats

48 Epiphytes, plants that live on other plants, are characteristic features of the rainforest. The most common ones are the different species of bromeliads, which form large rosettes of hard, rigid leaves (such as *Vriesia*), or the hanging fleshy leafless stems of the different species of *Rhipsalis* (which are members of the Cactaceae) (see figure 222).
[Photo: Roland Seltre / Bios / Still Pictures]

49 The presence of epiphylls, that is to say small epiphytes that grow on the leaves of other plants, shows the high degree of complexity of the equatorial forest, which is possible, among other reasons, because of the high environmental humidity. These leaf epiphytes are often mosses, as in the photo, which is of a leaf in the Pacific rainforest of the Ensenada de Utría National Park (Colombia).
[Photo: Xavier Ferrer & Adolf de Sostoa]

50 Columns of leaf-cutter ants of the genus *Atta* form part of the rainforest micro-landscape. A single colony of these ants may cut more than 132 lb (60 kg) (dry weight) of leaves per hour and transport them to their nest, which may represent the defoliation of 1% of the vegetation of the forest, 0.2% of the net primary production. The distance between individuals of a single species may be large enough to prevent catastrophic destruction, but these ants may become serious pests of tree crops. Once inside the nest, the cut leaves (normally cut from a few species, in this case *Banisteriopsis caapi* [Malpighiaceae] in Ecuador) are chewed into a paste the ants lay in a thin layer, on which they sow a fungus that later serves as food for the larvae and the adult ants. In fact, the ants create a pure culture, an artificial environment when the fungus can grow free of all competition; many of these fungi have still not been identified because it has not been possible to find sporophores among the mycelia. The grinding up of the leaves performed by the ants facilitates fungal access to the cell cytoplasm, and the breakdown of cellulose cell walls; otherwise the ants' fecal material provides the fungus with the proteolytic fermenting enzymes that it also needs to digest the leaf paste (see drawing 139 in volume 1).
[Photo: G.I. Bernard / NHPA and Michael & Patricia Fogden]

inconceivable in other latitudes. Freshwater invertebrates (planarians, leeches) can live among the branches a few meters above the soil in the understory, while earthworms occur in the canopy in the perfectly suitable habitat created by the leaf litter retained by the epiphytes.

With respect to vertebrates, the humidity means there are many types of frogs, some of which complete their life cycle on "dry land" by performing their entire metamorphosis within the egg. *Phytothelms*, the special water-retaining rosettes formed by the leaves, branches or flowers of many epiphytes provide water and food for mosquito larvae and tiny frogs as well as a good refuge for many small animals when conditions are dry.

Small is successful

Reducing their size is another way animals can exploit new niches, such as tiny cracks, small concavities, the hairy covering of leaves or animals, the body cavity of animals, feathers, etc. Everything may serve as a habitat, as food, or both to serve one way of life or another. To help their survival in the forest many animals make use of discretion and ambiguity: nocturnal habit, cryptic or mimetic shape and coloration. Or they may do just the opposite, exhibiting warning (aposematic) colors indicating they are dangerous, or mimicking animals that are genuinely dangerous.

The triumph of tree-dwelling

As the rainforest environment is so complex and intricate, it is not surprising that the proportion of the tree-living, or *arboreal*, fauna is high in all groups of animals, from the smallest to the largest. As already mentioned, fauna more typical of the soil or groundwater occur high above the soil. Many insects, even typically ground-living species like termites and ants build nests many meters above the ground, high up in the trees. A study in Guyana rainforest found 31 species of tree-living mammal, but only 23 ground-living species.

Arboreal animals have anatomical adaptations (prehensile hands, claws and tails, large nails, folds of skin for gliding, etc.) to help them move effectively through the branches. Birds are very abundant in the upper levels, but very few species live or lay their eggs on the ground. The tropical avifauna accounts only for a small proportion of the biomass, but shows much greater diversity than in temperate regions. Often, mutual relation-

51 Tree-dwelling life is highly developed in the rainforest as a consequence of the total dominance of the tree vegetation. Perhaps the most spectacular example of this phenomenon are the brachiate monkeys, such as these white-handed gibbons (*Hylobates lar*) from Sumatra. In fact, the term *hylobates* means "the one circulating in the trees."
[Photo: Xavier Ferrer & Adolf Sostoa]

ships between two or more species have led to speciation that is, to a large extent, coadaptation: pollinating insects, birds, and bats, all sorts of fruit and seed dispersing animals, and aphids reared as livestock by ants.

The different foods on offer
Only a small part of the plant biomass is truly accessible to herbivores, and even then only to specialized herbivores. A leaf's chemical composition often makes it unsuitable, if not actually toxic, to all but a few highly specialized consumers, mainly insects. Larger animals cannot chew the leaves finely enough to break the cellulose cell walls and release the nutrients within, and thus need the help of their symbiotic gut bacteria.

Predators are more varied and numerous than in other forest types but are less diverse than herbivores, at least in terms of the number of species. The wide range of insects means that most predators are insectivores, and they are mostly invertebrates, too. The characteristics of the food they eat ensure that most predators are small, although there are large exceptions, like the big cats that hunt large rodents, ruminants, tapirs, and peccaries. Rainforest carnivores include many birds of prey that feed on small arboreal mammals and birds. In contrast to the miniaturization so common in most animal groups, the high constant temperatures of tropical forests have made possible the development of giant forms of insects and other invertebrates that have taken the place of the vertebrates and eat small birds, lizards, small rodents and even small snakes.

The myth of stability

The ratio of production to biomass (P/B), or the rate of turnover, reaches its lowest values in the rainforests (see volume 1, pages 225-233). As already explained, this implies greater control of the cycling of chemical elements, and this control is so great that rainforests can be considered as closed ecosystems where everything is recycled. This may be the reason for the excessively simplistic association of the rainforest biome's complexity and diversity with its supposedly great stability. In fact, a system with a wider range of species and a more complicated web of interactions is more vulnerable than simpler and less

diverse systems to disturbances that are insufficiently frequent for them to have been interiorized by the system, or that are of unusual intensity. The rainforest is thus more fragile than temperate forest systems, which in spite of their lesser complexity, have a greater ability to regenerate after chance catastrophes, such as fire or felling.

In normal circumstances, the limited natural oscillations in the environmental conditions of the wet tropics allow the rainforest to grow and thrive within relatively restricted limits, as disturbances are localized and of little amplitude. Lightning strikes, wind and the modification of rivercourses may lead to clearings where the trees have fallen, but these disturbed areas normally only account for 1 or 2% of the area of the rainforest. In spite of this relative scarcity, this localized destruction followed by a gradual restoration of the original forest prevents the rainforest as a whole from remaining too long without renewing itself. Although the area of disturbed patches is small at any given moment, patches gradually reconstructing the original rainforest may account for 5-20% of the total area, bearing in mind the slowness of succession after a disturbance.

To sum up, natural catastrophes that occur with some degree of regularity lead to a diversification of forest stages that coexist and increase the rainforest's complexity: the highly changeable initial stages show low diversity and are surrounded by more persistent and diverse mature stages, and there are even clearly degraded and impoverished states. Large rivers flowing over plains that form meanders and gradually modify their courses show an arrangement of the vegetation on the relief that reflects the history of secondary succession; as the alluvial deposits modify the river's course, the new bank is colonized in bands running parallel to the river, so the initial stages of succession are closest to the riverbank and the most advanced stages are furthest.

Conversely, where the river is eroding the riverbank away, it often cuts across the successive strips representing the different stages of the previous secondary succession. Yet this dynamic stability requires that environmental conditions are virtually uniform (a requirement that the rainforest biome usually fulfills) and that the disturbances do not exceed a certain threshold; otherwise, the changes that occur are large and lasting.

2. The flora and the plant life

2.1 Plant structure and catching sunlight

Under the equatorial sun the rainforest grows in permanent warm, moist conditions and produces new plant tissue faster than any other terrestrial community. This high gross production is balanced and maintained by death, as the same amount of tissue dies as is produced, and its decay releases nutrients for new growth. The rainforest is in dynamic balance, with a rate of turnover that is extremely fast in comparison with forests in drier or colder regions. This dynamism is fueled by the speed of decomposition, as the rainforest is full of scavengers able to eat almost anything and also by the flow of water-bearing nutrients from the soil to the canopy, drawn by the suction exerted by evapotranspiration from the leaves.

From deep shade to the canopy

The life of the rainforest is structured according to overriding rules. One of these is that almost all the light is concentrated in the forest canopy, and with it the opportunity to photosynthesize sugars —the basis of growth and metabolism—from atmospheric carbon dioxide and water. It has been shown that 99.6% of the sunlight falling on the rainforest canopy is intercepted by the intermeshing branches of the trees, leaving the interior of the forest in deep shade. Thus, if a plant is to survive by photosynthesis (and there are alternatives, such as parasitism) it has to make do with 0.4% of the total light, or somehow ensure its leaves reach the canopy.

There are woodland plants adapted to the deep shade of the rainforest floor, but they represent a very small proportion of the total flora. These include several ferns and lycopods such as *Selaginella* and flowering plants such as begonias (*Begonia*); and broad-leaved grasses and sedges; and gingers (*Zingiber* and other genera of the Zingiberaceae). Often the areas of deep shade contain small palms, shrubs, seedlings, and young trees, which may eventually grow up to the

52 The undergrowth of the rainforest is in deep shade, so the plants living there must develop effective mechanisms to intercept and make the best use of the little light that does arrive. Thus their leaves are usually large and carefully positioned to catch light.
[Photo: Xavier Ferrer & Adolf de Sostoa]

53 Lianas (woody vines) are as typical of the rainforest as epiphytes. Their twisting stems twine between the trunks and branches of trees, or over themselves, forming tangled knots like this tangle of stems in a dipterocarp forest in the Bukit Timah reserve in Singapore.
[Photo: Wayne Lawler / Auscape International]

canopy as large trees or lianas. The rainforest is a gallery of trees, whose trunks provide the lowest level with a vertical structure and whose highest branches form a latticed roof.

The tallest trees may exceed 197 ft (60 m) and their trunks may be 16 ft (5 m) in diameter near the ground, where they are often strengthened by woody buttress roots. These reinforcements of the trunk may emerge from the bole, or trunk, 10 ft (3 m) or more above the ground and are distributed around the tree's base to increase its stability. These huge trees are in the minority, however, and their crowns usually rise above those of their neighbors, and this is why they are called *emergents*. One of the most spectacular examples is the Caesalpinoid legumine tree tualang, *Koompassia excelsa*, whose smooth, silver-white bark, pale green leaves, and majestic stature make it one of the gems of southeast Asia's rainforests.

Underneath the crowns of these emergents, the forest canopy is more continuous: At this slightly lower level, the crowns of most trees occur side-by-side in a thick interlocking layer that is between 49 and 148 ft (15 and 45 m) above the

ground. This is called the canopy. This main canopy stratum is translucent and creates a continuous gradient of light intensity from top to bottom, thus creating different opportunities for life for plants adapted to a specific level of illumination, and as the air inside the rainforest is more humid than outside, adapted to special conditions of humidity. Different tree species slot their adult crowns at different heights into this highly diverse matrix, each according to its physiological needs (each modified as necessary during its growth). Similarly there is also usually a profuse growth of lichens, moss, ferns and orchids on the leaves or bark, or both.

The interweaving of lianas

Much of the canopy is not formed by the crowns of trees but by the crowns of climbing lianas. Lianas are a prominent feature of the rainforest, almost its specialty, and they play an important role in its overall structure. Sprouting from fallen seeds or from their spreading root systems, lianas climb upwards by a probing shoots that grow in ascending spirals, sampling the surrounding environment until their tips find a firm support, often a tree trunk. Then the young liana grips tightly by coiling around the trunk or by means of specialized protuberances, and climbs up the tree, growing as rapidly as the supply of light and minerals allows, turning its extending stem into a bundle of tubes to conduct food and water to the vigorous apex. When it reaches the canopy, the liana sends out lateral shoots throughout the branches of its host, always growing upwards and outwards towards the light.

By spreading throughout its host's crown, the liana may eventually connect with the external branches of adjacent trees. These serve as a route for further expansion, until the liana has colonized, always in competition with other lianas and the trees themselves, a large area of the forest. As it grows, the liana will flower and fruit and produce new leaves that are eaten by the passing animals that use the multiple stems as paths for their daily movements.

By occupying tree after tree, a big liana will bind their crowns together, and in many places the canopy is like a woven mat of vegetation. If one of the trees supporting the liana dies after being weakened by competition with it, the rotten trunk may be held upright for months or even years by the other trees.

If the dead tree is the one the liana originally ascended, then after it has turned to dust, the liana's twisting main stem is left sagging in the air, like a huge over-stretched spring hanging from the other trees. These loops of liana, hanging without any apparent support from the canopy and leading down to a rootstock at ground level, are a common feature of the rainforest floor and middle levels.

Interlocking the different strata of the forest in this way can have dangers as well as advantages for the liana. One minor cost is that a climber's leaves fall on the soil far from its root system, and so, unlike the trees they grow on, the liana does not benefit from the nutrients that it releases. A greater cost is that if a large tree under the liana dies and then falls over, the liana's matted connections to the other trees may be pulled down by the force of the falling giant, probably destroying the entire climber.

54 **The many surprising growth forms of the intertropical lianas** include those known as monkey steps, turtle staircase, and snake climbers, which are members of the genus *Bauhinia*, often *B. anguina*.
[Photo: Tony Morrison / South American Pictures]

Climbing palms, or the rattans

The Old World rainforests contain many climbing palms (*Calamus* and other genera of the Lepidocaryoid palms), known as rattans. Most possess whip-like barbed structures up to 10 ft (3 m) long, which are either an extension of the rachis, the midrib of the frond (known as a *cirrus*), or grow from the tip of the leaf sheath (a *flagellum*). The hooks of these whip-like organs are sharp and recurved like grapnels, giving them a firm grip on other vegetation as the palm makes its way up to the canopy. Often the rest of the palm also bears spines or needles, especially the leaf sheaths protecting the stem. The New World has a similar group of spiny climbing palms, the genus *Desmoncus* and other related genera Cocosoid palms; their spines are paired specialized apical leaflets called acanthophylls. (Some African rattans also bear acanthophylls as well as thorns on their cirri.)

Rattan stems as long as 610 ft (186 m) have been found, in the case of a specimen of *Calamus manan* in the Malaysian Peninsula, and as long as 394 ft (120 m) in a specimen of *C. albus* in western Java. Their winding stems, firmly anchored to the canopy by their barbed fronds, bind the forest trees together.

Some species grow as a single stem, whereas others produce a clump of stems from suckers or from just below the ground. Rattans occur in many types of lowland forest, and some like *C. trachycoleus* are adapted to seasonal flooding. Rattans are abundant at medium altitudes, but are scarce or almost absent from montane forest.

Rattans are shade tolerant when young, and may spend several years after germination as small palms in the understory. Exposure to light triggers vigorous growth as the young palm seeks to support itself on the nearby seedlings or saplings that will serve as its pathway to the sunlit upper canopy. As a result of their exposure to sunlight, the edges of the rainforest, as well as riverbanks and clearings opened up by humans, are often overgrown with rattans whose spines may form impenetrable barriers.

Rattans vary greatly in the diameter of their main stem. The largest main stems are 8 in (20 cm) in diameter in exceptional specimens of *Plectocomia*; 4 in (10 cm) in *Calamus manan*; 2 in (4 cm) in some species of *Laccosperma*; about 0.8 in (2 cm) in *Eremospatha*; or 0.4 in (1 cm) or less in the smallest species of *Calamus*, *Daemonorops*, and *Plectocomia*. People collect rattan stems, canes, and use them for many purposes, such as handicrafts or furniture construction; in southeast Asia rattan canes are the second most valuable forest product after timber (see chapter 3.2.2).

Humans are not the only species to make use of rattans. Their fruits are part of the diet of monkeys as diverse as the drill (*Mandrillus* [=*Papio*] *leucophaeus*) in Nigeria, Cameroon and the island of Bioko (Fernando Poo) and the Mentawai macaque (*Macaca pagensis*) in the Mentawai islands off the west coast of Sumatra. A comparison of information on Mentawai macaque colonies in different river valleys has shown that their density is directly related to the abundance of rattans in the forest.

Although most of the 13 genera and almost 600 species of rattan are native to southeast Asia, nine species belonging to three genera also occur in western Africa. Inventories of primary forest in southeast Nigeria usually contain about five species of rattan per hectare (1 hectare=2.47 acres), the most common of which are *Laccosperma secundiflora* and species of *Eremospatha*, but there are also species of the genus *Oncocalamus*.

Strangler figs

Not all the living lattice covering the rainforest consists of lianas growing up from the ground to the canopy. There are also many species of fig (*Ficus*, Moraceae) living in the rainforest, a large and diverse genus. The stems growing down from the canopy include some of the latex-filled, fleshy, smooth-barked stems of strangler figs.

A lianoid fig (other species are normal trees, not even rainforest species, such as the Mediterranean fig tree *Ficus carica*) starts life as a tiny seed deposited on a tree branch in the excrement of a monkey or bird. Perhaps the best-known are the type known as the strangler figs. After germination, the plant lives for some time as an epiphyte, securing itself firmly to its host and accumulating reserves by photosynthesis. After a while, the fig begins to send fine roots downwards, one or two to begin with, and then many more as soon as the first one reaches the ground and finds a ready source of water. These roots, 98 ft (30 m) or more long, gradually wrap themselves around the host's trunk, fusing together to form a network embracing the tree. While these roots multiply and thicken, the branches and leaves compete for light and space with those of its host, gradually out-competing and shading

55 The unyielding network of stems of this strangler fig (*Ficus watkinsiana*) completely surrounds the trunk of this brush box (*Lophostemon confertus*, Myrtaceae) on which it germinated many years ago in the Frazer Island National Park in Queensland, Australia. The tree will eventually die and rot away, leaving the fig with the disconcerting appearance of a completely empty reticular trunk.
[Photo: Wayne Lawler / Auscape International]

its crown. Eventually the host's trunk is completely surrounded by the fig's linked roots, and as it now receives little light and cannot grow in thickness, it eventually dies. Its tissues decompose and fertilize the fig, which is now firmly supported by its own roots in spite of the hollow space left by the original host, whose place in the sun it now occupies.

2.2 The dynamics of succession

Few trees die as a result of the growth of strangler figs: most die for other reasons. Some are killed by the rare species of termite that eats living, as opposed to dead wood, and others are killed by the fungi that enter when gnawing animals or falling neighbors break the bark. A few die of old age: in this case, the first branches to die are the peripheral ones, followed by the main ones, until the crown falls to pieces where it stands. The increasingly necrotic trunk stands for a while, shaggy with bark falling off in strips, until it is so rotten that it cannot support its own weight and collapses.

The falling of large trees

In any case, the most common cause of the death of an adult tree is for it to fall over due to the action of the wind. Most rainforest trees are precariously rooted, and the problem of maintaining themselves upright increases with the height of the crown. When the wind moves the boughs of the crown, it generates enormous pressures in the tree's trunk. Tropical storms are usually preceded by strong gusts of wind, as air is displaced by raindrops hammering down on the forest. These gusts subject the trees to great stresses, swaying and twisting them and stripping their leaves.

The silence of the forest is broken by a noise like an exchange of gunfire, or even stronger explosions. This is due to millions of wood fibers in the branches or trunks breaking simultaneously as a result of the pressure, marking the end of their useful life supporting several tons of tropical hardwood. That is of course unless the root system is simply uprooted by the force of the wind. Either way, cracking and tearing noises precede the whistling roar of a falling tree or large branch, followed by an earth-shaking noise when it hits the ground.

After the storm, while the forest is still dripping wet, one may search for the fallen trunk. It is usually difficult to reach; the site where it has fallen is usually covered by a mass of climbing plants dragged down from the canopy, either because they were unluckily linked to the crown of the fallen tree, or because they were in the path of its fall. Most of the crown is crushed flat by the impact and this end of the tree is little more than a shattered mass of smashed branches and foliage. From the side, the trunk of a fallen tree resembles a convex wall with the bark and the young climbing lianas still adhering to its trunk. Often this trunk wall is surrounded by others lying in roughly the same direction. They are the trunks of smaller trees that were broken or dragged by the giant in its fall. These nearby trees and those dragged down by the lianas connecting the canopy mean that a big tree-fall may destroy a large area of forest.

The opening of clearings

Gaps formed by falling trees are an essential ingredient of the life of the rainforest. The largest clearings may even continue to increase in size for a while, as the trees at the edges are now more vulnerable to strong winds, but the forest starts working to close the clearings as soon as they appear, and it eventually succeeds. The key to this process is the sunlight that enters through the broken canopy to the formerly shaded forest floor. In spite of the apparent devastation caused by the tree's fall, most of the seedlings and young trees of the understory survive. They grow from seedlings that may have germinated many years before, but had only been able to send out a few roots and a couple of leaves in the dense shade.

In these conditions, the future trees are always ready to make use of the direct sunlight. The sudden illumination of the clearing opened by the tree's fall is the beginning of a race: Only a few of the many seedlings and plants present will grow to adults and close the gap. The light allows the growing plants to obtain more carbohydrates from photosynthesis, and these, together with water, serve to construct most of its new tissues. At the same time, the rapid decay of the fallen vegetation releases large quantities of valuable nutrients, and the death of the root system of fallen or crushed trees means even more nutrients for the survivors.

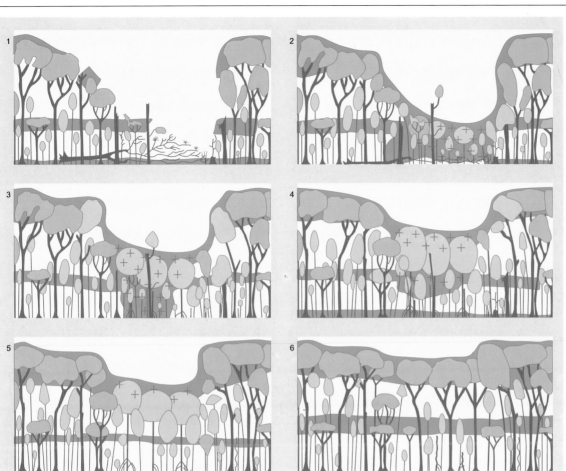

56 Forest regeneration in clearings has its own dynamic, the result of light attaining the levels it previously did not reach. The new situation created by a tree falling (1), which is common in forests as a result of cyclones, leads to the beginning of an orderly sequence of regeneration, called succession, that begins with the growth of pioneer plants (2), which compete with the species already present and are eventually replaced by more stable species (3-6). The diagrams show the area where growth is fastest in dark green, and the sites where competition is strongest with crosses. The list contains the main forest pioneer species of the biome's three biogeographical kingdoms. Some of the larger species are important for the timber industry.
[Drawing: Editrònica, from several sources]

TREE HEIGHT	NEOTROPICAL	AFRICA	EASTERN TROPICAL
Trees from 6-26 ft (2-7.9 m)	Cordia nitida Ocotea atirrensis Piper Vernonia patens Vismia baccifera	Ficus capensis Leea guineensis Phyllanthus muellerianus Rauwolfia vomitoria	Glochidion Macaranga Mallotus Phyllanthus Pipturus Trichospermum
Trees from 27-95 ft (8-29 m)	Trema Alchornea triplinervia Cecropia (20 species) Inga pezizifera Jacaranda copaia Ochroma lagopus Protium glabrum	Trema Anthocleista nobilis Canthium arnoldianum Cleistopholis patens Macaranga Maesopsis eminii Musanga cecropioides Spathodea campanulata Vernonia conferta Vismia guineensis	Trema Acacia aulacocarpa Acacia mangium Adinandra dumosa Alphitonia petrei Anthocephalus Macaranga Ploiarium alternifolium
Trees above 96 ft (30 m)	Ceiba pentandra Cedrela odorata Cedrelinga catenaeformis Goupia glabra Laetia procera Swietenia	Ceiba pentandra Chlorophora excelsa Chlorophora regia Lophira alata Nauclea diderrichii Pericopsis elata Ricinodendron heudelotti Terminalia ivorensis Terminalia superba	Eucalyptus deglupta Paraserianthes falcataria

m
50

40

30

20

10

0

a   b   c   d

57 The progressive simplification of the forest structure as a consequence of disturbances, in this case, human action (field notes taken in the Guinea rainforest, in the Fang country). The primary forest (a) is in this case a dense multilayered forest about 164 ft (50 m) tall. Agricultural clearings (d) are crops with some of the original trees. Abandonment of crops leads to the installation of an early forest community, or tertiary forest (c), dominated by fast-growing, opportunist species of tree. The partial exploitation of the primary forest, or the passing of time after abandonment of agricultural land, leads to the installation of secondary forest (b) less tall and dense than the original, with young individual trees, or perhaps with senescent (fully mature and older) specimens of the trees of the tertiary forest. In the Mata Atlântica, between (d) and (c) communities are usually established that consist of shrubs and low trees (3-10 ft [1-3 m]), known as *capoeira* and *capoeirão*. After an accident, the process of succession is similar.
[Drawing: Jordi Sabater Pi]

The plants that were present but not growing when the gap was formed are the offspring of trees that reproduce only under the mature rainforest canopy. Yet they are not the only ones in this race to the light. The seeds of most canopy trees do not remain dormant once they have found a suitable site. On the contrary, they soon germinate, thus putting themselves in a better situation than seeds to protect themselves from herbivores and to exploit any opportunities that arise.

The process of healing

There are many other species of trees, shrubs, and climbers whose growth follows different models. These specialized colonists have over the years buried their seeds among the other organic material falling on the soil from the rainforest's different strata. These seeds have to be very resistant to survive prolonged dormancy. As soon as a gap arises, they are stimulated to germinate by the hot sun, and their seedlings are adapted to outgrow the seedlings of mature rainforest trees by flowering and fruiting on fast-growing but weaker and less durable vegetative structures. If they can produce and disperse their seeds fast enough, they will have fulfilled their reproductive function before they are

finally overwhelmed by the shade cast by the mature forest trees.

Other species, both opportunists and the trees of the later stages of succession, base their success in colonizing gaps on the immediate germination of their air-borne seeds, which are continually drifting about the forest. Many of them are blown off their parent trees by the same winds that create the gaps in which they need to germinate.

With so many individuals of so many species seeking to reach maturity and reproduce, gaps are luxuriant and complex sites. Each gap passes through a sequence of development as it returns to mature forest, a process taking hundreds of years. The different growth strategies of the plants that were already present, or later arrivals, result in different waves of advance by different species: The first burst of growth is by the seedlings in virtual suspended animation, the seeds of fast-growing species or those of slow-growing ones that were already present in the soil and germinate when the gap forms and by both faster- and slower-growing plants borne on the seeds air or by animals. As the months and years go by, the individuals of each species gradually attain their characteristic adult size and begin to reproduce before they are shaded by other plants belonging to a more mature phase of the forest regrowth.

Accordingly, the identity of the dominant tree species in the clearing changes continuously over the decades, and their changing leaves, flowers and fruit attract different communities of herbivorous animals in each stage. Finally, the gap is closed, when its canopy is occupied by the adult trees typical of mature rainforest, bound together by lianas. Except for long low mounds marking where the trees fell or a shallow hole where they had been rooted, no traces remain of the large trees whose spectacular deaths started the long process of regeneration.

Meanwhile, other trees have fallen in other areas of the forest. The frequency varies between one in every 200 and one in every 30 adult trees falling each year, depending on the soil type, the terrain, and the floristic composition of different areas. Thus, the rainforest is never uniform but is a mosaic of disturbance and regeneration, an unending battlefield.

2.3 Coevolutionary processes

The permanently dynamic rainforest environment is paradoxically predictable for the species that live there. Whatever stage of forest maturity a species is adapted to, it is always available, somewhere. In very ancient rainforests, competition for light and space have produced plants well adapted to outmaneuvering their competitors. Any mechanism letting a tree grow faster or better than its neighbors, however small the advantage, will improve its chance of reproducing.

Symbiosis and commensalism: the case of ants and Barteria trees

The warm, moist air of the rainforest means that a tree's leaves are soon colonized by epiphytes, such as mosses and lichens. They interfere with light interception by the leaf they are growing on, a serious problem for a tree in perpetual danger of death from shading. Climbing plants are also a problem, as their weight limits the growth of the young trees and their leaves compete with those of the tree for light. A tree that could keep its leaves clean and its branches free of lianas would have an immense advantage in the struggle for existence.

One genus of trees of the passionflower family (Passifloraceae) has met this challenge. The trees of the genus *Barteria* have perfected a technique to keep epiphytes and lianas at bay, and their success can be measured by the fact that they are very common in the west African rainforest, can grow and reproduce without reaching the canopy, and live in the deep shade below it.

The key to the success of a *Barteria* tree is its close relationship with colonies of *Pachysima* ants. *Barteria* is an ant-plant, a *myrmecophyte*, that is to say a plant possessing special structures that encourage ants to live near it or even inside it. *Barteria* has hollow branches that fulfil this role; the long tubular galleries serve the ants as highways, grazing ground, breeding areas and hiding places in the sometimes dangerous world of the rainforest.

When a sapling of *Barteria* reaches a height of 3 ft (1 m), it grows its first horizontal branches. One day a winged *Pachysima* queen ant lands on it, after being fertilized on her nuptial flight from the colony of her birth. She quickly checks the *Barteria* to ensure no *Pachysima* queen has yet taken up residence and then chews her way into the hollow center of one of the side branches.

Once inside, she sheds her wings, begins to lay eggs and tends her first brood while surviving on previously stored fat and the tissues of her wing muscles. As soon as about 20 pupae have hatched, worker ants emerge onto the surface and search for the entrance holes of other *Pachysima* queens. If they find any, the workers enter and summarily kill the rival queen and all her developing offspring. From this moment, the *Barteria* has been adopted by the *Pachysima* colony, and their fates are now intertwined. Yet the tree is not totally dominated by the ants as there are too few of them.

The tree may still be patrolled by other animals, including ants of other species, which kill individuals of *Pachysima* caught outside their shelter. *Oecophylla*, for example, a very aggressive genus of red weaver ants dispute fiercely with the *Pachysima* workers seeking to share their foraging routes along the *Barteria*'s branches.

58 Symbiosis and commensalism between ants and plants are common in the rainforest. As an example, these ants from the Americas (*Azteca*) eat the glycogen-rich pilose nodules (Müller bodies, in photo at top left) at the base of the petioles of *Cecropia*, and they also live inside the plant's hollow stems (the photo at top right). *Cecropia* benefits from this as the ants remove epiphytes from its leaves. There is a similar relationship between ants of the genus *Crematogaster* and the myrmecophyte (ant-plant) *Duroia hirsuta* (Rubiaceae), whose branches' structure (center photo) favors ant nest construction (bottom photo).
[Photos: Adolf de Sostoa & Xavier Ferrer]

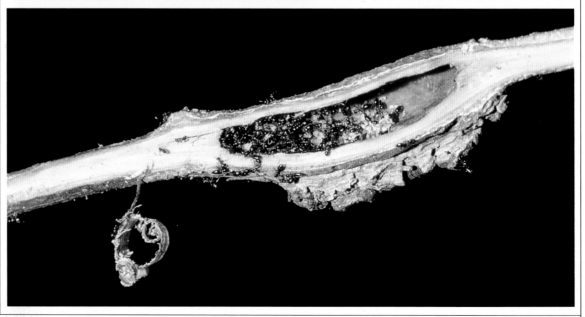

The *Pachysima* workers cut pits at regular intervals along the inner surface of the hollow *Barteria* branches. Small-scale insects (Coccidae), probably carried by the ants, attach themselves to these pits, and can be compared to penned livestock. The scale insects tap their mouthparts into the *Barteria*'s sap flow, which flows into their intestines, where they absorb some sugars and minerals, but much passes out through the anus as "honeydew," a nutritious, sweet liquid that is the ants' basic foodstuff. The rest of their food comes from fungi cultivated in "gardens" carefully prepared by the ants in the branches of the tree. If the *Barteria* is growing well, the ant colony is now self-sufficient in food thanks to the tree.

The tree cannot, however, grow in the dark, lower layers of the forest unless the black *Pachysima* ants take steps to help it. They cannot do this until the colony is about a year old, when there are enough worker ants for effective defense of the colony and the tree from their enemies. The worker ants, armed with potent, poisonous stings, move in strength against their opponents, such as the *Oecophylla* ants mentioned above, engaging them in single and multiple combat and carpeting the ground below the tree with their corpses. After their victory, the black ants move actively over the stem and leaves of their home. All larval and adult herbivorous insects are ejected from the tree as soon as they are found; the surfaces of the leaves are cleaned of moss, lichens and other contaminants, such as dried bird droppings, which are all removed and dropped to the earth below. In the meantime, the worker ants attack any leaves touching the branches of the *Barteria* and chew off the buds and shoots of all the plants growing under their tree. There is soon a bare circle up to 10 ft (3 m) in diameter, around the *Barteria* which, as it is now free of lianas and has clean leaves, grows vigorously at a rate of 24-35 in (60-90 cm) per year.

As well as defending their tree from overgrowth by other plants and from herbivorous insects, *Pachysima* ants also seem to be able to repel larger browsing animals. The workers regularly fall from the upper branches, as a slow rain that will land on any mammal foraging near the tree. If they come into contact with one, the ants react aggressively, locating an area of bare skin and then biting hard and finally injecting a virulent poison.

Human victims of these attacks say they are extremely painful and may even be incapacitating (in some areas of western Africa, the traditional punishment for an unfaithful wife was to tie her to the trunk of a *Barteria*).

The ant colony grows with the tree, gradually moving upwards as the lower branches are abandoned and shed. Both the tree and the colony stop growing at the same time, and the colony then contains about 4,000 workers. Nearby seedlings may now be adopted and protected by the workers of a large colony, as the colonies produce new queens from time to time and need new trees to house new colonies.

Poisons that feed

Complex mutual dependencies between different species, such as that just described between *Barteria* and *Pachysima*, are highly typical of the rainforest, and a basic and fascinating aspect of its ecology. They illustrate the complexity of *coevolution*—the adaptation of one species to a specialized role with respect to another. Yet not all relations of this type are benign: predator/prey relations may be just as specialized.

Thus, many plants protect their growing leaves from herbivores by filling them with toxins, such as alkaloids. This does not make them immune to predation but greatly reduces the number of animal species able to eat them. This increases their chance of reaching maturity before they are discovered by individuals of one of the few species capable of destroying them.

Both plants and animals have to administer their energy and nutrient reserves carefully. Animals are unable to produce their food by photosynthesis, and so live on particularly tight budgets, and detoxifying alkaloids is relatively costly. Invertebrates are small, and can only store limited reserves in their modest body, and so they tend to specialize. If a caterpillar is able to break down the alkaloid produced by a particular species of plant, its descendants can live on the leaves of that single species, and the caterpillar avoids competition with all other caterpillars by restricting itself to a single host plant. This may lead to

the loss of redundant metabolic pathways, making the caterpillar more and more efficient at feeding on its host plant, but less and less efficient at eating anything else. Adult butterflies of the species will seek out the shoots of the host plant to lay their eggs, because those laid on other plants will be seriously disadvantaged with respect to their competitors.

This specialization is gradually refined over many generations, until the species depends totally on its single host plant. This may lead to speciation, as the insects may radiate into different forms with different metabolisms, each race with its own particular requirements. For each race, everything in their diet that is not forbidden is compulsory.

The war of diversity

This specialization of invertebrates, in addition to generating a huge number of animal species, has at least two major consequences for plants. Both result from the fact that specialized predation is potentially very severe, as a plant's most delicate growing tissues are now vulnerable to a highly specialized herbivore. First, this means that the density of individual host plants may control and be controlled by the density of its predators. If the plants are in dense stands, egg-laying insects will find them with greater ease, and thus more will be damaged or killed, while if the plants are scarce, a smaller proportion is attacked. Thus, for many species, the number of individuals will be at a density in equilibrium with the demands and abilities of its predators and hosts, a fact that partly explains the high species diversity of the rainforest: Many relatively rare species are playing a deadly game of hide-and-seek with each other.

The other consequence of this system is the evolutionary "arms race." The insects most able to find their rare host plants will leave more surviving descendants, thus increasing predator efficiency. At the same time, host plants that improve their defenses and invalidate their enemies' adaptations have a better chance of not being eaten, and thus sharply increase their reproductive fitness. Adaptation leads to counter-adaptation, followed in turn by counter-counter-adaptation and counter-counter-counter-adaptation. In this game, the slightest advantage may be crucial, both in terms of the struggle between host and predator and in terms of the permanent competition between the host plant and other plants, and the predation pressure exerted on its predator. The hazards of life in the rainforest are very varied, and all species are fighting on many different fronts at the same time.

2.4 Spreading propagules

Reproduction is the third main imperative of living things, after obtaining nutrients and avoiding predation. Coevolution is also important in the reproductive strategies of rainforest plants and animals. In the rainforest ecosystem, sexual reproduction by plants is as complex and risky as the day-to-day maintenance of the growth and the form.

Dispersal systems

The individuals of a given species may be spread over a large area, isolated from each other by inhospitable space. Nevertheless, these individuals have to exchange pollen across this space in order to set seed, and then, the seeds must be dispersed to a suitable germination site. As the adult plants that produce the pollen and seeds are immobile, they must travel large distances and arrive safe and sound if the plant is to leave offspring.

Wind dispersal

To resolve the problem of dispersal, plants must use the moving features of their environment, making use of them in their reproductive cycle. Water, air, and animals are perpetually moving among the rainforest plants. Water is an adequate medium for the motile reproductive cells of some plants, but it is of no use to most plants. Many

60 The presence of wings on fruit or seeds favors their dispersal by the wind, as shown by these seeds (above) from a liana in the rainforest of the Palenque River in Ecuador and by these dipterocarp fruit (below) from the Sandakan rainforest (Borneo). The dipterocarps are especially interesting; the term *dipterocarp* refers to the two wings of the aerial dispersal mechanism of their fruits (three or five wings in some species) that slow its fall to the soil. The trees of this family may not begin to flower for 60 years, and after flowering they may not flower again for several years (7-11); yet when an adult flowers it induces the flowering of its neighbors that were waiting to do so. The fruiting that follows is irregular or isolated and does not allow the establishment of a specific link with animals, who as well as consumers may also be dispersal agents. This has obvious advantages for the tree (the seeds are hardly consumed and large production is not necessary), but there are also disadvantages, as dispersal suffers, and this is always problematic. In Borneo, for example, there are species that are present on one bank of a river but not the other. There are also species that stop between Borneo and Celebes, in the Macassar Strait. In the face of all these adversities, the dipterocarps' success at colonization is surprising; the family also contains immense trees that grow on poor, leached soils. [Photo: Adolf de Sostoa & Xavier Ferrer and Hans C. Heap / Planet Earth Pictures]

temperate plants use wind to disperse both pollen and seeds, but the densely matted rainforest vegetation makes air transport unreliable and limits its range. In addition, the rainforest's humidity tends to waterlog the pollen grains, further limiting their mobility. Small seeds or pollen may be blown long distances if they bear wings or plumes and are released from a sufficient height. Over a quarter of the upper canopy species are wind-dispersed. Some trees produce huge quantities of silky seeds that are blown off by strong winds, and look like a snowstorm falling on the rainforest.

The camphorwood forests (*Dryobalanops aromatica*) of peninsular Malaysia, for example, were maintained thanks to the reproductive pressure of their massive, regular and frequent crops of winged seeds. They were one of the rare forms of rainforest habitat dominated by a single tree species, whose seeds were the food of the migratory populations of a subspecies of the bearded pig (*Sus barbatus oi*). Unfortunately, the camphorwood forest was too attractive for the timber industry and these forests have been devastated.

Dispersal by animals

A few species use internal forces to spread their seeds; their fruits dehisce explosively, scattering seeds over a short distance. Yet animals are the key to the sexuality and seed dispersal of most rainforest plants. These animal-plant relations have been elaborated to the point of great complexity by natural selection acting strongly and very precisely over countless generations. Few plants use animals, like *Barteria*, during their vegetative growth; yet in reproduction it is specificity, coadaptation, and mutual aid that are the rule rather than the exception.

Flowers produce and receive pollen, and so they must attract animals if they are to serve the plant's interests. The rainforest's flowers are as varied as its vegetation: they may be bright or dull, fragile or robust, feathery or waxy, and they may be in the form of a funnel, dish, bowl, bell, trap, brush, gullet or flag. The rainforest houses species that flower in unusual places: growing on the midrib of leaves, or directly from trunks or branches; growing up from buried roots, hanging down from long stems, or sprouting from the outermost twigs in a tree's crown. There is no room for error in pollination. A plant that attracts too few animals, or animals of the wrong species, will pay an instant penalty in lost seeds and, likewise, more effective flowers will immediately benefit. This evolutionary accounting is much more exact than for other plant structures and is responsible for the great diversity of flowers, the result of complex adaptations by plants to their pollinating animals.

The animals most used as pollinators are those that regularly travel long distances from flower to flower; most have wings, such as bees, wasps, butterflies, moths, beetles, birds and bats. It is no coincidence that ants, despite being so common in rainforest, are almost never used as pollinators: They are too sedentary to be useful, and they are often counterproductive to pollination because they steal pollen and nectar.

The array of attractions in pollination

To load their pollen onto a flying animal, the plant must first attract them, and this can be achieved in several ways. In some cases, especially among the orchids, the flowers mimic objects, such as food plants or animal prey that encourage the insects to settle on them. Similarly, flowers may adopt the shape of members of the insect's own species, thus inciting the insect to copulate, or attack in defense of its territory.

Most flowers, however, show themselves for what they are, relying on their inherent suitability to attract potential pollinators flying by. Thus, most flowers act as signaling devices to make themselves as conspicuous as neon signs at night, and broadcast their location using color and fragrance. Carotenoids are among the most common pigments in flowers, giving them their yellow, red and orange colors, for example, rhodoxanthin and rhodoviolascin.

Curiously, no animal can produce carotenoids, yet these pigments are essential for the biochemistry of vision; it is as if plants had provided animals with vision just to exploit them!

Insect obsessions

Just like its shape and position on the plant, a flower's color and smell are tuned to the animals they seek to attract. There are several recogniz-

61 Cauliflorous (stem-bearing) trees bear flowers directly on their main stem and are not uncommon in the rainforest. The image shows a flowering and fruiting trunk of (*Couroupita guianensis*), a tree from the Guyana forest that is widely cultivated in tropical gardens throughout the world as an ornamental, as in this specimen in George-town (Guyana) (see figure 68).
[Photo: P. Burton / Natural Science Photos]

able "syndromes" in the rainforest, combinations of features that suggest the type of pollinator the flowers are intended for. Flowers that are purple, bristly and stink, such as the aptly named *Amorphophallus* (see "Extraordinary flowers" pages 106-109), use carrion flies as pollinators. Bees are attracted by more complex and highly colored flowers, as they are active during the day; these flowers are often equipped with footholds and pathways that reflect ultraviolet light, which is clearly visible to bees.

Curiously, bright red and orange flowers attract birds, especially sunbirds (Nectariniidae), while those with lighter and less conspicuous colors, generally trumpet-shaped, provide food for butterflies, which reach the base with their long proboscises.

Night-opening flowers with sweet scents and pallid colors are visited by moths, especially the long-tongued hawk moths (Sphingidae), whose long proboscis can reach to the bottom of the tubes formed by the fused petals. Many beetle-pollinated flowers open at night, when the rainforest is perfumed with a mixture of their odors. There are millions of tropical species of beetle,

and as they are clumsy animals, flowers that use their services tend to be open bowls or dishes to make access to the flower easy for them.

Bats and parkias

Bats are also highly diverse and ever present, and their wing beats fill the rainforest at night. They have many flowers to themselves; some flowers dangle outside the surrounding vegetation so they can be safely approached when flying, while others are on sturdy supports, such as the trunk or the branches. Bats are excellent pollinators, partly because they are large and furry (and can thus transport more pollen) and partly because they travel long distances when feeding, and also because they have mammalian memory and intelligence. This means that can remember the trees whose flowers they feed on and the paths between them, and so they can fly systematically from tree to tree, night after night, fertilizing flower after flower as they open.

This reliability is perfect for the trees, but it requires a heavy investment in structures suitable for this system of pollination. The genus *Parkia*, a Mimosoid member of the Leguminosae, which

62 The "hot pollination" of *Philodendron bipinnatifidum*, seen here in a specimen in the Beni Reserve (Bolivia), is one of the most elaborate reproductive strategies of the plant kingdom. Like the other members of the Araceae this species has a columniform inflorescence (spadix), surrounded by a protective bract (the spathe). The female flowers are at the base of the spadix and the male flowers are in its center, with a sterile part at the top. They are unusual because of the flowering sequence. The sterile part accumulates and oxidizes a large quantity of lipids and waxes—which is exceptional in the plant kingdom—raising its temperature to 63°F (17°C). This means that many insects that are attracted by the smell emitted by the inflorescence find a good site for mating and feeding (the sterile flowers are nutritious), so they stay there for a long time, mating and eating. During these operations their bodies rub against the pollen of the male flowers, or fertilize the female flowers with the pollen they have brought from a previously visited inflorescence. The spathes open at nightfall and the insects stay for 24 hours (thus ensuring accidental pollen capture and fertilization), and close again at nightfall the next day, and the spadix also cools down. The appropriate sequence of the opening of the flowers prevents self-pollination, and another no less opportune sequence in the days of opening of the spathes ensures cross-pollination between different inflorescences.
[Photo: Xavier Ferrer & Adolf de Sostoa]

includes some trees widely distributed throughout the rainforests, is a good example. Its blossoms consist of innumerable minute flowers in bulbous inflorescences reminiscent of shaving brushes, which hang from long specialized stems outside its crown, making them freely accessible from the air. The bananas (Musaceae), also have pendulous inflorescences to facilitate bat pollination.

In the rainforests of the coasts of the Gulf of Guinea, towards sunset on its one and only night of activity, the *Parkia* inflorescence starts to ooze nectar from the upper parts, intensifying as dusk falls. At first sunbirds (Nectariniidae) and bees can still take some nectar, as the sugar is a welcome source of energy before the long approach-

ing night. This ceases when night falls, when they are replaced by foraging nocturnal ants and perhaps by small mammals like dormice (*Graphiurus*) or primates such as pottos (*Perodicticus potto*). The dangling *Parkia* inflorescences are dangerously exposed to attacks by owls, their predators, but these mammals may sometimes be tempted to supplement their normal diet with nectar.

Finally, a bat arrives, remembering the route to a tree where it has recently fed, or guided by the sweet musky smell of the *Parkia* flowers. After flitting around the tree once or twice, it alights on the mass of hanging flowers, which bounce up and down because of the bat's weight. Clinging head up to the inflorescence, it starts greedily licking the sweet drops while it moves awkwardly around the flowers, rubbing its breast against the lower ones. Any pollen it has brought from other trees is picked up by the female flowers, which are thus fertilized. When the bat finally drops off the inflorescence, it leaves behind it a few fertilized *Parkia* ovules beginning seed formation.

By dawn, the inflorescence has served its purpose, although it may still attract some butterflies and bees to feed on the leftover pollen and nectar. In the daylight, the inflorescence wilts, all but the fertilized florets falling off. Soon, all that is left at the tip of the long *Parkia* stalks is a pale knob containing the rapidly-growing ovary sacs. These elongate to form pods about 28 in (70 cm) long, each one with a row of large, flattened seeds known in some areas as "locust beans." These pods hang for weeks awaiting maturity in bunches that look like gnarled many-fingered hand.

Compensation in food

Inducing pollinating animals to carry out their task effectively, avoiding any interference with the necessary chain of events requires complex adaptation. In most cases, the animal has to be rewarded for their visits to the flowers, so they will be repeated, and the usual "payment" is food. If there is enough sunlight, plants produce sugars with ease by photosynthesis and use them as a coinage to bribe their pollinators. So most nectars are essentially solutions of sugars in water, although some also contain amino acids, proteins, fats, and vitamins.

Except when a pollinator is totally committed to feeding on the flowers of a single species (in these rare cases, the plant must flower continuously), flowers must compete with each other and with other food sources for the attention of pollinating organisms.

For example, tropical moths and butterflies often feed on liquids other than nectar, such as mammalian urine, sweat and droppings, and the fluids of decomposing flesh. Moreover, there are times when flowers are superabundant in the rainforest, and then it is necessary to produce a competitive bribe by producing a very nutritious nectar, but sugar solutions cannot exceed certain concentrations without crystallizing. Many free-flowing

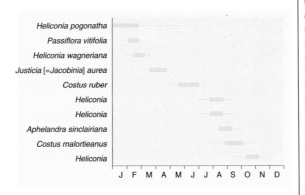

Heliconia pogonatha
Passiflora vitifolia
Heliconia wagneriana
Justicia [=Jacobinia] aurea
Costus ruber
Heliconia
Heliconia
Aphelandra sinclairiana
Costus malortieanus
Heliconia

J F M A M J J A S O N D

63 The flowering periods of some plants of the undergrowth, in the lowland rainforest of Costa Rica, that are pollinated by hummingbirds. It has recently been discovered that often, in the jungle, species sharing the same hummingbird pollinator flower sequentially. The chance of cross-pollination is higher if there are plants of the same genus (such as the species of *Heliconia* in the diagram) that flower simultaneously, and even more if those of other genera flower at other times. Four of the five species of *Heliconia* in the diagram share the same hummingbird as a pollinating agent.
[Drawing: Editrònica, taken from Stiles, 1977]

nectars have a taste that to humans is much sweeter than molasses, so that perhaps there has been selection for plants to use special sugars with a sweet taste and low viscosity.

Fats contain about twice as much energy per molecule as sugar, so oil droplets in nectar offer an added inducement to those animals able to use them efficiently. Bees and flies seem to be better at doing this than butterflies and birds are because they burn energy less rapidly and can afford to wait while the oils are slowly processed. Flowers pollinated by bees and flies usually produce a nectar richer in oils, and some orchids reward their specialized bees with oil alone.

Amino acids and proteins may also tempt passing insects to renounce searching for a richer food source elsewhere. Some of these molecules are secreted directly into the nectar, but this increases the problem of the solution crystallizing. Some flowers have a design that ensures the first insect visitor with a correctly shaped proboscis pushes pollen into the nectaries. In other cases, the insects soak the pollen in nectar and then suck the pollen dry; other insects may directly eat pollen grains, and some are specially adapted to doing so.

The fascinating case of nectar

One of the potential problems of nectar is that it may spoil before pollinators can find it. Once exposed to air, the nectar may oxidize, and antioxidants must be added to prevent this. One might expect sugary liquids to be colonized rapidly by bacteria and fungi, but they are protected by their very sweetness. Few microorganisms can tolerate life in such a concentrated sugar solution, as they would lose all the water from their cells by osmosis. Thus, nectar is protected, like the sweetened condensed milk that is so pop-

2. LIFE IN THE RAINFORESTS

ular in the tropics because open cans can be kept for a few days without refrigeration.

Like condensed milk spilled on a table, however, nectar is vulnerable to the depredation of animals it is not intended for, especially ants. When a plant has synthesized special sugars, concentrated them in nectar, added amino acids, proteins, fats and vitamins, it has obviously invested considerable metabolic activity and many nutrients to make its flowers attractive to pollinators.

Nectar is thus precious and not to be given away. Some animals are "nectar robbers" and take the pollen but cannot transfer it, such as hairless ants, while others take the nectar but are ineffective as pollen-carriers. Both are to be avoided at all costs.

Most flowers avoid potential nectar thieves by opening their flowers at restricted times, closing (or not producing pollen or fragrance) at night or during the day. The very structure of the flower may deny thieves access to the nectaries: Long, tubular corollas deny access to insects with an inadequate proboscis, while barricades of hairs pointing back towards the entrance or other similar features physically protect the flower's most vulnerable parts.

Precisely because some insects must reach the pollen and drink the nectar, these physical protections are intrinsically vulnerable, so plants also use chemical defenses to repel nectar robbers. Nectar is already a complex soup, and if protective chemical substances must be added without it solidifying, these must be simple molecules. Thus, toxins are more appropriate than digestion inhibitors, and the most widely used toxins are the alkaloids. They have the advantage of being very effective against animals unable to break them down, yet they are rapidly detoxified by "legitimate" pollinators adapted to them.

Normally, chemical defense of a plant's reproductive organs is not restricted to its nectar and pollen. The flower's structure is important and it must be protected from damage by over enthusiastic pollinators or attempts at theft. Tannins are effective against all animals and are thus often deposited in large quantities in flowers. One example is the genus *Pentadesma* (Guttiferae) whose large cup-shaped flowers are pollinated by monkeys.

Nectar is too rich a foodstuff for the leaf-eating colobid monkeys (*Colobus, Presbytis, Nasalis*) because it interferes with the biochemistry of fermentative digestion in their intestines but the cercopithecid monkeys are grateful for the abundant nectar flow of the *Pentadesma* flowers and go from bloom to bloom drinking it. When they drink, pollen adheres to the hairs of their chins, and is transferred effectively between flowers. Tannins deter monkeys, normally very destructive creatures, from eating the entire flower: they do not even nibble at it, because it is so bitter.

Seed dispersal

Other plants also a biochemical "carrot and a stick" approach to recruit and control the animals that disperse their seeds. About three-quarters of the rainforest's trees and lianas produce fruit with seeds with a fleshy, nutritious pulp attractive to vertebrates (mainly birds, fruit bats, and monkeys). Invertebrates are rarely involved in seed dispersal, as even the smallest seeds are large in comparison to most insects, and it is difficult to induce them to be effective carriers. Insects make a great contribution to pollination but are the great destroyers of seeds, which need to be well defended against insects and against damage by vertebrates.

Seed characteristics

Plants need to disperse their seeds for two main reasons. The first reason is that the repeated production of seeds year after year is likely to provoke increasing seed predation, as predator populations build up locally or are attracted from far away by the size of the feast awaiting them. An example is the way the Borneo bearded pig (*Sus barbatus barbatus*) seems to learn the location of regularly fruiting montane oak and bamboo groves, and returns year after year to eat the acorns and seeds on the forest floor. This type of response by seed-eating animals means that the closer a seed falls to its parent tree, or the longer it hangs temptingly on the branches, the more likely it is to be destroyed. To prevent this, selection makes plants increase their efficiency at removing their seeds from the danger zone, as only those that do so will in turn manage to fruit.

The second reason is that the adult seed-producing plant is by definition living in a suitable site with local conditions suitable for the species, but these conditions may change as a result of the rainforest's continuous cycle of tree fall and regeneration. Thus seeds have to be dispersed if they are to have a chance of occupying favorable sites elsewhere, which are unpredictable in space in time.

Seed dispersal may be greatly refined to ensure they are deposited in a site especially suited for their survival and growth far from their parent. This is clearly shown in the mistletoe family (Loranthaceae), such as the mistletoe *Viscum*, whose seeds have a sticky coat even after passing through a bird's gut. When the birds defecate they have to wipe themselves against the tree's bark to get rid of the seeds. Having their seeds rubbed into a branch is ideal for their germination and growth, as mistletoes are hemiparasitic plants that grow on trunks and branches.

Plants with animal-dispersed seeds have to make their fruits attractive to the species most likely to

64 The cross-pollination of many rainforest plants, especially those of *Heliconia*, *Passiflora*, and many genera of the Bromeliaceae and Gesneriaceae, is often the work of hummingbirds. These very small birds can hover in midair and suck the flower's nectar without having to perch on it. The flowers they visit are usually brightly colored, often red, and have a tubular corolla into which they thrust their beak and tongue, which are very long. Another feature of hummingbirds, which is more developed in some species than others, is that they can vary the intensity of their metabolism from very high values when flying to very low ones when roosting, so low that at night they may even suffer hypothermia. The photo shows a specimen of *Glaucis aenea* taking nectar from a *Passiflora* flower in the rainforest of Costa Rica. [Photo: Michael & Patricia Fogden / Bruce Coleman Limited]

65 Fruits must be conspicuous and attractive in order to disperse their seeds, because the animals that eat the fruits locate them by sight. So it is not strange to find fruit structures in the rainforest that have truly striking color combinations, such as red fruit with a black seed, as in the plants in the photos. The upper photograph is of an unidentified species in New Guinea, and the lower photo of a member of the genus *Connarus* from Cameroon. [Photos: Brian J. Coates / Bruce Coleman Limited and Michael & Patricia Fogden / Bruce Coleman Limited]

disperse them correctly, in other words, far away and in good condition. These animals should be alerted to the presence of fruits and rewarded for eating them. Bright colors usually fulfil the first function, and massive synthesis of bright pigments indicates the fruit is ripe and full of appetizing tastes and smells.

Ripe fruit pulp plays a role comparable to nectar: it is a reward in the form of food, programmed to please and sustain useful animals and deter others. Yet the complexities of animal-assisted seed dispersal are comparable with those of pollina-

tion, and there are many adaptations and counter-adaptations. Fruits adapted to the gut of birds often contain toxins noxious to mammals; many would cause severe diarrhea in monkeys without affecting birds, a solution that is perhaps beneficial to the seeds that are threatened by the monkey's digestive processes.

The characteristics of fruit-eaters (frugivores)

The number of animals capable of seed dispersal in the rainforest is limited, and seed producers must compete with others for the attention of appropriate dispersers. Dispersers belong to two different groups: specialists and opportunists. The two types have different needs and thus their activities have different consequences for the plants. Specialist frugivores (fruit-eaters) derive all or nearly all of their sugars, fats and proteins from the pulp of the fruit they eat, while opportunistic fruit-eaters are only interested in fruit as a source of sugar and water, as they obtain their fats and proteins by eating insects.

To establish an intimate evolutionary relationship with a specialist fruit-eater, the plant must present its seeds in a nutritious packet of pulp, and this represents a significant cost for the plant. Thus, the bigger the seeds the better, as they will have more food reserves and a better chance of establishment in the site where they germinate. Large seeds also discourage nonspecialists from eating the fruit, as they would fill the animal's gut with useless ballast.

Furthermore, the small animals unable to swallow large seeds have different energetic requirements than those of large animals. They burn energy faster and thus have to eat easily digested foodstuffs that release energy faster. Thus, they could hardly afford to digest the lipids and proteins in the pulp of specialized fruits, and certainly not at the added expense of slowing their guts down with blockages caused by large seeds.

Fruits with large seeds and abundant pulp are thus the domain of large-bodied specialist fruit-eaters, but their production is very costly for the plant. Thus, the crop is smaller, and so each fruit is of greater importance for the plant's reproductive future. By distributing its investment this way, the plant is opting for a high-quality dispersal system, based on a few seeds that have a high chance of successful dispersal.

The specialist fruit-eaters that plants have adapted to tend to be attentive and loyal, thanks to the generous reward. Thus, a high percentage of the fruit is consumed or removed from the tree before it rots or ceases to be usable by seed eaters. Large, intelligent, specialist fruit-eaters, including birds such as the hornbill family (Bucerotidae), have the added advantage that they are usually wide-ranging and can thus disperse the seeds over great distances.

66 Blue fruit are common in the shadiest understories because in the prevailing light conditions this color makes them easier to find. This is true for an unidentified shrub from the rainforest in Costa Rica (above) and the blue fig (*Elaeocarpus grandis*) from the Australian rainforests in Queensland (below).
[Photos: Peter Ward / Bruce Coleman Limited and Oriol Alemany]

Market supply, user demand

For plants using specialist fruit-eaters, improving fruit quality is not the only way of increasing the success of seed dispersal. If there are few specialists, the chance that the (rich and valuable) fruit are not eaten is unacceptably high, and plants compete with each other by increasing the nutritional value of their fruit's pulp. The fruit's other characteristics, such as its color, taste, texture, smell, and size are also subject to similar selection pressure. This is why there are so many types of fruit on offer in tropical markets: it is the result of millions of years of adaptation, unlike the situation in temperate areas. Few rainforest fruits have been modified by human horticulturists and their rich flavor and other attributes are still absolutely natural.

Dispersal by specialist fruit-eaters is usually reliable, but the small community of specialists can only process a small volume of seeds: quality is achieved at the cost of quantity. This does not always coincide with the plant's best reproductive interests, and many rainforest species adopt an alternative strategy based on the activities of opportunistic fruit-eaters. If a tree is to increase the number of useful dispersal agents, it must make the fruit's pulp sweeter and the seeds smaller and must strengthen the seed coats to protect them against the hazards of opportunists' excessively abrasive stomachs.

Specialists will be less attracted by this type of fruit, but they will be replaced by many other species of animal. These visitors may be distracted by the quantity and variety of fruit elsewhere, making them less reliable than specialists, but a large quantity of seeds will be eaten and voided by the opportunists as a whole. These seeds have cost little and their limited food reserves mean their future is uncertain, but if enough are dispersed, some will find their way to sites suitable for germination and the species will not become extinct.

Figs (*Ficus*, Moraceae) are a good example of opportunistic adaptation: They normally produce huge crops of fruit, each with many small, hard seeds. Some produce several million fruit in a season, and this is their defense: They all ripen at once and bear a huge number of seeds with a chance of germinating, thus overwhelming seed predators. Yet the fruit crop must be dispersed quickly if the strategy is not to backfire, with a free-for-all race between the fruit-eating dispersers and seedeaters or fruit thieves.

A rainforest fig fruiting on a massive scale is like a huge cafeteria. By day this noisy and crowded cafe's diners include many birds, such hornbills (Bucerotidae), pigeons (Columbidae), plantain-eaters (Musophagidae), toucans (Ramphastidae), bulbuls (Pycnonotidae) and starlings (Sturnidae); at night, the diners include fruit bats and the tree is the temporary home of mangabeys (*Cercocebus*) and guenons (*Cercopithecus*). This combination of opportunists, wasters and casual visitors may disperse less of the total seed crop than specialists might, but the number of seeds is so large that the fig's objectives are more than fulfilled.

Displays, brands and imitations

Rainforest fruits adapted to particular groups of animals have distinctive features comparable with the pollination syndromes described above. Fruit and flowers intended for bats, for example, are usually borne outside the crown on special stalks to make it easier for bats to land. They are usually in drab brownish or yellowish colors, with a strong musky smell. Fruit intended for monkeys and birds have brighter colors to make them stand out against the many background shades of green, making them attractive and visible from afar by daylight.

There are also subtleties and fine detail. Understory shrubs may produce fruit intended specifically for understory birds, whose eyes are adapted to the wavelengths of light typical of their habitat. Members of the Rubiaceae, such as *Lasianthus* in southern Asia, *Psychotria* in the Caribbean and western Africa, *Coccocypselum* in Amazonia, and members of the Liliaceae, such as *Dianella*, are all understory shrubs that use the same strategy of producing deep blue fruits.

Yet some of the brightest fruits are in reality fakes evolved to encourage birds to eat them, but without offering any reward. The seed cases split and fold over, often turning inside out, exposing their bright, showy seeds on a contrasting background. The seeds appear to be surrounded by a fleshy covering, like the fruits they imitate, but this is an illusion, a simple colored surface.

The groups of fruit types, each adapted to a different type of animals, such as monkeys, birds, bats, squirrels, genets, or lizards, often show a wide range of designs different enough to allow one to distinguish between those eaten by different groups of animals. Pigeons as a whole can be divided into a whole series of different species, each slightly different in body size, and each eating fruit of different sizes depending on their beak's size at its widest. Small monkeys may be frustrated by thick peel or spiny shells from reaching the interior; mangabeys (*Cercocebus*) are stronger than guenons (*Cercopithecus*), and drills (*Mandrillus*) are stronger than mangabeys, and this affects the fruit they choose to eat. But

these primate groups can be further subdivided by age and sex: For example, an adult male guenon may be as strong as a juvenile male drill or an adult female mangabey.

These cercopithecine monkeys (*Cercopithecus*, *Cercocebus* and *Mandrillus*) are among the most important fruit-eaters of Africa rainforests and have equivalents throughout the Old World. Yet the leaf-eating colobine monkeys (such as guerezas, langurs and proboscis monkeys) do not usually eat mature fruit because their digestion is not adapted to such a rich, sugary food. They are, however, important seed predators, as they can ferment their protective toxins without any problem; they may eat fruit before it ripens, indirectly damaging the plant's interests by preventing appropriate fruit-eaters from eating them when whole and ripe.

2.5 Rhythms and synchronies

In a given place in the rainforest, the number of trees in flower, in fruit or producing new leaves is changing over time. It is, however, very difficult to establish a clear pattern for these changes, as the many species and individual plants in question follow different cycles and rhythms of reproduction and growth that need not be synchronized with seasonal events, as in temperate forests.

A given activity may be performed in some species by all individuals at the same time, while in other species the individuals are not synchronized. Some species follow cycles that may be annual, or shorter or longer. Some species fruit at regular intervals unrelated to external factors like the weather or the season of year, while other species respond to environmental cues, such as drought.

Nonseasonal cycles

Detailed, long-term observations show some overall patterns. The commonest pattern in the rainforest is that plants produce new leaves twice a year, with the largest peak after the driest season; flowering is induced by water stress, and peaks just after the driest period; fruiting peaks occur five months later, just before the wettest season.

67 **Birds are the most conspicuous fruit-eaters** of the rainforest. The photo shows an Amazonian blue-and-yellow macaw (*Ara ararauna*) eating the fruit of a species of *Caesalpinia*. Birds' taste for fruit helps to disperse the seeds.
[Photo: Xavier Ferrer & Adolf de Sostoa]

Extraordinary flowers

Flower bud of *Rafflesia arnoldii* in Indonesia [Anna Motis]

Sir Thomas Stamford Raffles (1781-1826) founded modern Singapore in 1819. Raffles was a businessman and politician and also an enthusiastic naturalist. Thus, it is not surprising that in 1822 he created a botanic garden for the city, started experimental cultivation of nutmeg and cloves, and became a close friend of Joseph Arnold, a doctor and naturalist who lived in the colony. Arnold and Raffles (who was also Governor of Java [1811-1815] and the British East India Company's possessions in Sumatra [1818-1824]), were fascinated by the lush tropical vegetation and made excursions to Malaysia and the islands in the Strait, where they found a range of botanical wonders. In a letter to the Duchess of Somerset, dated July 11, 1818, Raffles excitedly described "a gigantic flower... perhaps the largest and most magnificent flower in the world... (measuring) across from the extremity of the petals rather more than a yard (ca. 1 m), the nectarium was... estimated to contain a gallon and a half (ca. 7 l) of water, and the weight of the whole flower is 15 pounds (ca. 7 kg)." He was right: It was in fact the largest flower in the world.

Sir Thomas Stamford Raffles [Mary Evans Picture Library]

Robert Brown (1773-1858), a famous Scottish botanist of the time, using the information received from Raffles and Arnold, named the remarkable flower after its discoverers; *Rafflesia arnoldii* required the creation of a new genus and family, the Rafflesiaceae, which later included other similar but less spectacular species (*R. micropylora*, *R. gadutensis*, etc.) found in the rainforests of Malaysia, Sumatra, Java, Borneo and the Philippines. All the members of Rafflesia are root parasites of lianas of the genus *Tetrastigma* (Vitaceae, the same family as the vine), but none is as famous as *R. arnoldii*, which not only has an enormous flower, but is lacking leaves, stem and functional roots. This plant, endemic to Sumatra and Borneo is an obligate parasite, so its nutrition is entirely dependent upon its host, the flower being the only part of the plant that emerges above ground. The flower is huge, 3 ft (1 m) in diameter, red in color and foul smelling.

Rafflesia arnoldii in Indonesia [Alain Compost / Visage / Bios / Still Pictures]

The five fused petals of this disproportionate flower are firm, fleshy and about 0.4 in (1 cm) thick. When it opens it starts to emit a fetid smell, like carrion: it seems to be pollinated by the small flies and carrion beetles that are attracted by its smell of rotting flesh and by its coloration, which they take for a decomposing corpse. The flowers of *Rafflesia* are unisexual and so each individual—and thus in this case, each flower—is either male or female, making it necessary for two flowers of different sexes to open near each other in order for pollination to occur. The fruit that forms does not fall from the plant, nor are the seeds spontaneously released: the plant simply rots away, and the seeds remain in the resulting putrid mass. The *Rafflesia* is thus not only notorious, but rather repugnant.

The way its seeds are dispersed is still not fully understood. Some authors maintain that it might be undertaken by mammals, such as rats, tree shrews, or tapirs, or that it might be birds, such as pittas (*Pitta*). It seems highly likely that the seeds become attached to the paws or some other part of fur or plumage while the animals are poking around in the decomposing flower. In any case, it has been shown that if the seeds are transferred to the bark of *Tetrastigma lanceolarium*, the normal host liana, they germinate and grow. This system is like that observed in other similar parasitic species, such as the very small but otherwise comparable yellow cytinus (*Cytinus hypocistis*) of Mediterranean matorral, also a member of the Rafflesiaceae.

In Sumatra, the rafflesias have competitors for sheer size. In the west of the island, there is another strange, enormous plant, the titan arum (*Amorphophallus titanum*). This was first described in 1880 by the Italian naturalist Odoardo Beccari (1843-1920). His description of the plant was considered an exaggeration in European botanical circles until 1889, when a tuber planted at the Royal Botanic Gardens at Kew flowered, revealing to the astonished British botanists of the time a flower that was 7 ft (2 m) tall! Strictly speaking, it is an inflorescence, because *Amorphophallus* produces a spadix like the arum lily (*Zantedeschia*), and is a member of the same family (the Araceae). Individuals with spadices 10 ft (3 m) tall have been found, and this makes them without a doubt the largest unbranched inflorescences in the world.

Tree shrew (*Tupaia glis*) eating dead insects in a *Rafflesia arnoldii* flower in western Sumatra [Alain Compost / Bios / Still Pictures]

Amorphophallus titanum is a sort of gigantic arum lily with a blotchy stem, up to 8 in (20 cm) across, that produces many leaves whose photosynthetic activity leads to the formation of a large tuber weighing 44-66 lb (20-30 kg) (one of 165 lb [75 kg] has been found) which finally produces the huge flower in question. It is not a parasitic plant, but it has the same disgusting smell of rotting flesh as *Rafflesia*. There is a closely related species, the equally foul-smelling *A. decus-silvae*, first described around 1920, which bears its spadices on a remarkable stalk up to 10 ft (3 m) tall, while the dark purple inflorescence is 4.9 ft (1.5 m) long. This vegetable structure is more than 13 ft (4 m) tall and is the largest unbranched flowering structure in the world.

Even the gigantic, smelly, and phallic inflorescences of *Amorphophallus* are dwarfed by the enormous branched inflorescence of *Corypha* palms, which produce the largest known floral structures. The inflorescence of the gebang palm (*C. elata*), native to the monsoon forests of the Lesser Sunda Islands in Indonesia, is an impressive 16-18 ft (5-6 m) long and bears millions of flowers that form hundreds of thousands of fruits. A similar and related species, the talipot palm (*C. umbraculifera*), produces a highly branched inflorescence 20-23 ft (6-7 m) tall, with about 60 million flowers. The leaves of these palms are quite remarkable, reaching 16-20 ft (5-6 m) in length. This is a record, too.

68 **When fruiting occurs it attracts the fruit-eating fauna** to the trees of the intertropical forest. The illustration shows a long-tailed macaque (*Macaca fascicularis*) eating the ripe fruit of a fig tree (*Ficus*) in the basin of the Kinabatangan river in the Sabah region of Borneo. [*Photo: Jean-Paul Ferrero / Auscape International*]

68 **When fruiting occurs it attracts the fruit-eating fauna** to the trees of the intertropical forest. The illustration shows a long-tailed macaque (*Macaca fascicularis*) eating the ripe fruit of a fig tree (*Ficus*) in the basin of the Kinabatangan river in the Sabah region of Borneo. [*Photo: Jean-Paul Ferrero / Auscape International*]

These general patterns have great impact on the rainforest community. For example, in Borneo, rutting (the mating season) by bearded pigs (*Sus barbatus barbatus*) coincides with peak flower-fall, leading to speculation that the fallen confetti-like petals may act as a visual signal that the pigs have adapted to. As the piglets are born five months later, coinciding with the fruiting peak, this timing synchronizes food availability with food demand during lactation and the early growth of the piglets. The temporary abundance of flowers in the canopy provides a good food supply for nectarivorous bats and insects, while fruiting peaks lead to changes in the ranging behavior of gibbons (*Hylobates*) and other primates, civets and fruit-eating birds to take advantage of the situation. Likewise, the sprouting

of tender leaves provides food for a great variety of animals from monkeys to caterpillars.

Physical effects also play a role, as wet periods may stimulate breeding by amphibians and those insects that need puddles to breed in. These different effects may interact. Thus, many birds eat fruit and insects, especially when breeding or molting, when they require high-value foodstuffs to support these demanding activities. If the birds can synchronize breeding and molting with environmental conditions favorable to insects, they obtain an added advantage.

For the human observer, it is tempting to try to unify and simplify the rhythms of the rainforest.

These rhythms, however, arise from varied, often species-specific, adaptive strategies. These rhythms can only be understood at a deeper level than is necessary in environments with marked seasonality.

Internal rhythms

Considering fruiting behavior, it may not be worth paying high rewards for the services of specialized fruit-eaters in seed dispersal, and other approaches are possible. One option is to produce fruit continuously, as this may lead to specialization by some animals and, at the same time, encourages the use of the fruit as a year-round food supplement, attracting specialists when their preferred fruit were scarce. This is, however, a heavy burden on the plant, as it must fruit continuously in spite of temporary fluctuations in light, water, and nutrient supply. Furthermore, a reliable food source for a specialist fruit-eater is also a reliable food source for a seed predator, with disastrous consequences for the plant.

The logic of the trees
Most rainforest trees thus tend to hoard nutrients and only flower and fruit from time to time, according to their own internal rhythm. This system ensures that they have the reserves necessary for fruiting and avoids the shortfalls in resources for other activities, while massive fruit production alerts fruit-eaters and overwhelms seed predators. Too many plants fruiting at the same time compete unnecessarily for specialist fruit-eaters, which may suffer hunger or even starve to death between two fruiting seasons.

A better solution for the trees needing animals to disperse their seeds is to fruit when as few other trees as possible are fruiting. This allows specialist fruit-eaters to attend to each tree species in turn, so the animals do not starve and the plants never lack dispersers. Thus, most rainforest trees and lianas have fruiting periods staggered over the year, so that neither too many nor too few trees are fruiting at a given moment.

The synchronization of fruiting may be counterproductive, except when the climate imposes seasonality (which rarely occurs in the rainforest) or when the fruits are not dispersed by animals. In this case, the rhythms of seed production are induced by the need to avoid seed predators, not the need to attract seed dispersers. One possible strategy is to glut then starve seed predators, and this is the strategy adopted by the mass-fruiting, wind-dispersed trees of the large Dipterocarpaceae family.

Dipterocarps and bearded pigs
The lowland or hill forests of southeast Asia are often dominated by dipterocarps, which greatly influence food supplies for ground-dwelling seed-eaters, because of their synchronized flowering and seeding ("mast fruiting"). Dipterocarps are very common on the island of Borneo, where studies of how wild animals manage to live in these forests despite erratic food supplies have highlighted the consequences of mast fruiting as a response to seed predation.

The Borneo bearded pig (*Sus barbatus barbatus*) is an opportunist omnivore that eats roots, invertebrates in soil and decomposing wood, small vertebrates, turtle eggs and parts of about 50 genera of flowering plant from 29 families. Despite this diversity of food sources, fruit supply apparently has most influence on their growth rate, fat accumulation and reproduction. The other normally occurring foodstuffs allow only slow growth at best. The oil-rich seeds of members of the Fagaceae and Dipterocarpaceae are very important to bearded pigs. Oaks are especially important as they fruit relatively continuously, and may dominate lowland habitats. The pigs can survive on the basis of this regular food supply and other temporary ones, including the fruiting peak of the dipterocarps.

Mast fruiting is well documented in Sarawak (Malaysian Borneo), because wild-collected dipterocarp seeds have for many years been commercially exported, and the export records provide data on natural fruiting in the forest. The seeds are exported because they contain oils that are important ingredients of hollow-molded chocolates (such as Easter eggs) and other products. The total weight exported varies greatly from year to year: in one third of the years since 1900 exports of less than 10,000 t have been recorded, and in the other years exports were between 11,000 t and just over 28,000 t.

69 The Borneo bearded pig (*Sus barbatus barbatus*) is an impressive wild pig with a hairy snout that is of great importance in the food economy of local people, and it is also linked to the fruiting cycles of the members of the Dipterocarpaceae.
[Photo: Roland Seitre / Bios / Still Pictures]

Heavy fruiting (10,000 t or more exported in a year) usually occurs only every 3-5 years, often with little or no production between the peaks. This illustrates the large variation of fruiting in the dipterocarp-rich rainforest, and at the same time shows the scale of the food supply problems faced by seed-eating mammals in this habitat.

The bearded pig has features that allow it to react and make use of the opportunities offered by this food supply, and to breed extremely fast. These features can be interpreted as adaptations to a habitat with food resources distributed discontinuously and capriciously. They are: large litter size (4 to 12 piglets); short gestation period (3-5 months), with the possibility of two litters per year; early age at first rut or pregnancy (as early as 10-11 months); efficient conversion of dietary fat into body fat; high growth rates; flexible group size; the synchronization of litter production with fruit fall; the social reduction of male feeding competition with females; and adaptations to traveling, such as long legs and the ability to swim.

Over time, bearded pig populations change due to immigration and emigration, in correlation with fruiting in each area. These are interpreted to reflect foraging movements dictated by the appearance of patchy and transient fruit sources in large areas of rainforest. These changes, however, are small on a regional scale in comparison with changes in overall population size. In 1983 there was a population boom, which was repeated in 1987. This is a repetition of what occurred in Sarawak in 1954 and 1959. The explanation seems to be widespread dipterocarp mast fruiting in paired consecutive years. Commercial exports of dipterocarp seeds show that since 1945 consecutive years of mast fruiting have only happened in 1953-54, 1982-83 and 1986-87.

In the last two examples, this fruiting coincided with repeated droughts in Borneo, a reflection of global climate changes. It is though that the bearded pig populations increased so rapidly because the afore-mentioned adaptations allowed them to make use of the sustained availability of oil-rich dipterocarp seeds.

3. Fauna and animal inhabitants

3.1 More insects than anything else

There is still no complete inventory of the world's animals or those of the rainforest. The dramatic destruction of the planet's forests has led to the extinction of many animals and plants species that were never scientifically documented or described. Even so, the rainforests still contain the largest and most important reserve of animal diversity on Earth.

It is hard to assess the number or characteristics of as yet undiscovered animals. Even some large animals were not discovered until the 20th century: the okapi (*Okapia johnstoni*) was first described in 1901, the giant forest hog (*Hylochoerus meinertzhageni*) in 1904, whereas the Congo peafowl (*Afropavo congensis*) was not described until 1936.

The overwhelming predominance of insects

Numerically, insects contribute more to the diversity of rainforest animal life than any other group. The number of species is hard to assess, estimates varying from at least two million (three times the number of known species) to as many as 80 million (almost 100 times the number of known species). Insects are the most important animal component of almost all terrestrial ecosystems, partly because they are small, specialized feeders.

Most insects are between a few millimeters to about an inch long, allowing them to form relatively small local populations that can survive in very small areas on food supplies too scarce to support larger animals. Many insects are highly specialized herbivores or carnivores. Herbivores may be restricted to feeding on one species or have a specialized feeding technique. A single rainforest tree may have up to a thousand different insect species living on or near it. Some suck sap from leaves by eating the leaf blade from the edge, while leaf-miners eat one surface of the leaf (usually the lower) by tunneling galleries within the leaf, and others produce secretions that make the leaf enclose them in a gall. Other species may attack the roots, stems, flowers, or fruits. Some even wait until the wood of a dead or dying tree is attacked by fungi.

Many insects can feed on a variety of plants, usually of the same genus or at least the same family. Between 1 and 5% of rainforest insects are estimated to be *monophagous* herbivores, i.e. they feed on a single plant species.

These rough estimates are incomplete, but the incredibly diverse rainforest flora includes thousands of tree species (at least 40,000). These rainforest trees house the richest faunal communities, and some of the most reasonable recent total estimates of biodiversity are based on considerations like these.

Harmonic and discordant populations

The enormous diversity of animals that inhabit rainforest makes the introduction of some differential factor necessary. The animals in African and southeast Asian rainforests are members of a large number of species, in turn members of a large number of higher taxonomic groups. In con-

70 Insects dominate animal life in the rainforest as a result of the high number of species and individuals. They have also evolved a fascinating range of seemingly capricious shapes that are, in fact, adaptations with precise functions. The morphological modifications of both *Anisoscelis flavolineata* (Heteroptera) from Costa Rica (above) and *Toxidera denticulata* (Dyctioptera) from Borneo (below) include legs with curious extensions, and are good examples of these modicications. Note just how well the insect in the lower photo blends in color-wise with the inflorescence it is resting on. [Photo: Michael & Patricia Fogden and Jean-Paul Ferrero / Auscape International]

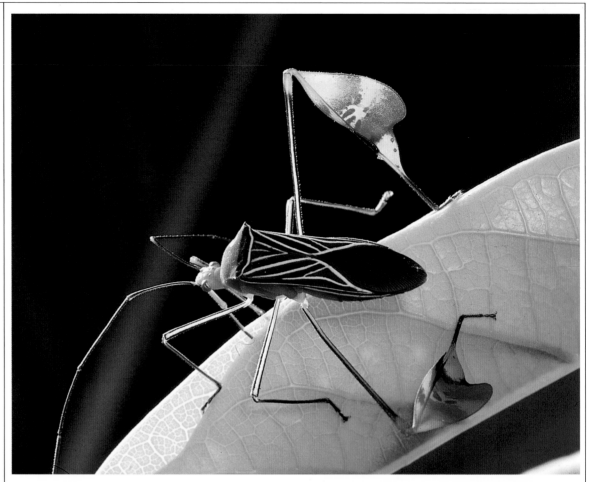

trast, rainforests in South America, Madagascar, New Guinea, and Australia contain many species, but they belong to a relatively small number of higher-level taxa. Biogeographers describe the type of inhabitants found in Africa and Asia as harmonic, whereas the other type are referred to as discordant.

These differences have historical origins. Australia, New Guinea and Madagascar have been isolated islands for a long time and have not been colonized by the animal groups that form part of the African and Asian rainforest fauna.

The existence of frequent but intermittent land links between South and North America has permitted many animals to cross between the two areas, but South America's fauna, especially its rainforest fauna, has developed in isolation.

The presence of, for example, the jaguar (*Panthera onca*) in South America must be seen as the result of relatively recent colonization. In contrast, the fact that lemurs are restricted to Madagascar and some of the Comoros Islands is not because they evolved there but because they are now extinct in the rest of the Old World. Lemurs are now restricted to Madagascar and Mayotte (Comoros Islands).

Uniforms and disguises

In a species-rich ecosystem such as the rainforest, the chances of being eaten are fairly high. This explains the many complex defensive or protective adaptations found in a wide range of animal groups. The situation is even more complex because many defensive adaptations can also be used offensively by animals when acting as predators.

This point is well illustrated by chameleons, arboreal lizards that are common throughout the rainforests of equatorial Africa, especially in Madagascar, where two thirds of all chameleon species occur. For lizards they move surprisingly little and exceedingly slowly, making them hard to spot among the foliage and branches of their natural habitats.

As is well known, they can change color to match their surroundings. This remarkable ability requires the animal's eyes to register color changes in their environment, and their chromatophores (pigment-containing skin cells) then expand or contract, and this controls the skin's overall color. As a predator, it is vital for the chameleon not to be noticed as it waits immobile for an unwary insect.

When a potential prey comes within range, it flicks out its long, sticky tongue in less than a twentieth of a second and then, just as rapidly, whips it back into its mouth with the captured insect. The chameleon's ability to remain immobile and to change its color according to its surroundings both help to reduce its risk of being eaten by one of its many potential predators (mammals, birds, snakes).

The ability to change color is unusual even in the rainforest, but camouflage is common. Many insects are effectively camouflaged by their protective coloration, complemented by their wing or body shape. Remarkable and well-known examples include the stick and leaf insects (Phasmatodea). The stick insects (Phasmatidae) are rigid and angular, resembling small leafless twigs, and one *Pharnacia serratipes* reaches 12 in (30 cm), making it the longest of all insects.

The leaf insects (Phylliidae), notably members of the genus *Phyllium*, have short, veined wings that look just like the venation of leaves. Many other members of the Orthoptera (crickets, grasshoppers, and locusts) imitate leaves, above all in southeast Asia, as do some butterflies. The upperwings of the Indian butterflies of the genus Kallima clearly show they are related to the vanessas (Nymphalidae), whereas the underwing, displayed when the wings are closed, gives the insect the appearance of a dead leaf, including the petiole.

A similar result is produced by the striped and spotted coats of many mammals that at a distance, help disrupt the animal's silhouette in the light and shade of the forest. This explains the striking, alternating light and dark vertical stripes on tigers (*Panthera tigris*), also present on some African antelopes, such as the bongo (*Tragelaphus euryc-

71 Many animals in the rainforest, whether as a means of defense or of attack, use cryptic coloration to blend in with their surroundings. In the photographs a mantis merges into a liana-covered tree trunk in the Mexican rainforest (above), a boa constrictor (*Boa constrictor*) lurks among the leaflitter at the foot of a tree (middle), and a small toad (*Eleutherodactylus latidirens*) sits camouflaged on moss in a Pacific coastal rainforest (below).
[Photos: Adolf de Sostoa & Xavier Ferrer]

eros) and zebra duiker (*Cephalophus zebra*), as well as on the hindquarters of the okapi (*Okapia johnstoni*).

These animals live in dense rainforest, and the okapi is one of the largest mammals present in the African rainforest.

Warning colors

However, coloration and patterning are not always designed to avoid being seen by predators or by potential quarries. Often, the complete opposite is true, and for many animals it is important to be highly visible, and not merely to members of the same species.

A good example of Müllerian mimicry in two Itomidae butterflies of different genera, *Dircenna jemina* (left) and *Godyris kedema* (right) in the Venezuelan rainforest. Müllerian mimicry, like Batesian mimicry, is based on patterning and coloration. The phenomenon was first described by Fritz Müller (1821-1897) and consists of the presence of similar markings and patterns in two different species, each with their own defenses. This similarity ensures that their defenses work more efficiently. The similarities in colors and patterns can be so great that it may be difficult to tell two species apart, even if they belong to separate groups such as the Heliconidae, Itomidae, and Danaidae. These three groups have very distinctive wing patterns, as the number of possible combinations of colors to warn of toxicity is limited. The known genera of Itomidae and Heliconidae have developed a defensive mechanism based on body toxicity: they are not actually poisonous but taste repulsive to potential predators. In animals exhibiting Batesian mimicry, on the other hand, inoffensive species benefit from their resemblance to toxic or foul-tasting species, thereby taking advantage of their defensive mechanisms. These similarities are so great that the males of many of these species emit highly specialized pheromones so that the females can recognize them correctly, in order to avoid fruitless and sterile matings.
[Photo: George Gainsburgh / NHPA]

Many rainforests species possess conspicuous *aposematic*, or warning, markings (see also vol. 1, pg. 218-219) that make them visible from afar. American rainforests are populated by vividly colored species, such as the highly venomous coral snakes (*Micrurus*), the small tree frogs of the genus *Dendrobates* (and other arrow-poison frogs of the Dendrobatidae), whose skin contains poisonous secretions used by local people to make poisoned arrows.

These creatures have fearsome natural defenses, although for them, as well as for their enemies, it is preferable not to have to resort to using them. The brilliant reds and blacks of many members of the Dendrobatidae and the distinctive white, black, and red rings of coral snakes are in fact highly visible, pre-contact warnings to potential predators to avoid confrontation with these animals, showing they can inflict poisonous bites, or provoke vomiting (or serious poisoning) in any creature that tries to eat them.

The English naturalist Henry W. Bates (1825-1892) observed that striking coloration sometimes has more subtle uses. He was one of the first to explore the Amazon, between 1848 and 1859, and studied some of the common genera of black, velvety butterflies with conspicuous red and white wing spots. Some of the commonest Amazonian butterflies with this coloration belong to the genus *Heliconius*, whose caterpillars feed on the leaves of *Passiflora*, making the adult butterfly completely inedible due to its high toxicity. Bates discovered that other butterfly species, for example members of the Pieridae and Papilionidae, present the very same markings as *Heliconius*, although they are totally unrelated and, unlike *Heliconius*, perfectly edible. The similarity between the inoffensive species and *Heliconius* is no coincidence, clearly shown by the fact that each inoffensive species "copies" the coloration and patterning of the *Heliconius* species it coexists with. Predators confuse the deceitful messages of edible species for the accurate aposematic warnings of toxic species. Resembling a toxic species thus, for many species, reduces the effective risk of being eaten. This is called Batesian mimicry, and for it to work the species copied must be more abundant than the inoffensive species, otherwise predators would detect the fraud.

3.2 Who eats whom

All more-or-less complex food webs contain carnivores and herbivores, specialists eating only a single type of prey, as well as organisms that can eat almost anything. This is true for rainforests, perhaps more so than in any other biome. Rainforest insects show many precise feeding

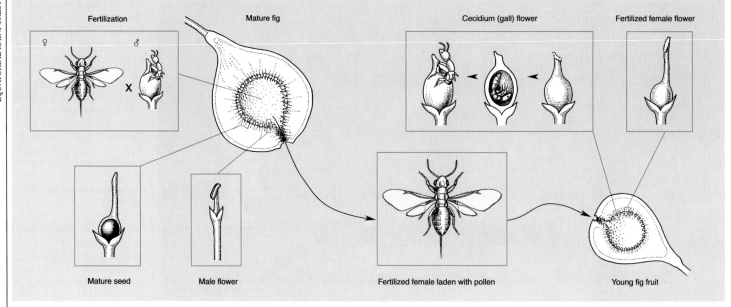

Fertilization Mature fig Cecidium (gall) flower Fertilized female flower

♀ ♂ X

Mature seed Male flower Fertilized female laden with pollen Young fig fruit

73 The life cycle of a fig-wasp, the insects that polli-nate *Ficus*. Fig trees pro-duce three types of flower: the pollen-bearing male flow-ers, the seed-bearing female flowers, and the specialized sterile cecidium (gall) flowers in which the wasps lay their egg. The maturation period of the wasps and their emer-gence from the different types of flowers are stag-gered. The male wasp, blind and wingless, hatches from a gall when adult, fertilizes the females and dies without ever having left the fig for the outside world. After fertiliza-tion, the females leave the fig, when they are coated in pollen from the male flowers located near the exit of the syconium, (the inside of the fruit) and then fly to another fruit. The gall flowers and the female flowers are very simi-lar when seen from the tip of the stigma, and so the female has to examine a number of flowers with her ovipositor, laying an egg in each gall. The greater length of the style in true flowers prevents the female from laying her eggs in fertile ovules, but the female's search ensures that the pollen she is carrying reaches its destination.
[Diagram: Jordi Corbera, from various sources]

specializations, and these are the basis of the enormous species diversity of the rainforests.

Parasitic and predatory insects

The role of plant-eating insects has already been discussed with relation to their coevolution with plants. However, the role of predatory and para-sitic insects cannot be ignored.

The most important parasitic insects are hymenopterans, often of very small dimensions, that are often as highly adapted to their prey as their prey is adapted to its food plant. The life cycle of these tiny wasps, for example, has to be synchronized correctly to the cycles of their prey, which are just as difficult to find as the leaves or the flowers of a given plant. In particular, the smallest of these hymenopterans (up to 500 dif-ferent species in the crown of a single tree in the Borneo rainforest!) develop within the eggs of other insects. A single butterfly or bug egg con-tains enough food for a wasp larva to grow to adulthood. After emerging, the adults mate and the females go off in search of other eggs of the same species of butterfly or bug in which to lay their own eggs.

These parasitic adaptations and the resulting complex food webs are not exclusive to the rain-forest biome and help prevent the explosive growth of herbivorous insect populations. Other types of relationships are, however, highly typical

of the rainforest and clearly explain the diversifi-cation of some insect families into thousands upon thousands of different species.

One of these relationships that leads to such diversification links fig plants of the genus *Ficus* and the fig wasps (Agaonidae). Almost all of the approximately 800 species of Ficus are rainforest species, especially in southeast Asia. Some are very large trees, others are small shrubs, many are lianas and some are even epiphytes. Yet all pro-duce the same characteristic inflorescence, called a syconium, consisting of many small inward-fac-ing flowers within a spherical receptacle linked only to the outside by a very narrow apical open-ing. To ensure cross-pollination, the pollen pro-duced by the male flowers inside one syconium has to reach the female flowers inside another. This is not simple, and can only be carried out by highly specialized pollinators, the fig wasps, minute (around 0.03 in [1 mm] long) insects that complete their entire life cycle within figs. To lay their eggs, the females have to leave the fig they developed in and enter another, thus ensuring its pollination. Each species of *Ficus* has its pollinating wasp, or more than one. The close relationship between the figs and wasps helps explain the large number of species of *Ficus* and of fig wasps.

Constricting and venomous snakes

The most remarkable of all vertebrate predators in rainforests are snakes. Within this biome, the

74 **The brute force of boa constrictors and the chemical complexity of poisonous snakes** are distinct strategies that lead to clearly different morphology and behavior: constricting snakes are large bodied and slow moving, while poisonous species are slender and agile. Boas and pythons such as the South American emerald tree boa (*Corallus caninus*, above) or the green python (*Chondropython viridis*, middle) from New Guinea are typical constricting snakes. In contrast, the green whip snake (*Oxybelis fulgidus*, bottom) is an excellent example of a poisonous snake. Note the similar green color of the adult emerald tree boas and the green pythons, and that they are dichromatic, that is to say, the juvenile and adult forms are different colors: the young of the emerald tree boa are reddish brown, but those of the green python—the photograph shows recently hatched young—are a yellowish color.
[Photos: Jany Sauvanet / Auscape International, Carol Farneti / Natural Science Photos and Adolf de Sostoa & Xavier Ferrer]

incredibly agile snakes that have evolved are perfectly at home in tree canopies, and not all are small and light-weight. Cryptic coloration is common among rainforest snakes, although it is essentially an offensive weapon to avoid being detected too soon by their prey. Some of the most important rainforest snakes are the reticulate python (*Python reticulatus*), green tree python (*Chondropython viridis*), emerald tree boa (*Corallus caninus*), the liana snakes (*Ahaetulla prasina*, *Dryophis*), and the green whip snake (*Oxybelis fulgidus*).

The first three species belong to the primitive family of the Boidae, or constricting snakes. These bulky animals kill their prey by constriction, crushing them in their coils. The reticulate python (*Python reticulatus*), widespread in southeast Asia and the Indonesian archipelago, is the second largest snake in the world. The largest is the anaconda (*Eunectes murinus*), an American species that swallows its prey whole, including kills weighing up to 110 lb (50 kg).

The other two members of the Boidae mentioned are much smaller. The emerald tree boa (*Corallus caninus*) lives in South American forests, whereas the green tree python (*Chondropython viridis*) is found in the rainforests of northern Australia and New Guinea. The skin markings of adults of both species are surprisingly similar—bright green on the back with white vertebral markings—although young snakes first pass through very different juvenile color phases. Young emerald tree boas are reddish brown, whereas the young of green tree pythons are yellow or occasionally brick red.

The liana snake (*Ahaetulla prasina*), an extremely agile and rapid species up to 7 ft (2 m) long, has poisonous fangs and a similar distribution to the reticulate python. Its conical head, narrowing towards the eyes, is unusually shaped for a snake but gives it binocular (and therefore stereoscopic) vision, a great advantage when hunting lizards and tree frogs. The American green whip snake (*Oxybelis fulgidus*) also has a venomous bite, and is probably the snake best adapted to arboreal life; its extraordinarily thin body is up to 7 ft (2 m) long.

Its back is bright green and is separated from its greenish yellow belly by a thin pale yellow border: perfect cryptic coloration for an animal living among leafy trees. It is active during the day and at night and is a relentless predator of lizards, frogs, and bird nests.

Although they are frequent in other biomes, some species of the much feared pit vipers (Crotalidae) also live in New World rainforests. The largest of the pit vipers is the bushmaster (*Lachesis muta*), 10 ft (3 m) or longer, the longest venomous snake except for the king cobra, or hamadryad, (*Ophiophagus hannah*) from southern Asia, a snake that can reach 13 ft (4 m) or more in length.

The bushmaster's venom is much less potent than that of another South American rainforest snake, the fer-de-lance (*Bothrops atrox*); although only half the bushmaster's size, it is responsible for most of the snakebite deaths in the Americas. The bushmaster is oviparous (egg producing) whereas the fer-de-lance is viviparous (bearing live young), like most members of the Crotalidae.

Specialized mammal and bird feeders

Some rainforest mammals, such as the three species of three-toed sloths (*Bradypus*) and the two species of two-toed sloths (*Choloepus*), are also specialized feeders. The three-toed sloths tend to eat *Cecropia* leaves, a specialization that is probably related to the sloth's singularly low level of activity.

They are undoubtedly the most sedentary of all mammals and rarely move more than 98 ft (30 m) a day, spending most of the day hanging from branches by their strong nails. Their long fur is usually covered by a layer of algae, like tree bark or any other inert substrate in the moist rainforest environment. Indeed, their silky fur is a miniature ecosystem, even containing a caterpillar that feeds on the flakes shed from the sloth's skin.

Another specialized feeding strategy practiced by birds and mammals is to eat ants or termites. The giant anteater (*Myrmecophaga tridactyla*) feeds almost exclusively on termites that are also the main food of the other two species of the Myrmecophagidae, the tamandua or lesser anteater (*Tamandua tetradactyl*) and the pygmy (or two-toed) anteater (*Cyclopes didactylus*), known in Colombia as the banana seraph because of its fluffy angelic appearance. In the Old World these anteaters' role is occupied by the pangolins or scaly ant-eaters (*Manis*). These anteaters have backs covered in scales and some, but not all, occur in rainforests.

75 **Sloths** and *Cecropia* **often occur together in the American rainforests.** In the photograph a pale-throated three-toed sloth (*Bradypus tridactylus*) is hanging from a branch of a *Cecropia* tree in the Amazon Basin. The characteristically slow-moving sloths move through the tops of these trees, eating the leaves as they go. There are two other species of three-toed sloths, the maned sloth (*B. torquatus*) and the brown-throated three-toed sloth (*B. variegatus*), and two more two-toed species, the southern two-toed sloth (*Choloepus didactylus* and *C. hoffmanni*), all found only in Central or South America and able to eat *Cecropia* trees.
[Photo: Jany Sauvanet / Auscape International]

The characteristic predatory habits of driver ant colonies are discussed later (page 138). In the New World and Old World rainforests they are represented by species such as *Eciton burchelli* and *Labidus praedator*. The waves of spiders, beetles and other small terrestrial invertebrates and panic-stricken vertebrates fleeing from advancing columns of ants, oblivious to all other threats, offer predators that are specialized in following driver ant colonies an excellent food source.

A number of birds of the family Formicariidae and, in particular, the black-crowned antpitta (*Pittasoma michleri*) and various species of antthrush (*Formicarius*), feed in this way.

The alimentary origins of the primates

It is clear that the primates, both the prosimians and the anthropoids, evolved in rainforest environments. All South American primates live in the rainforest biome. Only in the Old World (in both Africa and Asia) have some primate species secondarily colonized more open environments or more temperate forest zones. The situation in Madagascar, however, is similar to that in South America, and most of the world's extant species of prosimians live in Madagascar's rainforests, which are now, unfortunately, severely threatened.

The tree shrews (Tupaiidae) of the genera *Tupaia*, *Dendrogale* and *Urogale* are a zoological group

76 **The American anteaters and Asian and African pangolins are typical examples of carnivores with specialized diets**. Both are arboreal and myrmecophagous (ant-eating) species that are found in rainforests. The lesser anteater (*Tamandua tetradactyla*, above) eats mainly termites, whereas the African pangolin (*Manis tricuspis*, below) prefers ants. The photographs were taken in the Guyanan and Zairian rainforests respectively. Although they belong to different orders, the Xenarthra (anteaters, sloths and armadillos) and the Pholidota (pangolins), have comparable cranial structures and buccal systems adapted to capturing and eating ants and termites. They also possess enormous strong claws, apparently for breaking open the outer shells of nests and for rooting around in tree trunks.
[Photos: Jany Sauvanet / Bios / Still Pictures and John Newby / WWF / Still Pictures]

that may help reconstruct some important events in the evolution from shrew-like terrestrial mammals to the primates with their multifarious adaptations to arboreal life. The tree shrews are among the least showy of all rainforest mammals. The 15 known species have a body between 4 and 8 in (10 and 20 cm) long, with a tail 4-10 in (10-25 cm) long and look like shrews. Tree shrews were formerly classified, like moles, hedgehogs, and shrews, in the order Insectivora. However, in modern classifications they are placed in a separate order, Scandentia, and are sometimes believed to show close links with primates.

Although tree shrews move through the branches with great agility, they lack prehensile limbs. Their digits are, however, partly opposable and bear the long sharp claws they use to climb. Their long, highly mobile tails are also not prehensile and basically serve as a mobile counterweight to balance the rest of the body. Given their small size, these mechanical limitations are not too much of a handicap. Tree shrews are diurnal, very active, and seem to have color-sensitive eyes, an uncommon ability in mammals. Their feeding habits are essentially insectivorous, perhaps explained by their derivation from insectivores as some believe. Feeding on insects is one of the few good solutions available for small warm-blooded animals, whose high metabolic rates require a continuous supply of high-energy foodstuffs. Insects, along with other high-calorie foodstuffs, such as nectar and the sugary honeydew produced by insects that concentrate the sugars in saps sucked from plants, constitute an important part of the diet of some smaller primates, for example the cheirogaleids or mouse lemurs (*Microcebus*) of Madagascar, which are very similar in size to the tree shrews. Large primates, on the other hand, can get by on less nutritious but more easily found foodstuffs, such as leaves and fruit.

Some notable adaptive radiation has occurred in the lemuroids of Madagascar, as well as in the South American platyrrhine monkeys, basically affecting their feeding specializations. The most specialized of all feeding behaviors must be the aye-aye (*Daubentonia madagascariensis*), whose appearance is so weird that it was initially classified as a rodent, not as a primate. This incorrect classification was probably due to its dentition, as it has four chisel-like incisors, reminiscent of rodent incisors; furthermore, it lacks canine teeth and only has a total of 18 teeth. The aye-aye's dentition is unusual, but the structure of the aye-aye's hands and feet is bizarre. All its digits are long and thin and have curved claws, except the big toe, which has a flat nail; the third finger is especially thin and is used as a specialized tool. It feeds on fruit and insect larvae living under tree bark. To eat fruit, the aye-aye breaks the skin with its teeth and then uses its elongated third finger to scrape out the pulp and transfer it to its mouth. It also uses the same finger to root around in the narrow cracks between the bark and the wood of the trunk of trees in search of xylophagous (wood-eating) insect larvae.

3.3 A world of wonderful adaptations

Almost all the animal life in the rainforest lives in the forest canopy and in the crowns of the upper layers of the understory, between the vertical

77 A very specialized and rather forgotten fauna lives on the floor of the rainforest. Even medium-sized animals such as the curassow (*Crax rubra*), a turkey-like member of the pheasant family with a characteristic feathered crest and common in the understory of American rainforests, are often overlooked. [Photo: Adolf de Sostoa and Javier Ferrer]

columns of the trees and their interlocking foliage. The scarcity of life on the forest floor and in the subsoil has its causes and its clear and important consequences. There is no accumulated layer of leaf litter and detritus under the trees comparable with that in temperate forests, which is slowly broken down by a rich and varied community of microorganisms, fungi, and small invertebrates. In the rainforests, a part of the organic detritus is used before it reaches the soil, as it is trapped by the cavities in tree trunks, forks in large branches, tufts of moss or by the leaves and roots of the innumerable epiphytes. The materials that reach the floor decompose very quickly.

High up in the tree tops, among the leafy branches, there is much more food than on the floor and a much more structured and complex environment. Here, nests are built, hideouts are sought, and prey is stalked. For this reason, most rainforest animals have specific adaptations for life in the tree canopy, and this is very evident in quadrupeds, which might seem more adapted to life on the forest floor.

Moving through the branches

The most important adaptations are related to locomotion. The commonest and most efficient solutions are prehensile tails, and opposable digits with long, powerful nails. Over the course of evolutionary history, each of these adaptations has appeared more than once in very different lineages, and they have even appeared independently in different groups within a single class, such as the mammals. Locomotion strategies adopted by animals in Old World rainforests are much more diverse than those found in their counterparts in South America. In both areas, climbing species are abundant, although some adaptations like the prehensile tail are much more widespread in the New World than in the Old World.

The tail as a limb

Prehensile tails, for example, might seem to be a speciality of the mammals of the American rainforests, but they are also found in a wide range of other groups, such as the agile spider monkeys (*Ateles* species, Cebidae); kinkajous (*Potos flavus*, Loridae), which are medium-sized nocturnal carnivores; marsupials such as opossums (*Didelphis* species, Didelphidae); and even a large rodent with a prehensile tail, the tree porcupine (*Coendou prehensilis*, Erethizontidae), with a body 12-24 in (30-60 cm) in length from the snout to the base of the tail and weighing up to 11 lb (5 kg). This species also possesses the strong, robust claws found in some South American monkeys such as the tamarins (*Saguinus* species, Callitrichidae), and above all those of the tree-loving lesser anteater (*Tamandua tetradactyla*) and silky or pygmy ant-eater (*Cyclopes didactylus*, Myrmecophagidae), and the tree sloth (*Bradypus* and *Choloepus*, Bradypodidae).

Brachiation in monkeys

Another important adaptation for life among the branches is *brachiation*, the ability of primates to

78 Rainforest primates are very skilled at brachiation using, counting their tail, all five of their prehensile limbs, like this spider monkey *Ateles geoffroyi*, in Panama, bearing its young.
[Photo: François Gothier / Auscape International]

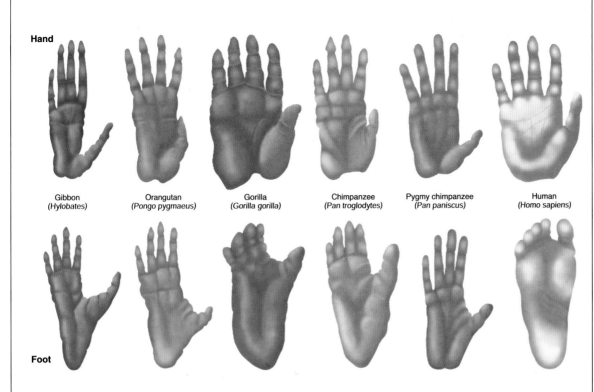

Hand

Gibbon
(*Hylobates*)

Orangutan
(*Pongo pygmaeus*)

Gorilla
(*Gorilla gorilla*)

Chimpanzee
(*Pan troglodytes*)

Pygmy chimpanzee
(*Pan paniscus*)

Human
(*Homo sapiens*)

Foot

79 **A comparison of the hands and feet of various great apes and humans**. The primates, originally quadrupedal plantigrades (users of all four legs to walk) like most mammals, evolved other postures over time that gave them more agility in trees and which, in humans, developed into bipedalism (using two legs to walk). Many primates' possession of prehensile hands and feet indicates their ability to brachiate (swinging from one arm to the other). Gibbons (*Hylobates*) and the more arboreal species of great apes (Pongidae) like the orangutans have feet that are much better adapted to brachiation than those of more terrestrial species like the gorilla. Human feet have become totally adapted to a terrestrial existence. During this transformation a change in the morphology of the hand and foot took place. The big toe has ended up parallel to the other toes, and the tarsus has become arched, making a stable, three-stage bipedal gait possible. First, the foot is braced on the floor (the taligrade stage), next the foot, still on the floor, prepares to push off (plantigrade stage), and finally the toes push the foot forward (digitigrade stage). The hand, however, has been transformed since brachiation was abandoned: humans have slender hands with longer thumbs than our closest relatives among the primates and a greater ability to manipulate objects using tools.
[Drawing: Editrònica, from various sources]

swing hand over hand from branch to branch. This skill occurs only in primates and not only requires well-developed arms and legs but also hands with opposable digits, which are thus prehensile (capable of grasping). Their hand has a thumb opposable to the four digits, almost like a human hand, and their foot has opposable toes; this means that many arboreal mammals are *quadrumanous* (i.e., they are four-handed rather than four-legged) and this is typical of most primates, with the single exception of humans who are bipedal. A similar modification occurs in chameleons, by far the best-adapted lizards to an arboreal existence, although the position of their digits is different from quadrumanous mammals. The first three digits on the chameleon's front limbs are opposed to the other two, whereas on the hind limbs, the first two are opposed to the remaining three.

The most widespread arboreal species of primate in Southeast Asia move by brachiation, from gibbons (*Hylobates*) with arm spans of 4.9 ft (1.5 m) and weighing 29 lb (13 kg), to male orangutans (*Pongo pygmaeus*), 4.9 ft (1.5 m) in height, weighing at least 198 lb (90 kg). The nine known species of gibbon live in the rainforests of southeast Asia, and in some respects are the most agile of all mammals. They move through the tree canopy using their upper limbs and often hurl themselves from one branch to another across distances of up to 10 ft (3 m). Occasionally they resort to leaping and can jump as a far as 29 ft (9 m). Gibbons and orangutans

rarely walk on the forest floor, unlike some African simians, such as the two chimpanzee species—the common chimpanzee (*Pan troglodytes*) and the pygmy chimpanzee, or bonobo (*P. paniscus*)—and the gorilla (*Gorilla*), although only some of various subspecies of gorilla live in rainforests.

Gliding flight

A remarkable number of animals in Asiatic rainforests have developed the ability to glide. This behavior is found in two different mammalian groups, two genera of lizards, one genus of frog, and astoundingly, some species of snake. Their common strategy is to broaden or flatten their bodies to create a type of parachute to support the animal in the air after launching themselves from a high branch towards a lower one or towards the forest floor. The adaptations used to glide do, however, vary from group to group.

Gliding mammals

One of the anatomical transformations for gliding in mammals is the development of a patagium, a cutaneous fold extending along the side of the body between the forelimbs and the hindlimbs. This is the case of the flying squirrels (Sciuridae) of the genera *Aeromys*, *Petaurista*, *Hylopetes*, *Petinomys*, *Pteromysus*, *Petaurillus*, and *Iomys*. Flying squirrels are not, however, restricted to rainforests, as other genera live in northern hemisphere temperate forests in Eurasia and in North America.

The minute order of flying lemurs or colugos (Dermoptera) is endemic to southeast Asia's rainforests; despite its common name, it is unrelated to the true lemurs of Madagascar. Two species survive: *Cynocephalus volans*, which lives in the southern Philippines and *C. variegatus*, found in southern Thailand, Indochina, the Malayan Peninsula, Sumatra, Java, Borneo, and various other smaller islands. Their gliding strategies are based on webs of skin joining the head, the forelimbs, the hindlimbs, and the tail. Their systematic position is unclear, but they are probably closely related to the insectivores in spite of the fact they are vegetarians that feed on tender shoots, leaves and flowers. Flying lemurs are nocturnal, weigh between 2 and 3.7 lb (1 and 1.7 kg) and measure between 13 and 16.5 in (34 and 42 cm) in length with a tail of between 7 and 11 in (17 and 27 cm). They spend the day in a hole in a tree trunk or hanging from the foliage of a tall palm tree. At night they glide long distances and are capable of gliding over 328 ft (100 m) with hardly any loss of altitude.

Gliding flight similar to that of the flying squirrels has evolved in a third group of mammals, the flying opossums (*Petaurus*, *Petauroides*, and *Acrobates*, Petauridae). The range of these marsupials covers northern Australia, New Guinea, and the neighboring Bismarck Islands.

Flying reptiles and amphibians

A number of species belonging to two families of lizards (Agamidae and Gekkonidae) and one family of snakes (Colubridae) have developed the ability to glide.

The flying dragons, or flying lizards (*Draco*), of southeast Asia belong to the Agamidae family and undoubtedly possess the most complex of all patagia. When motionless on a branch, these small reptiles (9 in [22 cm] long, including 5.5 in [14 cm] of tail) resemble nothing more than a normal, difficult-to-spot, cryptically colored lizard. However, when the animal launches itself suddenly into the air, raising its ribs perpendicularly to the axis of its body to spread its brilliantly colored patagium, its appearance totally changes and it looks more like a large, colorful butterfly. The best-known species, the flying dragon *Draco volans*, has a blue patagium spotted with black; other species of the same genus are yellowish and even red. As soon as the animal lands, the bright colors are hidden away as quickly as they were ini-tially unfurled. Naturally, this quick change, together with the difficulty of following an animal able to throw itself into the void at a moment's notice, help disorientate potential predators. Glides usually cover between 33 and 66 ft (10 and 20 m), sufficient to move from one tree to the next, although 328 ft (100 m) glides involving considerable altitude loss are possible. Nevertheless, flying dragons easily gain altitude by agilely scampering up branches. The patagium is used not only for escape from enemies but also for defense and even plays a role in courtship displays. The male and female unfold their striking patagia at the same time and observe each other. If the female is prepared to mate, she remains still on her branch with her patagium closed while the male glides over to her. He then mounts her with his patagium still unfurled and proceeds to inseminate her. The clutch generally consists of four eggs that hatch one or two months later. The flying dragon is insectivorous and feeds almost exclusively on ants, which it catches with its tongue.

The patagium is much simpler in the gliding geckoes (*Ptychozoon* species, Gekkonidae) from peninsular Malaysia, Sumatra, Java, Borneo, and the islands in the Malaccan Strait. These gliding reptiles have small folds of skin on their necks, along their flanks and tails, as well as along their limbs which, furthermore, terminate in five palmate digits. These gekkonids are very modest gliders compared with the flying dragons (agamids) and can only cover less than 10 feet.

Flying snakes (*Chrysopelea* species, [Colubridae]) keep themselves airborne by squashing their bodies, raising their ribs, thus flattening the front part of the body and making the underparts slightly concave. Their venomous bite is not very potent and they kill their victims—small birds, lizards, mice or bats—by holding them firmly in their jaws and crushing them to death with their coils.

The small "flying" frogs (*Rhacophorus*, Rhacophoridae) glide with the aid of webs stretched between their long digits, an obvious solution for an amphibian. The best known are probably Reinwardt's flying frog (*R. reinwardti*) from Java and Sumatra, about 3 in (8 cm) in length, and Wallace's flying frog (*R. nigropalmatus*) from Borneo.

Nightlife

A lot of animal life in the rainforest takes place at night. The first sign that creatures are stirring is the

80 Some reptiles and even some amphibians are capable of gliding. The most outstanding example are the flying dragons (*Draco volans*, right), while perhaps the most surprising are the flying frogs (*Rhacophorus*) of Southeast Asia, which, like this *R. pardalis* (left), glide on their exaggeratedly palmate feet. [Photo: Jean-Paul Ferrero / Jacana and Jean-Paul Ferrero / Auscape International]

81 Spectacular luminous nighttime display of thousands of luminous beetles and fireflies (Lampyridae) flying in the New Guinea rainforest. *[Photo: Jean-Paul Ferrero / Auscape International]*

sudden change at dusk in the noises of the rainforest.

Croaking frogs and luminous insects

Almost all frogs croak most at night. In the rainforest, these are full-scale concerts, not only because of their noisiness but also because there are so many different performers. A small section of rainforest may hold up to 50 different species of frogs that croak and each species, logically, has it own precise repertoire of vocalizations, all vitally important as a means of mutual recognition and for finding a mate. Another typical adaptation to the night, present in croaking frogs, is the development of large eyes: frogs need good nocturnal vision to be able to judge distances when jumping. Even more obvious adaptations such as digit shape are also present. Tree frogs often have enlarged finger and toe discs with mucus-secreting cushions that help them cling to leaves.

In the dense jungle, crickets and cicadas also make a lot of noise, yet many other animals are active at night and make no more noise than gently rustling, or occasionally stumbling, through

the rainforest. Silence is as vital for predators on the prowl as for their potential victims. Male frogs, crickets, and cicadas let themselves be heard because they possess no other effective way of finding a female; other nocturnal animals, such as fireflies, rely on other means and emit light.

In the equatorial forests the most spectacular insect light-emitters are the fireflies (*Pyrophorus* species), beetles belonging to the Elateridae family. They have entered West Indian folklore and the people of the Antilles are said to have attracted them with glowing coals placed on the end of sticks, and caught them to light their huts. They were also used, wrapped up in tulle and placed in the hair or on dresses of women, as living jewels in fiestas and traditional dances.

Nocturnal predators

However, the night is, above all, the stage for the silent roving of predators ranging in size from the big cats, such as the tiger or jaguar, through snakes and geckoes down to centipedes. Around any human settlement light attracts moths, bees and other insects, and their presence attracts predators such as geckoes and centipedes, fol-

82 Nocturnal or crepuscular predation is a hunting strategy practised by many felines in the rainforest. This ocelot (*Felis pardalis*) has been successful and has caught an iguana in an open space.
[Photo: Adolf de Sostoa & Xavier Ferrer]

2. LIFE IN THE RAINFORESTS

lowed eventually by other, more threatening visitors. The most feared are generally the big cats, not all of whom are linked to the rainforest biome nor strictly nocturnal. Nevertheless, some felines are undoubtedly well adapted to hunting at night in the rainforest environment.

Cats that hunt at night are highly dependent on information from their sense organs, especially their eyes. The placement of the eyes gives binoc-

ular vision, essential for judging the distance of a quarry. They also have the important ability to adapt their eyes to a wide range of light intensities. If there is little light, the pupil dilates greatly to make best use of it. A layer of reflecting cells behind the retina reflects the light reaching it, thus almost doubling its intensity.

Long whiskers are also useful and allow felines to use their sense of touch as an indication of

83 Perhaps the most characteristic of the rainforest's nocturnally active primates are the mouse lemurs (*Microcebus*) from Madagascar. The photo shows *M. murinus* from the forest station of Kirindi.
[Photo: Nick Garbutt / Planet Earth Pictures]

whether they can pass through a gap, even in pitch darkness. Other adaptations, such as retractable claws, are too well known to need explanation.

Big cats play an important role in almost all the world's rainforests. Asian felines are small in size, for example the jungle cat (*Felis chaus*), the marbled cat (*F. marmorata*), and the Asian golden cat (*F. temmincki*), although there are exceptions, such as the tiger (*Panthera tigris*); the leopard (*P. pardus*); which extends as far as Africa; and the clouded leopard (*Neofelis nebulosa*). African rainforests contain leopards, along with the African golden cat (*F. aurata*). In the Americas, the largest felines are the jaguar (*Panthera onca*), the ocelot (*F. pardalis*), the margay cat (*F. margay*), and the jagouarundi (*F. yagouaroundi*).

Heat-sensitive pit organs in snakes

Many snakes remain active at night, but not a single species possesses large prominent eyes like those of many frogs, lemurs, or other nocturnal mammals. Snakes have other means of precisely locating their prey when they hunt at night.

Most snakes can dilate their pupils like cats when there is little light, but they rely more on their other senses than on their sight. For example, snakes possess a special organ known as Jacobson's organ consisting of two sensory cavities located in the roof of the mouth. The organ's epithelium is highly sensitive to smells in the air, which are sampled by the incessant flicking movement of the snake's long, forked tongue.

However, some snakes, pit vipers, also have a sense organ that is unique in the animal kingdom. These organs are heat sensitive (thermoscopic) and consist of pits that can detect heat radiated by a warm body: They allow pit vipers to locate any creature (a bird or a mammal) with a body temperature warmer than the surrounding air. Some python species have rudimentary organs of this nature consisting of curious labial plates, although the most specialized heat-sensitive organs are found in the pit vipers (Crotalidae), which also includes the rattlesnakes. The pit organ (thermoscope) consists of a small sensory pit, divided into an internal and external chamber, situated in a depression in the upper jaw. These chambers are separated by a very fine membrane with around a thousand nerve endings per square millimeter connected to the trigeminal nerve, and they can detect temperature differences between the two chambers of a mere 0.003°C!

Nocturnal primates

Nocturnal habits have evolved in different groups of primates. The smaller species of lemur such as the mouse lemurs (species of *Microcebus*, *Phaner*, Cheirogaleidae), the dwarf lemurs (species of *Mirza*, *Cheirogaleus* and *Allocebus*, Cheirogaleidae) and the sportive lemur (*Lepilemur*, Megaladapidae) are nocturnal, although a reversion to diurnal (or occasionally) crepuscular habits seems to have occurred in larger species of lemur (*Lemur*, *Eulemur*, *Hapalemur*, *Varecia*, *Petterus*, Lemuridae), presumably because larger species run less risk of predation than smaller ones.

The four known species of tarsiers (*Tarsius*, Tarsiidae) occur in the rainforests of the Philippines, Celebes, Borneo and Sumatra, and are also nocturnal. The body of these small arboreal primates is only 3.3-7 in (8.5-17 cm) long, but the tail is 7-11 in (18-28 cm) long. Their limbs, in particular the hindlimbs, are very long, and their long, fine digits end in adhesive pads. Their eyes are very large, typical of night-hunting animals or birds, and like nocturnal raptors, they can swivel their heads through 180° and move very quietly. They move by agile leaps of 3 ft (1 m) or so, and can cover a distance of almost 0.6 mi (1 km) in a single night. Galagos (*Galago*, *Euoticus*, *Otolemur* and *Galagoides*, Loridae), an African group of prosimians related to the lemurs, are equally nocturnal. Most galagos (also known as bush-babies) live in rainforests and, like the tarsiers, have large, bulging eyes.

Among the Anthropoidea primates, nocturnal customs are the exception and are found only in the night or owl monkeys (*Aotus*, Cebidae), small American monkeys with large eyes.

Adaptations in birds

Typically terrestrial animals like reptiles and mammals show their adaptation to life in the rain-

84 Pigeons and doves are omnipresent in the Old World and especially in the African and Southeast Asian rainforests where they are among the most abundant of all frugivorous (fruit-eating) animals. Their discrete elegance and bills, perfectly adapted to their fruit-based diet, are evident in this female thick-billed green pigeon (*Treron curvirostra*) perched on a fruiting fig (*Ficus*) in Singapore.
[Photo: Morten Strange / NHPA]

85 **One of the few species of leaf-eating birds** is the hoatzin (*Opisthocomus hoazin*), here photographed in the Orinoco rainforest. Morphologically they are reminiscent of the cracids (see fig. 77), although they in fact belong to a completely different group.
[Photo: Roland Seitre / Bios / Still Pictures]

forest by possessing means of locomotion that allow them to live among the branches. The selection pressures acting on the bird families adapted to rainforest life have been very different. Rainforest birds are extraordinarily abundant and have diversified greatly: for example, a modestly sized section of the Amazon rainforest may contain 400-500 species, as many as are found in the whole of Europe.

Adaptations shown by beaks

Some of the most prominent adaptations by birds to rainforest life are related to their diet and this, in turn, is reflected in bill shape. In many frugivorous birds, above all in the large genera of pigeons and doves found in Southeast Asia and the tropical Pacific (*Ducula*, *Treron* and *Ptilinopus*, Columbidae), the problem seems to be limited to a matter of dimensions—i.e. avoiding close coincidence in bill size within species of the same group. Each parcel of rainforest may contain three or more differently sized species and with similarly shaped bills but the size of the bill is proportionate to the bird's length.

In other cases, the food sources chosen have forced drastic changes in bill shape. This is true for parrots, able to crack very hard seeds and extract the tasty pulp, and for hummingbirds, highly adapted to suck nectar from tubular flowers. It is, however, harder to explain the origin of the huge, but lightweight, multicolored bills of toucans and hornbills (see also "Remarkable feathers and beaks" pages 134-137).

Two curiosities: the hoatzin and the cassowary

The distribution of the hummingbirds is confined to the Americas, and at its center, in the Amazon rainforest, there is a quite remarkable bird, the hoatzin (*Opisthocomus hoazin*). Its exact taxonomic position has been revised repeatedly since it was first described in 1776. Owing to a superficial resemblance, it was initially, but unconvincingly, placed in the family of the guans and curassows, South American members of the Cracidae (part of the order of the Galliformes which also includes chickens, pheasants, turkeys and partridges).

However, recent research, using hybrid DNA techniques, suggests that the hoatzin has a closer affinity with the cuckoo family, Cuculidae. The most curious feature of the hoatzin is that fledglings possess well-developed claws, with the musculature required to move them, on the first and second digits of each wing. This means the young hoatzin (unlike any other bird) can hang from branches. Three weeks after leaving the nest, the claws fall off and the wing presents a more normal appearance. Adults reach around 24 in (60 cm) in length and frequent large rainforest rivers with abundant water where they dive and swim confidently. The wing claws have often been considered highly primitive, reminiscent of the oldest known bird, *Archaeopteryx* from the Mesozoic, a comparison that is only valid as an analogy and does not imply any direct phylogenetic relationship. The hoatzin also has a distinctive digestive tract: It is one of the few birds that feeds exclusively on leaves.

86 **The nest architecture of some rainforest birds** is very spectacular and complex. The photo shows the hanging nests of the Montezuma oropendola (*Psarocolius montezuma*), an American species found in the Central American rainforest, and in this case in the Tikal National Park (Guatemala).
[Photo: Adolf de Sostoa & Xavier Ferrer]

Its broad esophagus and stomach contain symbiotic bacteria that ferment the plant material eaten, as in ruminants, allowing its assimilation. It is so like a ruminant that it even smells of cow dung and takes two days to digest a meal, and for this time its powers of flight are severely limited.

Certainly, the cassowaries (*Casuarius*), enormous wingless birds, vaguely similar to the ostrich, that occur in New Guinea, northern Australia, and some neighboring islands and archipelagos, are even more primitive. Of the three known species, at least one, the one-wattled cassowary (*C. unappendiculatus*) from New Guinea, can be considered an inhabitant of rainforests. This cassowary is a powerful runner and can move at great speeds even among the intricate vegetation of the rainforest. For many years it was thought that its casque, a striking bony helmet, protected it from violent collisions with plants as it ran through the leafy understory.

However, recent observations have led observers to believe that in fact the casque is used principally as a type of spade for digging in sand and soil detritus for fallen fruit.

Nesting structures

Lastly, it is worth commenting on the nesting behavior of some rainforest birds. Many species nest logically, in natural holes in trees or excavate new holes. In addition to birds that normally nest in holes, such as the woodpeckers or the neotropical woodcreepers (Dendrocolaptidae), families that usually construct other types of nest normally nest in holes in rainforests. For example, the South American ovenbirds (Furnariidae) usually construct sturdy nests of sun-dried mud, but the rainforest species in this family nest in holes in trees.

The oropendolas (*Psarocolius*, Icteridae) construct even more singular nests. Colonies of these birds suspend their large nests (up to 4.9 ft [1.5 m] long) in groups from the branches of a tall, often isolated tree. The sack-shaped nests hang from a thin cord and are practically inaccessible to predation by tree-hunting snakes and mammals. The curious nests of many rainforest birds are another marvel to add to the many wonders of the rainforest.

3.4 The rhythm of animal life

The rainforest lacks clear seasonality but is affected by rhythms, often internal ones, as discussed in the section on vegetation. The same is true of animals, some but animal rhythms are so spectacular they deserve to be mentioned.

Remarkable feathers and beaks

At the end of the 19th century, western feminine fashions had a fondness for feather hats. A particular preference was for the feathers of the bird of paradise, which arrived by the thousand from New Guinea. Up to 50,000 birds a year were caught for export until, in the face of disaster, their capture was first regulated, then banned, in the first quarter of the 20th century. Worldly women impressed elegant gentlemen with their flowing feathers to such an extent that feathers and femininity became synonymous. This was certainly an error: The magnificent feathers of the birds of paradise occur exclusively on the males and are their greatest sign of ornithological masculinity.

Engraving of a 19th -century lady's hat with bird of paradise feathers [Mary Evans Picture Library]

Huli man decorated with bird of paradise feathers [Jean-Paul Ferrero / Auscape International]

The male birds of paradise have a remarkably showy plumage, varying greatly from one species to another, which they exhibit spectacularly in the courtship display. Depending on the species, they may display individually or in a group. Some perform their display on the ground, but most species position themselves on branches in the leafy canopy. The position adopted by the males of the blue bird of paradise (*Paradisea rodolphi*) is especially surprising: they hang upside down.

The family of paradisaeids consists of about forty species, almost all from New Guinea, although some occur in northeast Australia and the Moluccas archipelago. They are extremely beautiful birds, between 4.9 in (12.5 cm) and 3 ft (1 m) long, including the often much longer tail of the male. Except for the individuals of the genera *Manucodia* and *Macgregoria*, which are monogamous and do not show sexual dimorphism, all the birds of paradise (*Astrapia*, *Diphyllodes*, *Parotia*, *Lophorina* and especially *Paradisea*) are polygamous with pronounced differences between males and females.

The archetypal bird of paradise is *Paradisea apoda*. The first example to be seen in Europe was brought by Juan Sebastián Elcano when he returned from the first circumnavigation of the globe (1519-1522). He received it without feet, the traditional Melanesian method of preparing the skins, from the hands of a chieftain in the Molluccas and this presentation gave rise to the erroneous belief that they did not have legs: some held that they came from the earthly paradise and thus did not need to walk. Since then, they have been commonly known in the West as birds of paradise.

Engraving showing two male and one female bird of paradise (*Diphyllodes hunsteini*) published in *Monograph of the Paradiseidae*, by R. Bowler-Sharpe [E.T. Archive]

Interest in the feathers of the birds of paradise came later, but not from Europeans. In the middle of the 16th century the French explorer Pierre Belon reported that the Janissaries in the Ottoman court wore them in their turbans, and in the 17th and 18th centuries their use became widespread in India and the Far East. This led to the beginning of systematic hunting of birds of paradise by indigenous peoples, who used blunt arrows without tips so that they did not damage any of the feathers. Hunting birds of paradise is difficult because they are timid and hide among inaccessible branches: They like to display, but only in front of the female they are courting.

Engraving of a male bird of paradise (*Paradisea apoda*) [Dominique Halleux / Bois / Still Pictures]

Travies del.   Imp. Lemercier, à Paris.   F. Fournier sc.

Everything that is elegant about a bird of paradise is grotesque in toucans, which have the most disproportionate bills imaginable. The bills of the 42 known species of toucan, members of the family Ramphastidae, are prominent-colored horny structures supported by a dense network of bone fiber. The diet of these birds consists basically of juicy fruits, with flesh that could be eaten without problems with a smaller bill, but toucans are large animals and thus heavy, and a long bill is an advantage when it comes to obtaining fruit hanging from a thin branch. It is also thought that such a prominent bill served to intimidate other birds, whose nests area often raided by omnivorous toucans who take the eggs and young. However, these eating habits do not justify the diversity in bill coloration or even plumage from one species to another. Perhaps, as in the case of the birds of paradise, it does have a sexual role.

The green and yellow toucan Ramphastos sulfuratus, Costa Rica [David E. Rowley / Planet Earth Pictures]

These showy neotropical birds with their squawking calls have become symbols of the American rainforest. The largest and most spectacular are the green and yellow toucan (*Ramphastos sulfuratus*) from the jungles of Central America and the Orinoco basin, measuring nearly two feet from the tip of its bill to the end of its tail, and the even larger yellow and white toucan (*R. toco*) from the Amazon. Other Amazonian species include *R. tucanus*, *R. dicolorus*, *R. vitellinus* and *R. culminatus*. The group of toucans also includes less spectacular birds, such as the aracaris (*Pteroglossus*, *Selenidera*) and the toucanets (*Aulacorhynchus*, *Baillonius*) which are present in all the American rainforests.

The hornbills, members of the family Bucerotidae, have a bill comparable with the toucan's in size and shape but the birds are not related: while the toucans belong to the order of the Piciformes the hornbills are members of the Coraciiformes (like the kingfishers and bee-eaters). In fact, the bill of the hornbill is quite different, although it is also very prominent. It has a strange, horny frontal protuberance in the form of a casque, or helmet, growing from the bill itself that may rise like a small horn. Hornbills are from the tropical regions of the Old World, with a range including subSaharan Africa, except the Cape and Madagascar, and southeast Asia as far as New Guinea. One of the most singular aspects of the biology of the hornbills is their nesting behavior: The female lays the eggs (one, or at most two) within a hole made in a tree trunk, but she cannot leave because the opening is almost completely blocked by the remains of food and excrement, except for a small hole through which the male feeds her.

Asian hornbill (Buceros bicornis homrai) [Jean-Michel Labat / Auscape International]

Celebes hornbill (Aceros [=Rhyticeros] cassidix) [Alain Compost / Bruce Coleman Limited]

A total of 45 species of hornbill are known, most of them from rainforest, or at least very common in this environment. The largest and most spectacular ones, up to 49 in (125 cm) from bill to tail, are the Asian species *Buceros rhinoceros*, *B. bicornis* and *Rhinoplax vigil*, with its characteristic long tail feather. The genera *Anorrhinus*, *Aceros*, *Rhyticeros*, *Anthracoceros*, etc., are also Asian. In Africa and India, species of *Tockus* are quite common; these are small hornbills with small or non-existent horns. The African hornbills of the genera *Bycanistes*, *Tropicranus*, and *Ceratogymna* have more conventional appearances. In any case, seeing a crying hornbill glide among the canopy or watching a toucan about his business in the branches is an unforgettable image of the equatorial rainforest.

African hornbill (Tockus erythrorhynchus) [Hans Reinhard / Bruce Coleman Limited]

The case of the African driver ants

One of the most notable scourges of the African rainforests are the driver ants of the genus *Anomma*. These predatory ants are the result of a long evolutionary process totally unlike any bird or mammal. Swarms of workers attack in groups and can kill prey many times their own size. Most other ants species hunt individually and can take prey only a little larger than themselves. An *Anomma* colony may contain up to 20 million sisters, or, in other words, 20 million mouths, mandibles, and stings.

The mass of ants forms a front 33-66 ft (10-20 m) wide and advances through the leaf litter and small plants at a rate of 66 ft (20 m) per hour. The frenetic worker ants reconnoiter then retreat, functioning according to the colony's collective will, which is controlled by the gaseous hormones segregated by their fellows. As the army approaches, animals able to flee do so and their frenetic leaps and flights mark the progress of an advancing front of ants.

Most victims are immobile (poorly-hidden insect larvae, abandoned nestlings) or slow or unlucky creatures unable to escape, or panic-stricken animals that blunder into the advancing army. Few adult vertebrates are caught, normally only weak or wounded individuals, or perhaps torpid snakes digesting a large prey. When the ants locate an animal prey, they overwhelm it, paralyzing it and tearing it to pieces. The fragments are then taken back by the raiding party to the swarm, and thence along a thick column of ants back to its temporary headquarters, called a "bivouac," where the nutritious parts are processed to be fed to the large brood.

Anomma colonies have rhythmic existences. Each colony has a queen, an unbelievably fertile individual more than 2 in (5 cm) long, larger than any other ant in the world. The queen lays between three and four million eggs each month in 5-6 day bursts every three weeks or so. Depending on food supplies, the colony may remain in the same bivouac for a quiet period of between a week and three months, called the *statary phase*. The workers excavate and occupy an elaborate complex of tunnels that may penetrate 13 ft (4 m) into the earth. These redoubtable camps contrast with those built by their South American relatives *Eciton*, whose bivouacs are vertical columnar structures made out of the bodies of the ants themselves.

During the statary phase, *Anomma* swarms leave the bivouac every day and return later. Meanwhile, eggs hatch and the larvae are fed as intensely as populations of prey in the surrounding countryside permit. Before reaching the adult form, the larvae pupate, and when enough pupae accumulate this triggers the ants to change the site of their bivouac. The whole colony, carrying the queen and the pupae, leaves for a new place to settle, several hundred feet away. The number of ants taking place in the migration is so great that the column may take various days to move from one site to the next.

Bird migration

Driver ants perform rhythmic movements in search of new food, and birds do, too, but on a much larger scale. The phenomenon of bird migration also contributes to rhythms in the ecology of the rainforest. Many rainforest birds are migratory—they either breed in the rainforest but migrate to feed on the seasonal abundance of summer insects in temperate areas or breed in the temperate summer and shelter from the winter in the rainforest.

Collection studies have shown that birds often return to exactly the same part of the jungle, to the same tree or same patch of understory, after journeys of thousands of miles. Such site fidelity shows the highly conservative side of nature: If a habitat is predictable, why risk visiting any tree other than the one that kept you alive last year? Experimentation is best left to individuals that have no choice, having been expelled from their trees by territorial rivals or some major environmental upheaval.

Migration makes sense for rainforest birds for two reasons. Firstly, temperate summers offer abundant potential food as plant growth and production is packed into a few months during which insect populations reach very high levels. The increase in food supply in the summer always tends to exceed the capacity of local populations to exploit it efficiently. Secondly, the seasonal variation in food supplies in the tropics is minimal compared with temperate regions. If a bird knows what to eat and where to find it, and what to avoid and how to recognize it, it will never be short of food.

Thus, the rainforests are a good place to survive while waiting for the temperate summer to return, or waiting even to breed, as long as the bird is sufficiently well adapted to the peculiarities of the rainforest. Yet these peculiarities, such as sophisticated chemical defenses, mean the food supply for any given species are very limited; this severely restricts the rates a bird population can grow and its density.

Migratory birds in equatorial rainforests take advantage of a huge "bipolar" ecosystem. At one extreme is the predictable superabundance of the temperate summer and at the other is the no less predictable and in this case permanent—not seasonal—austerity within the abundance of the rainforest. Traveling between the two extremes allows birds to maximize their individual reproductive fitness abilities as well as, incidentally, their population growth rate.

Migration has a price, such as the hazards of a long journey, competition with faster rivals, the need for navigation skills and a good memory as well as the requirement for flexible social and feeding behavior. Investment in these adaptations means a migrant must be something of a generalist, and the rainforest has few niches for generalists. The nonmigratory birds that live in rainforests all year around tend to be specialists; because selection pressure forces them to eat and do fewer and fewer things more and more efficiently.

The hundreds of specialists in the rainforest leave little room for less specialized rivals. This makes the rainforest even less hospitable place for migrants than it would otherwise be, and makes migrating to the temperate summer even more attractive. Few species have this option, and the evolution of most rainforest birds (and other organisms of this biome) over the generations, in fact, tends to refine their specializations.

87 The capture, or ringing, of migratory birds is used throughout the world to study the behavior of migratory species. Birds are trapped in special harmless mist nets and are immediately released after ringing, in the hope that a second capture will permit their movements to be monitored. In the photo a bird is being freed from a net in Chajul, Chiapas (Mexico).
[Photo: Adolf de Sostoa & Xavier Ferrer]

Casiquiare

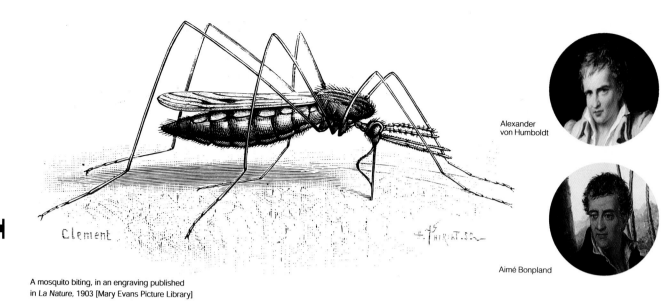

A mosquito biting, in an engraving published in *La Nature*, 1903 [Mary Evans Picture Library]

Alexander von Humboldt

Aimé Bonpland

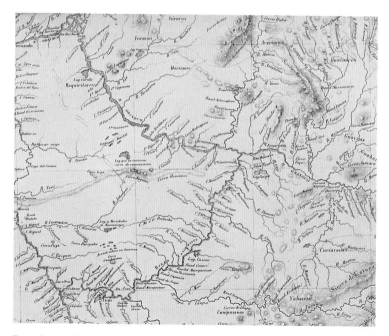

The confluence of the Casiquiare and the Orinoco, from the *Physical and Political Atlas of the Republic of Venezuela*, 1840 [Biblioteca de Catalunya]

Baron Friedrich Wilhelm Karl Heinrich Alexander von Humboldt could not swim, yet on the afternoon of June 5, 1799 in the port of La Coruña he had no doubts about boarding the ship Pizarro bound for Cumaná. Far from it: He had moved heaven and earth to obtain the necessary authorization for his long-dreamed-of voyage of exploration to the colony of New Granada. He did not know how to swim but was more worried by the Orinoco than by the Atlantic and rightly so, for he was to have more than one brush with death in the waters and turbulent rapids of this mighty river. Yet he survived to tell the tale of the vast and inhospitable waters of the Orinoco and the mythical Casiquiare, the only river in the world that forms part of two distinct river basins.

The expedition undertaken by the geographer, naturalist, and humanist Alexander von Humboldt (1769-1859) and the botanist and artist Aimé Bonpland (1773-1858) to the colonies of New Granada and New Spain —present-day Venezuela, Colombia, Ecuador, Peru, Central America, Cuba and Mexico— lasted five years (1799-1804) and was described in a book which was to become a classic of its genre: *Voyage aux régions équinoxiales du Nouveau Continent* (1805). Shortly before setting sail Humboldt wrote: "I intend to collect plants and fossils, and to make astronomi-

cal observations. However, this is not the principal objective of my expedition. I also intend to discover how the forces of nature interact and how the geographical environment influences animal and vegetable life. To put it another way, my task is to find the unity of nature." A naturalist wrote these words in the year 1799 yet they contain all the spirit of modern ecology, which likewise considers the biosphere as a whole. Humboldt was in spirit an ecologist *avant la lettre*, and could also be carried away by the simple beauty of the biological diversity of Venezuela. On landing he exclaimed, "What a fantastic and generous country we have under

our feet! Wonderful plants, electric eels, armadillos, monkeys, parrots and many, many authentically semisavage Indians. Up till now we have only wandered around like a pair of idiots. For the first three days we were unable to stop anywhere for long, as on finding one thing, we had to leave it to examine the next. Bonpland keeps repeating that he'll lose his head if the wonders don't stop."

The adventure proper began in San Fernando de Apure on March 3, 1800, the day that Humboldt and Bonpland loaded all their books, botanical presses and astronomical instruments into the canoe that was to carry them downstream to the confluence with the Orinoco. Over the next few days the adventure continued as they began to paddle up the swollen course of this great river, 4 mi (6 km) wide, where they nearly sank. The small canoe, with the two explorers, two other Europeans, a Creole pilot, and four Indian oarsmen, made everything even more of an adventure as they battled their way up through the Great Cataracts at Atures and Maipures, tossed around and taking on board too much water for comfort at every turbulent rapid.

Black uakari (*Cacajao melanocephalus*) from the Orinoco, from an engraving published in *Recueil d'observations de zoologie et d'anatomie comparée*, 1805-1832 [Bibliothèque Nationale, Paris]

The angry waters were a constant danger and the clouds of insects were a torment: "Which insect stings you depends on the time of the day. From half past six in the morning to five in the afternoon the air is full of a small biting mosquito known as the 'jején.' An hour before sunset, the 'tempraneros' (early ones), a very small sort of mosquito, take over and stay around for at most an hour and a half. They disappear between six and seven in the evening, or as they say here, at the 'angelus.' After a few minutes respite, you start to get stung by the 'zancudos' (long-legged), a species of mosquito with extremely long legs. The 'zancudos,' which have a very pointed sting, are very painful and leave you with a swelling which takes weeks to go down… It is not the small canoes and the savage Indians, nor the snakes, caimans, and jaguars that make the Spanish fear a voyage along the Orinoco. It is, as they say so succinctly, 'the sweat and the flies.'" In fact the Orinoco's waters are "white waters," full of life and human diseases.

Its waters were very different from the "black water" affluents (first the Atapabo and then the Temi and the Tuamini) that Humboldt and his fellow adventurers followed from the mission at San Fernando de Atapabo onwards. Here, in the headwaters of the river basin, the waters were crystalline and drinkable and the air clear and free of insects. They were at the watershed between the two most incredible river basins on earth: to the north from where they had come, lay the Orinoco, and on the other side to the south, downstream along the nearby Negro River, was the Amazon. They reached the top of the low ridge after fighting their way for four days through 7 mi (11 km) of impenetrable jungle, dragging their canoes behind them. First, they found the Pimichín River and then almost immediately afterwards, the River Negro and could then go downstream on the current to San Carlos, a isolated military post on the Brazilian border. It was the seventh of May 7th.

The pay and the salt for the small garrison at San Carlos arrived twice a year by river. Naturally, they were paid by the Spanish government and not the Portuguese, so their salaries had to come by canoe from the north along the Orinoco and the Casiquiare River, an affluent (tributary) which flows into the Negro River a few miles upstream from San Carlos. Yet the hateful "white waters" of the Orinoco flow in this affluent and drain into the Amazon Basin, first-hand evidence and an obvious contradiction of a geographic axiom: By definition the waters of two river basins never mix. So what was happening here?

"Raft on the Banks of the Guayaquil", engraving from the *Atlas pittoresque - Vues des Cordillères et monuments des peuples indigènes de Amérique*, by Alexander von Humboldt and Aimé Bonpland, 1810 [Aisa]

In 1599, Walter Raleigh (1542-1618), the English sailor and explorer, published a map of the Upper Orinoco in which the Orinoco and Amazon Basins appeared separated by a mountain chain (imaginary, but logical), crossed by a bizarre river connecting the two basins (illogical, but real). From then on, geographers refused to accept the existence of this impossible connection, even though it was in use to take their pay to the soldiers at San Carlos. In 1798, two years before the arrival of Humboldt at San Carlos, Philippe Bouache, the inventor of contours for showing relief on maps, published a map of the area without this "preposterous" connection and with the following footnote: "The communication between the Orinoco and the Amazon rivers is a geographical monstrosity which despite its foolishness has spread around the world." On May 12, 1800 Humboldt began to travel up this "nonexistent" connection, first pioneered by the Jesuit Manuel Roman in 1744 and habitually used by the garrison at San Carlos.

"Humboldt and Bonpland on the Orinoco" by Eduard Ender, 1799-1900 [Archiv für Kunst und Geschichte, Berlin]

This surprising phenomenon explained by Humboldt stems from the fact that the low ridge separating the two basins is below the level of the waters of the Orinoco at certain times of year. The "white waters" of the Orinoco thus flow on both sides of the ridge: Most flow north forming the Orinoco proper, whereas a small part flows south and is known as the Casiquiare.

Humboldt's understanding was as clear as the previous incredulity of geographers is understandable. Nevertheless, to ignore evidence, however startling it may be, is not a proper scientific attitude. Humboldt did what was necessary: he verified a fact experimentally and explained it scientifically. He had a clear mind and the courage to go there. This is how knowledge progresses.

4. Life in rivers and flooded forests

4.1 The biology and ecology of watercourses

Except for irrigated areas, there is nowhere else in the world with as much available freshwater as in the intertropical rainforests. In fact, their abundant rainfall supplies large and complex permanent river basins. Seasonality, and thus the rainfall regime and rises in water level, increase progressively and symmetrically with distance from the equator, which gives rise to variations in the behavior of the river basins. This is especially clear in the African continent.

The waters of tropical regions are characterized by their high temperature and low seasonal variation; the main course of the Amazon has an annual temperature of 84°F (29°C), with an annual temperature variation of 9° F (1°C), while streams running through the rainforest have a temperature of 73-75°F (23-24°C). The seasonal variations in the water level observed in tropical rivers are due to the wind and rain regimes, regularly flooding immense areas of fluvial plains and increasing the area of land under water on a scale that is hard to find outside the tropics.

River seasonality in the wet tropics

The river systems in the wet tropics are very large and in some cases they form immense watersheds, such as the Amazon or the Zaire, which flow through dense rainforest and have tributaries on both sides of the equator. The two periods of rises in water level occur at opposite periods of the year, coinciding with the peak rainfall in each hemisphere. The rainy season usually coincides with the period of the year when the sun is closest to its zenith, that is to say, between May and July in the northern hemisphere, and from November to January in the southern hemisphere. In spite of this, this period may be displaced depending on the characteristics of each continent, due to the presence of mountain chains or by the wind patterns.

88 **The recurrent flooding of the Amazonian forest**, with the consequent formation of areas of varzea (temporarily flooded, normally in "white," sediment-laden rivers) and of igapo (permanent flooding, usually in sediment-poor "black" rivers). This flooding is a phenomenon with far-reaching implications that creates extraordinarily beautiful landscapes, such as this photo of arapari (*Macrolobium acaciifolium*) silhouetted against the evening skyline and reflected in the waters, in Cuyabeno (Ecuador).
[Photo: Xavier Ferrer & Adolf de Sostoa]

89 The *encontro das aguas* is the confluence of the Solimões River with the Negro River, right in front of Manaus, the beginning of the Amazon as such. The upper photo of this remarkable river junction, clearly shows the very different colors of the waters of "white" rivers, (the Solimões, on the left) and "black" rivers (the Negro, on the right), and the difference between the two water masses as they flow along the first few miles of the Amazon virtually without mixing (shown in lower photo, in the top right). The same phenomenon occurs at the junction of the Solimões and the Manacapuru (lower photo, on the left hand of the photo). The false color satellite image, taken on August 2, 1989, shows the completely virgin areas of terra firme (solid dark red), the flooded varzea (less intense red by the river), the maze of restingas, islands of varzea, varzea lakes, igarapes, and tahuampas, (shown schematically in diagrams 26 and 27), as well as the deforested and built-up areas running along the roads (white and sky blue, respectively). [Photos: Tony Morrison / South America Pictures and by courtesy of Compton Tucker, Biospheric Science Branch, Laboratory for Terrestrial Physics, NASA Goddard Space Flight Center, Greenbelt]

In Africa, the basin of the Zaire River located between 8°N and 13°S, covers 1,544,402 sq mi (4 million km²) and is the world's second largest watershed. The alternating periods of rain in the two hemispheres, and the existence of tributaries both north and south of the equator give much of the basin a water level regime that is relatively stable, partly due to the water absorbed by the watermasses and wetlands of the fluvial plain. Even so, in the lower stretches of the river water level rises twice a year, with an amplitude of between 7-10 ft (2-3 m).

In Asia, the rainforest area reaches far to the north of the equator in the south and southeast of the continent and far to the south in the Indonesian islands and New Guinea. One of the main river basins is the Mekong River, which covers an area of 302,317 sq mi (783,000 km²). The rainfall is between 39 in (1,000 mm) in the lowlands and 118 in (3,000 mm) a year in the mountainous areas; the monsoon rainy season begins in May or June and marks the rise in the river level, with a peak in August and September in the higher stretches, and a peak a month or two later in the lower ones, which floods about 2,046 sq mi (53,000 km²). The Brahmaputra, outside its Tibetan headwaters, is an important river draining the rainforest regions in southern Asia.

In intertropical America there is a great diversity of river basins and river regimes. The basin of the Amazon is the world's largest water basin, covering an area of 2,702,704 sq mi (7 million km²) and is the definitive proof that tropical rivers show rises in level. Its flow is four times greater than the Zaire's and seven times greater than the Nile's. Annual rainfall is between 59 and 118 in (1,500 and 3,000 mm), but except in the northwest region, is distributed irregularly over the year; there is a dry season, with less rainfall, locally known as "summer" and a rainy season, called "winter," but they do not correspond to the calendar seasons. In the south of the basin, the rainy season begins in September or October, and the water level rises for at least six months, reaching its highpoint in April or May; in the Negro River, which is more equatorial, the rise in water levels begins in March and April and reaches its highest point in June and July; finally, in the northern part of the basin, in the headwaters of the Branco River, the rains begin in

April and end in September. There is obviously a delay between the rainfall peak and the rise in water level in the lower stretches of the main bed, as the water takes time to cover the basin (sometimes two or three months). The rainfall periods in these different tributaries follow each other in time, and one might expect the water level to show some degree of regularity, but surprisingly, this is not so; to the contrary, the lower stretches of the main course show a period of clearly defined rise in water level, with a maximum in May and a minimum in October or November. The differences in level between the two periods are between 20 and 66 ft (6 and 20 m), depending on the position in the basin and the topography of the terrain.

Classes of water and of environment

The rise in river water level brings a variety of biological mechanisms into operation in aquatic organisms, marking the beginning of their migratory activity. For example, many species of fish travel long distances upstream and downstream. Many fish move out from the main watercourse to the flooded areas, returning to the river when the water levels subsides. The flooding period is the period when there is most food for them, and when the many different types of refuges provide most shelter from predators, the best period for the reproduction.

90 The water types and flow of the main rivers of the Amazon. The immensity of the Amazon (a flow of 5.1 x 10¹² m³ per year) is clearly shown by comparing its flow to that of the Zaire (1.1 x 10¹² m³ per year), the largest river in equatorial Africa, or with the Mississippi (0.5 x 10³ m³ per year). The Solimões-Amazon flows 3,800 km (5,500 from the source of the Marañon, and 6,280 from the source of the Ucayali).
[Drawing: Editrònica, taken from M. Goulding (1979)]

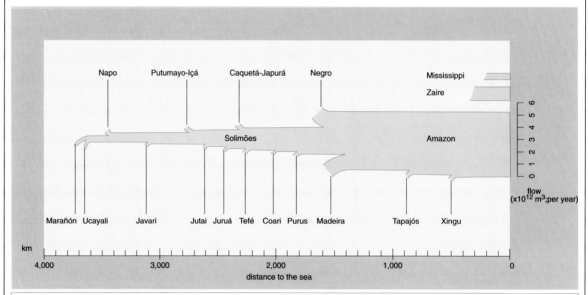

RIVER	TYPE OF WATER	FLOW (x10¹² m³; per year)	SALINITY (ppm)		SUSPENDED SOLIDS (ppm)	
			low water	high water	low water	high water
Madeira	very white	0.9	68	50	5	359
Amazon	white	5.1	148	28	22	123
Negro	black	1.4	6	4	1	9
Tapajós	clear	0.4	11	6	11	4

The case of the Amazon

When water level rises in the Amazon, a period lasting for several months, flooding a large area of rainforest (about 23,166 sq mi [60,000 km²]) on the lower sites of the alluvial plain, known as *varzea* (see section 1.4.3). The river then branches into many small arms, known as *paranas* or *igarapes* that join and separate again and again. For a time, much of the riverside vegetation is totally or partially covered by the water, and this leads to important processes integrating the river and rainforest ecosystems: in the flood period, the waters of the varzea are colonized by the aquatic fauna, especially fish, which play an important role spreading the fruits and seeds of many trees. In 1853, Alfred Russel Wallace tried to establish criteria for classifying the Amazon rivers, describing three types of waters on the basis of their optical qualities; white, black, and clear waters. Despite attempts to improve on this classification, it is still used and is often applied to other tropical basins; for example, some rivers in the Democratic Republic of Congo are known as black water rivers and some in New Guinea as white water rivers.

White waters, typical of rivers such as the Solimões-Amazon and the Madeira, are turbid and fertile, and loaded with sediment eroded from the Andes; these waters have a low transparency (visibility of 0.3 and 1.6 ft [0.1 and 0.5 m] measured with a Secchi disc), a pH tending to neutral (pH 6.2-7.2), and form soils that are nutrient-rich and support a relatively tall (131 ft [40 m]) and dense rainforest.

Black waters owe their caramel-brown color to the dissolved humic components derived from the rainforest soils; they are acid (pH 3.2 to 4.9) and typical of rivers that flow through lowland rainforest with poor, acid, sandy soils, such as the River Negro. They are much more transparent than white waters (visibility of 4.3-9.5 ft [1.3-2.9 m] measured with a Secchi disc).

Clear waters are typical of rivers like the Tocantins, Xingu, and Tapajós, which flow down from the ancient Guyana and Brazil shields; they contain very little sediment, are highly transparent (visibility of 14.1-36.1 ft [4.3-11 m] measured with a Secchi disc), and have a pH of 4.5-7.8.

These aquatic environments are very different from temperate ones and the same zonation models cannot be applied. The catchment basins are much more complex, with a large number of rivers and streams forming an intricate hydrographic network, with land subject to flooding; these include *varzeas* (temporarily flooded forest) and *igapo* (permanently flooded or

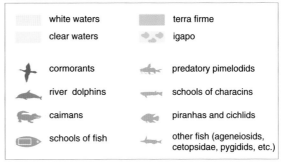

waterlogged forest, very open and poor), freshwater wetlands, floodable grasslands, lagoons and lakes, and alternating fast and slow stretches and drastic seasonal changes. Many river systems are very large and have suffered enormous modifications over their history. Tectonic changes have led to alterations in the level of the rivers, creating rapids and waterfalls that may have isolated some fish populations. Connections may however be formed between separate catchment basins, as in the connection between the Amazon and the Orinoco by means of the Casiquaire River.

Lake and delta environments

In most rainforest environments there are no true lakes, especially in the alluvial plains subject to large floods and retreats. Yet there are some permanent water masses, such as Lake Tumba (Mai-Ndombe)

91 The composition and behavior of the fish fauna varies, depending on the type of water. Thus, in the Madeira River, whose large flow consists of white waters throughout almost the entire year, there are many predatory members of the Pimelodidae (dourado and piraiba [*Brachyplatystoma*], caparari and surubim [*Pseudoplatystoma*], pacamum [*Paulicea*], "peixe lenha" [*Surubimichthys*], etc.), fish whose tactile organs allow them to move in conditions of almost zero visibility. The Madeira's tributary the Machado has "clear" waters ("black" waters but with higher salinity), and the fish tend to be herbivorous members of the Characidae (jatuarana and matrinchão [*Brycon*], tambaqui and pirapitinga [*Colossoma*], pacu [*Mylossoma*], etc.), and other species of conventional appearance. The fish in both types of river migrate in accordance with food availability, and this is related to the annual rise and fall of water levels, which generate changes in the nutrient levels (and thus in plankton growth) and cause variations of the flood level reached in the varzea and igapo. Characins, in the Machado spawn in the River Madeira, give rise to a different type of migratory movement, in this case reproductive, while the pimelodids migrate to escape their predators. Thus, in December and January, when the waters are highest, and the spawning period of the migratory characins commences, the confluence of the two rivers is a scene of great activity. The characins go downstream, the pimelodids go up the Madeira, while predatory members of the cichlids, sciaenids and characins remain in the igapo (tucunare [*Cichla*], pescada [*Plagioscion*], piranha [*Serrasalmus*]), and other predators enter the igapo, such as river dolphins (tucuxi [*Sotalia fluviatilis*], boto [*Inia geoffrensis*]), cormorants (*Phalacrocorax olivaceus*), caimans (*Caiman*) and human fishermen.
[Drawing: Jordi Corbera, from Goulding, 1979]

92 Main aquatic plants of the lakes of the Amazonian varzea, in the Brazilian region of Itacotiara, showing their biological characteristics. The dominant plants are *amphiphytes* (plants with leaves floating on the surface of the water), rather than *limnophytes* (completely submerged plants), and this is related to the instability of the flooding.
[Source: data from several authors, collected by N.J.H. Smith, 1979]

FAMILY AND SPECIES	rooted	floating	submerged
ARACEAE			
Montrichardia arborescens (aninga)	•	•	-
Pistia stratiotes (mureru)	-	•	-
AZOLLACEAE			
Azolla microphylla (mureru)	-	•	-
CABOMBACEAE			
Cabomba (cabomba)	-	•	•
ASTERACEAE			
Pacourina edulis ("tabokimha")	•	•	-
EUPHORBIACEAE			
Capirona castaneifolia ("tabokimha")	-	•	-
GRAMINEAE			
Hymenachne amplexicaulis (muri mole "tabokimha")	-	•	-
Luziola spruceana (uamã)	-	•	-
Oryza latifolia (cinauauà)	-	•	-
Oryza perennis (wild rice)	•	•	-
Panicum chloroticum ("tabokimha")	•	-	-
Panicum spectabile (canarana)	•	•	-
Paspalum fasciculatum (muri)	•	•	-
Paspalum repens (membeca)	•	•	-
HYDROCHARITACEAE			
Limnobium spongia (mureru)	-	•	-
LENTIBULARIACEAE			
Utricularia foliosa (samambaia)	-	-	•
LIMNOCHARITACEAE			
Hydrocleys nymphoides (mureru)	-	•	-
NYMPHEACEAE			
Victoria amazonica (giant water lily)	•	-	-
ONAGRACEAE			
Ludwigia natans (mama de pirarucú, murera "buchu" de pirarucú)	-	•	-
POLYGONACEAE			
Polygonum acuminatum (tabacurana)	•	-	-
PONTEDERIACEAE			
Eichhornia crassipes (mureru)	-	•	-
Pontederia rotundifolia (mureru "folha grande")	-	•	-
SALVINIACEAE			
Salvinia (mureru)	-	•	-
SOLANACEAE			
Physalis angulata (camapu)	•	-	-

in the Zaire Basin, which covers 295 sq mi (765 km²) and has a fauna rich in fish species (especially mormyrids, characins, bagrids, clariids, and cichlids); the Cambodian lake of Tonle Sap, joined to the Mekong by the tributary of the same name, may grow from 1,158-3,861 sq mi (3,000-10,000 km²), depending on whether the current is flowing towards the Mekong (when the river's level is low, from June to February) or towards the lake (when the Mekong rises). In the tropics it is difficult to speak of lentic (still waters) and lotic (running waters) environments in the same way as in other places. In the Amazon basin there are several bodies of still water, known as *lagos*, *cochas* or *madreviejas* that are stretches of river, or meanders, that have been abandoned by the river in the past, and they are sometimes joined to the main river by channels called *furos* or *canais*. These watermasses show high productivity, with many fish and, over time, they may rejoin the main watercourse. *Varzea lakes* also exist and are formed when the main watercourse overflows. The rise in water level may also lead to the blockage of some affluents (tributaries), forming water bodies with some lake-like characteristics.

All the large catchment basins have large estuaries or deltas, especially in South America and southern Asia, where the gradient of the relief is lower than in Africa. The quantity of fresh water is so large that it dilutes the seawater at a considerable distance from the estuary (93 mi [150 km] from the mouth of the Amazon the water is still not as salty as seawater). The slope of the lower stretches of some rivers is so low that tides move masses of brackish water tens of miles up or down (62 mi [100 km] in the case of the Amazon), and this is how many marine species enter the rivers, as in many rivers in Australia and New Guinea, where marine species now dominate the river fauna.

The plankton and the microfauna

When people talk of the high diversity of tropical environments, they are usually thinking just of the terrestrial communities. Aquatic environments, however, also show very high diversity, especially in terms of the macrofauna. However, more detailed analysis of the different groups using the information available shows that the potamoplankton, the zooplankton, and part of the benthic communities are no more diverse than those of temperate freshwaters.

The potamoplankton of tropical rivers and their associated environments is not especially rich in species and includes many cosmopolitan and pantropical species. The potamoplankton in the Amazon Basin varies greatly depending on the type of water. In the clear water rivers, such as the Tapajós, the dominant species are cosmopolitan cyanobacteria of the genera *Anabaena* and *Microcystis*, as well as diatoms (*Melosira granulata*) and desmids. Black water rivers rich in humic acids, such as the Negro River, are especially rich in desmids. The turbidity of many white water rivers prevents light entering, and this greatly impoverishes them. The potamoplankton of the varzea lakes is not highly diversified, either. The zooplankton follows the same pattern, and varies more on a local scale. In some environments, such as the varzea lakes, where seasonal differences are greater, production is higher in the dry season. The diversity of benthic (occurring at the bottom of a body of water) organisms is highly variable. There are small rivers, such as the Gombak, in

Malaysia, where up to 400 species, mostly (85%) insects, especially dragonflies (odonates), beetles (coleopterans), caddis flies (trichopterans), and mayflies (ephemeropterans). In the streams of the Amazon Basin, up to 100 species of blood midges (chironomids) have been found, and it is estimated the basin as a whole must contain at least a thousand species. Thus, the insect fauna of tropical waters seems to be highly diversified, but other taxonomic groups are poorly represented and, furthermore, inventories taken in streams and rivers show no major differences to those of temperate environments. Thus, the diversity of benthic organisms, especially insects, is highly variable and different in each river.

In general, insect diversity diminishes in the lower stretches of the river, and that of other invertebrates increases. Sediment deposition reduces invertebrate variability, but this increases with greater amounts of detritus.

4.2 The riverside forest

Water may be constantly present at the base of the large trees where gallery forest runs along the riverbank, or only seasonally. In the Amazon in particular, the large areas called *varzea* are subject to periodic seasonal floodings that may last for six or seven months of each year, when the water level may rise several meters. These seasonal floods obviously impose, as might be imagined, a precise regularity on the biological cycles of the rainforest animals and plants. The most affected are the soil-living organisms, some of which pass the months of flooding as dormant stages (in the form of eggs, for example), while other animals, depending on the change of water level, perform periodic vertical migrations up the trunks to escape from the flood.

For the organisms affected, the rainforest acquires a seasonality it would otherwise lack. The very many arthropods forced to migrate vertically, or into seasonal inactivity during the flood, show a tendency to develop a strictly programmed life cycle with a single generation per year. Those living in rainforest that is not subject to the limitations derived from periodic floodings have a reproductive season that is generally much less defined and may last all year round; the length of each generation need not coincide with that of the year and is, as far as we know, often shorter.

The types of flooded rainforest

The differences already mentioned between the rainforests of the different continents (fewer species in Africa, less seasonal variation and steeper topography in southeast Asia, etc.) are also true of gallery forests and floodable forests (see chapter 1.4). The flooded forests of the Americas are the most extreme and interesting example, with their unusual characteristics and dynamics, followed by those of southeast Asia. The African forests and the Australian fringing forests are less unusual. The different types of flooded forests are closely related to soil types (nutrient accessibility), to the periodicity of the flooding and to the characteristics of the water; in general, one can distinguish gallery forest, permanently flooded forest, and periodically flooded forests.

Gallery forests
Gallery forest shows irregular and scarce flooding, varying greatly from region to region. It usually possesses fewer endemic species than the other forest formations related to surface waters, and its main role is to ensure a higher level of humidity during the drier and hotter periods in areas that are already at the limit of the rainforest biome, acting as a refuge for the rainforest species. For example, in some cases in Australia, the gallery forest may contain half the species of terrestrial birds living in the area.

Periodically or permanently flooded forest
Permanently flooded forest does not occur frequently. It is typically dominated by palms, such as the moriche palm (*Mauritia*) and the assai palm (*Euterpe*). The type of water that periodically floods the forests appears to be a highly determining factor.

Thus, mangroves appear throughout the tropics in coastal areas that are in contact with salt water; mangrove is a formation that is closely related to the rainforest (see volume 10). In some estuaries and lowland areas, the rise and fall of the tides makes large volumes of fresh water retreat inland, leading to the formation of forests flooded by fresh water that are extraordinarily rich in palm species and contain many trees with stilt roots and buttresses. This type of waterlogged forest is well represented by the deltas of the Orinoco, the Amazon and the Magdalena in the Americas, and those of the large rivers of New Guinea, such as the Fly or the Sepik, and the islands of the Indonesian Archipelago.

93 The permanently flooded Amazonian forest is dominated by palms, especially assai palms (*Euterpe*, upper photo) and mauritia (*Mauritia*, lower photo). The upper photo shows a fringing forest with palmiche (*E. edulis*), and the lower photo a mixed formation in the Amazon estuary, with the highly characteristic buriti (*M. flexuosa*).
[Photo: Edward Parker / Still Pictures and Jacques Jangoux / Auscape International]

When the flooding does not have a daily periodicity, but one of a few months, different types of forest are formed, depending on the characteristics of the water. Nutrient-rich waters lead to the formation of varzea in the Amazon and other similar formations in the rainforests of Africa and in large areas of New Guinea, and to a lesser extent, in Sumatra and Borneo, where the same phenomenon occurs but to a lesser degree. Many of these Asiatic areas are now being brought into cultivation, mainly as rice paddies. These sites contain sago palms (*Eugeissona utilis*, *Metroxylon*), and the starch from their stems is an important basic foodstuff for the local human population. Flooding with nutrient-poor waters leads to the formation of igapo in the Amazon, and the corresponding Asian forest flooded by black waters in Borneo, and to a lesser extent in Sumatra, in the western part of New Guinea, and in some parts of the Malayan Peninsula. There is the special case of the peat forests in Borneo (and in also in some sites of Sumatra, the Malayan Peninsula, and western New Guinea), which also grow in a very nutrient-poor environment that is regularly flooded, although this flooding varies with the thickness of the peat they are growing on.

94 **The huge leaves of the giant water lily (*Victoria amazonica* [=*V. regia*])** and its magnificent flowers are typical of the backwaters and slow stretches of the Amazon and Orinoco. The flowers turn from white to pink after they are pollinated by a beetle. The rimmed leaf blades may reach 5 ft (1.5 m) or more in diameter and like a boat they can support a considerable weight without sinking. They are often chosen as resting places by animals, even small crocodiles. The Amazon water lily is not a floating plant but has a submerged stem rooted in the riverbed that bears the petioles attached to the center of the enormous peltate leaves. The underside of the leaves is brick red and its stout, spiny veins help to support the leaf blade. The photo shows a backwater of the River Ripununi, in Guyana.
[Photo: Tony Morrison / South America Pictures]

An estimated 2% of the total Amazon rainforest is floodable forest with a degree of flooding that varies from year to year. Only 80% of the total area of varzea, for example, is flooded in a normal year. The differences between the forest types affect species composition, the biomass and the physiognomy. As they receive waters richer in nutrients, the varzea has greater biomass and taller trees (reaching 131 ft [40 m]) than the igapo. In terms of the number of species, the varzea is also generally richer than the igapo, although there may be exceptions depending on the type of organism; for example, the aquatic invertebrates that live on decomposing organic material show lower numbers and species diversity in the varzea, doubtless because they have greater difficulty in finding food there, as it is covered by the fine inorganic sediment.

Igapo grows on poor (sandy) soils and is normally flooded by acidic, nutrient-poor, waters, and the trees are more open and lower-growing (about 98 ft [30 m] in the tallest areas). At the same time, some animal groups and species that are present in the neighboring terra firme are absent, and this is explained by the presence in the water of humic components, which are toxic to them. There is a physiognomic gradient from the sectors closest to the river, which are flooded more regularly and colonized by stunted shrubs and relatively low trees (around 26 ft [8 m]), to the zones farthest from the river, with few herbaceous and shrub species and a much taller and denser canopy.

The unusual features of the flooded forest

All periodically flooded forests share unusual features, due to the vigorous effects of the overabundance of water. Perhaps their most characteristic feature is their relative impoverishment in tree species.

The relative floristic poverty
The flooded forest is floristically poorer than the neighboring terra firme forest, and unlike them is often dominated by only a few species. This dominance is clearer in southeast Asia and Africa, where there are some almost monospecific communities of abura (*Mitragyna ciliata*, Rubiaceae). The fauna also shows differences, and there is a reduction in the number and diversity of coleopterans and termites; for example, in an igapo in Brazil there may be a dozen species of termites in comparison with more than 40 species in the neighboring terra firme, and roughly similar figures (about 30 species in flooded forest and about 60 in the terra firme) have been found in Sarawak, in the northwest of the island of Borneo. In a few cases, the opposite is true, as in the case of the epiphytes (which are favored by biotopes with greater environmental humidity) or in mobile groups, like birds and bats, especially in sites with relatively greater climatic seasonality. There is also a difference in human settlement patterns; for example, in the Amazon the population density of the terra firme forests is around 0.5 inhabitants/sq mi (0.2 inhabitants/sq km), but in the varzea it reaches 40.5 inhabitants/sq mi (14.6 inhabitants/sq km), largely due to the exploitation of fish resources.

The flooded forest has some tall trees, but they are not as tall as those of terra firme. In southern Asia, the cover is in general less dense and more open, but the trees are not distributed more or less homogeneously, as they are usually grouped in dense, shady patches with almost no understory that are linked by more open sectors dominated by lianas and shrubs. The Amazonian flooded forests are different and much more complex, with an understory almost lacking shrubs and dominated by tree seedlings and buttress roots.

Many species of fringing forest and flooded forests also occur in secondary forests, perhaps because of the high light intensity. For example, many flooded forests in Malaysia are dominated by niaouli (*Melaleuca quinquenervia* [=*M. leucadendra*]), which is also characteristic of the forests that grow after fires. The same is also true of cecropias *Cecropia* in the American rainforest. A comparable example from the animal world is the long-tailed macaque (*Macaca fascicularis*) in the Malaysian Peninsula.

The blurred limits of the flooding
Unlike temperate gallery forest, tropical riverside forests interact very strongly with the neighboring aquatic ecosystem, creating totally unique relations of use and dependence. For example, the macrophytes (floating and semisubmerged vegetation) of the South American waters show high biomass and many species but are hardly consumed by aquatic invertebrates, which use them only as shelter; they are, however, eaten by terrestrial invertebrates, especially crickets and other orthopterans, some of which like *Paullinia acuminata* are highly specialized in this diet. Another example is the fish *Osteoglossum*, from the Amazon Basin, able to leap 7 ft (2 m) out of the water to catch terrestrial prey, such as insects, bats and even small simians. On the other hand, the

water can serve as a means of transport for terrestrial species that live in the forest canopy, such as the sloth (*Bradypus*), which can swim perfectly.

These examples from the animal world are anecdotal, but more importantly there are no sharp limits in time and space between aquatic communities and terrestrial ones. In other words, there is no clear stage in the succession when a gradually changing area covered by surface water can be considered to have become a forest. It is very difficult to define the limit between aquatic and terrestrial ecosystems, especially in South America. The water hyacinth (*Eichhornia*), for example, lives on water and is a major colonizer of all types of tropical waters, but it also grows perfectly in soil, on recently emerged riverbanks. Yet mangroves (*Rhizophora*) and kapoks (*Ceiba pentandra*) can grow to a height of 98 or 131 ft (30 or 40 m) on sites that are flooded for long periods. So, where does the aquatic environment end and where does the terrestrial environment begin?

Succession from an aquatic community to a terrestrial one is similar in all the continents, although with variations from region to region. The first stages of colonization are by widely distributed (cosmopolitan) plants that float on water, such as

the water hyacinth (*Eichhornia*) mentioned above, the water lettuce (*Pistia stratiotes*), some aquatic ferns such as *Salvinia* and *Azolla*, and other plants, such as the insectivorous *Utricularia*. This is followed by a herbaceous community of ferns, reeds, sedges and grasses. Differences appear at this point between the continents. In Africa, for example, the next step is a community of papyrus (*Cyperus papyrus*) or screw pines (*Pandanus*). Yet the end result is the same rainforest. Floating plants make an important contribution to food webs, not because they are directly consumed (as mentioned above, few animals eat them directly) but because their remains are consumed by the floodable forest's abundant detritivorous organisms.

Adaptations to flooding

The trees in flooded forests in the Americas may be partly or totally submerged for months, and there are interesting plant and animal adaptations. For example, in the flood period about twice as much organic material is deposited in the sediment as in the dry season, because many plants drop all their leaves. Even so, many species keep their leaves, and grow new leaves, flowers and fruits above the still turbid water, or even within it, as in the case of some trees of the *rebalsero* forests of the Orinoco, which are flooded for eight or nine months a year.

95 The floating plants of tropical rivers can be highly obstructive, sometimes totally covering the river. The photo shows an Amazon river launch making its way in a stretch totally covered by water hyacinth (*Eichhornia crassipes*), a plant that reproduces extremely quickly. Its petioles are basically aerenchyma (spongy, cork-like tissue) and make it buoyant. It is a very effective colonizer, and in many warm areas water hyacinths cause veritable infestations.
[Photo: Tony Morrison / South American Pictures]

96 The surreal appearance of the igapo in a high water period, on the banks of the River Negro in the mid Amazon Basin. The igapo trees drop their fruit in the high water period, and fruit-eating fish concentrate there to feed.

[Photo: Luiz Claudio Marigo / Bruce Coleman Limited]

Trees show several adaptations to flooding, such as insulating corky materials around the bark, waterproof waxes on leaf surfaces, reduced metabolism during the flood period, many buttresses at the base of the trunks, stilt roots, and in some cases, aerial roots. The buoyancy of many aquatic plants is an excellent adaptation to fluctuations in water level. Yet the adaptations of the vegetation of the flooded forest and their detailed functioning is not yet fully understood; it seems reasonable to suppose, however, that root metabolism must be partly anaerobic, as the sediment is highly reducing (due to the lack of oxygen).

Animals have adapted to these seasonal rhythms and migrate or encyst during the unfavorable periods. Shortly before the rise in water levels many terrestrial vertebrates enter dormancy, attaching themselves to trunks, branches, etc. During the flood some will be eaten by aquatic predators, again showing the close relations between terrestrial and aquatic systems. Other animals adapt their breeding season to the period when resources are most abundant. For example, in the Amazon frugivorous animals reproduce in the highwater period, especially in June and July, when most of the trees of the igapo and varzea fruit, while insectivorous animals breed in the period when the waters begin to lower.

Vegetation dynamics

The highly regular nature of the flood periods in the Amazon explains the abundance of water-dispersed plants (plants that disperse their fruits and seeds by water) in the flooded forests. In many cases, legumes such as atapas and rosewoods (*Macrolobium*, *Dalbergia*) and palms like the assai (*Euterpe*) bear indehiscent fruit (remains closed at maturity) with a light, spongy cork-like shell that floats well. However, the fruit of their closest relatives in the terra firme are dehiscent (splits open at maturity) and usually depend on animal dispersal. The seeds of the rubber tree (*Hevea brasiliensis*) are so hard that few fish can eat them and may float around for two months, and the fruit of the zapoton (*Pachira aquatica*) begin to germinate while they are still floating.

The plants growing on the open riverbank include many with wind-dispersed fruits or seeds, such as the members of the Podostemaceae (*Apinigia*, *Podostemum*, *Mourea*), which are well-adapted to rapids; kapok (*Ceiba pentandra*, the sacred tree of the Mayans); willows (*Salix occidentalis*, *S. martiana*); and many lianas and epiphytes (especially orchids and ferns).

In flooded forests, as in the terra firme rainforest, animals are the most important vehicles of seed transport, especially bats, birds, monkeys, and rodents; for example, the agouti that live in the igapo of the Negro River, such as the green agouti (*Myoprocta acouchy*), commonly disperse palm seeds, as they have the habit of burying the seeds at a distance from the parent plant. Monkeys eat fruit in the flood period, such as the cacajao (*Cacajao calvus calvus*) that live in the

	CHARACIDAE					CICHLIDAE	PIMELODIDAE
	Brycon melanopterus (matrinchão)	Colossoma bidens (pirapitinga)	Colossoma macropomum (tambaqui)	Mylossoma aureum (pacu de renda)	Triportheus rotundatus ("sardinha")	Astronotus ocellatus (carauaçú)	Phractocephalus hemiliopterus (pirarara)
BIGNONIACEAE							
Tabebuia barbata (capitari)	-	-	-	-	•	-	-
CAPPARIDACEAE							
Crateva benthamii (catauari)	-	-	-	-	•	-	-
CECROPIACEAE							
Cecropia (embaúba)	•	-	•	•	•	-	-
Pouteria [=Neolabatia] cuprea (abiuarana)	•	•	•	-	•	-	-
EUPHORBIACEAE							
Hevea brasiliensis (seringueira, rubber tree)	-	-	-	-	•	-	-
Piranhea trifoliata ("piranheira")	-	-	-	-	•	-	-
MELASTOMATACEAE							
Mouriri ulei (socoro)	-	•	•	-	•	-	-
MYRTACEAE							
Eugenia (goiaba araça)	-	-	-	-	•	-	-
Myrcia fallax (araça)	-	-	-	-	•	-	-
MORACEAE							
Ficus (apuizeiro)	•	•	•	•	-	-	-
Sorocea duckei (caiembé)	-	-	-	-	-	•	-
LEGUMINOSAE							
Macrolobium acaciifolium (arapari)	-	-	-	-	•	-	-
POLYGONACEAE							
Ruprechtia brachysepala ("sardinheira")	-	•	-	•	-	-	-
RUBIACEAE							
Duroia genipoides (curuí)	-	-	-	-	•	-	-
SAPOTACEAE							
Gymnoluma glabrescens (cramuri)	-	-	-	-	•	-	-
SIMAROUBACEAE							
Quassia [=Simaba] guianensis (cajurana)	-	-	-	-	•	-	-
VERBENACEAE							
Vitex cymosa ("tarumã")	-	-	-	-	•	•	-
ARECACEAE (PALMS)							
Astrocaryum jauari (jauari)	-	-	-	-	•	-	-
Bactris [=Pyrenoglyphis] maraja (marajá)	-	-	-	-	•	•	•
Syagrus speciosa ("pupunharana")	-	-	•	-	•	-	-

varzea of the central basin of the Amazon, and so do other monkeys that preferentially exploit the flooded forest during this part of the year: squirrel monkeys (*Saimiri*), howler monkeys (*Alouatta*), and spider monkeys (*Ateles*).

Yet the most typical feature of the American flooded forests, distinguishing them from all other flooded forests, is the dispersal of fruit and seeds by fish. The very close relationship between the trees and fish involves many different phenomena. In the terra firme forests, many trees fruit when the water level is low; in contrast, most of the trees of the igapo and the varzea fruit when flooding occurs (high water), coinciding with the arrival of river fish in the flooded forests. In the most spectacular forests, some migratory fish, such as the catfish, perform their movements in big groups, locally known as the *subienda* (the rise), and fishermen take advantage of this moment to catch them at narrow stretches. This rise in water level also coincides with the fruiting period of the trees: for example, pacu fish

(*Mylossoma, Metynnis*) regularly consume the fruit of camapu (*Physalis angulatum*) and even the flowers of tabacurana (*Polygonum acuminatum*). In fact, each fruit makes a distinctive noise when it falls into the water, and this is recognized by both the fishermen and the fish. Expert fishermen in the varzea attract a catch by hitting the water with a stick to imitate the sound of a fruit falling. Some trees may drop their fruit over a period of a month, causing fish to concentrate under its branches, and fishermen in turn take advantage of this by setting nets there. The tambaqui (*Colossoma macropomum*) is a larger fish that not only eats the fruit of the giant water lily (*Victoria amazonica*) but also breaks seeds as hard as those of the rubber tree (*Hevea brasiliensis*) and the Brazil nut tree (*Bertholletia excelsa*). It and other large fish can be located by fishermen from outside the water due to the noise they make cracking the shells of the fruit.

The flood period is linked to the fruiting period, but the dry period is linked to flowering and the

97 The main plants of the *várzea* and igapo and the fish that consume their fruit when it falls in the high water period, in the Itacoatiara region (at the confluence of the Amazon and the Madeira). Only the principal species of fishing interest, mainly characins, are included: their eating habits are well known because fishermen bait their hooks and traps with the fruit of these plants.
[Source: N.J.H. Smith, 1979]

98 A group of butterflies on a rainforest riverbank in search of the salts trapped in the sediment. They belong to the genus *Catopsilia* (Pieridae), and the two odd butterflies are of the genus *Graphium*. They have gathered before their summer migration, in December, in the Kambas Nature Reserve in Sumatra. [Photo: Wayne Lawler / Auscape International]

massive appearance of terrestrial and aquatic insects. This is when aquatic invertebrates reach their peak, because when the waters are low the dissolved oxygen tends to increase. The water gradually withdraws to the river, and the fish abandon the varzea and igapo with it. The many terrestrial animals that fed on fruit now turn to leaves, nectar, insects and other forms of food. In this period red howlers (*Alouatta seniculus*), for example, eat the leaves of trees that are toxic to other animals. Another primate found in the varzea, the pygmy marmoset (*Cebuella pygmaea*), makes 4 in (10 cm) holes with its teeth in the bark of a tree and returns every day to suck the sap or resin. The recently exposed banks are covered in wet mud rich in organic matter deposited by the current, on which many butterflies feed, such as pierids (*Phoebis*, *Rhabdodryas*), uranids (*Urania leilus*), papilionids (*Protesilaus*, *Euritides*) and others. These colorful groups, dominated by yellows and whites, are the prey of many riverside birds, lizards, and amphibians.

4.3 The vertebrate fauna

The animals of the flooded forest are highly varied, including not only aquatic and semiaquatic species but also terrestrial species adapted to life in this environment. Anyway, it is obvious that the most abundant animals are truly aquatic ones. In any case, there is a surprising diversity of vertebrates.

The fish

The intertropical rivers and lakes have a very rich fish fauna. The Amazon alone, for example, has more than 1,300 species of fish, about a fifth of all the world's fish species! The Zaire in Africa has about 700 species (83% of which are endemic), and the Mekong in southeast Asia has about 500 species.

The fish of the Zaire Basin

About 2,000 species have been described in the freshwaters of the African continent, and 18 of the families they belong to are endemic, some, like the aplocheilids, with more than 260 species. The Zaire flows almost entirely through rainforest and contains about 700 species of fish, mainly silurids (catfish) (23%), mormyrids (elephant fish) (18%), cyprinids (16%), and characins (15%). The rivers of Cameroon and Gabon are also very rich in fish, including both endemic species and species shared with the Zaire Basin. In the rivers of the region of the Gulf of Guinea, as far as the northeastern limit of the African rainforest, most of the large basins run through different climatic regions, with two different types of fauna: the Sudanese, typical of open environments and with medium to large fishes of migratory habits, and the Guinean, typical of forest areas.

99 The elephant fish (**Mormyrops, Gnathonemus, Mormyridae**) are one of the most typical elements of the African fish fauna, especially in tropical areas. They are unmistakable because their snout is like a elephant's trunk, the reason for their common name. One of the most widely known is *G. petersii*, which can emit small, low-voltage electric discharges when disturbed. It is sensitive to very low concentrations of some elements in water, and is being studied as a biological indicator, as it emits detectable discharges when it detects, for example, heavy metals.
[Photo: Jean-Michel Labat / Auscape International]

The Zaire River has a large and highly branched basin, with tributaries of all sizes, zones of rapids, associated lakes, floodable areas, and marshes. Many of the fish that live in the basin change their habitat as they grow to adulthood, and others migrate in the reproductive period or when the river's waters begin to rise. Many enter the flooded forests to feed and reproduce. Some have special adaptations to use atmospheric oxygen for respiration, such as the lungfish *Polypterus* and *Protopterus*, which live in the oxygen-poor waters of the wetlands. Most species of the main watercourse or the large tributaries prefer the riverbanks and islands. In contrast, there are few species in the central channel; among these the most important are school-forming members of the clupeids (*Microthrissa*). The mormyrids, or elephant fish (*Mormyrops*) prefer the running waters of streams or rivers. The silurids, or catfish, such as *Clarias* and *Synodontis*, live in the main watercourse or in the large tributaries, although some species have specialized to live in rainforest streams. The cichlids live in streams and rivers. The cyprinodontids, or killifish, such as species of *Hepsetus*, are smallish fish that prefer small watercourses, pools, and wetlands. The anabantids, or climbing gouramis (*Channa*), are adapted to freshwater wetlands.

The fish of the Zaire show several feeding strategies. There are micropredators, including fish specialized in catching flying insects, species that feed in the benthos (the bottom), and species that catch only invertebrates near the riverbank. There are also fish-eating species, most of which swallow their prey whole, but some like the species of *Phago* (Citharinidae) are specialized in taking bites out of the fins of other fish. Some species are illiophagous (mud-eating), such as the cyprinids of the genus *Labeo*, and others are detritivorous, such as *Clarias*, catfish of the Clariidae. There are also many herbivorous species, such as tilapias (*Tilapia*) and other cichlids, such as *Pelmatochromis*, but many species are herbivorous, such as the cyprinid *Barbus*, the African species of *Alestes* (characids), or the species of the genus *Congocharax* (citharinids).

Many species make use of the rise in the river's water level to reproduce. Some species, including some cichlids, may show two spawning peaks, one in September or October, and the other between April and June, depending on the area they live in. Some clupeids, bagrids, and cyprinids do not leave the watercourses, but many species may enter tens of miles into the rainforest to spawn. Their eggs hatch in a few hours (at most, in a few days), and the young fish grow very rapidly. The juveniles usually form schools and either stay in the pools and backwaters or enter the creeks.

The fish of the Amazon and Orinoco basin
The freshwater fish fauna of the New World tropics contains almost 2,400 species, making it the richest and most diverse in the world. The Amazon Basin contains more than 1,300 species and is dominated by a few groups of fish—characins (43%), silurids (39%)

100 Rays are present in the rivers of the Amazon and are represented by the river stingrays, the potamotrygonids. The photo shows one of these members of the Elasmobranchii (*Potamotrygon*) in shallow water in the River Negro.
[Photo: Adolf de Sostoa & Xavier Ferrer]

and gymnotids (3%)—called Ostariophysi, with a swim bladder characteristically divided into two chambers and joined to the esophagus, and also an ability to emit an alarm substance. The characins have undergone a spectacular adaptive radiation and range from small species only an inch long to larger ones such as the piranha (*Serrasalmus*), and the tambaqui (*Colossoma macropomum*), which can reach a length of 3 ft (1 m) and a weight of 66 lb (30 kg), or the pirapitinga (*C. bidens*), which is slightly smaller and often confused with its relative. Some of the catfish silurids are also a very diverse group, with large fish-eating species, such as those of the genera *Brachyplatysoma* and *Pseudoplatysoma* (family Pimelodidae), some of which are important fishery species, such as the river dorado (*B. flavicans*), piraiba (*B. filamentosum*) and the surubim (*P. fasciatum*). The species of gymnotids typically use electricity for social communication, defense and to capture their prey; one of the best known is the electric eel (*Electrophorus electricus*). Other Amazonian families worth mentioning are the cichlids and osteoglossids, which includes the pirarucu (*Arapaima gigas*), one of the world's largest fish (7 ft [2 m] long and 276 lb [125 kg] in weight).

The great diversity of the Amazon's fish fauna is due to a variety of factors, such as the basin's size and age, the variety of habitats, the diversity of ecological niches, connections with other basins, the formation of environments isolated from the main bed where species have evolved, and finally, the relative stability of conditions in the basin over a long period of time. There is an immense range of waters and habitats.

The very steep rivers of the Andes have a fish fauna that is highly specialized in eating algae. In the headwaters of the basin, where the rivers flow through forests, there is a fauna that does not appear to be highly specialized: Many fish eat small prey, especially terrestrial insects, such as ants, as well as the larvae of aquatic insects, but others eat crustaceans, molluscs, fish, and organic matter. The small watercourses in the central region have a very diverse fauna (between 30 and 50 species per river), consisting above all species of characins, silurids, gymnotids, cichlids, and cyprinodontids. These rivers flow through dense rainforest where there is little light, nutrients are scarce and there is little aquatic vegetation; the food available for the fish is of external origin (flowers, pollen, leaves, fruit, insects, and spiders).

The *várzea* lakes have very complex food webs, include purely fish-eating species, such as the tucanare, or rainbow perch, (*Cichla ocellaris*, cichlid family), and zooplankton-eating species as well as mud-eating, insectivorous, herbivorous and omnivorous species. The juvenile phases of some fish, such as the two species of *Colosssoma*, known as boco and ruelo, feed in these waters. The flooded forests (*várzea* and igapo) are colonized by fish that make use of the external resources of the rainforest. These include fruit-eating species, such as the characin jatuarana (*Brycon*), and different species of *Colossoma*.

101 No other carnivorous fish from the Amazon is as famous as the piranha (*Serrasalmus*), undeservedly known as a pitiless predator. This specimen from the Manu Biosphere Reserve (Peru) shows their typical teeth, their location and the shape of the head. This arrangement allows them to swim just below the surface of the water, where they can even take prey swimming on the surface (see figure 229, volume 9).
[Photo: André Bärtschi / WWF / Still Pictures]

These fish reach a large size and store fat reserves that allow them to survive and develop their gonads when the river level goes down and food becomes scarce. In these areas, however, there are also predatory species; some are strictly fish-eating, while others eat terrestrial insects. Some eat leaves and even detritus.

One of the most special environments is formed by the masses of floating vegetation made up of *Paspalum* and *Echinochloa* that cover large areas in the middle of the riverbed. Many fish live here and use the vegetation as a refuge and often as a source of food, such as some characins (*Hemigrammus* and *Hyphessobrycon*) and cichlids (*Cichlosoma*); oxygen availability is also greater here. This concentration of fauna does not pass unnoticed by many predators, such as traíra (*Hoplias malabaricus*) and piranhas (*Serrasalmus, Rooseveltiella, Pygocentrus*).

One characteristic of the Amazon's fish fauna is that a large number of species are able to travel, many of them migrating seasonally from one area to another, depending on the availability of the food, their reproductive requirements, and the physical and chemical conditions. Many fish enter the varzea lakes when the waters are highest and rich in nutrients, and when plankton blooms occur, but then abandon them for a while to lay their eggs in more oxygenated sites in the river. Fish may perform reproductive, trophic (nutritional) and dispersal migrations. Reproductive migrations take place when the waters are rising and the fish seek suitable spawning areas. As already mentioned, many fish enter the flooded forests during the period of rising water levels to feed there. Other fish migrate upstream after feeding for several months in the varzea and igapo, especially the schools of characins. Finally, juvenile phases of different species usually undertake dispersal migrations upstream, especially those of the curimatid *Semaprochilodus*.

The fish of the Asian basins

In the tropical Asian fauna there are also many species of fish (more than 500 have been described in Thailand and around 400 in Peninsular Malaya). Wallace's Line represents a genuine boundary for strictly freshwater fish species. Thus, in Borneo (to the west of Wallace's Line) there are more than 300 species, while Celebes (to the east of the line) only has two species, and they were probably introduced by humans. There is also a great contrast between the freshwater fish fauna of the island of Java (like Borneo, to the west of Wallace's line), with 100 species, and the island of Lombok (on the other side of this biogeographical division), where there are only five species, three of them apparently introduced.

In southeast Asia, as in the other rainforest areas, the mountain streams have less selective species that are less specialized feeders, dependent on forest products and land insects, whereas in the

102 The number of species of reptile in the islands in the Strait of Sunda and different authors' lines separating the biota of eastern and western Malesia (see figure 31). The different lines reflect the fact that different groups of organisms have managed to spread different distances from their centre of origin. Yet it seems that the only lines that have a general significance are those of Lydekker and Huxley (modified), which coincide with the limits of the continental platforms, and thus indicate regions that shared long periods in the past when they were above sea level.
[Drawing: Editrònica, from several sources]

103 The distribution of all the known species of crocodile and diagrams of head shape in caimans, crocodiles, and gavials. The map shows their distribution in forests in all the continents except Eurasia; they are mainly freshwater, although there are some American and Indo-Pacific species that also live in brackish waters. Their shape, especially the head, clearly shows their adaptation to an aquatic environment. The positions of the eyes and the nasal orifices mean they can watch for potential prey to pass while they remain submerged. The fascination they exert on human beings is shown by their presence in ancient traditions. Crocodiles are still respected and feared, and an estimated 3,000 people fall victim to crocodiles every year. This does not prevent them being caught for their skins, which have been traded for centuries. The captive breeding of crocodiles has increased since the 1960s, for tourism, commercial and conservation reasons.
[Drawing: Editrònica, from several sources]

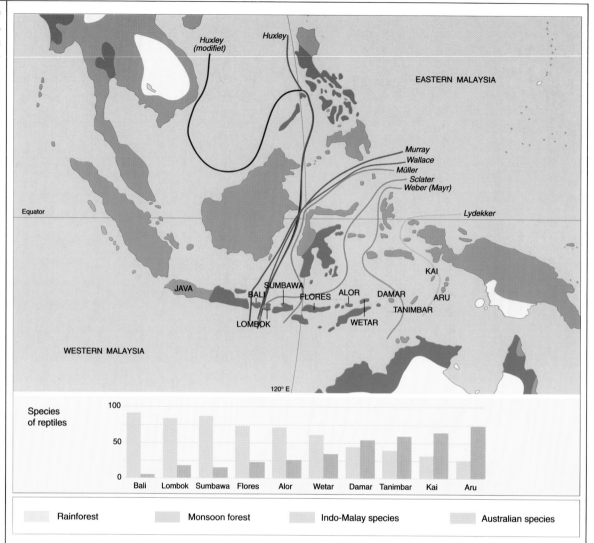

lower stretches the number of the more bottom-linked detritivores increases. The diversity of species increases with the scale and size of the river, which leads to greater niche complexity in the lower stretches.

The Mekong River, another of the world's largest rivers, has a varied fish fauna (500 species) dominated by cyprinids, including carnivorous, omnivorous, and herbivorous species. Fish migrations start when the waters start to rise; many migrate from the main river to the Tonle Sap, through the outlet channel of the same name and from there to the surrounding flooded forests; when the waters start to go down, the fish return to the main course of the Mekong.

The Tônlé Sap is a large lake area with a water level that fluctuates between the dry and flood periods (covering between 965 and 4,247 sq mi [2,500 and 11,000 sq km] to a depth of between 3 and 33 ft [1 and 10 m]). It is associated with the basin of the Mekong, and has a high fish production and supports intensive fisheries: more than 100 species move between the Tonle Sap and the river from October to February,

mainly following the lunar cycles; the large silurids move at night and the large cyprinids during the day. Some fish, such as the enormous catfish *Pangasianodon gigas* (pangasiid family), which reaches a length of 7 ft (2 m), travel hundreds of kilometers up and down the main course. In the delta of the Mekong there are also important fisheries; the abundant fish include catadromous species (which spend their adult life in rivers, but return to the sea to reproduce) as well as anadromous species (which live in the sea and reproduce in rivers), and amphidromous species (which move between the two environments, but not for clearly reproductive purposes).

The fish of the Australian and Papuasian river basins
The continental fish fauna of Australia and New Guinea has the unusual feature of lacking almost entirely strictly freshwater species. There are only two species of the osteoglossids, *Scleropages formosus* and *S. leichardti*, the same family as the piracucu in the Amazon, and a lungfish *Neoceratodus forsteri*: the other fish are of marine origin, with many catadromous species.

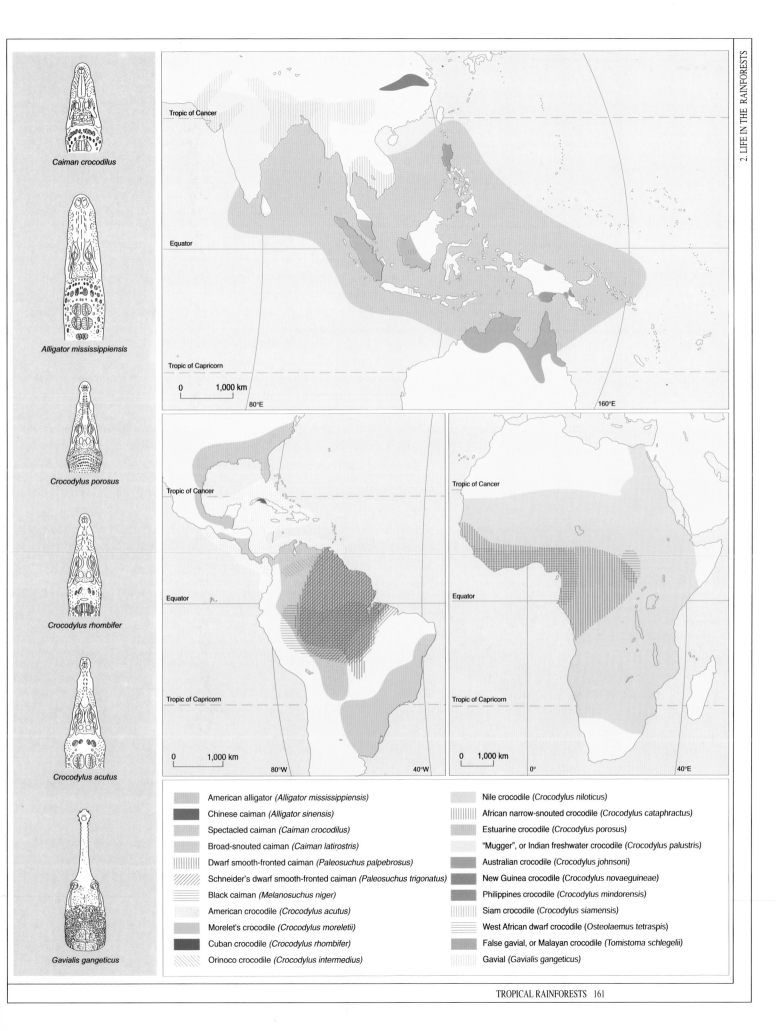

Caiman crocodilus

Alligator mississippiensis

Crocodylus porosus

Crocodylus rhombifer

Crocodylus acutus

Gavialis gangeticus

Tropic of Cancer

Equator

Tropic of Capricorn

0   1,000 km

80°E   160°E

Tropic of Cancer

Equator

Tropic of Capricorn

0   1,000 km

80°W   40°W

Tropic of Cancer

Equator

Tropic of Capricorn

0   1,000 km

0°   40°E

American alligator (*Alligator mississippiensis*)

Chinese caiman (*Alligator sinensis*)

Spectacled caiman (*Caiman crocodilus*)

Broad-snouted caiman (*Caiman latirostris*)

Dwarf smooth-fronted caiman (*Paleosuchus palpebrosus*)

Schneider's dwarf smooth-fronted caiman (*Paleosuchus trigonatus*)

Black caiman (*Melanosuchus niger*)

American crocodile (*Crocodylus acutus*)

Morelet's crocodile (*Crocodylus moreletii*)

Cuban crocodile (*Crocodylus rhombifer*)

Orinoco crocodile (*Crocodylus intermedius*)

Nile crocodile (*Crocodylus niloticus*)

African narrow-snouted crocodile (*Crocodylus cataphractus*)

Estuarine crocodile (*Crocodylus porosus*)

"Mugger", or Indian freshwater crocodile (*Crocodylus palustris*)

Australian crocodile (*Crocodylus johnsoni*)

New Guinea crocodile (*Crocodylus novaeguineae*)

Philippines crocodile (*Crocodylus mindorensis*)

Siam crocodile (*Crocodylus siamensis*)

West African dwarf crocodile (*Osteolaemus tetraspis*)

False gavial, or Malayan crocodile (*Tomistoma schlegelii*)

Gavial (*Gavialis gangeticus*)

Taking a dip

Very many rainforest animals may spend their entire life without ever touching the soil. Yet they may often come into contact with the water: A quick dip into the water may be an excellent way of fleeing a predator like a snake. The water below may be even more dangerous, but that is a different story.

Reptiles that enter the water

Many reptiles show some degree of aquatic behavior, exemplified by the common iguana (*Iguana iguana*). This sturdy reptile is common in the riverbank forests of the Americas from southernmost Mexico to central Brazil. The common iguana may reach a length of 87 in (220 cm) (including 59 in [150 cm] of tail) and leads a solitary life up to a height of 66 ft (20 m) in the tree branches. To climb up to the branches, they use their strong legs equipped with strong nails. Its emerald green body with dark transversal stripes, more obvious in the juveniles, makes it less visible among the dense vegetation. The iguana's favorite escape strategy is to jump into the water below rather than to climb to higher branches. It swims well in the water using vigorous flicks of its tail, and holding its immobile legs close to its body. It virtually goes down to the ground level only to lay its eggs, which it places in a hole in the sand. The young hatch after three months of incubation, just at the beginning of the rainy season, and at first eat mainly snails, grubs, and insects, while the adults are almost completely vegetarian.

A reptile even more familiar with the water than the common iguana is the soa-soa water dragon (*Hydrosaurus amboinensis*), a member of the agamid family that can reach a length of 43 in (110 cm), and lives near the rivers of the Indonesian rainforest. It too propels itself through the water using its tail, which has a large fin supported by bony projections (apophyses) from the vertebrae in its tail. It is virtually omnivorous, as is a third reptile linked to the water, the eastern water dragon (*Physignathus lesueueri*), another agamid that lives on the forest riverbanks along the rivers of New Guinea and eastern Australia.

Mammals with aquatic habits

Other semiaquatic animals include some of the largest vertebrates living in the rainforest, such as tapirs and capybaras.

There are now four species of tapirs (*Tapirus*), one from the rainforests of southern Asia, while the other three are from South America. The Asiatic tapir (*T. indicus*) is bigger (47 in [120 cm] at the shoulder and 71-87 in [180-220 cm] total body length) and is distinguished by the unusual color of the adult coat, mainly grayish black with whitish back and sides. The parts that will be whitish on the

104 The unusual habits and markings of the Asiatic tapir (*Tapirus indicus*) are clearly shown in this photo of a specimen in Malaysia. Half the tapir's body is light gray, the other half is black, and the animal is as usual half-submerged.
[Photo: Gerhard Lacz / NHPA]

adults are, until the fifth month of the tapir's life, a brownish color with white patches and stripes, with markings similar to those of the young of the wild boar. The coloration of the coat of the juveniles of the American tapirs (*T. bairdii*, *T. terrestris*, and *T. pinchaque*) is similar, but the adults have a uniform dark brown coat. All tapirs like water, especially the Asiatic species, which often passes long periods of time grazing on aquatic plants in areas under water, even staying for long periods completely immersed.

A typical visitor of the rainforest along the riverbanks of the rivers of South America is the capybara (*Hydrochoerus hydrochaeris*) which is by far the largest of all living rodents. It may reach a length of 51 in (130 cm) and a weight of 110 lb (50 kg). The location of the capybara's nose, eyes and ears is unlike that of other rodents and is related to its amphibious habits. They are found on the small part of the head that is above water when the rest of the animal's body is submerged. The same arrangement is found in other air-breathing animals that spend much of their life submerged in water, such as crocodiles, frogs, and hippopotamuses. Other features that clearly show the capybara's adaptation to water include the fact that the digits are joined by a short web that is more developed in the hind legs. This arrangement of its limbs means the capybara cannot dig a burrow, unlike almost all other rodents. In practice, it shelters within the water or any hole in

the ground. It is a peaceful and gregarious animal (living in family groups of 15 or 20 individuals) and has a vegetarian diet. Its large size makes it vulnerable to the attacks of larger terrestrial predators, such as the jaguar (*Panthera onca*), and boa constrictor (*Boa constrictor*), and aquatic ones like the black caiman (*Melanosuchus niger*) and anaconda (*Eunectes murinus*). Aquatic or riverside mammals, which are most common in India and southeast Asia, include the Amazonian giant otter (*Pteronura brasiliensis*) which may reach a length of 5 ft (1.5 m), the African otters (*Lutra maculicollis* and *Aonix congica*), different species of hippopotamus (*Hippopotamus amphibius*, *Choeropsis liberiensis*) that are exclusively African; the water buffalo of southern Asia (*Bubalus*); and swamp deer such as the tamang (*Cervus eldi*), which are also Asiatic.

Other aquatic vertebrates

Tropical rivers, flooded forest and adjacent watermasses also have their own interesting and diverse fauna of amphibians, reptiles and mammals, such as frogs, turtles, crocodiles and caimans, snakes, otters, freshwater dolphins, and manatees.

The amphibians
The amphibians are very numerous, especially in the American tropics, and there are many anu-

105 **The most unusual member of the Anura in the Amazon** is probably *Pipa pipa*, a strange looking frog with very odd habits. The adult female places her clutch of about 100 eggs on her back in a mass that, as shown in the photograph, is at first gelatinous and transparent. This gradually becomes opaque and compact, turning the same color as the rest of her body. When the eggs hatch after about three months, the tadpoles appear to be emerging from the mother's back, as if they were bursting out through her skin. [*Photo: C. Mattison / Natural Science Photos*]

106 One of the most remarkable skills possessed by any reptile is the ability of the Amazonian basilisk (*Basiliscus*) to run upright for short distances over water. This surprising ability requires very fast movements, captured in this high-speed photograph.
[Photo: Stephen Dalton / NHPA]

rans: frogs, toads and other tail-less amphibians. The most remarkable is the goliath frog (*Conrana goliath*). The largest anuran in the world, it can reach a length of 13 in (33 cm) and a weight of 13 lb (6 kg) and lives in the watercourses of the rainforests of the coasts of the Gulf of Guinea.

Frogs are very abundant in these environments, even in the areas of forest that are not waterlogged. The highly humid air means conditions are suitable for them, and not only for the adults. Many tree frogs (rhacophorids) make foam like nests among the leaves to lay their gelatinous eggs, and this is where the young undergo the first stage of their development. In the arrow-poison frogs (dendrobatids) of the Amazon, famous for their poisonous skins and their conspicuous aposematic (warning) coloration, the tadpoles often spend some time on their father's back.

Swimming reptiles

Typically aquatic reptiles occur in flooded forest, such as crocodiles, caimans, and freshwater turtles. In the Old World rainforest there are also monitor lizards (*Varanus niloticus*, on African riverbanks, *V. salvator* in southern and southeastern Asia, *V. dumerili* in the rainforests of Java and Borneo) and water dragons (*Hydrosaurus*). These water dragons play a similar role in the ecosystem to the basilisk (*Basiliscus*) in the Americas (which are commonly known as "Jesus Christ lizards" because of their unusual ability to walk on water, running straight over short stretches of water).

The freshwater South American turtles include remarkable species like the Arrau river turtle *Podocnemis expansa* and the terecay *P. unifilis*, which are important sources of food for indigenous peoples and *caboclos* in the Amazon Basin. In the months from October to December (coinciding with the lowest water level), many individuals of *P. expansa* congregate on the riverbanks to lay their eggs and bury them in the sand.

Crocodiles are widespread throughout most tropical basins but are declining alarmingly as they have been ruthlessly hunted for a long time; for example, the Siamese crocodile (*Crocodylus siamensis*) is almost extinct in the wild, although there are still a considerable number of individuals in captive breeding farms, especially in Thailand, where the last known wild population exists—some 50 individuals in the Bung Boraphet reservoir. It appears that during the Ming Dynasty (1368-1644) the range of the Borneo false gharial (*Tomistoma schlegelii*) reached the Canton (Guangdong) province in southern China, but now it is restricted to a few locations in eastern Sumatra, Borneo, and the Malayan Peninsula. The Amazonian crocodiles include the spectacled caiman (*Caiman crocodilus*), one of the most widely distributed crocodilians, with many local varieties and local races, and the black caiman (*Melanosuchus niger*), which is almost extinct in the Colombian Amazon and becoming rarer and rarer in the Brazilian Amazon; it is now common only in some watercourses in French Guyana. The water snakes of the tropics are not as highly diversified as the land snakes. In the Amazon there are species of the genera *Hydrops* and *Hydrodynates* and others, and especially the giant anaconda (*Eunectes murinus*), one of the most typically aquatic of all snakes. Anacondas can reach great sizes, although they do not reach the enormous sizes sometimes still attributed to them; even so, lengths of around 30 ft (9 m) have been recorded. The anaconda's geographical distribution covers a large part of South America, from Colombia to Peru, from Venezuela to Brazil, and also the island of Trinidad. It spends most of its life at the edges of wetlands, but may often spend an entire day underwater with only the tip of its snout out of the water. In addition to the capybara, its most frequent prey are other relatively large mammals, such as rodents like the agouti (*Dasyprocta*) and paca (*Agouti paca*) as well as fish, birds, snakes, and small caimans. Each brood the female anaconda produces may consist of up to 80 young, each of which is 28 in (70 cm) long when it hatches.

Aquatic birds

Because of their great mobility, birds can make use of the frontier between the water and the land, and this is why there are groups specialized for life on riversides, such as coots (*Himantornis*, or *Canirallus* in Africa, *Rallina* and *Gymnocrex* in southeast Asia, and *Aramides* in America), waterhen (*Amaurornis* in Africa, *Rallina* in southeast Asia and in some tropical Pacific islands), kingfishers (*Alcedo*, *Ceix*, *Ispidina*) and many species of cattle egrets, many of which have a cosmopolitan distribution. In addition to the totally aquatic fishing birds, such as the cormorant (*Phalocrocorax*) or anhinga (*Anhinga anhinga*), there is also the hoatzin (*Opisthocomus hoazin*), the only species of bird endemic to the Amazonian flooded forests, and other curious groups, such as the tree ducks (*Dendrocygna*), which nest in trees, or those of the genus *Cairina*, with an American representative that gave rise to the domesticated Muscovy duck (*Cairina moschata*), one of the few animals domesticated in the Americas before the arrival of the Europeans and now widely distributed throughout the world. The riverbanks also have nocturnal and diurnal birds of prey that fish.

107 The anaconda (*Eunectes murinus*) is perhaps the best known of all aquatic snakes and is one of the largest and most feared. The specimen in the photo is from Janauarí, near Manaus (Brazil).
[Photo: Adolf de Sostoa & Xavier Ferrer]

108 The cetaceans of the **Amazon and Orinoco rivers** are a major feature of the fauna. The upper photo shows a river dolphin, or boto (*Inia geoffrensis*) breathing on the water surface, while the lower photo shows a manatee, or "peixe boi" (*Trichechus inunguis*). The manatee is a peaceful and good-natured herbivore, but both the river dolphins, the boto and tucuxi, are very active fish-eaters (see figure 91). There are many legends about these dolphins in the mythology of local people, who are aware of these animals' mammalian features and consider they have supernatural powers. [Photos: Roland Seitre / Bios / Still Pictures and Ken Lucas / Planet Earth Pictures]

The river cetaceans

Some cetaceans have adapted to life in large rivers, such as the freshwater, or river, dolphins. In the Amazon Basin there are two species; the river dolphin, or boto, (*Inia geoffrensis*) which can reach a length of 8.5 ft (2.6 m) and a weight of 353 lb (160 kg), and the smaller tucuxi (*Sotalia fluvialis*), which reaches 110 lb (50 kg) and 5 ft (1.5 m). Both eat fish, but while the boto mainly catches solitary benthic fish by entering the *várzea* (or varzea) and igapo, the tucuxi lives in the main river courses and eats pelagic fish that form schools. The manatees deserve a special mention. Manatees are large herbivorous estuary-living cetaceans that have managed to colonize freshwater habitats. The Amazonian manatee (*Trichechus inun-guis*) eats aquatic plants from different groups: grasses, such as jungle rice (*Echinochloa*) or water grass (*Paspalum*); members of the Nympheaceae, such as water lilies (*Nymphaea*); members of the Pontederiaceae, such as water hyacinths (*Eichhornia crassipes*); labiates such as *Salvia*. Other sirens live in different basins in the tropics, such as the Caribbean manatee (*Trichecus manatus*) and the African manatee (*T. senegalensis*), which has been found in waters of the river Niger more than 1,243 mi (2,000 km) from its mouth, but in general they are more typical of estuaries and coastal seawaters. The dugong (*Dugong dugon*) is found in the Indian and Pacific Oceans and is basically marine, exploiting the populations of underwater flowering plants, although they are sometimes found in freshwater.

3
Humans in the rainforests

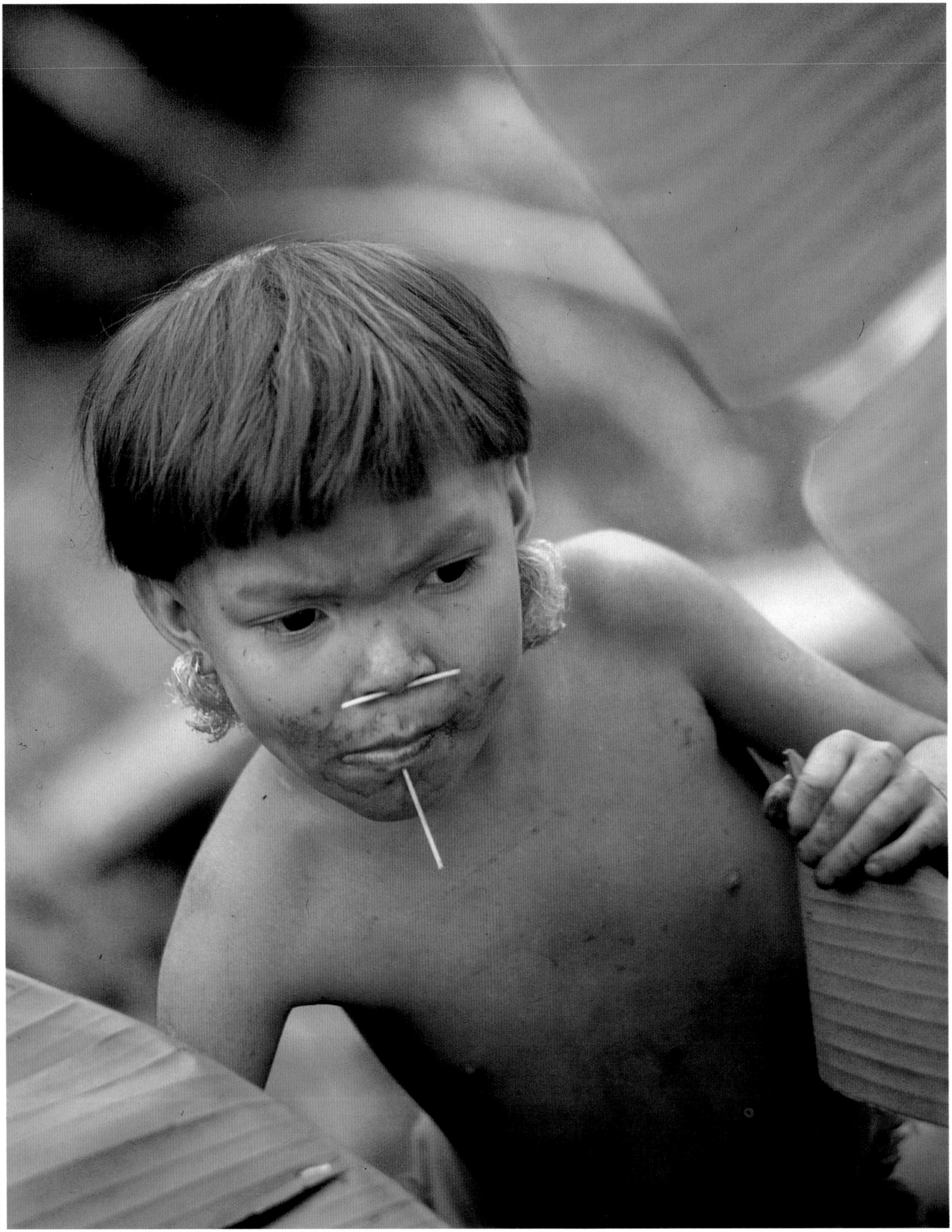

1. Human settlement of the rainforests

1.1 The economy and development of the rainforest dwellers

The tropical rainforest is not a favorable habitat for most terrestrial vertebrates. As most of the available plant food is high up in the trees, the vertebrates that best exploit these resources are birds, reptiles (especially snakes), bats and arboreal mammals (especially monkeys). Thus, the rainforest is not an easy environment for humans to colonize, but people live there just the same by making use of the resources it provides.

Rainforest nomads

The fact that human populations can live in the rainforest, even if only a reduced number still survive, shows the effectiveness of preagricultural and preindustrial human cultural adaptations; these populations are now generally marginalized, under serious threat and possess little technology (some do not know how to work metal, although they usually have some imported iron tools). Hunter-gatherer peoples can survive due to their low population density and their skills in extracting resources from their environment. They are now under threat, not from the natural environment, but from their agriculturist and stock-raising neighbors, inept governments, and destructive western cultural influences.

Most hunter-gatherers and many itinerant agriculturists do not have stable settlements, and settle in small camps built with the short-lived materials provided by the forest, as do the Pygmies of the African rainforest. These populations have very low densities, around one inhabitant per 1.5-2 sq mi (4 or 5 sq km). Thus, the areas of rainforest they move in can be considered to have virtually no human population. This is even more so, if it is borne in mind that, as now, their camps are not far from the settlements of more sedentary agricultural peoples, with whom they establish permanent trading relations and from whom they also obtain

other agricultural products; this is true of at least the Pygmies in Africa and of some other hunter-gatherer ethnic groups of the rainforest, such as the Aeta of Luzon and the Penan of Borneo.

Sedentary hunters, itinerant agriculturists

As already mentioned, there are in practice few rainforest peoples who are exclusively itinerant hunter-gatherers. Most hunter-gatherers also practice some form of agriculture, even if it is itinerant. They are thus peoples with more-or-less migratory, but not exactly nomadic, customs.

Many areas of the rainforest environment show the same population model highly conditioned by the relative fertility of the cultivated land and also partly by the agricultural techniques used. Thus, in Melaka, Peninsular Malaysia, while the hunter-gatherer Semang have population densities similar to those indicated for other hunter-gatherers (one habitant per 1.5-2 sq mi [4-5 sq km]), both the itinerant agriculturist Semang and the gardening Jakun have population densities up 10 or 20 times greater.

Colonial cities

The rainforest environment is seen as hostile to humans, a "green desert," and this may be appropriate description for some areas of the Brazilian terra firme, some interfluvial areas of the Zaire Basin or some areas of the interior of the Malayan Peninsula, Indochina and the large islands of Insulindia. It is, however, difficult to reconcile the fact that other rainforest areas are among the most densely populated areas of the planet, such as Singapore, some parts of Vietnam, Java, the other Indonesian islands (the source of many transmigrants), and some coastal areas in the rainforest areas of Africa and Brazil. In any case, native peoples occupy, with greater or lesser population densities, a space within the world's rainforests.

109 Human presence in the intertropical rainforests has had very different histories in each continent. Yet in all cases there are some peoples that have lived there since ancient times, and others that have arrived in the last two or three centuries. This child looking out from behind a banana leaf is a Yanomami, one of the most representative peoples of the Amazon and Orinoco (see photos 115 and 179).
[Photo: Mark Edwards / Still Pictures]

110 Missionary settlements in the heart of the rainforest often marked the beginning of western occupation. This mid-18th century map is from the work *El Orinoco ilustrado y defendido* ("The Orinoco, Illustrated and Defended"), published in Madrid (Spain) in 1741. It shows the different missions, especially Jesuit missions, that existed in the Orinoco area.
[Photo: Biblioteca de Catalunya]

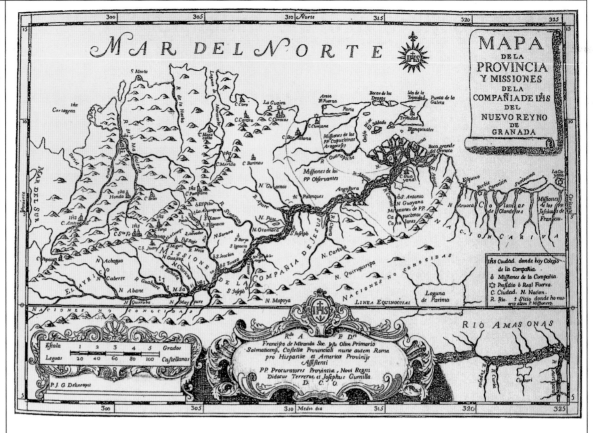

Since long ago urban civilizations have developed in some rainforest areas, leading to considerable population concentrations in some areas. This is true for the Mayan civilization, the Yoruba cities in Africa, and the Khmer empire in southeast Asia. After the beginning of European colonization 500 years ago, a new type of urban settlement began to appear in the rainforest. These settlements initially maintained stronger links with the distant metropolis than the surrounding countryside, were populated by migrants from the metropolis or brought from elsewhere, and pursued economic activities totally unrelated to the traditional activities of the surrounding established populations.

The first large colonial cities in the rainforest were founded in America. On his first journey in 1492, Columbus left a part of his crew as a settlement at a point on the northern coast of the island of Hispaniola that he named *Navidad* (Christmas), which is close to the current settlement of Cap-Haïtien, in Haiti. This first European settlement was destroyed and its inhabitants killed before Columbus returned. On his second journey, he founded La Isabela, and later his brother Bartolomeo founded the city of Santo Domingo. These settlements were the basis of the Spanish conquest and colonization of the New World until the founding of the first colonies on the American mainland at the beginning of the 16th cen-

tury. Yet the largest of these cities avoided the inhospitable environment of the rainforests that they were not adapted to (see "The Colonization of the Americas," in volume 8). The first Portuguese settlements on the Brazilian Atlantic coastline were almost all in the Mata Atlântica, such as São Vicente and São Paolo (1532), Santos (1545), Bahía (1549), Recife (1563), and Rio de Janeiro (1565).

The Portuguese had already explored the western coastline of Africa and had established some forts and trading posts (São Jorge de Mina, or Elmina, on the coast of present-day Ghana, in 1482, São Tomé in 1493, and Mpinda, on the mouth of the Zaire, in 1501). The colonization of the Americas led to the creation of the first colonial settlements on the African coastline in the Gulf of Guinea, founded to ensure the supply of slave labor for the American colonies. During the 17th and 18th centuries, all the European powers founded settlements, and in the 19th century they were the starting points for colonial exploration and entry into the interior of the African continent. Colonial trading posts of this type were also established in south and southeast Asia from the 16th century onwards, although there were already some native urban centers. This is true of Colombo, founded by the Portuguese in Sri Lanka in 1505, and Batavia (now Jakarta), which was founded by the Dutch in Java in 1619.

111 There are some large cities in the rainforest, such as Singapore, on an island at the southern tip of the Malaysian Peninsula. The photo shows the heart of the British colonial city, the completely transformed remains of part of the traditional city (the houseboat district has totally disappeared, for example), and the financial district of the modern city.
[Photo: VCL / TCL / Index]

The modern urban network

The many urban areas in the rainforest have very different histories. Like most other Third World cities, they have shown explosive population growth over the last few decades and the need to shelter the immense exodus from the countryside. They are relatively well-developed centers that are better connected to the centers of decision of the former or current metropolis than are the underdeveloped rural areas surrounding them.

Initially, these colonial cities were little more than a port, a garrison, warehouses and an administration center, but many American ones soon became real cities when the colonies developed, as all goods entering and leaving had to pass through their ports. During the 19th century, the spread of steamboats required the establishment of a network of supply depots, and some of them, mainly British colonies (Singapore, Hong Kong), grew into commercial centers. Most colonies, such as Jakarta (the former colonial city of Batavia), which ceased to be a colony in 1949, have grown continuously since decolonization.

Few of the 20 or so urban centers in the rainforest with more than a million inhabitants have a history going back more than 500 years. Almost all of them were insignificant centers at the beginning of the 19th century and secondary cities at the beginning, and even the middle, of the 20th century. Postcolonial development in the second half of the 20th century has led to a model of dependent urbanization, with high growth rates, major social imbalances and large sections of the population that are marginalized. São Paolo began to expand in the 17th century when it replaced Bahía as the capital of Brazil and was later boosted by the spread of coffee cultivation between 1870 and 1929, but its growth has been much faster in the second half of the 20th century, and it is now the third largest urban area in the world. Rio de Janeiro, also capital of Brazil from 1763 to 1960, underwent its first period of growth in the second half of the 18th century due to sugar cane and cotton cultivation and the discovery of the mines in Minas Gerais; it had periods of splendor as the seat of the Portuguese court and capital of the Brazilian Empire from 1808 to 1889 and did not stop growing (although not as quickly as São Paolo) even when it ceased to be the capital of Brazil in 1960.

The latest arrivals and transmigrations

Over the last 500 years, colonization has brought greater or lesser populations from outside the rainforest into this environment. These migrations occurred independently and the most important ones were white Europeans (mainly from the Mediterranean) and black Africans (mainly from West Africa) to the Antilles and to Central and South America, mainly the Atlantic coastline; and people from northern China to southern Asia, especially Malaysia and Singapore, where they are now large and important minorities.

More recently, often due to government initiatives, transmigrations have started to occur from overpopulated areas of the rainforest environment to less populated ones. This process has been especially important in Indonesia, where these programs began (1905) in the Dutch colonial period and have involved the movement and resettlement with government support of about two and a half million people; they were resettled from Java and also from Madura, Bali, and Lombok to sparsely populated or unpopulated areas of Sumatra, Kalimantan (Borneo), Celebes, and Irian Jaya (the eastern half of the island of New Guinea). This does not include the spontaneous immigrants who took the same path without any government support. The number of emigrants grew spectacularly between 1979 and 1986, when 60,000 families a year transmigrated, with a public investment of about $10,000 per family. The rate slowed down in 1986 due to the Indonesian government's falling oil revenues, and has now stabilized at a figure well below 10,000 families per year, a population reduction that did not, however, compensate for the very rapid natural growth of Java's population.

1.2 The colonization of the rainforests

Very few of the peoples now living in the rainforests of Africa, southeast Asia, Oceania, Central America, and South America are hunter-gatherers of wild foodstuffs, and many have now adopted some type of horticulture, which they may combine with hunting. Those who continue hunting and gathering also trade with the agricultural peoples settled in small villages, but they are able to find their own food in the rainforest, as shown by their diet and technology. When they reached the rainforest, these colonists learned to fit into their environment and manage it, both protecting it and extracting benefits to live on and for small-scale trade. It is estimated that up to 50 million people now live in the rainforest biome;

they are peoples who have developed environmentally harmonious lifestyles that do not over-exploit their resources.

A second type of colonization has been practiced since the 15th century, an expansive form, frontier colonization. This second types includes the colonists still felling and burning the Brazilian rainforest to establish unsustainable crop and grazing lands. Anyway, from the 16th to the 20th centuries (and probably into the 21st century), the need for land has driven more and more settlers into the rainforests. Normally, the recent arrivals have neither the knowledge nor the techniques needed to make best use of the resources and services provided by the rainforest, and thus contribute to its rapid destruction.

Before discussing archeology, it is worth pointing out that the rainforest's ecological characteristics mean that organic remains do not last long before they totally decompose. As ecologists say, the life of the rainforest converts all organic material and incorporates it into the biological cycle, as it is rapidly degraded by decomposers, such as fungi and bacteria.

Humans in the African rainforests

Human migration into the rainforests began in prehistoric times. The first traces of modern humans in what is now the rainforest biome are not bones but cultural remains. In the last ice age, between 30,000 and 40,000 years ago, a human population appeared in the eastern part of the Zaire Basin (then probably occupied by savannah-type vegetation). The *Sangoan culture* is known from its stone and bone tools, some of which were apparently not utilitarian but ornamental. Some authors have attributed the first deliberate attempts to domesticate a plant to this culture, namely the bottle gourd (*Lagenaria siceraria*, Cucurbitaceae), which has since spread to other tropical areas and has been present in New Guinea and the American tropics since the far distant past.

Human types in the African forests

It is not known for sure that the region of eastern Democratic Republic of Congo, where traces of the Sangoan culture have been found, was occupied by rainforest 40,000 years ago or that these humans were the ancestors of today's Pygmies or any other contemporary hunter-gatherers or itinerant agriculturist peoples. Yet the African rainforests are rela-

tively poorer in species than might be expected, and one suggested cause is the long, intense influence of human beings. Some authors consider that there is no true intact primary forest in Africa, that all Africa's rainforests are secondary forests of greater or lesser age, and that their floristic composition is thus in a permanent state of transition, as a consequence of their exploitation over the millennia.

Civilizations have developed in the African rainforest that concentrated population densities in urban centers, such as the *Yoruba* cities and states, as well as the *Edo* kingdom in Benin, which grew up around Ifé, their common religious center, between the 12th and 18th centuries. The Yorubaland and the Benin kingdom spread throughout the entire southwest of modern-day Nigeria, stretching from the river Niger to the river Mono in the west, and thus going beyond the western frontier of Nigeria and occupying part of the modern-day state of Benin (only a part of which formed part of the ancient Benin kingdom) and Togo. At least in the 12th or 13th century, after the foundation of Ifé, many city-states were founded in the area that later had periods of splendour and decline. Long before the arrival of the first Europeans, at the end of the 15th century, this was the most highly urbanized area in Africa to the south of the Sahara, and the cities were very large with a double row of city walls. Despite their generalized decadence in the late 17th century,

many of these cities survived until the colonial period and recovered their splendor under this regime or after colonization. Now two of these cities (Ibadan and Lagos) have more than a million inhabitants, another has more than half a million (Ogbomosho), and a further 20 have more than 100,000 inhabitants. The area as a whole has a population density of about 500 inhabitants/sq mi (200 inhabitants/sq km), comparable with that of Italy.

The central African Pygmies

The largest populations of Pygmies are in the African rainforest: the Mbuti (or Bambuti) in Ituri in Democratic Republic of Congo, and the Binga (or Babinga) in the northern tip of the Congo Republic and the adjacent regions of Democratic Republic of Congo, the Central African Republic, Cameroon and Gabon, with some small centers in central and southeast Gabon. Many of them, especially the Binga, are beginning to become sedentary, but their traditional forms of life are completely nomadic, consisting of groups of about 20 families that form a subsistence unit, both in terms of obtaining food and consuming it. In terms of morphology, it seems that there is a correlation between the height of the African Pygmies and the degree to which they have mixed with other local populations.

Pygmies live in small groups of about 20 families, with each family able to exploit a large area,

112 The Pygmies are among the most authentic inhabitants of the African rainforest, and their clearest anatomical trait is their low stature. They usually have little body hair (except the Mbuti), frizzy hair, a broad nose, thick but not everted lips, and a reduced jaw. The group in the photo are members of the population of the basin of the River Ituri, in the Democratic Republic of Congo. The Efe, bow hunters and gatherers of honey from wild beehives, maintain regular exchanges with the Lese Dese, a Bantu agricultural people of the same Ituri jungle. The Lese Dese exchange the products of their harvests, metal, cotton fabrics and aluminium pots and pans; the Efe in turn exchange meat, honey, construction materials and medicines from the jungle, and in some cases even help the Lese Dese to work their lands (see figures 132 and 165).
[Photo: Xavier Ferrer & Adolf de Sostoa]

113 One example of recently arrived or mixed populations in the rainforest are the inhabitants of the eastern part of Madagascar. They are of Austronesian origin (the xanthoderm settlers of Polynesia, originally from southeast Asia), more or less mixed with black populations from the nearby African coastline. The basis of the Malagasy language is Malayan-Polynesian, with some African borrowings.
[Photo: Nat Quansah / WWF / Still Pictures]

up to 386 sq mi (1,000 sq km). They normally settle in camps of about 20 hemispherical huts built with interwoven curved branches, fastened into the ground and covered with the leaves of the tilipi or mongongo (*Megaphrynium macrostachyum*, and other similar members of the Marantaceae), opening onto the central clearing of the camp, which is normally close to a watercourse. The men hunt with bows and arrows (the Efe) or nets (the Mbuti) and collect honey from wild beehives, while the women fish and collect a very wide range of plant and animal foodstuffs (edible leaves, roots and tubers, mushrooms, snails, and insects) without going very far from the camp.

Humans in the Asiatic rainforest

The vast rainforests of southeast Asia have a highly varied population. Most of the human populations consists of xanthoderms (yellow-skinned peoples) or mongoloids, but there are also groups of short-statured humans: the local race of Negritos in the Philippines and related groups in southeast Asia. These inhabitants of the Asiatic rainforest live, in some cases, as hunter-gatherers. The Semang of Malaysia form groups of 6-10 related families that exploit exclusively an area of about 19 sq mi (50 sq km) where they construct temporary camps of huts built of branches and leaves. The style of the hut is different from that of African Pygmies; they are not hemispherical huts with a structure consisting of curved branches fixed into the ground at both ends but windbreaks opening onto the common space, supported by a structure consisting of three or four thick stakes fixed into the ground, leaning slightly towards the clearing at the center of the camp with their free end resting in the forked branches of props leaning in the opposite direction. Crossbranches are tied to the stakes supporting the windbreak, and it is finished with interwoven leaves and lianas.

Outside Africa, the populations morphologically closest to the African Pygmies are the few surviving inhabitants (the Jarawa, Andaman, and Onge peoples) of the Andaman Islands in the Gulf of Bengal, although they can be distinguished as their body proportions are more slender, especially the head, which is not so large in relation to the body as in the African Pygmies, and the nose, which is not as wide and less flat. Other populations of short-statured humans in the southern Asian rainforest include the Semang, who live in the rainforest in the center of the Malaysian Peninsula on the frontier between Thailand and Malaysia, and the Negritos, or Aeta, of the Philippines, who mainly live in the mountains of eastern Luzon and in other areas of the same island and other smaller ones. There are small-statured populations in some of the islands of the Sonda Strait (Timor, Sumba, Badjawa, Celebes, Flores), in Sumatra, and in New Guinea as well as in the Nilgiri mountains in southern India and in some parts of southern Cambodia. All these short-statured populations appear to be descendants of the first wave of modern humans to reach south and southeast Asia, and who were then displaced to less hospitable areas by later Neolithic populations genetically related to more northerly mongoloid

114 The Dayak live in the Borneo rainforest, where they build their high-quality wooden longhouses. The photo image shows a group of Kenyah Dayaks from Sarawak, inside one of their typical communal houses (see figure 123).
[Photo: Nigel Dickinson / Still Pictures]

populations (see the chapter "Human populations in the monsoon forests," page 449).

Humans in the rainforest of Oceania

The first humans arrived on the shores of New Guinea at least 50,000 years ago, but there are no traces showing they reached the highlands of the island's interior until 26,000 years ago, although they reached Australia 40,000 years ago and New Ireland 30,000 years ago. Together with the ways of life of the few hunter-gatherer peoples left in the equatorial rainforests, this suggests that humans occupied and exploited these environments relatively late and that the groups arriving were marginal or forced to move by adverse circumstances (conflicts with other human groups, the exhaustion or reduction of the resources of the previously occupied areas in the adjacent savannah, etc.). (See the chapter "The settlement of Melanesia and Polynesia" in volume 9, which deals with isolated systems.)

The Melanesians are probably the humans most closely linked to the rainforests of Oceania. They all live in the rainforest or in the cloud forest of the equatorial highlands, except for some who live in tropical areas with a more marked dry season like monsoon forest or savannah. There are some popu-lations similar to the Semang and the Negrito in northeast Australia, mainly the Ngatjan, Tjapukai and Wultura peoples, who live in the rainforest of the Atherton Tableland around Lake Barrine and northwards to the headwaters of the Daintree River. These populations are known as Barrineans and there are an estimated 500 individuals who have not interbred with the surrounding populations. They might thus be the remains of the first waves of human beings to reach the isolated southern continent, and their ancestors might have settled the Atherton Tableland about 40,000 years ago.

Humans in the American rainforests

The oldest human remains in the American tropics appear to be those in the Pedra Furada cave, in the Brazilian state of Piaui, consisting of worked stone, traces of fire, and fragments of painted rock; some authors date them as 32,000 to 23,000 years old, but these datings are highly controversial. These finds are in an area of caatinga that has probably never been occupied by rainforest, and that is now about 435-500 mi (700-800 km) away from the nearest rainforest.

Most of the hunter-gatherers of the American rainforests now practice some form of agricul-

Pyramids in the jungle

The American John Lloyd Stephen (1805-1852) was a lawyer, whereas Frederick Catherwood (1799-1854) was a British architect. They travelled independently through eastern Europe and the Near East, producing some interesting materials, such as Catherwood's sketches, drawings and plans of Jerusalem and the Egyptian temples and Stephen's fascinating travel books, such as *Incidents of travel in Egypt, Arabia, Petraea and the Holy Land* (New York, 1837). For this alone, they would probably not have entered the history books. Their great contribution to archaeology and general culture took place later, between 1837 and 1843, when they discovered the Mayan cities and temples of Yucatán. This surprising world hidden in the rainforest lay in oblivion only a short distance from the young and thriving United States.

Stephen and Catherwood met by chance in London in 1836 when Stephen was on his way home from Arabia. The year afterwards Catherwood went to New York, which had just been devastated by a fire, hoping to find work there as an architect. He found work and also came into contact again with Stephen, and they renewed their shared interest in travel and archaeological research. In late summer of 1839, Stephen employed Catherwood as the artist for an expedition he had in mind. They set sail in a whaling boat for Belize on October 3, 1839. In mid-November, after a rough but spectacular journey they were amazed to discover the magnificent pillars and imposing ruins of the city of Copán, in present-day Honduras.

Stephen had previously received several recently published books mentioning major archeological remains found in Yucatán. Scholars of the time gave little credence to these accounts, just as they had ignored the countless reports from previous authors of the time of the Spanish conquest. This was because they were convinced the native people would never have been able to do anything good, let alone build immense constructions. They accepted what the historian William Robertson (1721-1793) wrote in his book *History of the Discovery and Settlement of the Americas*, when he stated, "... if the buildings in these descriptions had existed in the Mexican cities, there would still be visible remains...The reports of the Spanish must have been greatly exaggerated." Stephen thought otherwise, and decided to explore the area personally, and took the opportunity to go there as the United States Ambassador to the Federation of the United Provinces of Central America, supposing it still existed. (General Rafael Carrera had just deposed President Francisco Morazán, and the area was in chaos.)

The symbolic magic of his blue frock coat with gold braid saved him in many delicate situations. This ornament turned Stephen the adventurer into a diplomat and was a great help on several occasions. For example, it persuaded José María Acevedo, the owner of Copán, to sell him the ruins for $50—almost nothing—allowing Stephen and Catherwood to excavate and sketch their first great archeological find. Afterwards, they discovered

Jade mask from Tikal, Guatemala (3rd-9th century)
[Ancient Art and Architecture Collection]

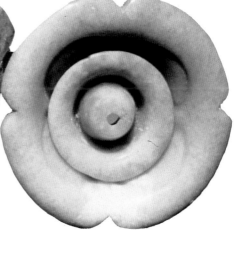

Palenque and Uxmal, and in a later voyage they discovered Kabah, Tulum, and Chichén Itzá, for a total of 44 sites. Yet they never saw the most impressive of all, Tikal.

Tikal was rediscovered by Modesto Méndez and Ambrosio Tut, together with the sketcher Eusebio Lara, in 1848 and was systematically studied by Alfred Percival Maudsley in 1881 and 1882. To say Tikal was systematically studied is rather an exaggeration, as even now, a century after Maudsley's work, there are many constructions still to be excavated. It is thus not surprising as this immense city, the jewel of the classic period of Mayan culture, covers 46 sq mi (120 sq km) of dense forest, and more than 3,000 constructions have been identified and listed. The central area, containing the large pyramidal temples, palaces and ceremonial platforms, contains over 200 monuments. There are countless altars, funeral steles, and *chultuns* (chambers dug in the rock). All this was built, destroyed and rebuilt over the city's 11 centuries of existence, between roughly 220 B.C. and 900 A.D. Excavations have found more than 100,000 instruments and objects, and more than a million ceramic fragments. The arrogance of the Europeans, such as the texts of William Robertson, was left in ridicule by these finds. However, Tikal unexplainably collapsed around the 10th century, as did virtually the entire Mayan civilization.

Tikal is only 820 ft (250 m) above sea level in the center of the Petén jungle, which overwhelmed it and then protected it. The tall pyramidal temples of the central area reached 197 ft (60 m) and were the tallest known constructions of the pre-Columbian civilizations. They emerge above the forest canopy, making the site especially striking. They must have been even more impressive when the city was flourishing, as it was the home of notable astronomers and mathematicians (the Mayan calender is more accurate than the one currently in use) and splendid artists. Although they did not know how to work metal, these artists worked stone with great skill to portray the fauna and flora of their mythology, above all the jaguar and the snake. They took both resources and artistic inspiration from the forest: an overwhelming jungle, but not as strong growing as might be expected, due to the highly permeable nature of the calcareous substrate, which makes it impossible for any lake or watercourse to form, as the water just drains away.

The temples of the Mayan city of Tikal, (3rd-9th century) in Petén, Guatemala [The Hutchison Library]

Fragment of pre-Columbian codex in Madrid [Museo de América / Scala]

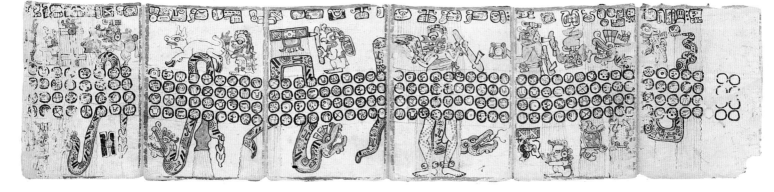

Ocellated turkey (*Agriocharis ocellata*) in the Maya Biosphere Reserve, Guatemala [Yves Lefevre / Bios / Still Pictures]

The forest is rich and diverse, with abundant sapodilla and cedrela, mahogany, amoreta, and palo campeche (*Manilkara zapota*, *Cedrela odorata*, *Swietenia macrophylla*, *Brosimum alicastrum*, and *Hemotoxylon campechianum*). The jungle still contains jaguar, spotted puma, and ocelot (*Panthera onca*, *Felis concolor mayanensis*, and *F. pardalis*), and its silence is broken by the capers and calls of spider monkeys and howler monkeys (*Ateles geoffreyi* and *Alouatta pigra*). The forest is paradise for birdwatchers, with more than 300 species of bird, including the dazzling ocellated turkey (*Agriocharis ocellata*). The Petén jungle, the former homeland of the Maya.

ture, if only itinerant. These are itinerant, but not truly nomadic, peoples and this applies to most of the peoples of the Amazonian terra firme. In terms of their habitat and occupation of space, there are no major differences between them and true nomads, although their settlements are normally more stable, and sometimes partially reused after a period of abandonment. In the Amazonian terra firme, population densities are little different from those in the forests of Ituri or Malaya, and the settlements consist of one or more huts, with a floor plan that is oval, or rectangular or has a rounded end. Each one is occupied by several families and has distinct spaces intended for different purposes or people.

In the varzea, the Amazon's floodable plain, population densities are higher (39 inhabitants/sq mi or 15 inhabitants/km^2). Settlements are logically more numerous and more permanent along the riverbanks than on the terra firme, as the soil is more fertile. This is because it is regularly renewed by flooding, meaning that clearings opened in the rainforest can be cultivated indefinitely, and it is not necessary to abandon them after a while and clear new ones. Furthermore, the wild plant and animal resources of the rainforest are more abundant, varied, and constant throughout the year.

The Warao of the Orinoco Delta are a special case much discussed by anthropologists. They are entirely hunter-gatherers but are sedentary, and they live in egalitarian societies with little or no social differentiation. The Warao have chiefs, counsellors and priests (*wisidatu*) who do not participate in the tasks requiring physical exertion, but control the work of obtaining and storing their basic resource, the pith of the mauritia palm (*Mauritia flexuosa*), which grows in waterlogged sites.

The differences between the Amerindian populations of the rainforests and the other American peoples are not as great as those between the melanoafricans and the peoples living in the deserts or Mediterranean regions of northern Africa (see the chapter on the human colonization of the Americas, in volume 8). As most Amerindian populations are derived from relatively small founder populations and arrived relatively recently in the Americas from Asia, genetic divergence between them is not as great as that found between the inhabitants of other continents. Even so, the inhabitants of Central America are genetically closer to the populations of North America than to those of South America. On the contrary, their

fragmentation and the almost uninterrupted migrations over the last millennia have led to great linguistic diversity.

Human occupation of the South American rainforest is more recent; the first immigrants reached Amazonia through Central America between 12,000 and 15,000 years ago. Agriculture in Amazonia must date from about 5,000 years ago. After the first wave of arrivals, Amazonia must have been relatively unaffected by the following migrations until the period of European colonization.

When the first Europeans arrived in South America, Amazonia was the home of diverse and complex native cultures, with elaborate artistic production and extensive commercial networks. There were an estimated eight million people living in Amazonia, but this number rapidly declined due to persecution, slavery, wars, and the illnesses the European colonists brought with them; the indigenous population is now only about 4% of the population that existed when the Europeans arrived. A few small groups of native peoples still have little or no contact with the outside world, but their traditional existence is at risk as the region is being rapidly deforested.

The rubber boom at the beginning of this century attracted many people to Brazil, and now the inhabitants of the rainforests are the descendants of these and other immigrants. The *caboclos*, of mixed native and European descent, live by agriculture, hunting, and gathering forest products. They have extensive knowledge of rainforest resources and understand the ecological processes of the rainforest.

During the last decades there has been a spectacular increase in the colonization of the Amazon. Immigrant peasants, rural landless workers, and miners have been encouraged to migrate to the most remote areas of the rainforest. The policies of the Brazilian government have encouraged these new settlers because they are a way of reducing the pressures resulting from the unfair distribution of land. In Brazil, for example, less than 1% of the landholders control almost half the cultivable land, while poor landless peasants are encouraged to move from south and northeast Brazil to the inland Amazonian states. In Colombia, 80% of the cultivable land belongs to 10% of the landholders, and the inhabitants are forced to move on. Unfortunately, these new settlers of the Amazon lack the knowledge of

115 **The Amerindian population of the rainforest**, once numerous and widespread, reached the rainforest between 15,000 and 10,000 years ago. The northern Asian origin of this group is clearly shown in their facial features, as in the face of this Yanomami man from the Orinoco Basin, decorated with macaw feathers.
[Photo: Antonio Rivera / Gamma]

the rainforest environment acquired by the indigenous peoples, *caboclos* and other groups that have traditionally lived in the rainforest.

1.3 Human adaptations within the rainforest

Despite the physical and cultural differences between different modern human populations, it is generally accepted that these populations diverged no more than 100,000 or 150,000 years ago. Since then human populations have crossed deserts and oceans, settling in the jungle or at the highest latitudes. They have acquired very different appearances and diverse ways of living, conditioned by the demands of the environment.

Human expansion over the planet has distributed polymorphic genes (molecules showing neutral genetic variation but coinciding in their function) that tell us about the different degrees of relationship between populations. Human appearance has been modeled by natural selection when a population has settled in a biome long enough for natural selection to act. The differences between humans are shown by both genetic characteristics and phenotypic ones. However, in spite of what one might intuitively suppose, it is the genetic characteristics showing the differences caused by 100,000 (or more) years of human history that allow the reconstruction of historic events, while visible characters (which show, moreover, variability that is continuous) show where the most recent ancestors lived. Thus, populations that live in the same type of surroundings, but have been separated for long periods of time may be very close in physical appearance but genetically quite distant. This is true of the Africans and the inhabitants of New Guinea; they look very similar, but the Papuans are genetically closer to the southern Chinese and the Vietnamese than to the Africans. External differences in no way imply different ancestries.

It has been the lack of physiological differentiation in humans, that is to say their great adaptability, that has allowed them to adapt to different climates. The capacity to use tools and reflective intelligence (the ability to learn, remember and foresee) has encouraged the development of an extrasomatic tool, culture. These special characteristics have allowed humans to adapt to all environments, and the human species now occurs throughout the planet. In reality the term *adaptation* is relative, but in any case it implies improvements in the quality of life of an individual in a given environment. In anthropology, adaptation may refer to the adaptation of a population to a given surrounding, or it may refer to the adaptation of an individual after a change in situation, in which case it is better to use the term *acclimatization*.

Natural selection leads to adaptations in a population; human genetic variation provided by ancient or recent mutations means selection has acted automatically to favor advantageous mutations and eliminate ones that do not favor a population living in a given environment; and so phenotypes have diversified in dissimilar biomes. Mutations that are favored in the Arctic environment are not favored in the tropics. Natural selection guarantees the survival of the best adapted to a specific set of conditions, the most important of which are climate, food supply and disease resistance. To sum up, external appearance is the result of life's tendency to try to reduce stress.

Despite the flexibility of humans, which has given them the means of surviving in very diverse climates, they need specific conditions of temperature, sunlight, humidity, etc. If these conditions move far beyond optimal values, this leads to physiological stress, which sets off a series of mechanisms intended to maintain homeostasis. This complex of reactions to restore homeostasis should be considered as acclimatization, discussed briefly above. *Acclimatization* is the organism's response to relatively sudden changes and does not involve genetic change, unlike adaptation. As human beings are warm-blooded, they have had to develop mechanisms to lose heat if the external temperature rises and to generate heat if the temperature goes down. In the same way, they also have mechanisms to maintain body moisture and other mechanisms to block ultraviolet radiation, a possible cause of mutations, but allow enough UV rays to pass for vitamin D synthesis to occur. This is why humans sweat, shiver, have wide or narrow noses, and get suntans in the summer. (See the chapter on human adaptations to high temperatures in volume 4.)

Acclimatization is thus an individual physiological response to a change in external conditions. When a human group has remained long enough in a given place, climatic conditions have favored some characteristics, the ones that are most suitable in these surroundings, so that the most successful individuals will be those with the phenotypes most suited to their climate and food sources or those most resistant to diseases. Thus, climate, not ancestry, has shaped human beings; the "design" of an individual's body reflects only where his or her ancestors lived. As human populations that have lived in the forests since antiquity have been subject to natural selection, their appearance has adapted to the climate. The most important changes in their morphology have affected the pigmentation of the skin (a defense against excessive sunshine), the width of the nose (a response to hot, wet, environments) and stature, which some authors also consider a consequence of the rainforest climate.

Skin color

Human populations living in the planet's tropical regions usually have dark skins. This protects the skin against ultraviolet radiation, much stronger in these latitudes than farther north or south. The mechanism by which human skin pigmentation has been selected is still unclear, and it is speculated that the ancestral forms might have had dark skin beneath their hair. Yet it seems that near the equator natural selection has favored phenotypes with skins possessing a protective layer to block ultraviolet radiation and to prevent photochemical damage, such as skin cancer or hypervitaminosis caused by excess vitamin D production. As human groups left Africa and moved to higher latitudes, the individuals with lighter skin benefitted in some ways; the relative lack of pigmentation in populations outside the tropics is thus a secondary characteristic, as light skins had a selective advantage in latitudes with less ultraviolet radiation as they were better at vitamin D synthesis; light skins were selected because they did not suffer from lack of vitamin D. In any case, selection continues to act, as in cases where light-skinned populations have returned relatively recently to the tropics in human evolutionary terms. For example, the nearer some Amerindian and some Polynesian peoples have lived to the equator and the longer they have lived there, the darker the color of their skin.

Vitamins and skin color

Vitamin D, or antirickets factor, is very scarce in normal foodstuffs (although fish, and especially fish-liver oil, is rich in it), but it is synthesized by the action of ultraviolet radiation on a steroid, 7-dehydrocholesterol, present in the lower layers of human skin. Vitamin D is essential for the metabolism of calcium and of phosphorus; it controls

116 A Barasana youth decorating a communal house or *maloca* in the Colombian Amazon, in the region of Vaupés. Malocas are the typical dwellings of the Amazonian indians. Those of the Barasana and Tukano are square with sides more than 66 ft (20 m) long, and walls about 23 ft (7 m) high, with a two-sided, sloped roof made of palm leaves. The front part is covered by a wall built with split palm trunks fastened with cross-beams of the same material, with a door in its center, the men's door. The side walls are at right angles and are enclosed to a height of about 7 ft (2 m) by interwoven screens of palm leaf. At the other end is a door for the women and children to enter the *maloca*. The center of the construction, within the main pillars supporting the roof, is a ritual space where they place the torches that light the inside at night on an empty tree trunk. They also use this trunk for making *chicha*, an alcoholic drink the Tukano obtain by fermenting cassava. The rounded rear space is the women's workplace and leisure space, while the side walls are lined by the private spaces of each of the eight or ten families living in the *maloca*. This is only a general account, and each ethnic group has its own type of *maloca*.
[Photo: Brian Moser / The Hutchinson Library]

117 Distribution of skin color before the great migrations of the last few centuries. Natural selection was responsible for the distribution of skin color before the major human voyages and migrations of the last 500 years. Many racists with white skins should remember that their not-so-distant ancestors had dark skins.
[Drawing: Editrònica, from data provided by the authors]

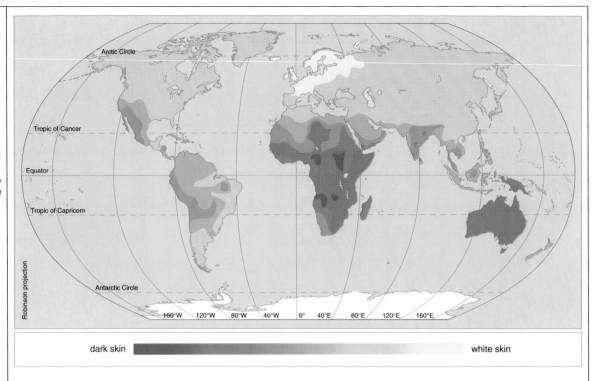

Arctic Circle
Tropic of Cancer
Equator
Tropic of Capricorn
Antarctic Circle
Robinson projection

160°W 120°W 80°W 40°W 0° 40°E 80°E 120°E 160°E

dark skin ▬▬▬▬▬▬ white skin

the absorbtion of calcium by the intestines, regulates its excretion by the kidneys and partly controls mineral deposition in the bones of the skeleton and, thus, normal growth in children. Children lacking enough vitamin D (hypovitaminosis) do not show adequate calcification of the skeleton during their growth, and this leads to deformations, mainly of the legs and pelvis, known as rickets, that may even lead to death. Mild cases of rickets in women may lead to problems in giving birth due to reduction of the birth canal. Excess vitamin D (hypervitaminosis) is also dangerous, because it leads to calcification of soft tissues and disturbances in kidney function.

Ultraviolet radiation is necessary for vitamin D synthesis but represents a risk of sunburn and skin cancer. Humans with dark skins rarely suffer from skin cancer, while relatively unpigmented populations show higher rates the nearer they live to the equator. As an example, in the population of the British Isles (about 55°N), the rate of skin cancer is about 28 cases per 100,000 persons in men and around 15 per 100,000 in women, while in the population of British origin living in South Africa (around 30°S) it is 133 and 72 cases respectively. The white population of Queensland, Australia (about 20°S), also mainly of British origin, has rates reaching 265 and 156 cases per 100,000 respectively.

It has been suggested that dark skin would not be a useful adaptation against excess radiation for rainforest dwellers, as they live in a habitat where the light reaching the ground is attenuated by the thick filter of plants. In fact, most rainforest dwellers are exposed to high levels of sunshine. Except for some exclusively hunter-gatherer populations that are constantly moving through the rainforest, most rainforest populations practice some form of agriculture. They clear spaces for crops and their settlements and spend most of their time working or resting there. Furthermore, most of the nonagricultural peoples chose sites on riverbanks, in clearings, or in forest margins for their activities and settlements, however provisional they may be.

The African continent is the home of the populations with the darkest skin coloration. The pigmentation of the melanoafricans is determined by the size of the melanosomes (twice the size of melanosomes in white Europeans), but these skins differ in more than their color: the dermis is tougher, the upper (corneous) layer is thicker, and the sweat glands are more active than in white skin.

Melanins and other skin pigments

The color of human skin depends mainly on the production of melanins (eumelanin and phaeomelanin), dark brown pigments produced by melanocytes, special cells with ramified extensions found on the border between the dermis and the epidermis. These compounds are derived from

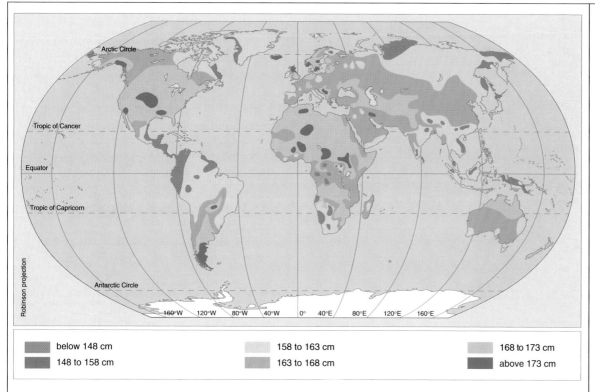

118 **Distribution of average human height before the great migrations of the last few centuries**. The morphological relationship between the shortest populations (red dots) reflects a phylogenetic (evolutionary) relationship; the local Negrito race in the Philippines and the low-stature populations of southeast Asia are descendants of the first wave of human beings to leave Africa, and are closely related to the Pygmies of the African rainforest, and more distantly, to the San, or Kalahari Bushmen. *[Drawing: Editrònica, from data provided by the authors]*

below 148 cm	158 to 163 cm	168 to 173 cm
148 to 158 cm	163 to 168 cm	above 173 cm

tyrosine, as are some neurotransmitters, and their production is stimulated by the action of hormones secreted by the hypophysis, especially *melanocyte stimulating hormone* (MSH).

The number of melanocytes varies little between individuals and between populations (around 1,500 per mm²), but varies greatly from one part of an individual's body to another. Melanocytes are most common on the face and on the back and least common on the lower trunk and the palms of the hands and feet, and their number is slightly lower in women than in the men of a single population. Members of populations with dark skin may have melanocytes in their peritoneum and darker retinas than individuals with lighter skin do. The quantity of melanin also varies with age: children are always born with less pigmentation than adults of the same group; the increase in MSH secretion occurs when they reach prepuberty. Melanins are synthesized in the melanocytes in the form of granules that are then transferred to the cells at the bottom of the epidermis, whose number, size and the way they are grouped determine skin color.

Other pigments, such as carotenes and hemoglobins, also influence the final color of an individual's skin, which is also affected by factors such as state of health (in anemia the skin is much paler, jaundice [icterus] leads to yellowness of the skin, and in serious liver or bile disorders, the skin may acquire a brownish tone); in pregnancy there is usually an increase in melanin deposition, especially in the areola of the nipple and on the abdominal midline. Skin color is also affected by environmental temperature, body pH, and the levels of vitamins A, B, C, and D and metals (copper and zinc).

The question of size

Clearly, the people living in the rainforest, where the climate is very wet, tend to be short. This is true of the Pygmies in Africa and in India, southern Indonesia, Philippines and New Guinea, the Mayans of Central America, and the inhabitants of the Brazilian rainforest. In an environment where the relative humidity is 100% (saturation), sweating, which is the human body's main mechanism to get rid of excess heat, is almost or totally ineffective; the sweat cannot evaporate easily and remains liquid, so sweating does not cool the body. Although they are not closely genetically related, all these populations share an unusual body size, habitat (the rainforest), and hunter-gatherer lifestyles. They also probably share the fact of being descendants of the first populations of modern humans to leave Africa and reach the different regions where they now live, although they have been relegated to marginal areas by successive expansions of other more powerful populations (see the chapter on the history of the population of Africa in volume 3).

119 Incisive tattooing, practiced by black African populations, relies on the scarring response of the conjunctive tissue of melanoderm skin. This leads to raised keloids, prominent scars, that form a kind of bas-relief on the cut skin. This practice is declining, but is still practiced in some groups following relatively traditional lifestyles. This photo was taken in 1907 and shows a Bakuba woman from Kasai (Democratic Republic of Congo), whose abdomen is very elaborately tattooed. These tattoos served to identify individuals as members of a group and to distinguish them from other groups (see figure 162).

[Photo: Royal Anthropological Society, London]

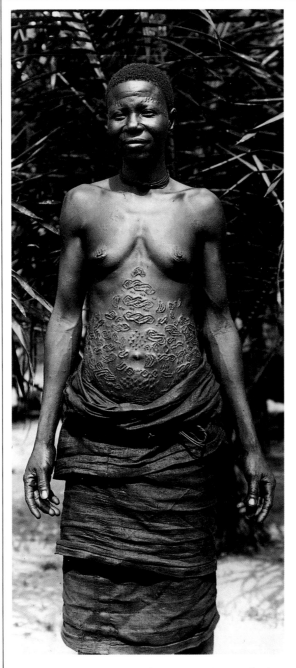

Pygmies and other diminutive humans have a further advantage: Their small size means they have less muscle mass, especially in the arms and legs, so they produce less body heat, and thus their metabolic expenditure to maintain homeostatic heat balance is less. It takes less effort for a Pygmy to move than for a larger individual, as the weight to be moved is less. It is not known if these populations have grown shorter over time, or if they have always been short. It seems the phenomenon might have been caused by the lack of response by the tissues to the *growth hormone* (GH) after puberty, when the adolescent growth spurt occurs in other human populations.

Some authors do not agree with this explanation for the short stature of rainforest dwellers, as not all the small-statured human populations live in the rainforest, and furthermore the Pygmies of equatorial Africa were displaced into the rainforest by the expansion of the Bantu 3,000 years ago, a very short time for such a large change; they previously exploited the rainforest-savannah ecotone. Discounting the theory that argues for the low height of rainforest-dwellers as a means of moving with greater ease through the dense branches, these paradoxes, they say, seem to indicate the existence of an evolutionary explanation in addition to that related to body temperature. This proposed evolutionary explanation is that the low availability of food for humans in the rainforest has maintained selection pressure on the pygmoid groups (short-statured human populations, but not necessarily Pygmies): Small individuals need less food to maintain themselves, and this explanation would also be valid for the Khoisan of the Kalahari desert, short-statured humans who do not live in rainforests.

The humidity of the rainforest

Populations that have lived in the rainforest since antiquity—the Pygmies are again a good example—have the widest noses in the world. This is also an adaptation to climatic conditions; the warm, moist air of the rainforest does not change when it is breathed into the body; all that can happen is some cooling when the air enters through the wide base of the nose, passing over the upper lip and evaporating some sweat.

The nasal index, the ratio of the width to the length of a person's nose, is mainly conditioned by selection factors due to variations in environmental humidity. The highest nasal indexes (and also the highest degree of variability, that recorded in the desert Bedouin) are found in Africa, especially among Pygmy groups. The nasal index of the Australian Aborigines is among the highest in the world, and the American rainforest-dwellers have the highest nasal index in the entire continent. This phenomenon of climate-related morphological convergence illustrates the fact that the width of the nose tends to be greater where the air is warmer and moister.

Other morphological differences

Dark-colored individuals, especially the melano-Africans, have thicker skin, with better blood and a greater number of sweat glands than do leucoderms.

Dark skins resist strong sunshine, parasitic attacks, and high temperatures better, but in cases of freezing (for example among U.S. servicemen of African origin in Alaska) they suffer more damage than the skin of leucoderms. Thick skin is due to the development of the skin's conjunctive tissue, clearly seen when scarring occurs as the scars are usually hypertrophic and keloid (i.e. they show excessive and raised fibrous growth). This type of scarring is culturally used by some African groups in tribal identifying marks; using sharp instruments they perform incisions in a geometric form, and on healing they leave a pattern that distinguishes one group from another.

The hair of the melanoafricans and other colored populations of the rainforest is short and frizzy, forming small curls tightly borne on the head. In cross section they are flattened oval, or reniform, in shape, and are intensely pigmented; except for albinos, they are always very black. This is thought to be to protect the cranium from possible photochemical (actinic) lesions.

1.4 Health and illness in the rainforest

The health problems of human populations in the rainforest are very different and have very different origins. They are related not only to environmental conditions but also to the social and sanitary conditions of the people of the Third World as a whole. The extreme biodiversity of the biome, however, is also shown by the wide and complex range of pathogenic agents, sometimes highly local, that affect humans and other organisms. There are some infectious, or transmissible, illnesses that are exclusive to the rainforest biome, and others that mainly occur there.

The main infections and their means of transmission

Many tropical diseases are transmitted through the digestive tract, almost always by infected water or food. Amoebic dysentery (caused mainly by the protoctist *Entamoeba histolytica*), ankylostomiasis (caused by the nematodes *Necator americanus* and *Ancylostoma duodenale*, which can both also be transmitted through the skin), ascariadiasis (caused by the nematode *Ascaris lumbricoides*), gnathosto-

miasis (caused by the nematode *Gnathostoma spinigerum*), giardiasis (caused by the protoctist *Giardia lamblia*), etc., are not exclusive to the rainforest but are common there, as are typhoid fever, bacterial dysentery and different forms of hepatitis. There is also the special case of trematode infections caught by eating infected snails or fish, specifically angiostrongyloidosis (caused by *Angiostrongylus cantonensis* and *A. costaricensis*), closely related to skin-transmitted schistosomiasis. There are also cases of cholera, especially in southeast Asia, and this disease is discussed in volume 3.

There are also diseases that are transmitted through the skin or the mucous membranes. Perhaps the most important in the rainforest biome is schistosomiasis, or bilharziasis, which are caught through contact with freshwater containing snails of the genera *Bulinus*, *Biomphalaria* and *Oncomelenia* that are infected by the trematodes responsible (*Schistosoma haematobium*, *S. japonicum*, etc.). Other important diseases include other forms of ankylostomiasis (mentioned above), strongyloidosis (produced by the trematode *Strongyloides stercoralis*), sexually transmitted diseases, some serious viral diseases that generally cause hemorrhagic fever, non-venereal treponematosis, especially *pian* (caused by the spirochaete *Treponema pertenue*) and *pinta* (caused by *T. caretum*).

The most important diseases are those transmitted by a vector, such as an insect or other arthropod, and especially the many different types of mosquito. By far the most frequent vector-spread disease is malaria, but there are others: trypanosomiasis, yellow fever, dengue and other viral fevers, and some forms of filariasis. Leishmaniasis is caused by different protoctists of the genera *Leishmania* and also has an insect vector; one form, kala-azar, is discussed in the section on monsoon forests.

Malaria

Malaria is a parasitic infection of the red blood cells and causes typical bouts of shivering, fever and sweating, swelling of the spleen, and anemia. The parasites are species of the protozoan *Plasmodium*, protoctists belonging to the apicomplex subtype (and called until 1984 sporozoites) whose complicated life cycle includes an asexual phase that parasitizes vertebrates and another stage, including the sexual and sporogenous phas-

120 Distribution of malaria and sickle-cell anemia, two common tropical diseases, the first infectious and the second genetic. Since the mid-Pleistocene, during the last ice ages, humans have suffered from malaria, or ague, a disease caused by protoctists of the genus *Plasmodium* that are transmitted by mosquitoes of the genus *Anopheles*. This mosquito can breed in any wetland (lakes, pools or even abandoned containers) and the parasite is transmitted by the bite of the female mosquito. Malaria, which can still result in death, was in the past a major cause of mortality, especially after the Neolithic. Some mutations in the gene for hemoglobin mean the plasmodium cannot develop normally in the red blood cells, so the people who are carriers of these genes have been positively selected in areas where malaria is endemic.

[Drawing: Editrònica, from data provided by the authors]

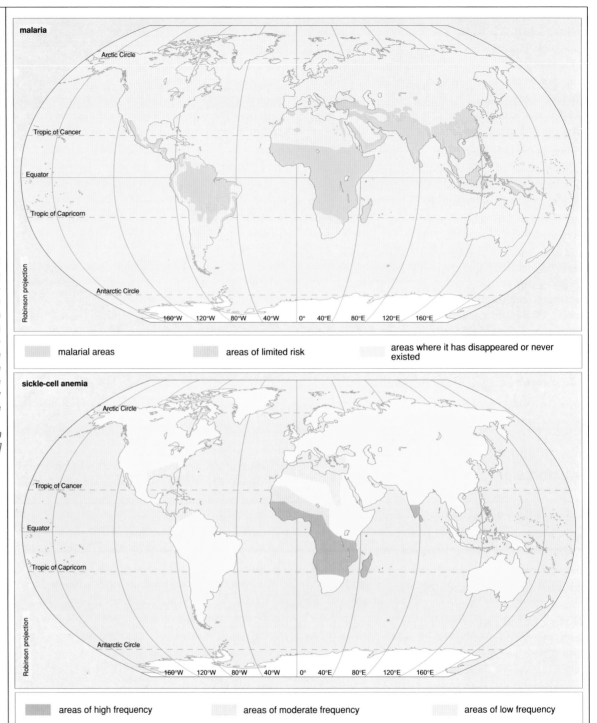

malaria

| malarial areas | areas of limited risk | areas where it has disappeared or never existed |

sickle-cell anemia

| areas of high frequency | areas of moderate frequency | areas of low frequency |

es, that parasitizes the arthropods (mainly mosquitoes and ticks) that are the disease's vectors. Now considered an essentially tropical disease, malaria was until recently widespread in all wetlands in warm and hot areas. It was endemic throughout the Mediterranean Basin until the mid-20th century and there are still some isolated foci of infection in the eastern Mediterranean and in the Mahgreb. At the end of the 1940s there were still some foci in the Rhine Delta, in the Netherlands. Apart from isolated spots in some countries with a temperate climate, malaria is now a tropical disease that affects mainly rainforest areas, where it is hyperendemic (more than 100 million cases a year).

The malaria life cycle

The plasmodia that cause malaria have two hosts, human beings and mosquitoes of the genus *Anopheles*. The asexual phase that occurs in humans begins with a bite by an infected mosquito (a female *Anopheles*) and the inoculation of the *sporozoites* (elongated cells with unusual structures at the apex, known as the *apical complex*).

The sporozoites penetrate a liver cell, where they grow into another type of cell, the schizont, which divides by multiple fission (this process is typical of the apicomplex and some groups of protoctists). The schizont gives rise by budding to many cells, similar to the sporozoites, called *merozoites*. In the case of the malaria plasmodium, these invade the red blood cells, at whose expense they in turn grow into schizonts that can repeat the process several times, releasing successive generations of merozoites into the bloodstream of the infected person. Some merozoites do not, however, develop into schizonts, but give rise to sexual forms that remain within the human red blood cells. If a female *Anopheles* ingests some of these erythrocytes in a bite, the sexual phase of the plasmodium's life cycle can then take place in her stomach, leading to the formation of new sporozoites.

Plasmodium and fevers

Malaria's characteristic attacks of chills, fever and sweat occur when the merozoites are released by the rupture of the affected red blood cells and occur with a rhythm that is typical for each species: every 48 hours in the case of *P. ovale* and *P. vivax* (tertian fevers) and every 72 hours in *P. malariae* (quartan fevers), although in *P. falciparum* they occur at brief and undefined intervals, most often 48 hours (malignant tertian fevers). For centuries the preferred antimalarial treatment has been quinine (see "The Viceroy's Wife's Fever," pages 374-377), but no vaccine was developed until a team of Colombian doctors under Dr. Patarroyo prepared the first "synthetic" vaccine in 1993, a vaccine that has been tested with encouraging effects.

Of the four main species of *Plasmodium* that attack humans, the most widespread and dangerous is *P. falciparum*, which is the dominant species in Africa, in southeast Asia, and in some countries in the Americas and the only one that can be fatal, as it may cause acute and serious neurological, renal or cardiovascular complications. This species is considered to have evolved more recently as a human parasite, and it cannot remain latent in the sufferer's tissues to cause a recurrence a few years later. The other species can remain latent (*P. ovale* and *P. vivax* survive in the liver and *P. malariae* in the red blood cells). Thus, paradoxically, in areas intensely infested by *P. falciparum*, especially in Asia and the Americas, infections by this species in adults who survived a childhood infection by this parasite may be less serious than those caused by *P. vivax*, which is less virulent. *P. ovale*, an exclusively African species and characteristic of forested areas, seems to be the most highly host-adapted of the species of *Plasmodium*; it causes benign infections, with frequent relapses and is almost unaffected by eradication or control campaigns. The malaria produced by *P. malariae* is also more benign. Other species of *Plasmodium* cause illness in primates, birds and other animals, and mosquitoes are again the vectors.

The associated genetic anomalies

The long time that some human populations have lived with malaria has led to the selection of some spontaneous genetic anomalies causing the synthesis of abnormal hemoglobins. These may cause serious genetic diseases in some individuals but represent a protection against malaria for the population as a whole. This is true of the anomalies that produce sickle-cell anemia and thalassemia.

Sickle-cell anemia mainly affects the populations of western and central Africa, eastern Anatolia, the Arabian Peninsula and India, and consists of the presence in the red blood cells of sickle-cell hemoglobin, hemoglobin S, with a changed amino-acid sequence (valine instead of glutamic acid) in the ß-chain. This apparently insignificant alteration leads to a characteristic deformation of the red blood cells, which become sickle-shaped; during physical exercise or any other circumstance giving rise to high oxygen demand, the hemoglobin molecules precipitate and the sickle-shaped red blood cells elongate. They may then block the capillaries, leading to their destruction by the body's immune system, until the typical symptoms of anemia appear, with all their consequences.

This alteration is the result of a recessive mutation in a specific gene on an autosomic chromosome, so it is inherited but is not sex linked. One of every four descendants of a couple that are both carriers of the recessive gene is homozygotic, in which case the disease manifests itself. Two of the four descendants will be heterozygotes, carriers and potential transmitters, but they will be relatively resistant to malaria, and the fourth will neither suffer nor transmit the disease. When the heterozygotes are infected by *Plasmodium*, the infected red blood cells become sickle-shaped more easily, restricting the exchange of potassium ions, causing the parasite to die. This explains why such a lethal genetic anomaly is maintained in some populations: it will defend two out of every four descendants of a pair of carriers against an even more dangerous parasite, at the cost of one victim. This selection pressure also explains the differing levels of this gene in African (around 40%) and Afroamerican (around 9%) populations; African populations are still in permanent contact

121 **The world distribution of yellow fever, filariasis and trypanosomiasis**. The development of infectious diseases in the tropics is related to many factors, not only ecological ones. Serious social problems, poverty, and wars do not allow effective information and vaccination campaigns in precisely the countries in which infection rates are highest.

[Drawing: Editrònica, from data provided by the authors]

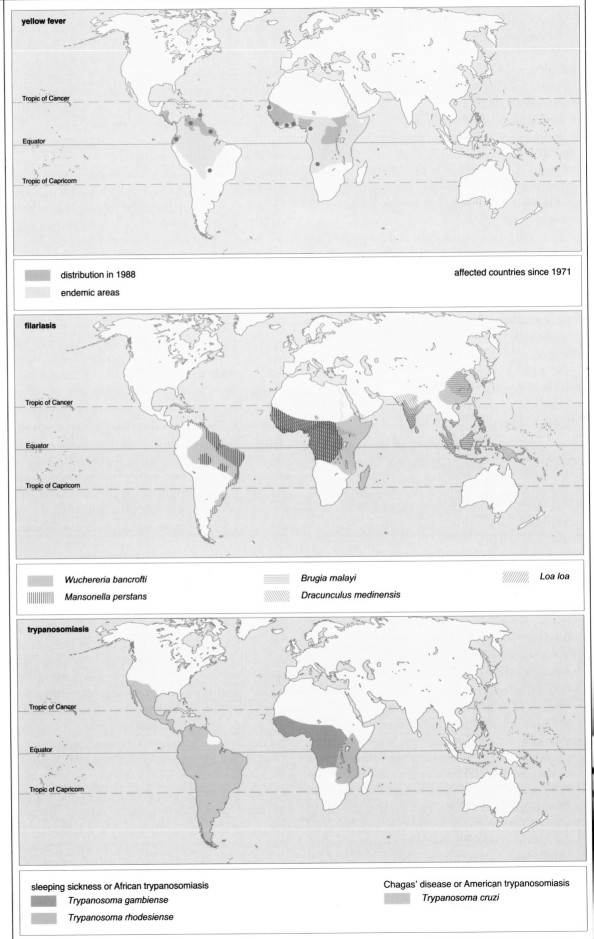

yellow fever

Tropic of Cancer

Equator

Tropic of Capricorn

distribution in 1988

endemic areas

affected countries since 1971

filariasis

Tropic of Cancer

Equator

Tropic of Capricorn

Wuchereria bancrofti

Mansonella perstans

Brugia malayi

Dracunculus medinensis

Loa loa

trypanosomiasis

Tropic of Cancer

Equator

Tropic of Capricorn

sleeping sickness or African trypanosomiasis

Trypanosoma gambiense

Trypanosoma rhodesiense

Chagas' disease or American trypanosomiasis

Trypanosoma cruzi

with *Plasmodium*, but the AfroAmericans are not, and so the lethal effect of the mutation prevails over the useless protection from a nonexistent parasite.

In populations of the Mediterranean Basin, southern India, southeast Asia, and New Guinea there is a frequent genetic anomaly that confers resistance to malaria, but which affects a different site in the amino-acid sequence of the ß-chain and leads to the presence in the red blood cell of the protein called hemoglobin E. Thalassemia in the Mediterranean Basin is discussed on page 212 of volume 5.

Yellow fever and dengue fever

Yellow fever is another tropical disease transmitted by mosquito bites. Fever starts suddenly, accompanied by an intense headache and general illness. The fever subsides after three or four days and then returns, accompanied by jaundice due to liver necrosis and often by black vomiting of blood and bile. Mortality is high in adults and much lower in children, because in regions where the disease is endemic, they often have antibodies without having suffered the illness, just by having been in contact with the pathogen.

Yellow fever is originally a disease of monkeys (and apparently in the Americas, the didelphid marsupials) that may sporadically infect some humans if they are bitten by the vectors of the virus, mosquitos of the genus *Haemagogus* (*H. spegazzinii*, *H. equinus*) in the American forests and of the genus *Aedes* (*A. africanus*, *A. simpsoni*) in the African rainforest. When a carrier reaches a human settlement where the species *Aedes aegypti* (a species closely linked to human communities) occurs, then yellow fever may enter an epidemic phase. Its name might suggest it is restricted to Africa, but in fact *A. aegypti* occurs in all the world's tropical and subtropical regions, mainly in Africa and the Americas, but also in India, Malaysia and northern Australia.

In the American tropics, the great epidemics of yellow fever were especially devastating, and in the 19th century epidemics even affected cities as far from the tropics as Philadelphia and Boston. Although its epidemic form has hardly occurred for many years, its forest form is endemic in many rainforest regions, mainly in Africa, and it is not possible to rule out outbreaks in human communities in contact with populations of *A. aegypti*. In 1985, the Asiatic mosquito *A. albopictus*, which is a vector of

dengue but also of yellow fever, accidentally spread from Japan to the United States, and since then yellow fever has reappeared in some cities in the American tropics. It has also had a comeback in Africa as a result of the renewed activity of *A. aegypti* and the presence of the recently arrived *A. albopictus* and has increased from a few hundred cases in the 1970s to many thousands in the 1990s.

Dengue is another viral disease that is transmitted by mosquitoes of the genus *Aedes*, mainly *A. aegypti* (and now *A. albopictus*, too). The symptoms consists of fever, generalized pains in the joints and muscles, and a rash on the face, arms and chest on the fifth day of the disease. In some cases, mainly in children and especially in southeast Asia and New Guinea, it may also lead to hemorrhagic fever. Other viral hemorrhagic fevers are also transmitted by mosquito bites, such as *chicunguña* fever and several forms of viral encephalitis.

Filariasis

In addition to *Plasmodium* and virus, mosquitos may also be the vectors, in the rainforest, of other important parasites, such as some filaria worms (*Wucheria bancrofti*, *Dracunculus medinensis*, *Brugia malayi*, *Loa loa*, *Onchocerca volvulus*, *Mansonella perstans*, etc.). The vectors of *W. bancrofti* may be any of several mosquitoes (*Aedes polinesiensis*, *A. fijensis* and *Culex cinquefasciculatus* in the most easterly islands of the tropical Pacific, *Anopheles punctulatus* in New Guinea, the Melanesian archipelagoes and the most westerly Polynesian archipelagoes, *A. gambiae*, *A. funestus* and *A. melas* in Africa and *A. darlingi* in South America). *Brugia malayi* is mainly transmitted by mosquitos of the genera *Mansonia* (*M. annulifera*, *M. uniformis* and *M. longipalpis*) and some species of *Anopheles* (*A. barbirostris*).

Filaria worms are parasitic nematodes whose larvae, called microfilaria, are transmitted by arthropods (mosquitoes, horseflies (tabanids) and black-flies (simuliids). When the larvae grow into adults they may invade the lymph vessels and glands, causing inflammation of the limbs and the male sexual organs, accompanied by shivering, fever, pain and general illness. If the illness becomes chronic, the obstruction of the lymph vessels by the numerous parasites may lead to elephantiasis, which is also localized, mainly in the lower limbs and, in men, in the scrotum.

Trypanosomiasis

Trypanosomiasis are tropical diseases caused by protoctists of the genus *Trypanosoma*. They basically affect livestock, but some species produce disease in humans, although there is always an intermediate host, either a domesticated or wild animal, in their complex life cycles.

Trypanosomiasis in Africa

In the African tropics there are high levels of a human trypanosomiasis, known as sleeping sickness. In fact this is two different diseases, the first in dry savanna areas and the second in the wet areas more-or-less corresponding to the rainforest. In both cases, the cycle involves an intermediate carrier host (wild ruminants and domesticated pigs, respectively) and a dipteran fly vector, the tse-tse fly (*Glossina morsitans* and *G. palpalis*, respectively). Eastern, or savanna, sleeping sickness is caused by *Trypanosoma brucei rhodesiense*, and is discussed in volume 3. In the rainforest, the most common form is the less serious western sleeping sickness, transmitted by *Glossina palpalis* from the domesticated pig or from dogs. Once they reach the bloodstream of a person bitten by an infected mosquito, the trypanosomes attack the lymphatic system, causing fevers and eventually affecting the central nervous system, leading to aboulia and somnolence that in many cases leads to death, although it is almost never fatal immediately. To sum up, it is a serious zoonotic (communicable from animals to people) disease that, including both forms of the disease, is present permanently in about 200 loci of infection with about 50 million people at constant risk of infection.

Trypanosomiasis in the Americas

In the Americas, trypanosomiasis affects the rural areas of the entire continent from Mexico southwards, but it is especially common in the rainforests of Central America and Colombia. There it is known as Chagas' disease, in honour of the Brazilian physician Carlos Justiniano Chagas (1879-1934), who worked out its precise etiology in 1909.

Chagas' disease is caused by *Trypanosoma* [=*Schizotrypanum*] *cruzi* and is transmitted to humans and other mammals by the heteropteran triatomid *Triatoma infestans*, a blood-sucking bug known throughout South America as the *vinchuca*. Other triatomids are also vectors of the protoctist pathogen, such as *T. dimidiata*, *Rhodnius prolixus*, *Panstrongylus megistus*, but they are of less importance, essentially because they do not have domestic habits. Unusually, the vinchuca has adapted to life in human communities, especially huts and cabins with a roof of plant fiber, where they nest. The vinchuca bites any mammal it can, and may infect them all, as well as birds, reptiles and amphibians, which become carriers but do not develop the disease. Humans contract this trypanosomiasis when bitten by infected vinchucas, through blood transfusions from infected persons or through the placenta. This is highly possible as the trypanosomes may remain in the blood stream of the sufferers for a long time. If infection occurs, after an incubation period of 1-3 weeks, the blood stream is full of parasites, and the illness shows its severe form (fever, general illness). Especially in children, the mortality rate is high (up to 13%). If the sufferer survives, he or she will be symptom-free for 10-20 years, and during this period may infect other vinchucas, while developing myocarditis, meningo-encephalitis, ophthalmia, and swelling of the internal organs. The prognosis for a symptomatic chronic sufferer, and their prognosis is very serious. This trypanosomiasis is the cause of most heart disease in the rainforest biome.

The acquired immune-deficiency syndrome (AIDS)

The origin of AIDS is uncertain, as was that of syphilis 500 years ago, and that is still unresolved. AIDS has recently spread as a pandemic, ending a relatively long period in which humanity had almost forgotten what worldwide pandemics were like. The acquired immune-deficiency syndrome was first described in 1981, although the first signs of the epidemic, which were not identified as such, appear to have occurred in California and New York in the mid-1970s.

Although the earliest signs of the current AIDS pandemic appeared in North America, it is almost certainly of African origin and from the rainforest. It is transmitted by the HIV-1 retrovirus (Human Immunodeficiency Virus-1), which is similar to other members of the same group that have been isolated from monkeys, mainly STLV-III (Simian T Lymphotrophic Virus III) which has been found in wild populations of the grivet-guenon monkey (*Cercopithecus sabaeus*) and in 1998 in the mortal remains of a female chimpanzee (*Pan troglodytes troglodytes*) raised in captivity. Antibodies to HIV have been found in blood donation made in 1959 by a person in Belgian Congo (present-day Democratic Republic of Congo),

122 The rapid spread of AIDS, probably from the African rainforest, is a major global phenomenon in the last quarter of the 20th century. It was first recognized when it appeared in the United States, from where it spread to Europe and the rest of the world. The African continent is by far the worst affected. This is because it is the cradle of the disease and the cultural difficulties of introducing preventive measures. The photo shows an educational session in a women's collective on the correct use of the condom, as part of a campaign against AIDS.
[Photo: Arkell Katie / Gamma]

and the illness seems to have appeared, long before in small isolated populations in the African rainforest. The highest levels of AIDS are in subSaharan Africa, where the number of infected people is estimated to exceed 23 million people, in sharp contrast to the half million in Western Europe, 890,000 in North America and 8.7 million in the rest of the world. Not all those infected develop the illness, but their death rate is much higher than that of the general population. Many epidemiologists consider that the possibility of contagion was limited while the initially infected populations had little or no contact with the outside world, but when these contacts became common this allowed the formation of reservoir of infection large enough to unleash the current pandemic. The epidemic spread among intravenous drug addicts and European and North American male homosexuals, but there is now a tendency for it to increase among the heterosexual population.

The HIV infection has a wide range of pathological manifestations. Many infected persons may not develop any symptoms for years, maybe more than 10 years. In other cases, they start to show nonspecific symptoms, such as fever, skin eruptions, and general illness, from the moment they begin to produce antibodies. What distinguishes AIDS is that it affects the sufferer's immune system—above all as a consequence of the destruction of a special type of lymphocyte, the T-4 cooperator-inducer—and this makes the individual much more vulnerable to opportunistic pathogens that rarely affect people with a normal immune system (such as the rhizopod *Pneumocystis carinii*, coccidia of the genera *Cryptosporidium* and *Toxoplasma*, fungi such as *Candida albicans*, herpes virus of the cytomegalovirus group, etc.). They are also susceptible to some uncommon tumors, such as Kaposi's sarcoma, or Burkitt's lymphoma, which is especially common among AIDS sufferers in Africa.

In a short time, AIDS has ceased to be an unknown ailment and has become the most feared, controversial, and studied of all diseases. It is transmitted across the mucous membranes and in bodily fluids, and so the main risk of infection is through transfusion of contaminated blood and through contacts involving exchange of bodily fluids, thus AIDS is to some extent a sexually transmitted disease. Until 1981, AIDS was unknown to medicine. By 1983 at least two laboratories, one in France and the other in the United States, had isolated HIV-1 and the related HIV-2 was isolated in 1985 in western Africa. In 10 years AIDS has become a health risk throughout the planet, the object of preventive campaigns, research and social debate in many countries, especially in the United Sates, Europe and Africa. In some African countries, 20-40% of the sexually active population of some cities may be infected, and it has also spread widely through rural areas. In cities like Abidjan, where not a single case was recorded until 1983, AIDS was by 1993 the main cause of death in the male and female adult population. Social and economic factors help to accelerate the spread of AIDS; population movements caused by war and the search for work far from home foster frequent contacts between men and prostitutes, and the problem ceases to be exclusively medical, because when they return home temporarily they may infect their partners, who may in turn give birth to infected children; or they may return home to die. This leads to an alarming increase in the number of widows and orphans.

2. The use of plant resources

2.1 Harvesting without planting

The equatorial rainforest provides a wide range of useful plant resources that have traditionally satisfied the basic needs of its inhabitants, but are now increasingly important sources of income through local trade of forest products. Some of these products are internationally traded commodities of importance to the exporting country's economy. Much of this plant wealth is still unexplored, but the rainforest's vast potential as a storehouse of plant biodiversity is now being recognized.

The diversity and number of plants used by rainforest cultures is astounding. The Yukuna of Colombia, for example, use more than 160 different species of wild plants as wood for canoes or other materials to make household, hunting or fishing implements, or as building or decorative materials; they also obtain medicines, curare poisons for hunting, poisons for fishing, items for ritual practices or shamanism, dies to stain their body and even materials for their games. The most important plants, however, are the food plants.

Food plants

Some tropical crops of global importance originated in the rainforest. Some major crops—discussed later in the sections on agriculture—such as cocoa (*Theobroma cacao*), pineapples (*Ananas comosus*), bananas (*Musa*) and the oil palm (*Elaeis guineensis*), have been developed over many centuries of cultivation and selection and are now very different from their wild relatives.

Most kitchen spices, from black pepper to nutmeg, that are now cultivated on a large scale are derived from rainforest ancestors. The wild relatives of crop plants are often still important local food sources, as are many other plants gathered

123 **Collecting wild plants** for medicine, fruit or food is a custom deeply-rooted in many rainforest peoples. This Kenyah woman is collecting medicinal plants in the forest in Sarawak (Borneo).
[Photo: Nigel Dickinson / Still Pictures]

from the rainforest. Almost every plant form found in the rainforest is a possible food source for the indigenous peoples under certain conditions. Fungi, ferns, tubers, leaves and fruit are all collected, whether as basic foodstuffs, snacks, and flavorings, or as emergency foodstuffs in times of hardship.

CROP	ORIGIN	CURRENT PRODUCTION					
		Africa	Asia	Europe	America	Australia	Pacific
CEREALS							
rice (*Oryza sativa*)	Asia	*[1]	***		**		
maize (*Zea mays*)	America		**	±	***		
STARCHY ROOTS AND TUBERS							
cassava (*Manihot esculenta*)	America	***	***		*		
sweet potato (*Ipomoea batatas*)	America	**	***		*		
yams (*Dioscorea alata*)	Africa	***	**				*
SWEETENERS							
sugar cane (*Saccharum officinarum*)	Asia		**		***	*	
OIL PRODUCING PLANTS							
peanut (*Arachis hypogaea*)	America	***	*		**		
coconut (*Cocos nucifera*)	Asia / Pacific		***		*		*
oil palm (*Elaeis guineensis*)	Africa	**	***		*		
VEGETABLES							
squash (*Cucurbita pepo*)	Africa?	**	*		***		
beans (*Phaseolus*)	America		**	*	***		
red pepper, chillies (*Capsicum annuum*)	America		**	*	***		
tomato (*Lycopersicon esculentum*)	America	*		**	***		
SWEET FRUIT[2]							
avocado (*Persea americana*)	America	**	*		***		
breadfruit (*Artocarpus*)	Asia / Pacific	*	***				**
macadamia (*Macadamia*)	Australia	**				***	*
mango (*Mangifera indica*)	Asia	*	***		**		
papaya (*Carica papaia*)	America	*	**		***		
pineapple (*Ananas comosus*)	America	*	***		**		
STIMULANTS							
coffee (*Coffea*)	Africa	**	*		***		
kola nuts (*Cola acuminata*)	Africa	***			**		
SPICES							
cinnamon (*Cinnamomum verum [=C. zeylanicum]*)	Asia	**[3]	***		*		
cloves (*Syzygium aromaticum*)	Asia	**	***		*		
nutmeg (*Myristica fragrans*)	Asia	*	***		**		
black pepper (*Piper nigrum*)	Asia	*	***		**		
vanilla (*Vanilla planifolia*)	America	***[3]	*		**		
OTHER CROPS							
caucho, rubber tree (*Hevea brasiliensis*)	America	**	***		*		
quinine (*Cinchona*)	America	***	*		**		

1. Much of the rice produced in western Africa is species of African origin. The main producer of true rice is Madagascar.

2. Table fruit, except for the macadamia, which is a nut.

3. Especially Madagascar and the islands in the Indian Ocean (the Comoros, Réunion)

124 The origin and spread of the world's most important tropical food plants. The table shows the crop's origin and the continents with the greatest production. The asterisks indicate the scale of production. [*Source: data provided by the authors*]

The limited food value of rainforest plants

One of the rainforest's basic characteristics, the chemical diversity of its plants, is an important limitation on human use of its resources. Many secondary metabolites have evolved to give the plant possessing them some degree of immunity from herbivores, parasites, or other pathogens. In very few biomes does the vegetation have such effective chemical defenses as in the tropical rainforest, suggesting its plants are subject to such intense selection pressure that they are forced to use some of their resources as chemical defenses. There are at least two reasons for this. The first is that in the rainforest it is hard to obtain both light and mineral resources due to the intense competition; so the tissues the plants have managed to grow are especially valuable and have to be defended. The second reason is that there is no winter, and so there are no seasonal "holidays" from predation, and no chance of growing and reproducing rapidly in the spring before the number of predators increases.

Over the millennia, the twin forces of the threat of being eaten and the subtler threat of starving to death have transformed the rainforest into an ecosystem full of poisons, where only the fittest or the most specialized can survive. The vegetation of the rainforest has an enormous range of secondary defensive compounds with different actions. Latex, resins and gums all obstruct the mouthparts of herbivores and phytohaemagglutinins coagulate their blood. Terpenoids and phenolic oils suppress neighboring plants and burn the skin of animals or cause cancer. Alkaloids, such as cocaine, caffeine, morphine, nicotine, mescaline and codeine act as neurotoxins. Compounds disguised as hormones, amino acids or vitamins alter animal physiology and may cause sterility or prevent development. Saponins break cell membranes, burst blood cells, and stop food absorption by the intestine. Cardenolides attack muscles, and some flavonoid poisons attack energy metabolism. Lignins and tannins—indigestible phenolic polymers—bind to cellulose and proteins, thus interfering with digestion and reducing the plant's food value to animals undeterred by their astringent taste.

Humans in rainforests have had to make a place for themselves to be able to live in this complex and dangerous environment. Their simple digestive systems cannot cope with most of the plant tissues in their biome, and they have to restrict themselves to picking pulpy mature fruit (undefended, and whose edibility is often displayed), meristems (small-celled formative plant tissue) and the storage organs they can reach with simple tools, or those foodstuffs that can be detoxified by cooking. Humans show great intelligence when seeking foodstuffs, but in the rainforest they have found few trustworthy plant foods, and where they are consumed, it is mostly because selected species are cultivated in small, cleared plots.

Subsistence gathering

Most rainforest dwellers in Amazonia practice some type of agriculture, with different varieties of cassava (*Manihot esculenta*) as staple crops but complemented with other cultivated species and many that are harvested from the rainforest. Here are some examples to show how many plants different peoples may collect: the Ka'apor people of Brazil are said to use 34 different species from a single 2.47 acre (1 ha) plot, while the Chaboco people use 38 species in an equivalent plot. The Kayapo people use about 250 species for their fresh fruit, and hundreds more for their nuts, tubers, and leaves. One of the most interesting cases is the milk-tree (*Brosimum galactodendron*, Moraceae), which can be tapped for its runny, white, and edible latex, long used by the Orinoco.

Wild plants continue to be the most important source of leafy vegetables in many tropical areas where itinerant, or shifting, agriculture is practiced. At least 1,650 rainforest plants contain about as much protein in their leaves as the seeds of leguminous plants, and are also an important source of vitamins. Of the many examples from Africa, one of the most important is the composite, made from *bologi* (*Crassocephalum biafrae*), a perennial climbing plant that is cultivated and collected from the wild in southern Nigeria and other countries of the Gulf of Guinea, and a wild African eggplant (*Solanum aethopicum*, Solanaceae) that is more important for its leaves than for its fruit.

The most important rainforest food in southeast Asian, especially in Papua New Guinea and Borneo, is wild or semiwild sago, extracted from the pith of *Metroxylon sagu* and other sago palms, such as *Eugeissona utilis*. Sago complements the traditionally cultivated plants, such as tapioca, maize and yams. Other food resources available in the rainforest throughout the year include the edible parts of some ferns (*Athyrium esculentum*, *Achrosticum aureum*, etc.) and some wild sweet potatoes (*Ipomoea*), roots, rhizomes and corms. Rainforest fruits, either seasonal or available all year round, are eaten fresh, roasted, boiled, made into cakes or preserved.

One example of a diet based exclusively on rainforest products is that of the Baroi people who live in the Purari River delta in Papua New Guinea and cultivate sago palm as their staple food crop, together with a range of fruit and vegetables. The Baroi also collect wild plants from the nearby rainforest and swamps: the shoots of the *Arenga* palm, the fronds of several ferns, the leaves of *Gnetum gnemon* and of species of *Ficus*, *Cassia*, *Morus* and *Evodia*. The fruit of the mangosteen and related species (*Garcinia*, Guttiferae), the fruit of *Myristica*, and Mlaya apple (*Syzygium malaccense*)—all add variety to their diet.

Large-scale collection

Collecting wild nuts may be of economic importance. This is true of trees whose products have a good market, but are not yet successfully cultivated in plantations. One example is the Brazil nut (*Bertholletia excelsa*, Lecythidaceae), an important item in the traditional diet of many Amazonian peoples and an economically important export for some American countries, like Bolivia, Brazil, and Peru.

In addition to the internationally important tropical fruits, there are many others of local or regional importance, both wild and cultivated. In some regions of Peru, for example, fruit from more than 200 species of plant, are regularly consumed, 120 of which are exclusively collected from the wild while another 19 are both collected and cultivated. More than 500 native and introduced fruits are eaten in Peninsular Malaysia, of which only 60 are cultivated. The durian (*Durio zibethinus*), popular throughout southeast Asia and famous for its delicious taste and unpleasant smell, is only known in the wild from Borneo and Sumatra. In Peninsular Malaya there are 13 species of the genus *Durio*, at least five of which have edible fruit. The fruit of the rambutan (*Nephelium lappaceum*), langsat (*Lansium domesticum*), rambai (*Baccaurea motleyana*) and rose-apple or jambu (*Syzygium jambos*) are also appreciated in the region. The mangosteen (*Garcinia mangostana*) grows wild in the rainforests of Indochina, Malaysia and Indonesia, although it is also cultivated in Sri Lanka, the Philippines and India. Most of the mangosteen sold in the countries of its natural distribution are harvested from the rainforest.

Some Amazonian palms are of proven value in the international market place. The cabbage palm (*Euterpe oleracea*) grows in dense populations in the estuarine areas of the Amazon rainforest near the city of Belem. Locally, its fruits are used to produce a drink, its roots for medicinal purposes, and its leaves and trunks for a wide range of uses. Its apical meristem is of economic importance as an expensive luxury food, the palm heart, whose extraction kills the palm. This has led to the destruction of entire populations of closely related species, such as the assai palm (*E. edulis*) in southeast Brazil, and threatens the huassi palm or *yuyu-chonta* (*E. precatoria*) in Peru. Fortunately, the cabbage palm is a species with many stems that produce new shoots with greater ease than these other palms.

125 Finding water fit to drink is not always easy in the rainforest. A traditional method is to drink the water stored in the tissues of some plants, such as this Brazilian liana in the basin of the Negro River, which produces abundant water when the vessels are cut with a machete.
[Photo: Francesc Serrat & Angela de Dalmau]

126 **The tender growing tips of several species of palm** of the genera *Acrocomia, Chamaedorea, Geonoma, Iriartea, Oenocarpus, Orbignya, Prestoea, Sabal,* and especially *Euterpe* are highly valued foodstuffs. The most appreciated is the palmito or juçara (*E. edulis*), and the upper photo shows the extraction of the palm heart in the Brazilian Mata Atlântica. The fruit of a species of the genus *Orbignya*, the babassu palm (*O. martiana*), are greatly valued for their oil and are shown in the lower photo taken in Maranhao (Brazil).
[Photos: Xavier Ferrer & Adolf de Sostoa and Luiz Claudio Marigo / Bruce Coleman Limited]

The *caboclos*, the name given in the Amazon to the local peasants of mixed descent, manage the assai palm in a way that produces a good crop of palm hearts and also increases fruit production. They obtain good income from the exploitation of a plant resource, selling the fruits and palm hearts, without overexploiting the species. The pataua palm (*Jessenia bataua*) also grows in the Amazon rainforest. The pulp of its purple fruit contains an oil of quality comparable to that of the olive. There is considerable interest in developing the cultivation of this species, and scientists from Colombia and Malaysia are working together to raise yields and improve other desirable characteristics.

There is now research into the potential of several rainforest trees, such as the Brazil nut, for sustainable production and sale. Two promising candidates from the Amazon rainforest are the babassu palm and the aguaje palm. The babassu palm (*Orbignya phalerata*) produces many items of use that can also be sold, and is of economic importance to many rural populations in the state of Maranhão, in the Brazilian Amazon. The edible parts are the palm's protein-rich kernel, which is similar to a small coconut and the oil it produces; the mesocarp, which is used to make flour; and the fronds and stems hearts, eaten as salad. Like many palms, the moriche palm (*Mauritia flexuosa*) is a dioecious plant, whose male and female flowers are on different unisexual plants. Its small, scaly fruit are oily and slightly acidic, and in Brazil and Peru they are used to flavor ice cream. The entire female plant is felled to collect the fruit, and so they are now sought further and further from market centers; unfortunately, the fruit rot easily and often spoil on the journey. The male plants also have products that the people of the rainforest use: The leaves are used to weave screens and roofing, the leaf-bases are used as corks for bottles, and beetle larvae extracted from the trunk are considered a gastronomic delicacy.

Semi-cultivated wild fruit

Between strict gathering and itinerant agriculture there is a wide range of intermediate situations in the rainforest, which are difficult to assess quantitatively and in terms of their local importance. Traditional itinerant agriculturists often did not cut down useful trees or fruit trees already present in the plots they cleared for cultivation. Some nomadic peoples even planted wild fruit trees along migration routes as a source of food and to attract wild animals. Some trees may even be "owned," and looked after within the rainforest, as happens in New Guinea with many specimens of the breadfruit (*Artocarpus altilis*). In total, about 2,500 different edible fruit are known from the world's rainforests, some collected only from the wild, while others are collected and cultivated without having been improved by selection, and others have been developed as major crops. Only a tiny part of the diversity of tropical fruit is available for consumption around the world, and only about 15 are produced commercially.

The fruits still gathered in the rainforest include the wild parents of tropical fruits that are now major plantation crops. Wild species of the banana (*Musa*) can still be found in southeast Asia and the Pacific, where, in addition to collecting the fruit throughout the year, the indigenous people prepare vegetable dishes with the flowers and eat the heart of the plant. Another wild plant related to a major crop is the wild mango, a group of 35 species of the genus *Mangifera* native to southeast and southern Asia.

Medicinal and poisonous plants

About 80% of the inhabitants of developing countries depend on traditional medicine, mainly herbal. On a local scale, a wide range of plants species is used, largely still collected from the wild. For example in Malaysia, most herb traders and local healers use resources collected from the wild. Unlike fruit trees, which are often in semi-cultivation around settlements, medicinal plants are being lost as their habitats are destroyed.

Traditional uses

Rainforest dwellers following traditional lifestyles have maintained their knowledge of the uses of these plants, although this varies from tribe to tribe. The Woarami of Ecuador use a relatively small number of medicinal plants, about 30, while their neighbors, the Kofan, use at least 80 species to cure 27 different diseases. On the other hand, the distinction between medicinal and culinary plants is often artificial when it comes to traditional usages. A single plant may be used to spice a meal, to promote good health or to cure an illness. A culinary plant as well-known as cardamom is used in India to cure coughs, asthma, and some diseases of the bladder and the kidney.

It has been estimated that in southeast Asia traditional medicine uses at least 4.5% of the indigenous flora —560 to 900 species of plant from the lowland rainforest of Malaysia, Borneo, and New Guinea alone. Traditional healers in eastern and southeastern Asia use more than 6,000 species, mainly derived from the rainforest. In Malaysia, many species of medicinal plant, members of families such as the Apocynaceae, Annonaceae, Rutaceae, Dioscoreaceae, Leguminosae, Lauraceae, and Zingiberaceae are species of the declining rainforest. In this and other tropical countries, protection within national parks and support for traditional usage are two important aspects of the conservation of medicinal plants.

The inhabitants of Gunung Leusur National Park, a tropical forest protected as a biosphere reserve in Indonesia, use more than 170 species of medicinal plant. In the reserve there are two settlements whose inhabitants have virtually no access to modern medicine, and rely almost entirely on medicinal plants administered by local healers, called *dukuns*. They use both native and introduced plants. Some native are still only collected

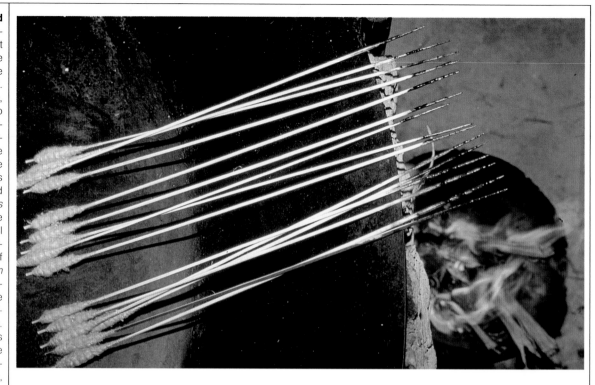

127 Blow darts tipped with curare, a careful prepared mixture of rainforest barks, seeds and herbs, made by the Waimirí-atro-arí of the Negro River Basin in Brazil. Note the bundle of fibers, probably wild cotton, to ensure the blow dart fits correctly in the bore of the blowpipe. It was for a long time erroneously thought that the active ingredient of curare was strychnine from the seeds and bark of species of *Strychnos* (Loganaciae), but in 1938 the ethnologist Richard Gill showed that the active ingredient came from the leaves of *Chondrodendron tomentosum* (Menispermaceae). The alkaloid responsible, isolated the following year, was named D-tubocurarine hydrochloride. When this compound enters the blood stream, it blocks the transmission of nerve impulses to the skeletal muscles, causing death by paralysis. This is why it is now used, in adequate dosages, as a muscle relaxant in neurological surgery and in the treatment of rabies and tetanus.
[*Photo: Xavier Ferrer & Adolf de Sostoa*]

from the wild, such as *konyel*, the bark of some *Ficus* species, which is used to treat abdominal pain and diarrhea. Medicinal plants are collected and cultivated for local use and for sale at the traditional medicine stalls in local towns.

The Kenyah Dayak people of the Apo Kayan plateau, in eastern Kalimantan, the Indonesian part of the island of Borneo, use more than 200 plants as medicines and poisons. Traditional medicines still continue to be used to treat more than 65 ailments, but this ancestral knowledge is no longer held in high esteem. In each community, only a few elderly people know the medicinal plants and their uses. Younger people now consider the use of plant remedies is outdated. Furthermore, the medicinal plants in the rainforest on the Apo Kayan plateau are becoming scarcer and scarcer. Some medicinal species are cultivated around the communal longhouses, in the gardens at the edge of the village, or farther away in the rice fields. Even so, most medicinal plants are still collected from the wild, about half coming from primary forest or mature secondary forest. Deforestation means these plants are no longer easily found.

Modern pharmaceutical applications
Some of the first Europeans to explore the tropics were interested in the local use of medicinal plants. The first botanical exploration of the Americas was organized by Philip II of Spain in 1570. One of his physicians, Francisco Hernández, spent seven years in Mexico collecting specimens and information on local plants used as medicines. He compiled a six-volume work on the medicinal traditions of the Aztec civilization, whose originals were unfortunately lost in a fire in the Escorial Palace. Pharmaceutical companies are now investing in screening the rainforest flora for new medicinal substances, but the task is immense. The Amazonian flora alone contains about 80,000 species, and nothing at all is yet known about the chemical composition of 99% of them.

In fact, only a relatively small number of rainforest plants have been used in modern medicine. Even so, the catalog of species of proven value continues to grow. In 1993 the United States imported rainforest plants worth over 20 million dollars for medicinal purposes. An example of an important natural drug is the alkaloid D-tubocuranine which is used in surgery as a muscle relaxant; it is derived from pareira root (amphihuasca, [*Chondrodendron tomentosum*, Menispermaceae]), a jungle liana used by many Amazonian peoples to make curare. Chemists have still not managed to produce a synthetic form of this alkaloid with all the properties of the natural product, and so commercial production still comes from the wild.

Another example of an internationally important rainforest-derived drug is reserpine, a hypotensive agent extracted from the roots of the snake

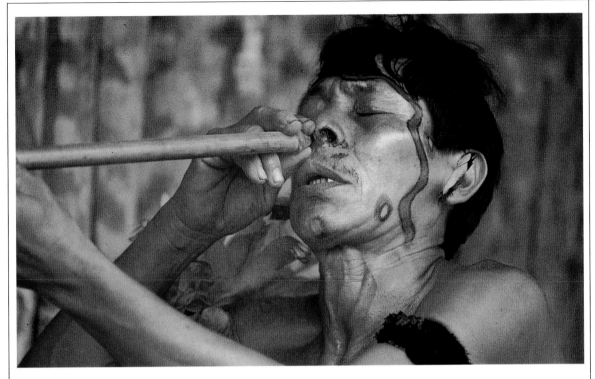

128 Sniffing hallucinogenic drugs for ritual purposes, or perhaps simply for fun, is a widespread custom among Amazonian indians, such as this Yanomami man. This shows these peoples' great empirical knowledge of the properties of rainforest plants.
[Photo: Index Editora / South American Pictures]

root (*Rauvolfia serpentina*, Apocynaceae). This shrub has been used in traditional medicine in India and other parts of southeast Asia for 4,000 years to treat snakebites (the reason why it is known as snake root), nervous disorders, dysentery, cholera and fever. Furthermore, for the last 50 years reserpine has been used in the industrial production of tranquilizers, and extraction from roots of *Rauvolfia* is still cheaper than synthesis. Snakeroot is still collected in India and Thailand, and it is cultivated in southern Asia and the American tropics. In the Democratic Republic of Congo, Mozambique and Rwanda, other wild species of *Rauvolfia* are collected. Another plant of great pharmaceutical interest is the ipecacuanha (*Cephaelis ipecacuana*, Rubiaceae), an American rainforest plant whose roots are rich in the alkaloids cephaeline anemetine that are effective against amoebic dysentery.

Both reserpine and tubocuranin are obtained directly from rainforest plants for use in modern medicine. Other plant extracts are used as the base for the production of semisynthetic derivatives. Plant extracts have been used to produce steroids. Until recently, 95% of all steroid production was from extracts of neotropical yams (*Dioscorea*). Diosgenin, which is derived from the Mexican yam (*D. mexicana*) and other related species, such as *D. composita* and *D. floribunda*, all Central American rainforest species, is the basic material for many steroid drugs, including the contraceptive

pill. Over the last ten years or so, price increases imposed by the Mexican government have stimulated the pharmaceutical industry to produce synthetic diosgenin and to search for it in other natural sources. It has been found in the western Africa Calabar bean (*Phytostigma venenosum*) and in other species of *Dioscorea* from India and China.

As well as the proven botanical drugs from the rainforest, there are countless other plants that may have curative properties. A recent exciting example is that the seeds of the Australian rainforest species called the Moreton Bay chestnut (*Castanospermum australe*, Leguminosae) contains an active ingredient, castanospermine, that might help to combat AIDS.

Poisons from the rainforest

The rainforest dwellers have accumulated knowledge about the poisons that can be extracted from plants, not just the medicines. Some poison preparations have been studied scientifically as potential sources of compounds of medicinal interest, such as the many arrow poisons or curares used by Amazonian tribes. Most curare preparations are combinations of different plant materials. Normally, they are species of *Abuta, Curarea, Chondrodendron* and other genera of the Menispermaceae, or of *Strychnos* (Loganiaceae), the genus that produces strychnine. Other species used by different ethnic groups in the Amazon include: gingive'-ko (*Ocotea venenosa*); porson (*Schoenobiblus peruvianus*); ko-yo-vi-fan'-ti (*Anaxogorea*), used by the Kofan indians of

Colombia and Ecuador to prepare several types of curare and for medicinal purposes; and the "ka-ho-gaw" (*Vochysia columbiensis*), used for similar purposes by the Maku people of Brazil.

In southeast Asia, the main active ingredient of blow dart poisons is normally the latex of the tree *Antiaris toxicaria* (Moraceae), and sometimes the sap of some members of the same genus as the nux vomica (*Strychnos nux-vomica*, Loganiaceae), or an extract of tuba-root (*Derris*, Leguminosae). These plant poisons are more stable than animal ones and last longer in the quiver before use. The active principle of *Derris* is rotenone. This and other equally toxic substances found in plants (such as *Mundulea sericea, Phyllanthus brasiliensis, Ryania speciosa, Euphorbia cotinifolia, Adenia lobata, Olax gambecola, Paullinia pinnata, Hura crepitans, Tephrosia toxicaria*, etc.) are used throughout the wet tropics to catch fish by temporarily stunning them (see section 3.3.5).

Plants for dress and ornament

In the rainforest, dressing is more about elaborate body decoration than wearing clothing. Palm leaves are a good raw material to weave simple items of clothing, for example the clothing using the fronds of *Astrocaryum chambira* made by the Yagua people in Amazonia, or the raincoats and hats using *Phoenix hanceana* variety *philippensis*, which is only found in the Batanes Islands in the Philippines. The indigenous peoples of New Guinea weave cloth from grasses and bark fibers to make into skirts, capes to protect them from the rain and other clothing.

Apart from fibrous materials that can be woven, many other plants are used for bodily decoration. Many tribes use dyes to paint their bodies and for other decorative purposes. The seeds of the annatto or urucú, (*Bixa orellana*) are used by the Colorado peoples of Ecuador to make a thick red paste to decorate their hair. It is believed that this orange dye, *achioto*, provides magical protection from forest spirits; moreover, its oil is a mosquito repellent. The same dye is processed industrially to produce annato (commercially known as E-160b) to color butter, cheese, and margarine. Another common Amazonian dye is obtained from the genip or xagua *Genipa americana*, whose sap turns dark blue on exposure to air; Amazonian tribes use it to dye and paint their

bodies. This tree grows from Mexico to Brazil is also valued for its very hard wood and is used to make a drink.

Some rainforest plants also are used to make items of jewelry. The black shiny seeds of the fruit of *Astrocaryum* palms are used to make beads and earrings. Beads are also made from the aromatic wood of the Brazilian tree, pau santo (*Kielmeyeria coriacea*). In Papua New Guinea, the seeds of Job's tears (*Coix lacryma-jobi*) are used to make nose decorations (such as those used by male Huli) and to make mourning necklaces (widows in the Enga tribe).

Plants with a cultural or ritual meaning

In addition to satisfying the most basic domestic needs of rainforest dwellers, many plants are used in different activities of a purely cultural or spiritual nature.

In Vanuatu, for example, it is believed that the tree ferns of the rainforest are in contact with the hidden world of the spirits, and figures carved from their stems are of great importance in the cultural life of this island chain in the Pacific. In the cultures of the northern islands of Vanuatu, social status is acquired by the accumulation of wealth, measured by the number of pigs an individual owns. At a certain point on this scale, the men pass through a grading ceremony that requires the preparation of a tree fern carving, produced subject to many taboos. The finished carving is the center of the ceremony which involves dances, rituals and sacrifices. Sometimes, the statues of these tree ferns are placed outside sacred huts, as they are believed to be shelters for ancestral spirits. Figures placed in pairs are believed to ensure the fertility of vegetable plots and plantations.

The Kenyah Dayak people of the Apo Kayan plateau in east Kalimantan formerly used many plants in their mamat rituals, associated with headhunting and ritual cures. They are now little used, although about twenty species still have some cultural or ritual significance as protective charms or offerings. The leaves and roots of the lung bileng (*Homalomena rubra*) are collected from the wild in the rainforest and are used as amulets to protect children from wandering spirits. The fruit of the "beleng la" (*Litsea cubeba*,

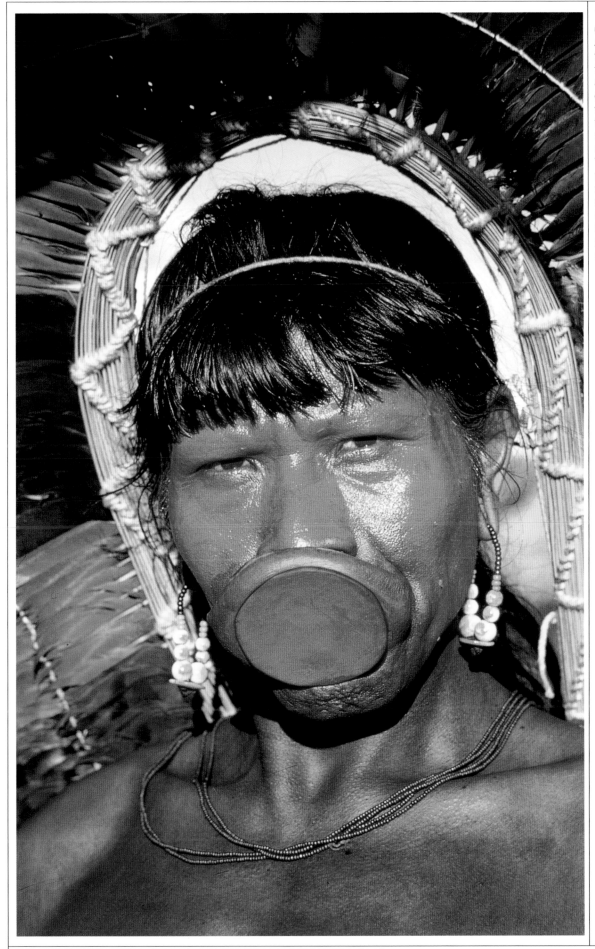

129 **Annato is widely used to dye the skin** among Amazonian people, such as this Kayapó from the basin of the Xingu (Brazil), and also among the Colorado people of Ecuador, who dye their hair with it. Annato is obtained from bixa or urucú (*Bixa orellana*). It is decorative and also protects from insect bites. To make application easier, they usually prepare the skin with a base of oil from the seeds of the piquí (*Caryocar brasiliense*), an oil that is also a foodstuff.
[Photo: Bill Leimbach / South American Pictures]

Lauraceae) is one of the nine ingredients used to make the incense burned to treat diseases thought to be caused by curses.

2.2 Building and furnishing materials

It is impossible to separate the idea of the rainforest from that of the dense forest—a community full big trees with very large trunks that can supply enormous quantities of timber. The rainforest has always been an abundant source of wood that has been both used and abused, but rainforest trees are more than trunks and logs. In addition to their primary biological function as the elements forming the rainforest, they are the source of countless other products, including those used traditionally by indigenous peoples and others used in modern industry. They are, above, all the basic material traditionally used by rainforest peoples to build their dwellings.

Wood is one of the basic construction materials, whether for simple shelters in the rainforest or for the large communal houses of South America and southeast Asia; bamboo is also an important construction material. Palms are the most versatile rainforest plants for building purposes, because they are lightweight and their leaves make excellent roofing for huts and shelters.

The uses of palms

In the Malayan Peninsula, the palms used for roofing include sago palms (*Metroxylon sagu*), which produces the best thatch, and nipa palm (*Nypa fruticans*), which provides a valuable thatching material called *atap*. Other species of palm are also used locally, such as the umbrella leaf palm (*Johannesteijsmannia altifrons*), bertam (*Eugeissona tristis*), *Arenga obtusifolia* and several species of the genus *Livistonia*. Atap is now being replaced by corrugated iron sheeting, which lasts longer but gets very hot and does not let the air flow.

In Sarawak and in Sabah, on the island of Borneo, the use of materials from wild palms is more widespread than in Peninsular Malaysia. The Penan of Sarawak and the rest of Borneo rely on palm products for roofing and matting for their temporary shelters and to make blowpipe darts, baskets and rope. The nipa palm (*Nypa fruticans*), which the coastal Malays collect from the estuaries to thatch their houses, is used in Sarawak to make hats, baskets, cigarette papers, brooms and string. Its nuts are also edible, and the sap is used to make sugar, alcohol and vinegar. Nipa fronds are also the preferred material in the Philippines for thatching and house walls. At the beginning of Spanish colonization, much of the Philippine coast was covered by nipa, including the sites of the cities of Manila and Cebu, but nipa populations are now declining, and even disappearing. Many other species of palm are used in the Philippines as thatching, such as the four species of *Livistonia* that occur, especially the cabbage palm or anahaw (*L. rotundifolia*), whose trunk also provides durable posts for house construction in rural areas. This exploitation is also leading to this species' rapid disappearance from natural forests and commercial plantations have not yet been developed.

130 **Weaving plants for building huts** in a village of Kangarasem (New Guinea). The Melanesians are highly skilled at this type of technique that, like all construction-related techniques, is, in New Guinea, restricted to men. It is mainly used in the coastal regions and the lowlands and is largely inspired by Malayan models.
[Photo: Manuel de Sostoa & Adolf de Sostoa]

131 Rattan canes are a highly valued product in southeast Asian markets, such as this market in Blankegerem in Sumatra (left-hand photo). The most important producers of rattan are the Philippines, China, India, and above all Indonesia, which produces 90% of all the raw material, known as rattan cane, which is used to make furniture. Most rattan comes from the wild, and only 10% is supplied from the plantations of central and southern Kalimantan. In Indonesia, over-exploitation has reduced natural rattan populations so much that the species producing the stems of greater diameter, such as *Calamus manan* and *C. inops* (right-hand photo), are harder and harder to find. In 1989, Indonesia banned the export of unprocessed rattan. In the Philippines almost all the rattan, whether for local use or for export, comes from wild plants.
[Photos: Adolf de Sostoa and Wayne Lawler / Auscape International]

The rattans

The rattans, the general name for a group of climbing palms, are second only to timber trees as generators of economic income. These climbing palms are enormously useful to the rainforest's inhabitants, and are also important items of international trade as raw materials for furniture production. There are about 600 species in several genera (*Calamus*, *Daemonorops*, *Korthalsia*, *Plectocomia*, *Plectocomiopsis*), mostly from south and southeast Asia. They are used by the inhabitants of the Peninsular Malaya to make cordage, including ropes to lash the framework and floorings and to secure the thatch, as well as basket making and fish traps.

The Philippines has about 60 native species of rattan, about 10 of which are of commercial importance. The tender young shoots of most of these rattans are edible, especially those of *Daemonorops melanochaetes* and *D. halleriana*, which are the most appreciated as foodstuffs. They are cooked with fish and coconut milk in a dish prepared for important guests. The juice of rattan fruit is used as a dye or as a medicine to treat rheumatism, asthma and snakebites. The center of rattan species diversity is in the Malayan Peninsula, where 104 species have been recorded, 38% of which are endemic and about 20 species, all wild, are commercially important.

Indigenous people use many of these plants for a wide range of purposes.

Timber and palms in communal constructions

All these building and household items are best exemplified by the complex communal houses that, all over the world, are very typical of many rainforest peoples. The discussion of the Amazonian peoples (section 3.1.2) mentions their malocas, large collective huts that are covered with yapó palm (*Parascheelea*) fronds, but there are other similar constructions.

The riverside settlers of northeast Peru, mostly descended from Cocama natives, although some maintain they have European ancestry, build settlements of houses built near the river from several hardwoods and palms, selected from the local flora. The split trunks of palms such as Iriartea deltoides and Socratea exorrhiza are used for walls and floors. Insect-resistant and rot-proof wooden pillars come from Minquartia guianensis (Olacaceae); the wood of several species of the genus Guatteria (Annonaceae) is used for beams and roof supports, as they need to be flexible and able to resist the wind. The secondary supports are made with stems of the grass Gynerium sagittatum (Poaceae). Several lianas are used to lash the structure together, mainly Heteropsis jenmannii (Araceae).

132 Pygmies are highly skilled at working plant fibers, as shown by this woman in the central African rainforest making a basket by the side of her hut, which is also built of plant materials. The Lese Dese build *mafikas*, or covered kitchens, that are open at the sides, whereas the sleeping huts and shacks have woven walls covered in mud. The huts are built when the strongest rains in December have finished, taking advantage of the fact that the soft earth can be used to cover the walls and dries out during the dry season. Beginning at the bottom, the women weave the leaves of the tilipi (*Megaphrynium macrostachyum*) they have gathered and prepared. They cover the walls and roofs with waterproof cloth and lash it all together with flexible lianas and strips of bamboo. This covering may last for five years. The Efe live in simple dome-shaped huts constructed from bent and woven saplings covered with tilipi leaves. Each family has its own hut, arranged around a central communal space for socializing (see also photo 112).
[Photo: Rick Weyerhäuser / WWF / Still Pictures]

FAMILY AND SPECIES	COMMON NAMES
ANACARDIACEAE	
Astronium (several species)	king wood, urunday
Dracontomelon (several species)	paldao, dao, senal
ANNONACEAE	
Oxandra lanceolata	lancewood, senal
APOCYNACEAE	
Dyera costulata	jelutong
BOMBACACEAE	
Ceiba pentandra	ceiba, cotton tree, kapok
Ochroma pyramidale	balsa
BURSERACEAE	
Aucoumea klaineana	okoume, gabun
LEGUMINOSAE-CAESALPINOIDEAE	
Caesalpinia echinata	Brazil wood, Pernambuco wood
COMBRETACEAE	
Terminalia alata	Indian laurel
Terminalia bialata	chuglam
Terminalia ivorensis	idigbo
Terminalia superba	limba, afara
DIPTEROCARPACEAE	
Anisoptera (10 species)	mersawa (*A. laevis*), palosapis (*A. thurifera*), krabak (*A. curtsii*)
Dipterocarpus (several species)	keruing, gurjun, yang, apitong
Dryobalanops (several species)	kapur, Borneo camphorwood
Parashorea malaanonan	white seraya, bagtikan, white lauan
Shorea (several species)	meranti, Philippines mahogany (dark red meranti)
Shorea (several species)	sal, yakal, balan and selengan-batu, "chan"
EBENACEAE	
Diospyros (several species)	ebony, abenuz, macassar ebony, coromandel persimmon
STERCULIACEAE	
Heritiera (6 species)	mengkulang
Mansonia altisima	mansonia
Pterygota (several species)	pterygota
Triplochiton scleroxylon	obeche, whitewood, wawa
LEGUMINOSAE-PAPILIONOIDEAE	
Afzelia (several species)	afzelia, African mahogany
Dalbergia (several species)	rosewood, palisander
Dalbergia melanoxylon	African blackwood
Dalbergia retusa	cocobolo
Dicorynia guianensis	basralocus, angelica
Gossweilerodendron balsamiferum	tolawood, agba
Guibourtia demeussii, G. pellegriniana, G. tessmannii	bubinga, African rosewood
Guibourtia ehie	ovangkol
Intsia bijuga, I. palembanica	merbau, Borneo teak
Microberlinia brazzavillense, M. bisulcata	zebrano, zebrawood, zingana
Millettia stuhlmanii, M. laurentii	panga panga, wenge (respectively)
Oxystigma oxyphylum	tola (Angola), tchitola, lolagbola
Peltogyne (20 species)	amaranto, zapatero
Pericopsis elata	afrormosia
Pterocarpus (African species)	African padauk, muninga
Pterocarpus indicus	amboina, Burma rosewood, Andaman padauk, pink padauk
FLACOURTIACEAE	
Casearia [=Gossypiospermum] praecox	zapatero, Maracaibo boxwood
LAURACEAE	
Endriandra palmertonii	Australian endriandra, Queensland walnut
Ocotea rodiaei	louro, green duramen wood
MELIACEAE	
Cedrela odorata	cedrela
Entandrophragma cylindricum	sapele
Entandrophragma utile	utile
Guarea cedrata, G. thompsonii	white bosse, dark bosse (respectively)
Khaya (5 species)	African ebony
Lovoa trichilioides, L. brownii	African walnut, tigerwood, Congo wood
Swietenia (several species)	Venezuela mahogany, American mahogany, Honduras mahogany, Mexican mahogany (*S. macrophylla*), mahogany (*S. mahagoni*)
MYRISTICACEAE	
Virola (several species)	virola, ucuuba, baboen
MORACEAE	
Chlorophora excelsa	iroko, African teak
Brosimum [= Piratinera] guianensis	breadnut, ramón, leopard wood, cardinal wood
OCHNACEAE	
Lophira alata	ekki, ironwood
RUBIACEAE	
Mitragyna foliata	abura
Nauclea diderrichii	bilinga, opepe
RUTACEAE	
Chloroxylon swietenia	satinwood, Ceylon satinwood
Flindersia brayleyana	yellow-wood, Queensland maple
SANTALACEAE	
Santalum album	sandalwood
SAPOTACEAE	
Aningeria (several species)	aningeria, anagre, aningre
Tieghemella heckelii	makore, baku, cherry mahogany
THYMELAEACEAE	
Gonystylus bancanus	ramin
VERBENACEAE	
Gmelina arborea	gumari
Tectona grandis	teak

ORIGIN	APPEARANCE	MAIN USE
Central America and Brazil	reddish with black streaks, decorative	cabinetmaking (veneers)
Philippines, New Guinea	grey or brownish with dark stripes	cabinetmaking (veneers)
Caribbean	dark	wheels for carriages, rods and bows
Insulindia	ordinary, yellowish	industrial and craft uses
tropical Africa and America	pale, light	veneers, simple packaging, insulating material
tropical America (especially Ecuador)	white or pink, very lightweight	industrial (DIY, insulating material)
western Africa	light rose, fine	cabinetmaking (veneers), cigar boxes
Brazil	orange and fine	bridges for violins
Indomalaysian region	decorative, brown with dark streaks	high-quality carpentry (train carriages), handles for tools.
Andaman Islands	variable color (white chuglam, silver chuglam)	high quality carpentry (veneers)
western Africa	yellowish brown with prominent growth rings	carpentry, interiors (paneling, veneers)
tropical Africa (especially Democratic Republic of Congo)	variable in color (pale limba, black limba)	carpentry, interiors (panelling, veneers)
Indomalaysian region	yellowish, ordinary	simple carpentry (veneers)
Insulindia	dark brown	outdoor carpentry, boats
Insulindia	yellowish brown, ordinary	outdoor carpentry
Borneo and Philippines	yellowish or pinkish	fine cabinetmaking (boarding)
Malaysia (pale red meranti and white meranti); Philippines (red meranti and white meranti); Myanmar (white meranti)	variable color (pale red, white, yellow, dark red meranti)	construction, outdoor carpentry, cabinetmaking
India, southeast Asia	dark, resistant, heavier and denser than meranti	construction (beams and docks) and boats
India and Sri Lanka, tropical Africa	black, or dark brown with black streaks	cabinetmaking, carving, musical instruments
Insulindia	dark brown	outdoor constructions, leisure boats
western Africa	dark brown, decorative	luxury carpentry
western Africa and Asia	yellowish or whitish	indoor carpentry and cabinetmaking
tropical Africa	yellowish and shiny, lightweight	cabinetmaking and indoor carpentry
tropical Africa	red with yellowish streaks	cabinetmaking
tropical regions of all continents	reddish brown with black streaks	luxury cabinetmaking, turnery (handles)
tropical Africa	dark or black, smooth	turnery, carving (wind instruments)
Pacific coast of Central America	dark reddish brown	turnery (handles) and carving
French Guyana and Surinam	dark reddish or brown	construction (columns, dikes, docks)
western Africa	reddish brown	indoor and outdoor carpentry, cabinetmaking
tropical Africa	reddish with purple streaks	cabinetmaking (veneers)
eastern Africa	yellowish or brownish with black streaks	cabinetmaking (veneers)
Insulindia, Indochina	a reddish ebony color	high-quality cabinetmaking
Cameroon, Gabon	decorative, light with dark streaks	cabinetmaking (veneers), turnery
tropical Africa	dark brown, almost black, very attractive	cabinetmaking (veneers), boarding
tropical Africa	yellowish with dark streaks	specialist cabinetmaking (televisions)
tropical America	shiny purple, heavy	decoration, turnery and industrial uses
tropical Africa	teak-like	boatmaking, luxury cabinetmaking
western Africa (especially Cameroon and Nigeria)	delicate	many uses (fine cabinetmaking, shipbuilding, handles, boarding)
Indomalaysian region	delicate	many uses (fine cabinetmaking, shipbuilding, handles, boarding)
Caribbean	yellowish	turnery (rulers and drawing tools), carving
northeastern Australia	greyish or brown with dark patches	high-quality cabinetmaking and carpentry
tropical America (especially Guyana)	yellowish green or darkish	industrial construction (beams, docks)
tropical America	similar to mahogany	many uses (cabinetmaking, cigar boxes, boats)
western America	similar to mahogany	quality woodwork
tropical Africa	dark, similar to African ebony	luxury woodwork
tropical America and Africa	similar to ebony	cabinet making
western Africa	pink or brown	reproduction furniture
western Africa	similar to African mahogany	cabinetmaking (veneers), turnery
tropical America	reddish brown	luxury cabinetmaking and finishes for boats.
tropical America	pink-brown, lightweight	cabinetmaking (veneers) and interiors
tropical Africa	like teak	boat-building
tropical America (especially Guyanas)	attractive mottled dark mahogany red	turnery (walking sticks, umbrellas), string instruments
western Africa	dark reddish brown with light streaks	construction (beams, railway sleepers)
western Africa (especially Nigeria)	ordinary	normal woodworking, often stained
western Africa	shiny orange-yellow	construction (boats and sleepers) and outdoor carpentry
India, Sri Lanka	elegant, golden, decorative	many uses (veneers, turnery oboes)
northeast Australia	pale pink-brown or darkish	luxury cabinetmaking, rifles and shotguns
India, Australia and Pacific islands	brown, oily and sweet-smelling	perfumery (distillation of shavings) and carved goods (boxes, frames, combs)
tropical Africa	yellowish pink, heavy	cabinetmaking (substitute for mahogany)
western Africa	pale pink or reddish, resistant, abrasive	luxury cabinetmaking and construction of boats and carriages
Sarawak	light in color, almost white	cabinetmaking (imitation of other woods)
India, Bangladesh and Myanmar	pale straw color, shiny	woodworking
Indomalaysian region	golden or dark-streaked, with visible growth rings	boat-building

133 **Main commercial wood producing trees** of the world's rainforests and equatorial and tropical monsoon forests. The diagram includes the wood's main characteristics and the main producing areas.

[Source: data drawn up by the authors]

3. HUMANS IN THE RAINFORESTS

The Dayak communities of Sarawak that live in communal longhouses also rely on rainforest plants for their construction materials. The main forest products collected for the longhouse are rattan canes (*Calamus rotang* and many other climbing palms), which they also use to make curtains, baskets and many other objects. Another very important product is the wood of the billian or Borneo ironwood (*Eusideroxylon zwageri*, Sapotaceae), whose very hard wood is used for construction, roofing, and to make buckets and other recipients for water. This species used to be common in the dipterocarp forests of Borneo and Sumatra, but is now becoming scarce due to deforestation and commercial exploitation.

In northeastern Democratic Republic of Congo's Ituri forest, there are two communities whose lifestyles are very different, but both obtain all their construction materials from the rainforest: the Lese Dese, who are agriculturists and the Mbuti pygmies, who are hunter-gatherers. The Mbuti pygmies build huts, kitchen shelters (mafika), and shelters for the

social reunions of the males (baraza), using small trees and saplings tied by climbing palms and young bamboo shoots; woven tilipi leaves (*Megaphrynium macrostachyum*) are used for roofing; the latticework sides are covered with mud. The Efe, however, live in simple dome-shaped huts, built using bent saplings woven together and covered with tilipi leaves.

2.3 Timber and timber-producing trees

The rainforest's main economic product is timber. An enormous number of rainforest trees reach a size suitable for timber exploitation, but generally only a few species are commercially exploited. There are thousands of species of tree in Amazonia, but only about 50 are intensely exploited, although about 400 have some commercial value. In the 1970s, 35 main species of timber were exported from the African rainforest, and only 10 species accounted for 70% of total commercial value. In spite of growing efforts to diversify this trade, there is still great reliance on traditionally used species. Ghana alone has 674 species that reach a size suitable for use as timber, of which about 60 species have been exported over the last 20 years. The most exported species is wawa or obeche (*Triplochiton scleroxylon*, Sterculiaceae), which accounted for 45% of unprocessed timber and 23% of processed timber exported between 1972 and 1989.

Despite the abundance of trees producing wood, high-quality cabinet making using tropical hardwoods is usually restricted to a small number of species: American and African mahogany (*Swietenia*, *Khaya*, *Entandrophragma*), ebony (*Diospyros*), American and African rosewood (*Dalbergia nigra*, *D. sissoo*), tigerwood on Congo wood (*Lovoa*), limba or afara (*Terminalia superba*) and okoume or Gaboon mahogany (*Aucoumea klaineana*).

Dipterocarps and ebonies

The most important source of tropical hardwoods for the international market is southeast Asia, where lowland rainforest contains many species of commercial use, and more types of tree are exploited here than in the other regions. This diversity is masked as different woods are grouped under a single commercial name.

134 **Ebony is one of the most appreciated of all tropical hardwoods**. It comes from several different species of *Diospyros* and is the deep, black heartwood. Imitation with dyed wood is frequent, especially in African sculptures carved for sale. In fact, the ebonies are not from Africa, although some species are cultivated in this continent. [Photo: Sandra Mbanefo / WWF / Still Pictures]

135 **Mahogany has a characteristic reddish color**, whether it comes from the American true mahoganies, such as this Honduras mahogany (*Swietenia macrophylla*) in the left-hand photo) in the Tikal rainforest (Guatemala) or from one of the African mahoganies, such as this recently felled sapele (*Entandrophragma cylindricum*), in the right-hand photo) in the Democratic Republic of Congo (see photos 22 and 188).
[*Photo: Xavier Ferrer & Adolf de Sostoa and Sylvain Cordier / Jacana*]

The Dipterocarpaceae alone provides about 80% of the wood exported from southeast Asia; the most important timber trees in the family are keruing or dau (*Dipterocarpus*), kapur (*Dryobalanops*) and meranti or lauan (*Shorea* and *Parashorea*). In Peninsular Malaysia alone, there are at least 3,000 species of tree, 400 of which have been traded on the international market. Indonesia has more than 4,000 species of tree and more than 260 are considered commercially important sources of timber.

The different species of ebony (*Diospyros*) are among the most highly valued of all tropical hardwoods, especially for cabinet making and carving. Ebony's main characteristic is the dark, almost black, color of the heartwood, in addition to its hardness and its shininess, although this is not true of all the species in the genus. The black ebonies include true or East Indies ebony (*D. ebenum*), from the rainforests of India and Sri Lanka, and Sulawesi ebony or macassar (*D. celebica*), an attractive black wood streaked with brown stripes, as well as *D. philipinensis* and *D. reticulata*, from Mauritius. Some ebonies have light-colored woods, called white ebony, such as the coromandel or white African ebony (*D. quaesita*) and another extratropical species of the same genus.

The mahoganies

Mahogany (*Swietenia mahagoni*, Meliaceae), also known as American mahogany, Cuban mahogany, or Honduran mahogany, is from Central America and the Caribbean. It has been internationally traded since the 16th century. Very few trees are now left, and the species is an extreme example of genetic erosion. Depletion of this species stimulated the search for other mahoganies, and at the beginning of this century the trade turned to Mexican or Honduran mahogany (*S. macrophylla*), widely distributed throughout Central and South America, although the already small populations are widely scattered. The rate of exploitation of this mahogany has raised concern about its future in several countries. Both these mahoganies are a characteristic reddish color, and it is this that has made them famous; they are highly valued in cabinet making.

The so-called African mahoganies are different species of the genera *Khaya* and *Entandrophragma* (both members of the Meliaceae, like the American species). These trees have been intensely exploited over the last century, especially for export to Europe, and in some countries they are now scarce in the wild. Red African mahogany (*K. ivorensis*) dominated exports until the 1950s, but now it and other species of *Khaya* and *Entandrophragma* are legally protected. *K. ivorensis* is also overexploited in Ghana, and since 1979 its export as raw timber has been prohibited. The most important species of *Entandrophragma* are tiama (*E. angolense*), sapele (*E. cylindricum*) and sipo or utile (*E. utile*). These trees are becoming scarcer in western Africa, and are now being extracted from the relatively intact forests of central Africa. Sapele is one of the most important timber trees in Cameroon, and one of the few that is logged for export from the remote forests of eastern Cameroon. The rainforest of northern Democratic Republic of Congo is also a source of sapele.

Real furniture

Even at the beginning of the 20th century, in Europe it was still fashionable to own a chest of drawers made of jacaranda, or mahogany. Jacaranda is not a rainforest tree, but mahogany is, like most fine hardwoods. Tropical hardwoods are excellent materials, of unequalled pleasure to the touch and pleasing to the eye, with a silky grain emphasized by cutting the trunk's growth rings obliquely. They glisten once they have been polished, and this is brought out with a touch of matte or gloss varnish. They are hard wearing and resistant to woodworm and other wood-boring animals. The furniture made two or three centuries ago using these hardwoods has a double value, material and historical, and is more and more appreciated. This furniture in solid hardwood has been copied but never equaled, as nowadays veneers are used to give a surface appearance of elegance to structures built of more modest wood.

Furniture made of tropical hardwoods has embellished European households for the last four centuries. In the 17th century the main hardwoods imported into Europe were true mahogany (*Swietenia mahagoni*), coromandel (*Diospyros quaesita*), several species of palisander, or Brazilian rosewood (*Dalbergia*), and Burmese rosewood or amboyna wood, the reddish and black streaked wood of the asiatic *Pterocarpus indicus*. These woods were the raw materials preferred by European manufacturers of wardrobes and sideboards, such as Thomas Chippendale, George Hepplewhite, Richard Gillow, and Thomas Sheraton. Currently, the main imported tropical hardwoods, already cut for use in the furniture industry, are African mahoganies—such as the sapele and utile (*Entandrophragma utile* and *E. cylindricum*), Honduras mahogany (*Swietenia macrophylla*), teak (*Tectona grandis*), basically exported from areas of seasonal monsoon forest, afrormosia (*Pericopsis elata*), and ramin (*Gonystylus*), from Indonesia.

Originally, true mahogany (*Swietenia mahagoni*) was used by the inhabitants of the Caribbean to construct canoes, which was the reason why the Spanish chose it to repair their ships. The first time mahogany is known to have been used in Europe, in 1584, was wood brought as a gift for Philip II of Spain. This consignment was used to construct the furnishings of the library at the Escorial Palace, furnishings that still exist. The removal of taxes on the importation of wood into Great Britain, together with the destruction of most of the walnut trees in Europe in 1704 by a devastating frost, increased the demand for mahogany in the 18th century. After 1715 mahogany was used in Britain to make tables, chairs and other items of furniture. Often as cargo captured by corsairs from the Spanish, mahogany was usually available for British cabinetmakers as timber merchants accumulated large quantities in London and other ports.

True mahogany (*Swietenia mahagoni*) was considered the finest wood, although Honduras mahogany (*Swietenia macrophylla*) was also greatly appreciated. Honduras mahogany became widely used in Britain after large-scale imports began from the colony of British Honduras, now Belize whose coat of arms of features a mahogany tree with the motto *Sub umbra floreo* (we prosper under the trees). In the mid-19th century the port of London became the European center for hardwood imports. There was a steady supply of mahogany logs from Honduras, Cuba, Costa Rica and Santo Domingo, and sales were held in the famous coffee houses of the time. Thus, mahogany has been the typical hardwood for several centuries.

Detail of furniture with inlay of different rosewoods (*Dalbergia nigra, D. sisson*) [Christie's Images]

Wardrobe made from ebony (*Diospyros ebenum*) with copper decorations, built by A. C. Boulle (1732), preserved at the Louvre, Paris [Aisa]

There are other hardwoods, such as ebony; the South American word *ebenisteria* (ebony-working) serves to distinguish the delicate and artistic manufacture of high-quality furniture such as cabinetmaking, from ordinary carpentry. A lot of furniture has been made of coromandel, the white African ebony (*Diospyros quaesita*) but few items have been made from ebony, whether true ebony or macassar (*D. ebenum*, *D. celebica*), because it is expensive and hard to work, although greatly appreciated for artistic carvings.

The different types of palisander, or rosewood, are also greatly sought after by cabinetmakers. The Brazilian rosewood, or true palisander (*Dalbergia nigra*), has been traded for more than 300 years, and Brazilian tulipwood (*D. frutescens*) was the preferred wood of the classic French furniture makers, especially in the Napoleonic era. A dozen species of *Dalbergia* produce true rosewood, which is easily worked and features distinctive, rich colors and a beautiful grain. Small quantities of palisander are still used in decorative veneers for high-quality furniture and in the manufacture of musical instruments. Combining these two uses, some European manufacturers produce pianos with a rosewood veneer. In the past pianos were made of solid mahogany with a substantial rosewood veneer, but now thin rosewood veneers are used to cover structures made with mahogany substitutes.

Detail of polished padouk (*Pterocarpus*)
[Christie's Images]

Another of the first hardwoods imported into Europe was padau wood (*Pterocarpus*). This beautiful and highly decorative wood is as good as mahogany and teak. After becoming famous for its use in furniture making and in cabinet making, padau has been in great demand from furniture makers, for carving, parquetry and for boat-building. The best padauks are Andaman padauk *P. dalbergoides*, one of the most sought-after of all hardwoods, the West African padauks *P. osun*, and *P. soyauxii*, species that are excellent for making furniture and decorative veneers, and Amboyina wood or Andaman redwood (*P. indicus*), a beautiful pinkish color, one of the most elegant woods used in cabinetmaking. It is the national tree of the Philippines, and also grows in Malaysia, Indonesia, and Papua New Guinea.

Nowadays, furniture made of solid tropical hardwood is a luxury that few can afford. Copies of historical styles, modeled on traditional designs like those of Thomas Chippendale, are now made with cheaper woods, stained to make them resemble mahogany. Chipboard or particleboard is used to make the structure and this is then faced with a thin veneer of hardwood. The rapid destruction of the tropical rainforest makes it important to realize the true value of tropical hardwoods, by using these precious materials with the restraint they deserve. Nowadays, furniture made of solid tropical hardwood belongs in museums.

The rainforest provides firewood for domestic fuel, normally from fallen trees. This woman from Kivu (Democratic Republic of Congo) is returning home with a bundle of wood on her back, a scene common throughout tropical Africa. Scarcity of firewood is not a problem in the rainforest but is in savannahs and arid areas.

[Photo: Nigel Smith / The Hutchison Library]

The lightest and heaviest woods

One of the most noteworthy tropical woods is balsa wood (*Ochroma pyramidale*, Bombacaceae) from the rainforest of Central America and the northwest of South America. It is the lightest of all commercially important woods, with a specific gravity only 0.12. Aircraft manufacture originally used balsa wood structures. The famous Mosquito fighter plane was mainly built of balsa, and stood out for its speed and efficiency in the Second World War. Balsa wood is still the wood preferred by airplane model-makers. About 80% of total production comes from Ecuador, partly from plantations and partly from the rainforest.

On the other end of the scale are the woods known as ironwoods. South American ironwood (*Krugiodendron ferreum*) is the heaviest wood known, and its specific gravity of 1.3 means that it sinks in water. Ekki or African oak (*Lophira alata*), from the African rainforest of the Gulf of Guinea, is another hard, heavy ironwood. Other heavy tropical hardwoods are billian or Borneo ironwood (*Eusideroxylon zwageri*) and the lignum vitae or guayaco (*Guaiacum officinale*, *G. sanctum*), of the drier areas of tropical forest in Central America and the Caribbean. Billian is traditionally valued for house construction, and among the Chinese to make coffins; its main commercial applications are heavy construction (mainly bridges and jetties), boat building and industrial flooring.

2.4 Raw materials for industry

Wood is by no means the only material provided by rainforest trees. To the contrary, many commercially interesting substances are spontaneously synthesized by countless forest plants and accumulate in their bark, trunk, resin, or latex ducts. These substances are collected directly from the rainforest by tapping or simply removing entire parts of the tree. It is difficult to imagine the modern world without the manufactured products made from all these types of latex, resin, wax, oil and colorings. The absence of these materials must have been even harder for the first rainforest dwellers because most of them, without industrial processing, have always formed part of the daily life of rainforest dwellers.

Oils and resins

Essential oils, as well as fragrances and essences extracted from the rainforest, are important raw ingredients for the perfumery industry. Rosewood (*Aniba rosaeodorae*, Lauraceae) used to be widespread throughout Central Amazonia, and was intensely exploited for its bois-de-rose oil. Other essential oils derived from rainforest trees are also very important for the perfume industry.

137 **Many of the most appreciated perfumes on the international market** include as a basic component the essence distilled from the ylang-ylang (*Cananga odorata*, Annonaceae). This is a small tree that is widely cultivated in the tropical islands of the Indian Ocean, such as Réunion, where the photo was taken. A similar tree, with the same use, is *Artabotrys odoratissimus*, which is cultivated here, in the islands in the Sonda Strait and the Philippines.
[Photo: Michel Viard / Jacana]

Guiac wood oil is obtained from the wood of different species of the tropical genera *Guaiacum* and *Bulnesia* (both members of the Zygophyllaceae) mainly found in the dry forests of the Caribbean and the Chaco. Its exploitation for international trade has increased so much in the last few years that some species are now becoming scarce. Brazilian sassafras oil comes from Brazilian sassafras (*Ocotea pretiosa*, Lauraceae), a plant of both the Mata Atlântica and the *Araucaria* forests, and is used to make soap, cosmetics, and disinfectants. The flowers of ylang-ylang (*Cananaga odorata*, Annonaceae) produce a sweet-smelling oil of great value in high-quality perfumery. It is originally from southern Asia, but ylang-ylang is now one of the main cash crops in the Comoros Islands.

Oleoresins are more viscous than essential oils. In Peninsular Malaysia, the oleoresin tapped from *Dipterocarpus kerrii* is sold as an essential oil, and yang oil is still extracted in Thailand from some species of *Dipterocarpus*, although it is legally prohibited. Copaiba balsam, an oleoresin obtained from several Amazonia copaiba trees (*Copaifera*), is used by native peoples as a medicine and a scent, and is still used in both the pharmaceutical and varnish industries. Sometimes so much accumulates in the resin ducts that it exudes from the trunk. Maracaibo copaiba comes from *C. officinalis* and Para copaiba from *C. reticulata*.

Balsams are oleoresins that contain benzoic acid or cinnamic acid, and so they are highly aromatic. Peru balsam is a thick resin, pharmaceutically used as an antiseptic and to protect mucous membranes, which exudes from the wounded trunks of *Myroxylon balsamum* var. *peireirae* (Leguminosae), a mahogany-like Central American tree. Tolu balsam is obtained from a single species (*M. balsamum*) in the rainforests of Venezuela, Colombia and Peru and is used in perfumery and soap production, and pharmaceutically as an expectorant and antiseptic. Benzoin or gum-Benjamin (a corruption), a balsamic resin rather than a balsam, is a vanilla-smelling solid that has similar uses: Siam benzoin obtained from *Styrax tonkinense* and *S. benzoides*, can be distinguished from the Sumatra benzoin produced by *S. benzoin*.

True resins are the product of the spontaneous oxidation of essential oils within the resin ducts; their composition varies greatly from resin to resin, but all are soluble in alcohol and insoluble in water. Many paints, varnishes and lacquers contain products refined from the resins of rainforest trees. Among the most important are copals, resins with a low oil content that are used to make hard, elastic varnishes. The white kauri (*Agathis alba*) is a conifer that is not only widely appreciated for its high-quality wood, but also produces Manila copal, traditionally used in batik textile production, torches and to caulk boats. In the Philippines, the commercially exploited species is *A. philipinensis*. Other important copals are derived from African copals (*Copaifera demeusii*, *C. mopane*, *C. copallifera*, *C. salikounda* and *Daniellia ogea*).

138 The stunningly rich colors of Central American textiles, such as these ones on sale in this Mayan market in Antigua (Guatemala), would be inconceivable without the tradition that developed thanks to the presence of the palo campeche (*Haematoxylon campechianum*), a universal fixative for colored dyes derived from other plants. Although some of these fabrics are now dyed with synthetic pigments, some ancient traditions are still maintained.
[Photo: Ramon Folch]

Some southeast Asian dipterocarps of the genera *Neobalanocarpus*, *Hopea*, *Shorea* and *Dipterocarpus* produce a resin, known as dammar, as valuable as their wood. Chengal (*Neobalanocarpus heimii*) produces dammar penak, *Shorea hypochra* produces dammar temak, *S. robusta* produces dammar sal and *S. weisneri* produces Batavian dammar. Dammar is collected in the form of the lumps that form spontaneously on the bark or by regular tapping. Rainforest dwellers regularly use dammar as fuel for lighting and to waterproof boats and baskets. Another species of dipterocarp, Borneo camphorwood (*Dryobalanops aromatica*) produces a camphor comparable to true camphor from *Cinnamomum camphora*. It is used locally for medicinal purposes, and is exported to China. For thousands of years products from south Asia's rainforests, such as dammar, camphor and gaharu have been traded with China for Chinese pottery. Gaharu, a valuable commodity product that cannot yet be cultivated, is the resinous diseased heartwood of *Aquilaria malaccensis* (Thymelaeaceae), which is used as a medicinal product and burned as incense. At times gaharu provides good cash income for forest-dwellers, but the trees are now too widely scattered for exploitation to be profitable.

Dyes and colorings

The exploitation of a tree for its dye was one of the first extractive operations performed by European settlers in Brazil. Brazilwood (*Caesalpinia echinata*, Leguminosae) in fact gave its name to the country of Brazil: It produces a beautiful scarlet dye but is now close to extinction in the forests of the coastal Mata Atlântica. Its exploitation began in 1503 and continued for about 300 years, until wild stocks were exhausted and synthetic dyes were developed. The name brazil had previously been applied to sappanwood (*C. sappan*), a tree the Portuguese had found in the forests of southeast Asia and that also produces an intense red dye, the first known red dye to be produced from wood. It is a good coloring agent, but tends to run, which does not occur with hematoxylin.

There is probably no other plant-coloring agent as famous and important as hematoxylin. For centuries hematoxylin has been used to dye cotton and wool, and has been of great importance in the development of the textile industry, the basis of the 18th century industrial revolution. Hematoxylin ($C_{16}H_{14}O_6H_2O$) is also used in histological stains, and is more of a color fixative than a color, so it can be mixed with different additives to give varied and stable colors, but especially a dark black. Hematoxylin is responsible for the deep red color of the heartwood of campeche (*Haematoxylon campechianum*), a spiny tree of forest edges from Yucatán, that from the 17th century onwards was widely exported to British dyers from British Honduras (present-day Belize).

In addition to the red colors derived from brazilwood and sappan, and the deep black from campeche, fustic provides a yellow dye for wool, cotton and synthetic fibers as well as hides and leather. Fustic is obtained from the heartwood of *Chlorophora tinctoria* (Moraceae) from the American tropics. Yellow paints have long been made using gamboge, a gum-resinous dye exuded by *Garcinia hanburyi* (Guttiferae) from southeast Asia. Annato (discussed in section 3.2.1) is a red dye produces from bixa or urucú (*Bixa orellana*). Catechu, or cutch, is a brown dye or tanning agent obtained from the heartwood of *Acacia catechu*, a tree from India and Myanmar.

Latexes

Latex is an internal secretion produced as a defense against herbivores and other environmental attacks by a large number of plant species—about 12,000—belonging to 20 different families. Latex forms in specific channels, known as latex ducts or laticifers, and is usually stored under slight pressure, the reason why it flows abundantly on incision. The different types of latex (which should not be confused with gums, which are amorphous substances consisting of the neutral salts of organic acids formed by the spon-

taneous decomposition of plant tissues) are always watery solutions or milky emulsions that may be white, yellowish, or pink, with variable quantities of proteins, alkaloids, enzymes, coagulating agents, and especially starch and terpenes. It is this high terpene content that makes the latex of several rainforest trees suitable for industrial use.

The best known of all these products is Pará rubber, the latex of the rubber tree (*Hevea brasiliensis*, Euphorbiaceae) from the Amazon. Other important latex-producing plants include the following members of the Sapotaceae: the Asiatic gutta-percha (*Palachium gutta*), balata (*Manilkara bidentata* [=*Mimusops balata*]), and the zapote or sapodilla (*Manilkara* [=*Achras*] *zapota*). For more information on latex and latex-producing trees, see pp. 218-221 "Tires and chewing gum" and pp. 306-309 "From Henry Wickham to Chico Mendes."

2.5 Traditional agricultural activity

The origins of agriculture in the rainforest are little known and more speculative than in regions where a more complete archeological record has been intensively studied, as in the Middle East and the Mediterranean. The areas pre-adapted to exploitation which seem to have been required by the earliest domesticated plants and animals from different parts of the world (see volume 1, page 291) are scarcer in a relatively constant climate, like that of the rainforest, than under more sharply seasonal climatic conditions. Yet some archeologists consider that the terracing and

139 Slash and burn cultivation forms part of the cultural habits of many rainforest peoples, such as these Amazonian Yanomami, who have burned a patch of rainforest to plant bananas (*Musa*) and cassava (*Manihot*).
[Photo: Mark Edwards / Still Pictures]

Tires and chewing gum

At this very moment, millions of people around the world are chewing a product from Yucatán—chewing gum—a plastic gum made from the latex of a tree from the Central American rainforest. Further millions are also moving around on another product of the New World rainforest, vehicles whose tires are made of vulcanized rubber. This is made with the latex of another rainforest tree, in this case from the Amazonian rainforest. Tires and chewing gum: both symbols of the modern American way of life. But these materials are nothing new to the native Americans: in pre-Colombian times the Maya knew of *chicle*, or chewing gum, and played ball games with balls made of rubber. After all, the word *chicle* comes from the Nahuatl language.

Bubble gum [Hamilton / Index]

Latex extraction and the waterproofing of a shoe in an 1867 engraving [Archiv für Kunst und Geschichte, Berlin]

The people who harvest chicle, *chicleros*, still tap wild trees. They roam the rainforest equipped with machetes and rubber cups, containers that were originally made with the latex of uli (*Castilla elastica*, Moraceae), the plant that provided the first rubber seen by Europeans and the first waterproof material. The chicleros search the Central American jungle for acras or sapodilla trees (*Manilkara [=Achras] zapota*, Sapotaceae). The incisions (tapping) are normally made early in the morning when humidity is higher, and in a single day up to 77 lb (35 kg) of latex (the "chicle") may run into the cup from each tree. It cannot be tapped again for another six or seven years, and a tree can only be tapped three or four times in total. The day's harvest is first boiled in the jungle until the water content has been reduced to 33%. Then it is solidified into blocks and sent to shipping centers.

Commercial chewing gum contains only about 15-20% chicle: the rest consists of colorings, flavorings, and sweeteners, but mainly of other substitute gums. People in fact use the latex of other similar species in the manufacture of bubble gum, including other Amazonian species (*Manilkara achras, M. chicle, M. inundata*), the Trinidad balata or bully tree (*M. bidentata*), species of *Dipholis* (*Dipholis stevensonii*) and especially that of the Malaysian jelutong (*Dyera costulata, D. lowii*, Apocynaceae). In any case, many of these species are cultivated so that *chicleros* tapping wild trees are becoming scarcer.

Making the incisions to obtain the latex of the rubber tree (*Hevea brasiliensis*) in the Alto Juruá extractive reserve. Brazil [Edward Parker / Still Pictures]

The latex of the bully tree (*M. bidentata* [=*Mimusops balata*]) has other important uses in the production of golf balls and in the plastics industry. It is harder than chewing gum and does not expand with heat. This is why it is used industrially in transmission belts and conveyor belts, applications that it shares with another famous latex, gutta-percha, (*Palaquium gutta*, Apocynaceae), a Malaysian plant now widely cultivated in the Sonda Strait and in the Philippines. Balata and gutta-percha latex are unsurpassed insulating agents, and before the invention of plastics they were used to cover all electric wires and are still used today for waterproof cables.

The waterproofing of materials was the first application of uli latex, and it was also one of the first uses for another American latex, produced by an Amazonian tree that wept drops from its leaves and from wounds on its trunk, and for this reason the natives called it the *caáuchu* (the weeping tree). This cauchu latex is very rich in isoprene, a highly elastomeric substance that also rubs out pencil lines on paper, which is why it is known as rubber. At the beginning of the 19th century many objects were waterproofed with rubber, using a technique invented by the Scotsman Charles Macintosh (1766-1843). They all, however, had the disadvantage of deforming with

heat and becoming brittle with cold. The situation changed in 1839 when the American Charles Goodyear (1800-1860) invented, at the same time as the Englishman Thomas Hancock (1786-1865), the process of vulcanization: Heating the rubber with sulfur at a high temperature (130-140°C), causes further polymerization of the isoprene, and the bonds made with the sulfur give the rubber a three-dimensional structure. This creates a new substance that is slightly elastic, malleable but not plastic, highly adhesive, waterproof and resistant to organic solvents, and that can be molded and keep its form per-

Gutta-percha (*Palaquium gutta*), part of a 1905 engraving [Archiv für Kunst und Geschichte, Berlin]

Tapping the latex of the rubber tree (*Hevea brasiliensis*) in Kerala [B.N.S. Deo / Planet Earth Pictures]

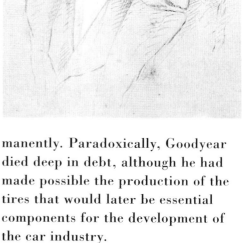

manently. Paradoxically, Goodyear died deep in debt, although he had made possible the production of the tires that would later be essential components for the development of the car industry.

The freshly collected latex is an emulsion of sap, terpenes (including isoprene), proteins, starch and water. At the base of the tree, it is made into a ball that is spitted and then heated over a fire. It emits a dense smoke, consisting of creosote, acetic acid and tar, leaving a mass of polyterpenes, the raw rubber (*borracha* to the Brazilians). These large balls of raw rubber, 132-198 lb (60-90 kg) in weight, are the raw material that arrives at the shipping centers. The chemical industry has learned to substitute these isoprene-rich balls for synthetic chemical products (neoprene, polymerized butadiene, etc.) but has by no means replaced rubber. Production in the Amazon Basin, from wild trees is very low (1% of the world total), but the plantations in southeast Asia and west Africa cover five million hectares (1 hectare=2.47 acres) and produce six million tons of raw rubber a year, 70% of which is used in tires. The difficulties and suffering linked to the extraction of latex and the cultivation of heveas is quite another story: a different story, but one worth telling (see insert "From Henry Wickham to Chico Mendes" pp. 306-309).

The typical rubber tree, or Pará rubber tree, not the Panama rubber tree, which is the uli mentioned above, is a species of the genus *Hevea* (Euphorbiaceae), commonly called the seringuiera in Brazil, or simply hevea. Strictly speaking the seringuiera is *H. brasiliensis*, commonly found growing wild throughout the basins of the Amazon and the Orinoco, although acceptable rubber also comes from *H. benthamiana* and *H. guianensis*. They are large trees (66-131 ft [20-40 m]) preferring a well-drained soil and can live 200 years. It is not known exactly why the trees produce this latex, but the fact is that if they are tapped correctly the latex does not cease flowing for many hours. When the wounds heal, the seringueiros (the people who extract the latex from the wild heveas of the Amazon Basin), or the rubber growers of Asia, repeat the process, and so the bark of old trees may be covered in scars.

channeling in the Kuk valley (New Guinea) under 9,000-year-old peat deposits are some of the earliest traces of agricultural or pre-agricultural activity. There is no conclusive proof that this transformation of the valley was for agricultural purposes, but some authors consider that the environment was deliberately modified to cultivate taro (*Colocasia*). Agriculture presents many problems in the rainforest, starting with the unsuitable nature of the soil.

The limited suitability for agriculture of rainforest soils

The equatorial rainforest is a system with a relatively closed and fragile nutrient cycle. The biomass immobilizes the large quantity of nutrients that the roots have taken up from the infertile soil. The kaolinites so abundant in rainforest soils are clays with a low cation (positively charged ions) exchange capacity, and thus a low nutrient storage capacity. Nutrients are thus easily lost by leaching, as the high rainfall favors such transfer processes in these soils. Fertility is even lower when iron oxides dominate over kaolinites, as their cation exchange capacity varies with pH and is almost nil in these acidic environments, meaning that they cannot retain nutrients.

Humans have empirically discovered that the biomass is the compartment of the ecosystem where they can find the nutrients lacking in the soil. Unlike the use of technology and mineral fertilizers, the traditional solution has been to slash and burn the rainforest to practice subsistence agriculture in an itinerant or rotatory system. Farmers burn the plant mass when preparing the ground for cultivation and thus recover the nutrients it contains, as the ashes increase soil fertility for a number of years, providing the nutrients for food production.

Nutrient exhaustion

This, however, interrupts the incorporation of organic material into the soil, thus breaking these systems' fragile nutrient balance based on the supply and breakdown of organic material. The cultivation of this land implies the increasing exhaustion of the organic material present in the soil. In the rainforest of the central Zaire Basin, it is estimated that during the first year of cultivation of former forest with almost 22,046 lb (10,000 kg)/ha of organic matter, partial mineralization may supply about 882 lb (400 kg) of nitrogen in forms available to plants. As cultivation

continues, this quantity of organic nitrogen decreases, as does available nitrogen. After a few years, the organic material ceases to be the main source of nitrogen, and unless nitrogen-fixing legumes are cultivated, the lack of nitrogen may become a major factor limiting agricultural production.

The other nutrients are leached away and extracted in the harvests, becoming exhausted after a few years of cultivation. The good harvests of the first few years are because the ashes may supply, per hectare, between 20 and 68 lb (9 and 31 kg) of phosphorus, 273-1,631 lb (124-740 kg) of potassium, and from 278-5,644 lb (278-2,560 kg) of calcium, according to measurements from different African rainforest countries, such as Ghana, Democratic Republic of Congo, Liberia and Nigeria. In Colombia, this nutrient release per hectare is estimated at between 280 kg and 360 kg of calcium, 240 kg of magnesium, and 90 kg of potassium. This incorporation of basic cations supposes an addition to the soil that increases its pH, and this in turn diminishes the solubility of aluminum, and thus its toxicity.

The diminishing fertility of rainforest agricultural systems therefore depends on the soil's characteristics, its content of organic matter, nitrogen and other elements; its clays, pH, and soil structure and its biological activity. The characteristics of the system (rotation or monoculture, the intensity of exploitation and protection against erosion) control the rate of the inevitable loss of fertility. Depending on these factors, the area has to be abandoned after a period of 2 to 5 years, and the process begins again somewhere else in the jungle. Traditionally, fertility was recovered by leaving the area to recover for between 8 and 30 years. Now, in many countries' population pressure has forced many shifting farmers to return to the same plot after a shorter period. The rainforest cannot regenerate if a secondary forest or a degradation savanna is formed that does not attain the original forest's fertility, and this reduces its potential for future agricultural use. A historic disaster of this type is one of the explanations given for the disappearance of the classic Mayan culture. To study and foresee the effects of forest degradation, the Food and Agriculture Organization of the United Nations (FAO) created some years ago the Tropical Forest Development Committee.

The problem of soil aluminum

Another major problem of tropical agriculture is the presence of soil aluminum. Traditionally, the problem of soil aluminum has been resolved by burning the natural vegetation or by applying lime. Burning tropical rainforest may release 4,163 lb (1,890 kg)/ha

140 The low fertility of **many rainforest soils** is well known. Slash and burn cultivation not only clears the site but also supplies ash, thus enriching the soil with some mineral elements. This is why the crops are sown directly in the ash, as this woman in Sabah, Borneo, is doing. *[Photo: Richard Matthews / Planet Earth Pictures]*

3. HUMANS IN THE RAINFORESTS

of calcium, 639 lb (290 kg)/ha of magnesium and 1,872 lb (850 kg)/ha of potassium, enough to raise the pH above 5.5 and provisionally solve the problems raised by aluminum toxicity. This means rational soil management must include soil conservation measures to avoid the loss of ash in runoff and soil leaching.

In degraded forests, where the amount of nutrients in the vegetation is far less than the quantity of cations necessary to neutralize the aluminum, it is necessary to apply calcium, in the form of agricultural lime, limestone, or dolomite. This raises the problem of the presence of quarries nearby, the feasibility of transport to the farm, and the farmer or landowner's ability to afford and apply the improvements. When calculating the quantity to be supplied, the soil's content of organic matter must be taken into account, as part of the calcium will be immobilized by the organic matter.

The roots of agricultural activity

Despite these objective difficulties, agriculture has been practiced in the rainforest for many centuries. It seems to be accepted that a complex of plants was domesticated in southeast Asia and then spread throughout tropical and sub-tropical Asia and the Pacific and later throughout the entire world. The most important of these plants is rice (*Oryza*), but this set of domesticated plants also includes a series of roots and tubers, such as yams (*Dioscorea*) and taro (*Colocasia*); fruits like bananas (*Musa*) and mangos (*Mangifera*); and other plants, such as the sugar cane (*Saccharum*).

In America, there seems to be indirect evidence of cassava (*Manihot esculenta*) cultivation in Amazonia 8,000 or 9,000 years ago. Some authors consider that increasingly intense cassava cultivation, and its spread to new areas (such as the Andes, Central America and the Caribbean coastline and islands) with a climate unlike the Amazon riverbanks, marked the origin of other centers of plant domestication that are better documented, such as the Central American and Peruvian ones. Associated with cassava cultivation, there was apparently an entire agro-horticultural complex comparable with that of southeast Asia. This included fruit, such as the avocado (*Persea americana*), pineapple (*Ananas comosus*), and papaya (*Carica papaya*) and many other plants producing colorings, fishing and hunting poisons, stimulants, etc., that are still grown as semidomesticated plants in the vegetable plots around malocas and villages.

The origins of agriculture in the African rainforest are even less clear, although many authors believe it may be very old. Some authors suggest the bottle gourd (*Lagenaria*) was domesticated very long ago and that the oil palm (*Elaeis guineensis*) was protected in clearings and forest edges for thousands of years before its deliberate cultivation in the colonial period.

Most tropical plants that are basic foodstuffs have been cultivated for thousands of years, but none had a pantropical distribution until the European colonial period. After colonialism began in the late 15th century, bananas, maize, cassava, and sweet potatoes, to name a few, spread rapidly throughout the tropics, and even traditional rainforest dwellers now cultivate plants originally from other continents. Cassava and maize are American crops that were introduced into Africa in the 16th century and into Asia in the 18th century. The Americas received several crop plants from the Old World; for example the Portuguese introduced sugar cane and bananas from western Africa. The introduction of plantation crops during the colonial period, especially rubber, tobacco, oil palm and coffee, significantly affected the economies of many countries.

Itinerant agriculture

Some human groups still obtain all their resources from the rainforest as hunters and gatherers of wild plants. Indigenous peoples practicing traditional lifestyles and more recent colonists both, however, normally produce their food by cultivating certain domesticated and selected plants, often by itinerant agriculture. Many traditional systems of itinerant agriculture have given rise to agricultural practices that rely on the detailed knowledge of the plants of the rainforest and their ecology. Many plants, both wild and domesticated, are used in practices combined to make the best possible use of the plant resources present.

Horticulture in clearings and "slash and burn" agriculture

Some authors consider that agriculture in the strict sense arose in the Middle East, based on the cultivation of plants with hard seeds (cereals, legumes) that were sown by hand and on rearing flock-forming herbivorous animals. They contrast it with the horticulture that arose separately in the rainforest regions of southeast Asia and Amazonia, based on plants producing starchy roots or rhizomes that are multiplied by cuttings and lacking herd-forming domesticated animals. *Agriculture* in the first case implies the extensive, long-term use of land and requires the permanent location of agricultural and stockraising activity in a given space. *Horticulture* in the second case implies intensive, but temporary, use of spaces cleared and prepared within the rainforest for itinerant agriculture; this by no means excludes returning to previously cleared and cultivated sites.

In fact, itinerant or shifting agriculture based on "slash and burn" remains the main form of sub-sistence cultivation practiced in the rainforests of southeastern Asia, Oceania, Latin America and Africa. Shifting agriculture predated the single-species-plantation form of cultivation of the colonial period by thousands of years and arose independently in all the world's tropical areas. Shifting agriculture is often regarded as the main cause of tropical deforestation, but these traditional forms of cultivation have shown over the centuries that they are sustainable.

Shifting agriculture involves clearing patches of rainforest by felling the trees and burning them. The cleared area, enriched by the nutrients released from the ashes, is cultivated for a few years until soil fertility and crop production decline. The plot is then abandoned for the rainforest to reoccupy, and a new plot is cleared. In its simplest form, shifting agriculture is a natural extension of the collection of food plants directly from the wild. The Siriono people of northern Bolivia still practice a simplified form of nomadic cultivation, obtaining most of their food by hunting and gathering, but at certain times of year they clear small gardens and cultivate crops. These plots are left untended while they continue their hunting trips, and they return several months later to harvest their crops. After the harvest, the plots are abandoned and revert to the rainforest. In more sophisticated forms of itinerant agriculture or horticulture, as practiced in Melanesia, a range of clones of the main crop plants are cultivated in carefully prepared plots, with raised ridges to plant yams and irrigated terraces for taro; the plot is left to revert to the rainforest for 10-20 years, when the agriculturists return to the same plot.

The Lacandon Mayans of Chiapas

The Lacandon Mayan people of Chiapas, Mexico, cultivate more than 70 different species of food and textile plants on single-hectare (1 hectare= 2.47 acres) garden plots cleared in the lower montane forest. After clearing and burning the plot, the first crops planted are fast-growing species, such as papaya (*Carica papaya*), banana (*Musa*), cassava (*Manihot esculenta*) and sweet potato (*Ipomoea batatas*). These help to retain the nutrients released by burning before they are leached by the heavy rainfall. Then, at the appropriate time of year, they plant a wide range of vegetables, fruits and herbs, as well as maize and rice. The natural events of the rainforest's calendar act as cues signaling the best time to plant: When the flowers fall from the mahogany (*Swietenia*), it is time to plant the spring corn, and tobacco is plant-

141 **The struggle between farmers and the jungle** is clearly shown in areas of rainforest that have not been cleared. It is not uncommon to see crops halfway between itinerant and fixed that are in direct contact with the forest area, as shown by this photo from New Guinea. There is a clear lack of precautions against erosion, despite the care with which the crops have been arranged.
[Photo: John Downer / Planet Earth Pictures]

ed when the Manila tamarind (*Pithecellobium arboreum*) flowers fall.

In addition to planted crops, the Lacandon Maya allow some wild plants to flourish in their plots, for example, trees with edible fruit, such as mammee apple (*Mammea americana*), wild pineapple (*Ananas comosus*), sapodilla (*Manilkara achras*), breadnut (*Brosimum alicastrum*) and chaya (*Cnidocolus chayamansa*), together with others that provide raw materials for building and making bows and arrows. The diversity of food species attracts wild animals, an important component of their diet. After tending the plots for seven years, the Lacandon farmers cease intensive cultivation, and plant tree crops, such as rubber, citrus fruits and avocado, that can be harvested for 5-15 years while the natural rainforest regenerates. Meanwhile,

142 **A cleared area in the Lacandon jungle**, specifically in Loma Bonita, Chiapas (Mexico), with a more or less stable settlement. The Lacandon Mayans living in these precariously cleared areas practice a very skilled and highly diversified agriculture.
[Photo: Xavier Ferrer & Adolf de Sostoa]

143 A Barol woman preparing sago on the river-bank in a Karawari village in the Sepik region of New Guinea. Sago is the starch obtained from the sago palm (*Metroxylon sagu*). The palm's pith is cut and repeatedly washed until it is free of undesirable fibers, and is the basic foodstuff of this and other southeast Asian peoples. [Photo: Jean-Paul Ferrero / Auscape International]

another plot has been prepared in the rainforest, and the agricultural cycle is repeated. The agricultural techniques of the Lacandon Maya have been passed down from generation to generation since pre-Colombian times. Unfortunately, much of the Lacandon rainforest has now been destroyed. Recent colonists and cattle ranchers lack this intimate knowledge of the rainforest and awareness of all the resources it can provide. The cultural changes and marginalization the Lacandon Mayans are experiencing are leading to rapid loss of this ancestral knowledge.

The case of the Baroi of Papua New Guinea

In Papua New Guinea, the Baroi people of the Purari delta farm and fish in large settled villages installed in sites chosen on the basis of the availability of cultivable land, fishing and crab collection. Their basic foodstuff is sago, the starch of the sago palm, (*Metroxylon sagu*), which they cultivate on the banks of the estuaries. They plant 12 different varieties of sago palm, mainly selected for the flavor of their starch. After planting, the Baroi do not put a lot of work into tending the plot. In the same area, there are large stands of wild sago palms, but they are rarely used, as they are some distance from the settlements.

The Baroi also plant coconuts (*Cocos nucifera*), banana (*Musa*), taro (*Colocasia*), sugarcane (*Saccharum*) and betel-nut (*Areca catechu*) around their sago plots on the riverbanks. Swampy areas are cleared of nipa palm (*Nypa fruticans*) to make bush gardens for these and other crops. They also clear small areas on drier ground within walking distance of their homes. These clearings are made each year and are planted with cassava (*Manihot*), banana (*Musa*), sugarcane (*Saccharum*), squashes (*Cucurbita*), taro (*Colocasia*), maize (*Zea mays*) and watermelon (*Citrullus*) and are left untended until harvesting time. The settlement's vegetable plots are normally abandoned after a single harvest and are allowed to lie fallow.

The male Baroi fell and trim the sago palms from the riverside plots and float them down river to the village. They are left floating in the river for up to two weeks, until they are needed. The women extract the starch from the pith. It is eaten in a variety of ways, such as sticks baked in nipa palm leaves, often with grated coconut, or as soup, accompanied by green leaves, smoked fish or crabs. Some beetles, considered a delicacy, are extracted from the stumps and branches of the palm trees left after felling. The larvae of the rhinoceros beetle are greatly appreciated, baked in nipa leaves. The sago palm has a wide range of uses among the Baroi. The pith discarded after sago extraction attracts wild pigs, which are hunted; its leaves are used in house construction, providing materials for floor coverings, walls, and roofs.

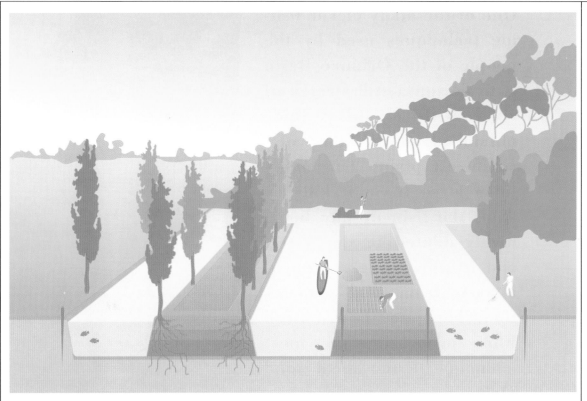

144 **The chinampa system of cultivation** developed in pre-Colombian America. It makes use of the floating layer of plants (atlapalácatal) that forms spontaneously on lakes, consisting of growing plants and dead remains of different species of *Lemna*, *Salvinia*, *Typha*, *Nymphaea* and other aquatic plants. To construct a chinampa, the first step is to cut three or four rectangles of this layer of vegetation. They are then moved like rafts to the site of the chinampa, and placed so that only the top layer rises a little out of the water. Then they are covered with silt dredged from the bottom of the lake with a special tool, the *zoquimaitl*, a sort of canvas bag mounted on a bow at the end of a pole about 16 ft (5 m) long. Then a number of specimens of "ahuejote" (*Salix bomplandiana*) are planted to stabilize the floating chinampa as their roots help to retain the soil at the edges. The system is regularly fertilized with mud from the bottom of the channels. The chinampas soil is totally organic, and porous in texture, facilitating watering and drainage, and is extraordinarily fertile. The use of natural fertilizers mainly of plant origin and very careful cultivation techniques allow intensive production of a wide range of plants, with up to four harvests a year.
[Drawing: Jordi Corbera, from several sources]

They are also used to make bags and baskets, grass skirts and fish traps and nets.

2.6 The basic permanent crops: roots and tubers

Other more stable agricultural systems have also evolved in the rainforests. Before European colonization, the indigenous peoples of Amazonia permanently cultivated the seasonally flooded riverbanks, and some groups continue to do so using similar methods. The Mayans of Central America, before the conquest, were also sedentary farmers who grew crops on raised plots. The chinampas system of central Mexico is an example of permanent cultivation that still continues. In any case, the basic crops of both itinerant farmers and sedentary horticulturists are plants producing edible roots and tubers, such as cassava, yams, sweet potatoes, taro, and others.

Cassava

Cassava (*Manihot esculenta*) is one of the world's main food crops and in the tropics provides a basic foodstuff and an export crop for the production of industrial starch, tapioca and animal feeds. It is fermented to produce popular alcoholic drinks, such as pinarri in the Caribbean. World production is over 90 million tons, split more or less evenly between South America, Africa, Asia, and Oceania.

Cassava was first cultivated in South America, where it has been grown since antiquity. The oldest remains of cultivation are in the Orinoco Basin and date from 4,000 years ago. It is thought to have been one of the food plants used by the very first humans to reach the region, and its trade was already important between 4,000 and 5,000 years ago. The species no longer exists in the wild, but the centers of diversity of closely related wild species are in Brazil and southwest Mexico. Cassava was introduced into western Africa in the late 16th century, and reached the eastern coastline by way of the islands in the Indian Ocean, at the end of the 18th century. It has been cultivated in India for about 200 years.

Indigenous peoples' knowledge of cassava is highly sophisticated. For example, the Jarawara people of the Purus River in the south of the Brazilian Amazon, cultivate 22 different types of cassava, and the Tukano people of the Colombia-Brazil border cultivate 140 varieties. The Machiguenga people of the Madre de Dios Valley on the border between Peru and Bolivia also cultivate many varieties of

Cassava: from poison to food

One of the many clever fishing techniques used by the people of the Orinoco Basin is to poison a still stretch of river with a milky juice obtained from the tubers of a rainforest plant. This milky juice is so toxic it kills or stuns the fish, despite being highly diluted in the water, and is, surprisingly enough, a waste from food preparation. The juice is produced when processing the most common of the local food plants, cassava.

Peeling cassava tubers (*Manihot esculenta*) in Brazil [Edward Parker / Still Pictures]

The leaves, stems, fruit, and tubers of cassava (*Manihot esculenta*), and other species of the same genus) are all poisonous—or more precisely, they are pretoxic. They do not contain any poison as such, but they have high levels of substances that turn into poisons. They contain cyanogenetic glucosides, that is to say, sugars that release the extremely toxic cyanide ion. Cassava thus needs to be treated with some respect.

Growing plant and tuber of cassava (*Manihot esculenta*) [Rudolf Konig / Jacana]

There is a fascinating series of phenomena and processes behind the toxicity of cassava. It starts with the cyanogenetic glycosides, linamarin and lotaustralin, sugars containing a cyanide group, and abundant in all parts of the cassava. The plant tissues also contain the enzyme linase, which is however separated from the linamarin and lotaustralin, so that these pre-toxic sugars do not act as poisons. The situation, however, changes when the plant is consumed: if the raw cassava is broken by the process of chewing and digestion, the linamarine and lotaustraline come into contact with the linase, which hydrolyzes them. This transforms the two apparently inoffensive glucosides into innocuous glucose and acetone molecules, and the tremendously toxic cyanide ion. So eating a raw cassava tuber is like taking a large dose of cyanide.

Toasting cassava (Manihot esculenta) flour in Brazil [Edward Parker / Still Pictures]

How, then, is it that the manioc is the main source of carbohydrates in tropical countries? The answer lies in the cooking and pre-treatment of the raw tubers. Heat destroys the cyanic groups, so that cooked manioc—e.g., the leaves eaten as vegetables—are not at all toxic and the empirical wisdom of the peoples of the Amazon and Orinoco also provides a proper treatment of the raw manioc, which should be used depending on the way it is to be eaten. The trick consists of provoking hydrolysis of the cyanogenic glycosides, as occurs in the intestines, and then separating the edible glucose, in the form of starch, from the hydrogen cyanide.

The process begins with the grinding of the tubers, the part of the cassava containing the most edible carbohydrates. This grinding brings the linase into contact with the cyanogenic glucosides, causing their hydrolysis and the liberation of hydrogen cyanide, which is released into the milky juice. The paste is then very thoroughly washed until only the starch remains, or it is placed in long funnels of woven plant fibers called tipiti or cibucán that are generally shaken by two people like a sieve. The milky liquid that runs from this "strainer" may be used as already explained, in fishing.

Preparing cassava (Manihot esculenta) flour in Brazil [Luiz Claudio Marigo / Bruce Coleman Limited]

Macuna woman washing cassava (Manihot esculenta) in Santa Isabel, Colombia [Harriet Logan / The Hutchison Library]

Wayana child straining cassava (Manihot esculenta) with a tipití in French Guyana [Tony Morrison / South American Pictures]

Many of the wild species of cassava are eaten to some extent by the indigenous populations of Central and South America (*Manihot carthaginensis*, *M. aesculifolia*, *M. isoloba*, *M. guaranitica*, *M. tripartita*, *M. orinocensis*, etc.). The only form that is now eaten is the cultivated cassava (*M. esculenta*), of which there are no known wild specimens. All these wild and cultivated cassavas contain cyanogenic glucosides, but in different concentrations, depending on the species and the part of the plant. The cultivated cassava is one of those showing the highest levels, although there are some varieties with almost none, (known as "sweet" cassava, in contrast to the toxic ones, called "bitter" cassava). The tubers of bitter cassava may contain concentrations of cyanide, in the form of cyanogenic glucosides, of 136-160 mg/lb (300-350 mg/kg); bear in mind that eating raw untreated tubers with concentrations of 32-41 mg/lb (70-90 mg/kg) is lethal for human beings. The potential toxicity of cassava is a very serious problem.

It is a especially serious problem with worrying health consequences in Africa, where the relatively recent introduction and spread of cassava cultivation means that the commonly-used methods of preparation lack the refinement of those in South America. Cassava was introduced into Africa when the Portuguese took it to Angola in the late 16th century. Cassava cultivation did not, however, spread throughout the continent until the 18th and 19th century through the efforts of the European colonists who needed an abundant foodstuff for their plantation workers. Inadequate treatment of the raw cassava means that it is common for populations in Africa to eat cassava starch with the equivalent of 3-8 mg/lb (6-17 mg/kg) of cyanide. This can lead to several disorders, especially where the deficiency disease goiter is endemic because of iodine scarcity (the Ubangui region of Uganda, for example). Furthermore, its low protein content (only 2.2-2.7% dry weight) means that cassava is a far from nutritionally complete food.

In any case, cassava is one of the world's main dryland crops, and in the 1980s it was cultivated on 12 million hectares (1 hectare=2.47 acres), producing 135 million tons of tubers a year. It is the staple foodstuff of 300 million people, and is eaten fresh, both the treated leaves and tubers (such as the foufou, atieké, chikwangue, etc.), which have to be eaten shortly after preparation because they spoil in a few hours. It is also eaten in the form of toasted flours and dry starches, such as tapioca, which is popular throughout the world, and the forms known as farinha in Brazil, gari in Africa and glapeck in Indonesia. Until recently cassava crops were almost pest free due to their high toxicity, but in recent years they have been attacked by virus, bacteria, fungi and several insects that must also have found a way around the problem of cyanide poisoning. Agricultural research centers in Africa, Asia, and the Americas are searching for new poisons as pesticides, as well as working to breed varieties of cassava that are totally free of these cyanogens—which just goes to show that every species looks after its own...

cassava and believe that the tubers, like other cultivated plants, are daughters of the moon (which in their culture is the male civilizing hero who gave the tubers to them with instructions on correct cultivation, so they no longer had to eat earth).

The many varieties of cassava can be distinguished by the appearance of the shrub and the color and starch content of the tuber. They are generally divided into two groups: the sweet and the bitter. The tubers of sweet cassava are cooked like any other vegetable but the bitter varieties contain toxins and have to be prepared correctly before they can be eaten. The toxic juice extracted in the treatment is used by some Amazonian groups as a fish poison and to rid dogs of fleas. More than half the wild species of *Manihot* are endemic species of Latin America with restricted distributions. It is important to conserve these wild relatives of cassava so they can be used in crop improvement programs. The wild *Manihot* gene pool is now being eroded as rainforest is being turned into pasture, and the wild cassava plants are eliminated because they are poisonous to livestock.

Yams

Yams (*Dioscorea*) are another major root crop cultivated as a staple throughout the tropics. They are climbing plants with large roots full of food reserves, although they sometimes also form a sort of aerial tuber. Diosgenin and other irritants and even toxic substances are present but are destroyed on cooking. World production of yams is about 20 million tons, of which Nigeria produces about half. About 50% of African subsistence farmers depend on yams as a basic foodstuff, and their cultivation is an integral part of daily and ceremonial life. Yams are also very important in several parts of southeast Asia, Melanesia, the Caribbean, and other parts of the Americas.

Cultivation of yams for consumption occurred independently in Asia, Africa and tropical America, and dozens of different species were used (in Asia the species *Dioscorea alata, D. esculenta, D. hispida, D. japonica*; in Africa the species *D. cayenensis, D. bulbifera, D. dumetorum, D. rotundata*; and in the Americas, the species *D. trifida, D. floribunda, D. hastata, D. racemosa*, and many more). There is

145 A roadside stall selling yams (*Dioscorea*) in Buea, at the base of Mount Cameroon (upper photo). After shredding, yam roots are usually left to dry on improvised threshing floors, such as this one in Kabasha, in eastern Democratic Republic of Congo (lower photo). Despite the importance of yams as food plants, they seems to be suffering severe genetic erosion, so steps should be taken to conserve the wild yams that are still common.
[Photos: Mauri Rautkari / WWF / Still Pictures and Xavier Ferrer]

146 The taro's large leaves make taro (*Colocasia esculenta*) fields look like tropical gardens, as shown in this photo of a field in Viti Levu, in the Fiji Islands.
[Photo: Jean-Paul Ferrero / Auscape International]

3. HUMANS IN THE RAINFORESTS

evidence showing yams have been eaten in southeast Asia for at least 10,000 years, and it is thought their history in western Africa may be just as long. Little is known about the history of yam cultivation in the American tropics, where they have historically been overshadowed by cassava. In times of scarcity, wild yams are still eaten in the areas where they grow wild, for example, *Dioscorea lecardi* in western Africa, *D. schimperiana* in eastern and western Africa and *D. luzonensis* in the Philippines. The Semang in Malaysia eat at least 10 different species of wild yam.

The sweet potato

Like cassava, the sweet potato (*Ipomoea batatas*) is of neotropical origin, and the earliest archeological remains found in Peru might be 10,000 years old. Its cultivation had spread throughout the American tropics in pre-Colombian times, and the sweet potato then spread throughout the world even to nontropical climates, such as the Mediterranean coastline of the Iberian Peninsula in the northern hemisphere, and New Zealand in the southern hemisphere. Nowadays, in southeast Asia and Oceania it is an important subsistence crop. Thus, for example, in many places in southeast Asia it is used to complement rice, and in Oceania it is grown with yams and taro; even the Maori, who live far from the tropics, cultivate several varieties of sweet potato. It seems it may even have been taken to Polynesia in pre-Colombian times.

Taro and other aroids

Several species of the Arum family (Araceae), such as taro and cocoyam, are also important subsistence foodstuffs. Taro (*Colocasia antiquorum* [=*C. esculenta*]) and the variety *globulifera* known as dasheen are thought to have been first cultivated in India, from where it spread east to southeast Asia, China, Japan and the Pacific islands. It spread west to Arabia and Egypt, where it has been cultivated for over 2,500 years, and from there to tropical Africa.

In English-speaking western Africa *Colocasia* is known as "old coco-yam" or "eddoes," and is less important than coco-yam or tania (*Xanthosoma*), which was introduced into the region from the Caribbean in the days of the slave trade. The production of coco-yam ranks third in western Africa after yams and cassava. Other edible species of the Araceae include the giant Taro (*Alocasia macrorrhiza*) and the giant swamp taro (*Cyrtosperma*), which are important subsistence crops in parts of the Pacific.

2.7 Cultivated and semicultivated fruits

Many rainforest species produce edible fruit, and those of most interest have to some extent been regularly cultivated. Initially, interest was centered on those fruit with the greatest food value, but fresh fruit is becoming more important. Some of these fruit are important raw materials for derivative products, such as alcoholic drinks or sweeteners.

In the rainforest there are many trees, and even lianas and herbaceous plants, that produce edible sweet fruits: in the Philippines alone a list includ-

147 One of the most popular tropical vegetables is the chayote (*Sechium edule*, Cucurbitaceae). The very nutritious fruit is like a small squash and is native to the Central American rainforest. [Photo: Tony Morrison / South American Pictures]

The following summary includes some of the most important fruits, beginning with some wild fruit that are collected as table fruit.

Mangos and similar fruit

The most important of all these fruit is probably the mango (*Mangifera indica*, Anacardiaceae), originally from India but now widespread throughout the wet tropics. In fact, the mango is one of the few tropical plants that has undergone genetic improvement in cultivation by agricultural selection, with more than 500 known varieties. The best varieties produce delicious fruit, with a typical smell, with relatively few of the fibers that are so disagreeable in the coarser varieties or in immature fruit. Mangos are eaten as table fruit, and also in salads. World production is estimated at 100,000 tons annually.

ed 250 fruits. Most are in no way cultivated, and many others that are locally exploited are not tended, as they are wild plants whose growth is merely protected by clearing away the surrounding vegetation. Only a few species, half a dozen or so, have been used in large-scale plantations, known as plantation agriculture. There is a wide range of intermediate situations between plantations and simple collection from wild specimens, most of which can be considered kinds of cultivation. It is the fruit of these randomly cultivated plants that is normally found in local markets, and is even in some cases exported. Some of these species are also cultivated more regularly.

The true mango (*Mangifera indica*) is the most widespread species, and what most people consider a mango, but Peninsular Malaysia possesses more than 20 other species of *Mangifera* with edible fruit, 11 of which are cultivated in villages for local consumption. In the markets of the island of Borneo it is possible to find 14 indigenous species of mango, 5 of which grow only in the wild, while the others have been brought into semi-cultivation. These mangos are unknown outside their area of origin and are highly appreciated locally and have been given specific names: binjai (*M. caesia*), lanjut (*M. lagenifera*), bachang (*M. foetida*), bambangan (*M. panjang*), kuini (*M. odorata*), etc. Throughout southeast

148 An African market stall selling kola nuts. Kola nuts, the seeds of two tropical African plants (*Cola nitida* and *Cola acuminata*, Sterculiaceae), are both cultivated and collected from the wild. Chewing kola nuts is very popular because they contain caffeine. These seeds' worldwide fame is due to their use in extremely widespread cola drinks.
[Photo: Jean-Pierre Champrouz / Jacana]

149 There are many different shapes and varieties of mango (*Mangifera indica*) in the area where it is cultivated, which includes most of the tropics. The unripe mangoes in the photo are of the lancetilla variety, one of the many varieties, and are under cultivation in Roatán Island (Honduras).
[Photo: Xavier Ferrer & Adolf de Sostoa]

Asia kundang, gandaria or ramania, a tree with diminutive mango-like fruits of *Bouea macrophylla*, is greatly appreciated.

The amabarellas, or hog plums (*Spondias*, Anacardiaceae), are also similar to mangoes and belong to the same family, but are not from Asia. The true hog plum (*S. cytherea*) is from Réunion Island, but it is widely cultivated in the tropics. In the Americas there are several native species, some of which are cultivated, such as the mombin or Spanish plum (*S. mombin*, *S. purpurea*) and others are collected from the wild (*S. vanulosa*)

Papayas, custard apples, durians, and other fruits

Mangos are followed by papayas and custard apples (including cherimoyas) as the tropical fruits most widely cultivated on small plantations. Papayas can be found in almost any market, and may even be exported. Yet there are many other tropical fruits of the rainforest, such as rambutan, guava and mangosteen that are highly appreciated in local markets. They are rapidly increasing in importance as international markets are more and more influenced by the search for exotic tastes.

The pawpaw (*Carica papaya*) produces the most commonly consumed papayas. It is a tree-like, dioecious herbaceous plant that is probably from Amazonia but is now cultivated throughout the tropics in any small plot or backyard: no wild specimens

are known. The female plants produce many large fruit directly on the main stem, with a smooth orange skin and flesh that is full of seeds; papayas can be eaten as fruit or in salad. There is also a series of similar species, many of which are semiwild, whose fruit can be found in South American markets: *C. caulifolia* which is from Central America, *C. microcarpa* which is cultivated by the natives of Darién, *C. stipulata* and *C. pubescens* which are from montane forest.

Custard apples and cherimoyas (*Annona*, *Rollinia*, Annonaceae) come from the American tropics. There are about 70 different species, mostly small trees, a dozen of which are cultivated. The cherimoya or custard apple (*Annona cherimola*) is more typical of montane forests, but the sweetsop (*A. squamosa*), the tastiest of all and perhaps the most widely cultivated, and lowland rainforest species include the soursop or guanábana (*A. muricata*) which produces enormous fruit (8-12in [20-30 cm] and 7.7-9.9 lb [3.5-4.5 kg]) that are used to make water ices; other valued species include *A. reticulata*, *A. diversifolia*, and *A. purpurea*, as well as biriba (*Rollinia deliciosa*, *R. jimenezii*, *R. emarginata*), whose fruit are similar to the custard apple, but rougher, and contain just as many seeds.

The durian (*Durio zibethinus*, Bombacaceae) bears a superficial resemblance to the custard apples and shares their characteristic of rapidly oxidizing on opening. Their origin and nature are, however, very different. The durian belongs to a different family and is from Malaysia, from where it has hardly spread, although it is intensely cultivated. Durians, which look like spiny melons, travel very badly as they spoil easi-

150 The herbaceous structure of the papaya plant (*Carica papaya*) does not prevent its tree-like stem growing tens of feet tall. The flowers, and thus the fruit on the female plants (the species is dioecious), are at the top of the stem and borne directly on it. The fruit are the size of a melon and turn yellow when they ripen, as shown in the photo of a Machiguenga child from Manu (Peru) gathering a ripe papaya. The fruit's pulp is very rich in papain, a proteolytic enzyme that explains why the papaya is famous for helping digestion.
[Photo: André Bärtschi / Planet Earth Pictures]

ly. They are highly appreciated locally, although their rancid stench is disagreeable to the unaccustomed.

The Sapindaceae family includes several fruit highly appreciated in Asia's tropical markets and increasingly popular throughout the world. They are typically in the form of a dense infructescence with a hard skin and gelatinous pulp. The best known is the lychee (*Litchi chinensis*), from southeast Asia, which has a reddish, leathery skin and is served in Chinese restaurants throughout the world preserved in syrup. Throughout Malaysia, however, rambutans (*Nephelium lappaceum, N. mutabile*) are more common; their skin has spikes with soft hooks, and they are cultivated in other tropical regions. The longans (*Dimocarpus longan, D. malaiense*), are also from southeast Asia and resemble the lychee but have a light brown skin.

The guava (*Psidium guajava*, Myrtaceae) is a neotropical plant that has been cultivated since antiquity. The Incas spread the consumption of its fruits through most of South America, and it is now cultivated throughout the tropics. The guava's fruit is a kind of berry with a vitamin-rich, tasty pulp that varies in color. It can be eaten fresh or made into a jelly due to its high pectin content. A related species of Brazilian origin, the strawberry guava (*P. littorale* [=*P. cattleianum*]) is also locally cultivated, together with an enormous array of other species—more than 100—of the same genus, whose fruit are also to some extent eaten.

Eugenia and *Syzygium*, members of the Myrtaceae and closely related to the guavas, also produce a large number of edible fruit, as well as the very well known spice, cloves (*Syzygium aromaticum* [=*Eugenia caryophyllata*]), which is discussed in the section on spices. The most widely spread species are the jambu or rose apple (*S. jambos*), jambolans (*S. cumini, S. malaccense, S. aquea*) from Asia, and Brazil/Surinam cherry or pitanga (*E. uniflora*), and related species (*E. brasiliensis, E. dombeyi*).

There are many more different plants from different families that produce fruit, sold in local markets or on a larger scale. These include, in no particular order: mangosteen (*Garcinia mangostana*, Guttiferae), another of the more than 100 species in this Malaysian genus that has edible fruits, which have a delicious smooth white pulp; mammee apple (*Mammea americana*, Guttiferae), from the Antilles, whose fruit are also delicious; santol (*Sandoricum koetjape* and langsat *Lansium domesticum*) both Indomalaysian members of the Meliaceae with fruits somewhat similar to the

151 The wonderful range of tropical fruits is clearly visible in the markets. Some are a riot of shapes and colors, such as at this stall (upper photo) in Kandy, Sri Lanka. The fruit on display include several species of custard apple or cherimoya (*Annona cherimola, A. mamillata*), with their typical scaly skin, mangosteens (*Garcinia mangostana*) with their smooth, brownish peel, the spiky durian (*Durio zibethinus*), the red and even spinier rambutans (*Nephelium lappaceum*) in a basket just next to the stallholder, and many others. This photo (center) of a stall in Pointe-à-Pitre, on Guadalupe, shows the unusual cross-section of the carambola, the rose-apple (*Syzygium jambos*), a few yellow passion fruit (*Passiflora*), a guanábana, which is a relative of the custard apple (*Annona muricata*) and some bananas (*Musa*). The display is rounded off (lower photo) with one of the most typical of tropical fruits, the guava (*Psidium guajava*), in this case on a stall in Brazil. [Photos: Montserrat Ferrer, Rosa Carvajal and Christian Errath / Jacana]

152 The breadfruit tree (*Artocarpus altilis*) is a staple food plant in the islands of the tropical Pacific, and is inseparably associated with the voyage of HMS Bounty in 1787. This voyage was an expedition to transport seedlings of the breadfruit from Tahiti to the British colonies in the Caribbean for cultivation as food for the slaves. Lieutenant Bligh was in command, and David Nelson, a gardener from the Royal Botanic Gardens at Kew, was contracted to collect the breadfruit seedlings. On the journey back from Tahiti, the master's mate, Fletcher Christian, and other members of the crew mutinied. Bligh, the loyal officers and David Nelson were cast adrift. David Nelson died 11 weeks later in Java, but Bligh lived to repeat the voyage. The mutineers returned to Tahiti. From there they sought an uninhabited island and established a community in Pitcairn Island, where their descendants still live. The breadfruit tree was successfully introduced into Saint Vincent, in the Lesser Antilles, after Bligh's second voyage in 1793. The two botanists from Kew Gardens that accompanied him on this occasion were Christopher Smith and James Wiles; the first breadfruit tree they planted is still growing in the St Vincent Botanic Gardens. [Photo: John B. Free / NHPA]

mangosteen; carambolas (*Averrhoa carambola*, *A. bilimbi*, Oxalidaceae), which have unusual fruit, star-shaped in cross-section, with an acid taste that are popular in southeast Asia; several sapotes, the normally very tasty fruit of different rainforest members of the Sapotaceae, such as the marmalade plum *Calocarpum sapota* [=*C. mammosum*] and the star-apple *Chrysophyllum cainito*, which are very popular in the Antilles under the local name of "mamme zapote" and "caimito," sapote itself or sapodilla (*Manilkara zapota*) that provides one of the gums used in chewing gum; sapote, lucuma or canistel (*Pouteria campechiana* [=*Lucuma nervosa*]), etc.

Finally, there are some rainforest fruit that are not eaten raw but are cooked or treated as a nonfruit foodstuff. Perhaps the best example is the breadfruit (*Artocarpus altilis*, Moraceae), which occupies a place of importance in the history of European colonialism. An almost unknown foodstuff to contemporary Europeans, early descriptions of the breadfruit by Captain Cook and other mariners in the 18th century, spread this humble food plant's fame as a "wonder crop." The first European explorers of the Pacific were truly impressed by this tree "from which bread itself is gathered as a fruit." The fruit of the breadfruit tree, cooked in a variety of ways, is still a staple foodstuff in some Pacific islands, though it is now also widely cultivated in other lowland tropical areas. The tree also produces timber, fiber, and latex. Despite its importance in subsistence economies, the bread-

fruit tree has received little scientific attention as a food plant. Other related food-producing species include *A. integer* and *A. heterophyllus*, which are mainly cultivated in southeast Asia. Some wild species are also eaten in southeast Asia and the Pacific.

Palm fruits

The importance of palms in the local economy of rainforest dwellers has already been mentioned (as food, construction materials, etc.). They also deserve special attention as a source of edible fruit. The babassu palm (*Orbignya phalerata*) and the moriche palm (*Mauritia flexuosa*) have already been mentioned as species collected on a large scale (see 3.2.1), while oil palms (*Elaeis* and other genera) are discussed in the section on plantation agriculture (see 3.2.8) because they are so widely cultivated. Yet there are many palms that are scarcely cultivated, although they produce fruits that are important in local markets. The New World tropical area includes edible palm fruits, such as the acrocomias (*Acrocomia panamensis*, *A. totai*), astrocaryas (*Astrocaryum aculeatum* [=*A. vulgare*], *A. tucuma*, *A. chonta*), ataleas or pissava palms (*Attalea spectabilis*, *A. agrestis*), pataua palms (*Jessenia bataua*), bacaba palms (*Oenocarpus*), and especially the peach palm (*Bactris gasipaes*), whose racemes (clusters) of fruits are found on sale in almost the entire American tropics, despite the difficulty of collecting them because of the ferocious spines covering the stipe (short stalk).

In southeast Asia the fruit of the salak palm (*Salacca zalacca*) are also widely eaten, and are similar to those of the moriche, while those of the betel nut (*Areca catechu*) play an extremely important social role as a masticatory; they are mixed with a little lime, wrapped in fresh betel pepper leaves (*Piper betle*, Piperaceae) and chewed.

Fruits used as sweeteners and for alcohol production

Many palms have been widely used for local production of sugary substances, such as the now rare kitul palm (*Caryota urens*) from the moist forests of southern India and Sri Lanka. The sweet sap tapped from its young inflorescence can be fermented to make the juice toddy, or concentrated to make jaggery, a crystallized candy that is very popular as a substitute for sugar and sells well in local markets. Kitul tapping is a well-established cottage industry

153 The most important fruit-producing tropical palms regularly found in markets, include the peach palm (*Bactris gasipaes*) which produces the clusters of red fruit, as in the left-hand photo, which in this case are from Iquitos in the Peruvian Amazon; and salac (*Salacca zalacca*) which produces shiny brown reticulate fruit (right-hand photo, taken in Celebes).
[Photos: Ramon Folch and Josep M. Barres]

in parts of Sri Lanka that uses traditional methods handed down from generation to generation. Unfortunately, centuries of extraction from the wild have led to wild plants becoming scarce, and the species has never been established in cultivation. Other palms tapped for their sap include the nipa palm (*Nypa fruticans*), whose sap is used to make sugar, vinegar, and a popular fermented beverage known as tuba in the Philippines, where the gebang palm (*Corypha elata* [=*C. utan*]) is used in the same way. The fruit of the palm *Acrocomia vinifera* from Central America are also used to make a fermented beverage.

Other rainforest plants have aroused great interest for their commercial potential as natural sweeteners, including three from west Africa. The *katemfe*, or miraculous fruit (*Thaumatococcus danielli*, Marantaceae), is a west African rainforest plant with crimson fruit containing a gelatinous substance, thaumatin, a protein up to 2,500 sweeter

than sucrose. The fruit are sucked as sweets and are also used to sweeten cooked dishes. Thaumatine is widely used in Japan as an additive in drinks, chewing gums and cigarettes, and as a flavor enhancer. The serendipity berry (*Dioscoreophyllum cumminsii*, Menispermaceae) produces red fruit containing a protein, monellin, used as a sweetener that is also much sweeter than sucrose. The fruit of the miraculous berry (*Synsepalum dulcificum*, Sapotaceae), produces another protein, miraculin, that can make bitter foods taste sweet.

2.8 Plantation agriculture

Since European colonization of the tropics, and specifically of the rainforest areas, many large plantations have been established for the large-scale production of foodstuffs or other export

154 Two of the most popular cold drinks in Brazil are guaraná and yoco. They are made with the fruit of the guaraná and yoco lianas (*Paullinia cupana* and *P. yoco*, both members of the Sapindaceae). They are from the Orinoco-Amazon Basin and are now widely cultivated. Guaraná and yoco are very stimulating drinks, as the seeds contain 3.4% caffeine, twice as much as coffee beans. The drink was formerly prepared in a very simple way by the Siona people of the Putumaya-Caquetá Basin in the Colombian Amazon; other species of the same genus (*P. macrophylla*, *P. perophylla*) were also used in making the drink. The photo shows a typical raceme of fruit of the guaraná (*P. cupana*), with what looks like a pair of eyes peeping through, the seeds.
[Photo: Luiz Claudio Marigo / Bruce Coleman Limited]

155 **No other major tropical plantation crop** is as famous as sugar cane (*Saccharum officinarum*). The photo shows the harvest (*zafra*) on a plantation in Panama. This has long been performed using machetes, after burning the fields to eliminate the troublesome leaves.
[*Photo: Mark Edwards / Still Pictures*]

products. Often, this has led to the clearing of large areas of natural forest, displacing subsistence agricultural systems that are better adapted to the environment. Industrial production of plantation crops for export markets sharply contrasts with the everyday subsistence agriculture practiced by millions of people in the rainforest and on its edges. Whereas export crops considered profitable are grown in monocultures, traditional agriculture produces a large range of harvests, normally without using artificial fertilizers, insecticides, or other agricultural chemicals.

In fact, large plantations were the main economic activity of the colonial administrations, and later became the main economic activity in most newly independent countries, with all the problems inherent in monocultures (lack of diversified food crops in the colonial period, subjection of prices to those of monopoly markets currently). In the rainforest, the most important plantations are rubber trees (see "From Henry Wickham to Chico Mendes," pp. 306-309), followed by oil palm and cocoa.

Sugar cane

For more than 5,000 years, the sweetness of sugar has been a source of pleasure. All green plants produce sugars, and for centuries they have been sources of sugary syrups; even honey, the archetypal sweetener, comes from the nectar that bees take from flowers. Nowadays, two plants provide most of the world's sugar production: sugar beet (*Beta vulgaris*, Chenopodiaceae), a European plant, that was first cultivated to produce sugar in the early 19th century and now provides a quarter of the sugar consumed in the world; and sugar cane (*Saccharum officinarum*, Poaceae), a cane-forming, fistular (hollow-stemmed) herbaceous plant, provides the other three quarters of the world's sugar crop.

Sugar cane today, for which no wild ancestor is known with security, is a grass between 8.2 and 11.5 ft (2.5 and 3.5 m) tall that grows into a thicket of canes and leaves. Sugar accumulates in the canes as a byproduct of metabolism, reaching its peak concentration 10-14 months after sprouting, when the leaves wither. The canes are then cut to the ground, almost always with machetes, in a harsh operation that forms part of the story of the plantations and its literature. New plants are propagated vegetatively by cuttings.

Sugar cane is thought to have been domesticated in New Guinea, which is still the primary center of diversity for the crop plant. Sugar cane was already cultivated in India 3,000 years ago. The Arabs took it to Egypt, to Sicily and to al-Andalus between the 8th and 10th century A.D. In the 12th century, some sugar from sugar cane was consumed in Christian Europe, proceeding from Sicily, the Valencia region, and the eastern Mediterranean, but it was

156 **The main part of the traditional sugar factory**, where the sugar was obtained from the sugar cane, was the mill. Mills were powered by water, or during the 19th century by steam engines. In the sugar factories the sugar cane is pressed by passing it through metal rollers. The resulting juice was concentrated by evaporating the water in the boiler room. The impure crystallized sugar, raw or brown sugar, was then molded into the typical shape, a sugar loaf. Processing this brown sugar turns it into white or refined sugar. This process is described in the first volume of the *Recueil des planches sur les sciences, les arts libéraux et les arts mechaniques avec leur explications* of the engravings of the *Dictionnaire raisonné des arts, des sciences et des métiers* (Diderot and Alembert's encyclopedia) and is essentially unchanged today.
[Photo: Biblioteca de Catalunya]

an expensive product that not everyone could afford, and ordinary people used honey as a sweetener. The Portuguese introduced sugar cane cultivation first into Madeira and then into Brazil, while the Spanish introduced it first into the Canary Islands and then to the Antilles. From the 16th century onwards, the development of New World plantations with slave labor ruined the formerly prosperous sugar mills of Valencia, Mallorca and Sicily, but sugar consumption became much more widespread. In the 17th century, Brazil dominated world sugar production, which was controlled by Portuguese and Dutch planters. Sugar cane plantations were mainly established along the coast, where the soil was fertile and access to seaports was relatively good. The European colonists adopted the slash and burn technique to cultivate sugar cane, and also consumed large quantities of firewood to fuel the furnaces needed to refine sugar. This led to the rapid deforestation of large areas of northeastern Brazil.

Today, sugar cane is cultivated in many hot countries, and the main producers are still Brazil, the Caribbean and India; total world production is about a million tons. The cultivated plant's genetic base is very limited, and this has led to *ex situ* programs to collect and preserve its varieties. It is also necessary to protect the valuable germ plasm of wild species related to the sugar cane, which are being lost as a consequence of the destruction of their natural habitats in Malaysia, Indonesia, and Papua New Guinea.

Bananas and pineapples

The two most widely cultivated tropical fruits are the banana, the fruit of the banana "tree," a large herbaceous member of the Musaceae, and the pineapple, the infrutescence of a member of the Bromeliaceae.

Bananas and plantains
Bananas (*Musa*) are from originally from southeast Asia, but are now grown in plantations throughout the tropics in any clearing in the rainforest or in any domestic vegetable plot, and some isolated specimens may even have more or less reverted to the wild. They are almost always the result of vegetative reproduction, because bananas do not contain viable seeds. Banana plants produce a huge inflorescence (77-110 lb [35-50 kg]) with a characteristic appearance, hands of bananas, and are covered by the colored bracts that protect the bunches of female flowers. Their large inflorescences, and their palm-like growth-form with large frayed leaves

whose petioles form the plant's apparent stem, makes their appearance quite unmistakable. The large vegetative structure reaches a height of 10-13 ft (3-4 m) within a few months and is cut down after each harvest, sprouting again without any problems.

In fact, three species are cultivated, two of which produce medium or small fruit, eaten as table fruit (*Musa sapientium*, *M. cavendishii* [=*M. nana*]), while the third species (*M. paradisiaca*) produces very coarse bananas that are eaten cooked or used to make flour, as they contain a great deal of starch. There is, however, disagreement between authors about whether three and different specific taxa really exist, because these three species or basic varieties are sterile, so their possible hybridization has not been tested. There are also many varieties of each type, greatly complicating the situation. The many forms, especially those eaten as table fruit, vary greatly in size and color.

The early history of the banana is unclear. It seems clear that it must have been domesticated thousands of years ago. There are records of banana cultivation around 1100 B.C. in Assyria. They must have reached Polynesia a long time ago, considering their degree of integration, and the same is true of tropical Africa. At the beginning of the 16th century they were introduced into the Antilles, and from there they spread throughout the New World tropics. Plantations in the Americas (especially Brazil and Central America), India and the Philippines produce most of the internationally traded crop, which is about 40,000 tons a year. Some companies have or have had a monopoly on the trade, giving them an enormous power over the producer states (the "banana republics").

In the rainforest of southeast Asia and the Pacific there are still wild bananas (*Musa acuminata*, *M. balbisiana*) whose fruits are fertile and form part of the local diet. These wild bananas may be important in future breeding programs. The genetic base of the cultivated banana, as mentioned above, is very limited and depends on a few triploid clones developed from these two wild species. They have adapted very well to commercial cultivation and long-distance transport, but are not very resistant to some diseases.

Pineapples
The different species of pineapple (*Ananas*) are from the neotropical lowlands. *A. comosus* ([=*A. sativus*]) was discovered and first domesticated by the Guarani people, and has been the species most

157 The banana is the most widespread of all tropical fruits, including all the very many different species and varieties (*Musa esplendidum*, *M. cavendishii*, *M. paradisiaca*, etc). The bananas, or plantains, are borne in bunches that hang from "hands" topped by purple bracts (top photo). In cultivated varieties, the fruit are sterile, but this does not prevent them reproducing vegetatively. The banana is a herbaceous plant with a tree-like growth form (see figure 189). Bananas are very rich in carbohydrates and vary in size and color, as shown in this photo of a stall in Chimaltenango, in Guatemala (bottom photo). They can be eaten raw or cooked. Transporting bananas over oceans forced the development of a special trade that, before the invention of cold storage, had to ship the unripe bunches and ripen them on the voyage. Due to the hormone given off by mature bananas, shippers ran the risk of ripening prematurely and this could lead to the loss of the entire cargo. [*Photos: Richard Chesher / Planet Earth Pictures and Ramon Folch*]

systematically cultivated, but others are occasionally gathered by indigenous populations (*A. bracteatus*, *A. guaraniticus*, *A. microcephalus*, etc.). They all share the typical bromeliad growth form: a rosette of elongated leaves, in whose center the inflorescence forms, followed by the infrutescence, the "pineapple."

Surprisingly, the agricultural varieties of pineapple now cultivated throughout the wet tropics did not originate in the Americas but in Europe. The pineapple was already cultivated in the Antilles in pre-Columbian times and then in the Orinoco Basin. At the beginning of the 19th century, specimens of varieties cultivated in Guyana were taken to the greenhouses

158 **The pineapple** is the infrutescence of the pineapple (*Ananas comosus*). It got its name because it looks like a pinecone. The pineapple is not a conifer but a herbaceous plant that forms a rosette at ground level. A single pineapple grows from the center of the rosette, with a second leaf rosette at the top of the fruit.
[Photo: Fritz Prenzel / Bruce Coleman Limited]

159 **Pressing the fruits of the oil palm (*Elaeis guineensis*)**, by industrial or craft methods, like those shown in this photo, releases the oil for which the plant is grown.
[Photo: Dominique Halleux / Bios / Still Pictures]

at Versailles, where the current commercial varieties were bred. The main pineapple plantations are in Hawaii, Central America, and the Ivory Coast. Much of the crop is sold canned.

Palm oils

The oil palm (*Elaeis guineensis*) lives in the clearings and forest edges of the African rainforest, where there is little shade. Its small oval fruits are from 1-2 in (3-5 cm) long, and grouped in dense spherical infrutescences and produce two types of oil: the first, palm oil, is extracted from the dried pressed pulp, while the second is pressed from the seeds which are separated from the pulp before pressing. The first is more like olive oil, while the second is more similar to coconut oil. Both are export crops used in the food industry in industrialized countries, though palm oil is also consumed in the local market of the producer countries in western Africa (from Guinea to Angola). The leading exporters are Malaysia and Indonesia, where the crop was introduced only a century ago, and the Americas, especially in Colombia and Ecuador, where production is now increasing greatly.

The American oil palm (*Elaeis oleifera*) is also cultivated on a modest scale in the Amazon Basin. Oil is also obtained from a series of other palms of the babassu group (*Orbignya martiana*, *O. oleifera*, *O. cohune*) and from the astrocaryas (*Astrocaryum murumuru*, *A. tucumal*, *A. vulgare*).

Cocoa

Cocoa (*Theobroma cacao*, Sterculiaceae) is a small tree of the understory of the upper Amazon. It has been cultivated since ancient times by the Central American people, from whom its common name derives: *cacahuatl* is a Nahuatl word, derived from the Mayan *cacahu*. It is one of the rainforest's many cauliflorous plants, with fruit borne directly on the trunk. The fruit contain many seeds, the cocoa grains used to make chocolate. The neotropical area has about a dozen species (an exaggerated twenty species have been named), but only five species produce edible fruit: *T. bicolor*, *T. canumanense*, *T. subincanum* (locally known as "cupuí" or "caca-co de monte"), *T. grandiflorum* (known as "capauçu" by the indians of Para and Maranhão, where the species still grows wild and has also been cultivated since pre-Columbian times) and *T. cacao*.

Cultivated cocoa (*Theobroma cacao*) has, like the other members of its species, fruit with an edible pulp, but they are mainly appreciated for their seeds. There are three different types, corresponding to the three centers of genetic diversity of the cultivated crop: the central American criollo cocoa, surely descended from the first varieties to be cultivated, with rough fruit that are yellow or reddish; the Amazon forastero variety, with smooth greenish or whitish fruit, which is the most widespread; and Trinitario cocoa, which spread from Trinidad and Venezuela, with very rough fruit that were formerly greatly appreciated.

Cocoa, true to its origins, needs to be cultivated in semishade in a hot, wet climate. Until the 19th century it was only cultivated in the neotropical area and in the Philippines, but later it spread from Brazil to Bioko and from there it spread throughout the wet African tropics, and to Java and Sri Lanka. The huge present-day plantations in Africa and Brazil (Ivory Coast, Nigeria, Ghana, and especially the Brazilian state of Bahía), and to a lesser extent in Malaysia, are the main producers, with an annual harvest of about a million tons. In fact, only the seeds (25-40 seeds per fruit) are exported, after being removed from the pulp and fermented for a few days: It is during this drying and spontaneous fermentation that they lose their initial bitterness, turn a toasted reddish color and acquire their typical smell. These cocoa seeds contain a lot of fat or cocoa butter (45-50%), protein (12-14%), and an unusual alkaloid, theobromine (1.5%), which is responsible for many of the properties of the product made from the seeds, chocolate (see "Chocolate, a food fit for the gods," pp. 246-259).

2.9 The taste and smell of spices

Food-related rainforest plants include a special group, those used as kitchen spices, partly collected from the wild and partly cultivated. Tropical spices were highly valued even in ancient times and were normally collected from wild plants. They are still important, but they are now generally cultivated, though collection from the rainforest is by no means uncommon.

The world of spices

The general term spice includes many plant products, buds, fruit, seeds, bark, roots, etc. All they have in common is their possession of an unusual smell, essence, or another chemicals usually lacking in the European flora of the time, and therefore of exotic provenance. These plants are nearly always from Asia. The term *spice* is still used today to refer to these products, but the list has grown greatly with new additions of American, African and even European origin. In any case, some of the plants considered as spices are not derived from the rainforest, such as saffron, paprika, star anise, mustard and the seeds of many members of the Umbelliferae (coriander, cumin, aniseed, dill, etc.).

In Europe, the trade in spices from the Orient has been operating for more than 2,000 years. The busy routes were those that ran west from China, India, Sri Lanka, and Indonesia, through Afghanistan and Iran to Europe. Europeans first perceived the tropical rainforests, above all those in Asia, as sources of spices that were invaluable as means of masking the taste of their daily food, often dubiously preserved, as well as the basis for preparing (real and imaginary) medicines, perfumes, and drinks. International trade in each of the nine main rainforest spices now has a value of about 150 million dollars, a figure that can be doubled or tripled when they reach the retail trade.

The main spices: cloves, nutmeg, and pepper

Historically, the three most important spices have been cloves, nutmeg, and black pepper. Cloves, the flower bud of *Syzygium aromaticum*

Chocolate, a food fit for the gods

Fray Bernardino de Sahagún (1499-1590), a Franciscan missionary in the Vice-Royalty of Nueva España and assiduous collector of information on Nahuatl customs, recorded in 1571 that for the feast of Atemozotli (the 16th month in their calendar) the native people offered small gourd cups filled with cocoa seeds to images of the permanently snow-covered mountains (Iztaccihuatl, Popocatepetl, Citlaltepetl). Some areas of Mexico still maintain the custom of including cocoa in their offerings to the plants they consider divine to reinvigorate them, or if they are medicinal, to strengthen their curative effect. Cocoa was for centuries considered a food fit for the gods, and this was recognized by the Swedish botanist Carl von Linné (Linnaeus) (1707-1778) when he gave the cocoa plant its scientific name, *Theobroma*, meaning "food of the gods."

The Mayans probably cultivated cocoa 2,500 years ago. They gave it the name cacao which combines the words *cac* (the fruit's color, red, in the Mayan language), and *cau* (a particle expressing the idea of force and fire). The fruit of the cocoa represented the human heart and chocolate the blood. The Aztecs learned cocoa cultivation and use from the Maya and called cocoa *cacahuatl*, and gave the name xocolatl to the aromatic drink obtained from it, often flavored with flowers or other fruits, especially those of the tlilxochitl (vanilla). In any case, the first reference by a European to cocoa and chocolate (1519) was by Bernal Díaz de Castillo (1495-1584), a chronicler of the Spanish conquest of Mexico. In his description of a banquet with the Anahuac emperor Montezuma (Moctezuma) II, he explains that "from time to time they brought, in a sort of cup made of fine gold, a certain drink made of cocoa, that they said was to have use of women; but we said this was not for us; what we saw is that they brought about fifty jars of fine frothy cocoa and drank it all."

Cocoa was of great importance in Nahuatl culture. Not only was chocolate appreciated as a drink that gave strength and increased sexual potency, but its seeds were also used for trading and eventually as money by the Aztecs, who demanded a tribute in cocoa seeds from the peoples living in the hot areas where the plant was cultivated. The monetary unit was the *xiquipilli* a bag of 8,000 seeds, but fractions and multiples of this unit, such as the *uquipilli*, a bag of 24,000 seeds were also used. Fakes were not unknown, and in 1537 the Viceroy of Nueva España, Antonio de Mendoza, sent Charles I of Spain samples of fakes, which were empty seeds filled with mud. The use of cocoa beans as money lasted long after the Spanish Conquest. Hernán Cortés paid his soldiers with cocoa beans, and even in the early 19th century, Alexander von Humboldt recorded the use of cocoa beans as money in southwest Mexico.

Cocoa (*Theobroma cacao*) fruits [Michel Viard / Jacana]

In the 16th century chocolate became famous in Europe as a stimulating drink. Whether cocoa broke a fast and could be taken during Lent or before mass gave rise to labyrinthine debates. Ana and Maria Teresa of Austria (1601-1666, 1638-1683), the sister and daughter of Philip IV of Spain (both queens of France by marriage, to Louis XIII and Louis XIV, respectively) introduced the taste for chocolate into the French court, and from there it spread to the rest of Europe. The British, French, Dutch and Central Europeans all competed to find the best way to prepare it, the start of a burgeoning food industry. Yet it was not the Spanish who promoted the cocoa industry, which remained basically in the hands of the Dutch, and British, while chocolate manufacture was dominated by the British, French (and later Belgians), and above all, the Swiss.

Engraving of cocoa cultivation (*Theobroma cacao*) from the Ausländische Kulturpflanzen (1894), by F. Dannenberg [Archiv für Kunst und Geschichte, Berlin]

the Swiss Rudolf Lindt had the idea of mixing the cocoa paste with cocoa butter to make a new smoother-tasting form of chocolate, the chocolate we know nowadays. Years later, in 1875, in the city of Vevey, the Swiss Daniel Peter Nestlé and Henry Nestlé added condensed milk to the mixture pioneered by Lindt: thus milk chocolate was born.

Chocolate production [Michel Viard / Jacana]

Simply grinding the seeds produces a dark, bitter, oily paste that is pure, raw chocolate. This paste liquefies on heating, and is aromatized with vanilla and sweetened with honey to make the chocolate the Aztecs drank. Europeans replaced the honey with sugar, and used other flavorings, such as cinnamon. Its medicinal use as a tonic led to its spread in the form of solidified cold paste—cooking chocolate—which was the beginning of modern bars of chocolate. The first bars were sold in 1779 by the French company Pelletier. The industry soon learned to separate the fat from the chocolate (40-50% of the paste) to leave a dry powder, soluble in water or milk, called cocoa powder. In 1840,

Poster advertising chocolate (1925) [Mary Evans Picture Library]

Since then, chocolate has been combined with many other products, flavored with different fragrances and filled with a huge range of delicacies, even mint paste, a British invention. Dark or bitter chocolate, contains 50-70% pure ground cocoa paste (the rest is mainly cocoa butter, sugar, and often vanilla), but in normal chocolate the cocoa content is much lower (30-50%), as it contains more cocoa butter or milk products. The bars of chocolate for preparing drinking chocolate by mixing with warm milk or water usually contain flours or other thickening agents, so that this popular drink is now very different from the beverage the Aztecs drank, which was pure liquid chocolate.

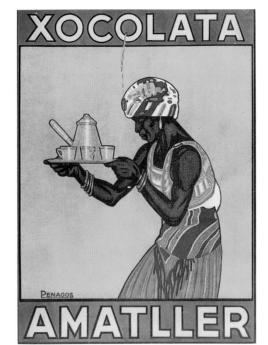

Poster advertising chocolate (1930) original from Rafael de Penagos (1889-1954) [Mary Evans Picture Library]

Chocolate has played and still plays an important role in confectionery, as shown in the famous Austrian *Sachertorte*, the Catalan *mona* (Easter cake), and an immense number of sweets. And it is also used in the kitchen, especially in Mexico, where it is used in guajolote sauce, and in Catalunya, where it is an essential ingredient in many *picades* or pastes used to flavor and accompany fricasseed fish or fowl. Chocolate has a vast number of followers. It produces addiction (after all, its active ingredient theobromine, is an alkaloid), and in addition to its virtues, it has drawbacks. It may cause headaches, it promotes tooth decay, it damages the liver and more importantly in affluent societies, it is fattening. But it is a food fit for the gods themselves.

Chocolates [Eric Sander / Gamma]

160 The structure of the fruit of the nutmeg (*Myristica fragrans*) is very complex. The white globular epicarp and mesocarp are of little interest. The shiny black endocarp, or seedcase, is covered by a red aril. The seed-case is dried in the sun for two months and broken with a stick to obtain the brownish-grey seed, the nutmeg.
[Photo: Michel Viard / Bruce Coleman Limited]

[=*Eugenia caryophyllata*], Myrtaceae), and nutmeg, the dried kernels of *Myristica fragrans* (Myristicaceae), are both from the Molucca Islands of Indonesia. Peppers are the fruit of the pepper (*Piper nigrum*, Piperaceae), and are originally from India.

Historically, cloves and nutmegs were so important that the interest in finding a better route to the Moluccas led to the discovery of the Americas. Later, at the beginning of the 16th century, the Portuguese, in their search for cloves for the European market, discovered a group of small volcanic islands in the North Moluccas, known as the Spice Islands. They established a monopoly on the spice trade that a century later fell into the hands of the Dutch East India Company. Most cloves are now produced in the islands of Zanzibar and Pemba (part of Tanzania), off the eastern coast of Africa, and Madagascar and Indonesia are also important producers. Much of Indonesia's production is used in *kretek* cigarettes, which consist of a mixture of cloves and tobacco.

The nutmeg tree (*Myristica fragrans*, Myristicaceae) is originally from the Eastern Moluccas. The Dutch dominated the trade between the middle of the 17th century and the early 19th century, by forcibly restricting nutmeg cultivation to Banda and Amboina, two small islands in the Moluccas. The nutmeg's spread to other islands has been attributed to the fruit-eating pigeons that fly from island to island. Indonesia is now a major producer, and Grenada, in the Lesser Antilles is another center of cultivation. The parts of the nutmeg that are used include both the seed (the nutmeg) and the fimbri-

ate red aril partially covering the seed, which is dried and ground to form the spice called mace.

Pepper is the other main rainforest spice. Wild specimens of pepper grow in the Western Ghats of Malabar, probably the crop's center of origin. Pepper was taken from India to southeast Asia as cuttings. The search for routes to the centers of spice production in southeast Asia stimulated the major sea voyages by Europeans in the 15th and 16th centuries. The introduction of the pepper into other tropical areas is relatively recent. It is now mainly cultivated by smallholders in Malaysia, Indonesia and Brazil. In addition to "black pepper," (*Piper nigrum*, Piperaceae) there are also other peppers, such as the long peppers, (*P. retrofractum*, from Java, and *P. longum*) from Assam and Bengal, which produce the pepper that was most appreciated in antiquity.

Cardamom, vanilla and other seeds and fruits

Cardamom is an expensive spice, obtained from the dried or pickled fruit or seeds of cardamom *Eletteria cardamomum* (Zingiberaceae), a species originally from India. It is now mainly cultivated in Central America, India and Sri lanka, but the wild fruit are also sold. In Sri Lanka, the variety *cardamomum* is widely cultivated in the shade of the natural forest cover in mountain areas; the wild variety (*major*) is common in Sri Lanka's lowland rainforest.

Vanilla (*Vanilla planifolia*, Orchidaceae) is the most important spice from the New World. Native to Central America, the Aztecs already used the

161 **The economic value and aesthetic beauty of spices** go hand in hand. This illustration features (from top to bottom and left to right), fresh and dried cloves (*Syzygium aromaticum*), fruit and seeds of black pepper (*Piper nigrum*), vanilla pods (*Vanilla planifolia*), quills of cinnamon bark (*Cinnamomum verum* [=*C. zeylanicum*]), and rhizomes of turmeric (*Curcuma longa*). The spice clove is the dried flower bud. Black peppercorns are the dried immature fruit of the pepper, while white peppercorns are the same fruit, but mature and slightly fermented (both peppers are usually sold ground, and sometimes mixed together); pepper's smell, sharp taste, and culinary value are due to an oleoresin, a volatile oil and some alkaloids. Vanilla is an orchid, but it has small, inconspicuous, flowers. Self-pollination is prevented as the flower's stamens are effectively separated from the stigma by a sterile stigma, a rostellum, and fertilization can only be performed by some hummingbirds and bees of the genus *Melipona*. As these pollinating agents are only present in the Americas, attempts to cultivate vanilla in Asia and Africa, where other species of the genus grow, failed repeatedly. The problem of vanilla's pollination was scientifically resolved in 1836. In 1841, a former slave from Réunion called Albius managed to hand pollinate vanillas in Mauritius, and this led to its successful cultivation, especially in the islands of the Indian Ocean. Yellow powdered turmeric is the basis of curry powder, a preparation from India that consists of mixture of several ground spices (turmeric, coriander, cinnamon, cardamom, ginger, nutmeg, black pepper, red pepper, and cloves), in varying proportions and types, depending on the dish to be spiced. [Photos: *Christiana D'Hotel / Jacana and Michel Viard / Jacana*]

pods of this climbing orchid as a flavoring for chocolate in pre-Colombian times, a custom the Europeans followed and spread to sweets and ice creams. Vanilla is prepared by leaving the dry pods to cure so that spontaneous enzyme actions converts some glycosides into crystals of the aromatic substance. Vanilla was first introduced into Europe around 1510. The main producers are Madagascar, the Seychelles, Réunion, and the Comoros Islands.

Substitutes for vanilla include the fruit of *Vanilla pompona*; a synthetic aroma, vanillin, derived from euglenol; and especially, the fragrant seeds of the Tonka bean (*Dipteryx odorata*, Leguminosae), which is used to give a vanilla-like flavor to meals and tobacco (formerly and most importantly, snuff). The large Tonka tree is abundant on the banks of many large rivers in northern Amazonia and the Guyanas, especially in Venezuela, the main producer. Recently trade in Tonka beans has declined because of the possible toxicity of coumarin, one of its active ingredients.

Two further spices deserve mention. Allspice (*Pimenta doica*, Myrtaceae) is a small Central American tree whose dried green fruit are used to make allspice, a spice that resembles a mixture of clove, cinnamon and nutmeg. Jamaica, where the tree grows almost wild, is the main commercial producer. Melegueta pepper is produced from the seeds of the herbaceous plant *Aframomum melegueta* (Zingiberaceae) and is a substitute for cardamom; it is generally collected from the wild in several countries in western Africa, although it is also cultivated.

Cinnamon bark

The tree producing cinnamon (*Cinnamomum verum* [=*C. zeylanicum*] and *C. aromaticum*, Lauraceae) is native to Sri Lanka, and its bark, cinnamon, has been famous since antiquity. Seven or eight more species of cinnamon grow in Sri Lanka, including *C. sinharajensis*), recently discovered in the Sinharaja forest, but none has the delicate flavor of *C. zeylanicum*. Cinnamon is the dried peeled bark of the young shoots, and is sold as "quills," in rolled strips of bark, or as a powder. Its very typical smell is due to cinnamic aldehyde, and is highly valued in pastry making and perfumery. It has been collected from the

wild in the Sri Lankan rainforest for centuries: Cultivation began during Dutch colonization of the island in the 17th and 18th centuries, after the Dutch, Portuguese and British gained control of the Ceylon cinnamon trade from wild cinnamon trees.

China bark has been traded even longer. It is similar to that of the common cinnamon from Sri Lanka but is coarser and is obtained from Chinese cinnamon, or cassia (*Cinnamomum cassia*) and from other southeast Asian cinnamons (*C. tamala*, *C. burmannii* and *C. loureirii*). Finally, white cinnamon is obtained from *Canella winteriana* (Canellaceae) a small tree from the Caribbean.

Turmeric, ginger, and other rhizomes

Turmeric is obtained from the rhizomes of *Curcuma longa* [=*C. domestica*] (Zingiberaceae), a herbaceous species from southeast Asia. Turmeric has two different uses, as a coloring to turn food yellow, and as a spice: it is a basic component of curry powder. It is widely cultivated in India and Malaysia. Wild turmeric (*C. aromatica*) is also collected from the rainforests of southern India and western Bengal, and is used as a headache cure.

Ginger (*Zingiber officinale*, Zingiberaceae), another highly valued herbaceous member of the same family, is native to southern China. Its rhizomes are dried and cured or boiled in syrup. Ginger's characteristic smell is due to an aromatic essential oil containing a nonvolatile oleoresin, zingiberene, that is responsible for ginger's slightly biting taste and its dilatory effect on blood vessels. This causes sweating followed by a cool feeling, the reason why ginger is so appreciated in hot countries. Ginger is used as a condiment and to prepare ginger beer. Ginger is cultivated almost throughout the tropics and also in Japan.

The Zingiberaceae contains other plants producing rhizomes of interest as spices that are only known locally: galangal (*Alpinia officinarum* and *A. galanga*), from southern China and southeast Asia respectively; and two other Indomalaysian species widely used in southern Asia, false galangal (*Kaempferia galanga*) and zedoary (*Curcuma zedoaria*).

3. Using animal resources

3.1 The rainforest, a source of animal protein

Rainforest animals are a basic source of nourishment for many human groups. Even today, many indigenous people, unaccustomed to the domestication of animals and with only occasional access to industrially processed animal products, depend entirely on hunting and fishing for animal proteins. On the other hand, recently established colonists tend only to resort to hunting in times of need or for sport and prefer to consume domesticated cows, pigs, and poultry. Both indigenous and colonist hunters prefer mammals to all other animals, then birds, and then reptiles. The inhabitants of the rainforests also consume many kinds of fish from many sources.

The use of animal resources extends far beyond mere consumption as food, because for forest people many products have a ceremonial, medicinal, and social value. The sale of skins and leather is often part of the rural economy. Trade in live animals for pets, zoos, and biomedical research can be locally important. Sport hunting and tourism, especially with the recent growth of ecotourism, also adds value to the rainforest's animal resources. As sustainable development schemes evolve, native species will be evaluated as sources for new domesticated species, and recognition of the direct and indirect benefits produced by these animal resources will show the obvious value of conserving them.

The predatory action of humans

Within their evolutionary limitations, humans are consummate predators. They have binocular color vision, dexterous hands, sufficient mobility to cover wide areas, memories efficient at learning the habits of their prey, and social abilities that allow collaboration and communication. On the other hand, their simple, globular stomach does not allow fermentative digestion, meaning they are vulnerable to many food toxins and unable to digest most plant fibers. Thus, like their close relatives the anthropoid simians and cercopithecoids, they exploit food resources selectively, aiming always for the largest available sources of nutritious, nontoxic and easily digestible food.

There has never been any reason for humans to evolve individual constraints on methods of acquiring food. Human evolutionary experience consists of picking up and eating any high-quality food item that can be found, saving it for later only if it is certain that no one else will take it, or, in the event of a surplus, trading it quickly for maximum gain. This strategy served humans well in most biomes in which good foods were scarce and food acquisition was limited to hunting, fishing, and gathering.

Social cooperation applied another kind of selection pressure. Groups of allied peoples or kin could secure a territory and lay claim to the food within in a way that individuals could not. The brains that evolved by trading surplus wild-caught goods were also able to support codes of social behavior that governed access to foods and regulated relationships among and between groups of people. At the same time, acquisition techniques also gradually improved.

For a long time these technologies were stable and in many hunting and gathering societies they remain so. They typically include a set of simple projectile weapons (darts and blowpipes, bows and arrows, spears and spear-throwers), traps or nets for catching fish, sharpened implements for digging and butchering, and fire for smoking out bees, cooking meat, and detoxifying certain foods. Limits on food acquisition were imposed by social rules governing access to resources that operated between and within groups. In stable human ecologies, therefore, a balance was maintained whereby humans continued to exploit resources to the full (limited by social rules and by technology) and bred as often as they could

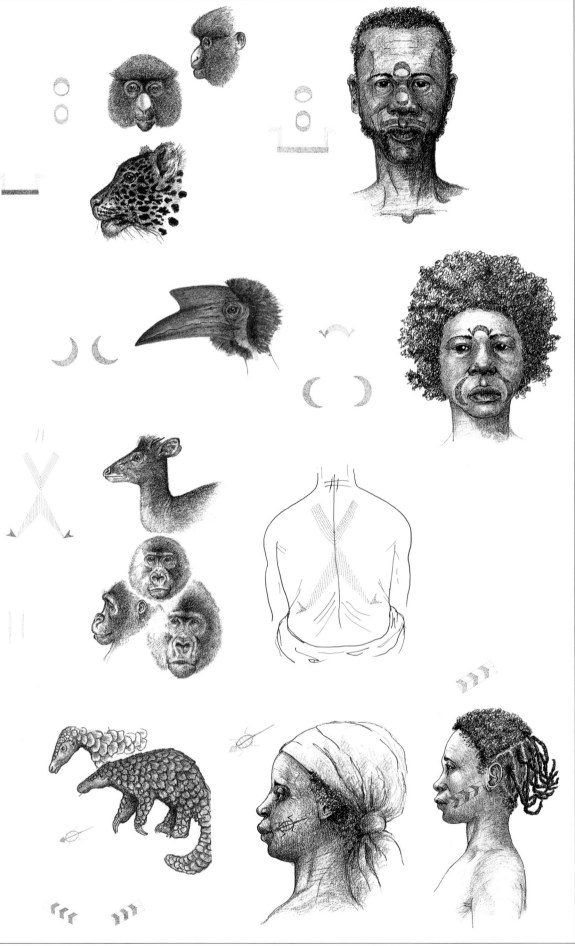

162 Scarified tattoos of animal motifs show the veneration felt by many people of the African rainforest for wild animals. These sketches were taken from life in 1953-1955 by Jordi Sabater Pi, an anthropologist who worked with the Fang people of Equatorial Guinea and Cameroon. From top to bottom: leopard whiskers (*Panthera pardus*) and the eye-rings of a white-faced cercopiteco (*Cercopithecus nictitans*) on an Okak man; the bill of a black-casqued hornbill (*Ceratogymna atrata*) on a young Bulu man; the body of a bay duiker (*Cephalophus dorsalis*) and a cryptic symbol for a western lowland gorilla (*Gorilla gorilla gorilla*) on the back of an old Okak man; a pangolin (*Manis gigantea*) body and scales on Okak women (see also figure 119).
[Drawing: Jordi and Josep Oriol Sabater]

(subject to high infant and early adult mortality). Since their prey species did the same, a balance was ultimately achieved and could be maintained indefinitely.

By the time humans entered rainforests they were well equipped to make a living there. They were not, however, predisposed to exploit the forest's resources sustainably, even though the ecology of modern rainforest-dwelling humans may give that impression. The rainforest is an immensely complex and dynamic place. There is more biomass per unit area and a higher sustained rate of primary production than in any other terrestrial habitat.

The importance of hunting

Since most rainforest vegetation is poisonous or otherwise inedible, humans must use other animals to help them find nutrients and to convert them into a form that can be eaten safely. This confers an exceptional importance on hunted animal meat as the primary source of food. It also explains why the dominant themes of traditional human activities in rainforests are about finding ways to catch animals or to use their products (for example, honey), whether by gathering invertebrates or honey or by hunting or fishing for vertebrates.

Predatory activities are the key to human adaptation to life in rainforests; wild vertebrates, above all mammals, provide most of the proteins and fats consumed by humans. Nevertheless, rainforests are, in fact, a very marginal habitat for humans, and hunting, albeit complemented by fishing and by the gathering of invertebrates, does not always completely satisfy all food needs. The majority of humans living in rainforests depend on basic plant products for food which are gathered wild, cultivated in the forest or obtained from other peoples living outside the forest.

Detailed studies of hunting and fishing by tropical forest-dwellers are few and far between despite their obvious importance. Early studies frequently only compiled lists of species consumed and methods employed. Only recently have researchers begun to look into issues of human use of animal resources in much greater detail. For example, until the 1980s forest animals were not included in calculations of forest value, nor featured in attempts to calculate the benefits obtainable from a forest. Animals, particularly those killed for food, have remained a "subsidy from nature," often undervalued and understudied by the institutions and governments in whose hands lies the fate of much of the remaining rainforests. In many instances, the existence of various indigenous groups, rubber tappers, colonists, and other forest-dwellers of the Americas is contingent on this "subsidy." For this reason, hunting pressure is increasing on the numerous species that the growing number of colonists hunt to meet their daily needs.

Some examples

An exceptional case is that of the Penan hunter-gathers of Borneo. They have no traditional agriculture, although their distribution within the island is closely linked to that of the hill sago palm (*Eugeissona utilis*), which they use as a starch staple. In general, the forests of the Bornean interior are exceptionally inhospitable to mammals because of the dominance of trees belonging to the family of Dipterocarpaceae, which set fruit too rarely to support large mammal populations. The forests of the interior of Borneo, lacking sufficient game, are uninhabitable in those areas without hill sago or agriculture to compensate. The Penan—not an agricultural people—have settled only in areas where they can exploit the starch given by the sago palm. Likewise, the Mbuti and related peoples of central Africa are hunter-gathers who maintain long-term relationships with agricultural peoples and at least half their diet comes from cultivated food. This evidence suggests that rainforests are very marginal habitats for humans and cannot be occupied fulltime without an agricultural food supply.

Many natives populating the Amazon Basin developed complex agricultural techniques, although hunting and fishing have remained important activities. As European expansion and domination progressed along water courses, the indigenous inhabitants of the *várzea* were either displaced or exterminated. Some of these displaced groups were forced to adopt new life styles, and relatively recently many have had to begin to rely more heavily on hunting and gathering. Although marvelously adapted to their environment, numerous Indian cultures do not represent precontact development in the areas they currently inhabit. Linguistic elements of certain Amazonian huntergatherer groups reveal former agricultural backgrounds that are not obvious in their current life styles. A complex set of factors have combined to produce the societies and resource management strategies seen today.

3.2 The gathering of invertebrates

The role of gathering invertebrates in the ecology of rainforest-dwelling humans is one of opportunistic exploitation of carefully chosen species or life-stages of insects, molluscs and crustaceans as supplementary rather than as primary foods. This is combined with the occasional specialized use of invertebrates in magic and medicine and more commonly as an aid in catching larger vertebrate animals by hunting (poisons) or fishing (as bait). Millipedes (diplopods) are innocuous herbivorous animals, but in Malay magic their ashes and juices have a variety of uses, mainly in potentiating poisons. Some species secrete corrosive liquids as a means of defense, and these may be mixed with other ingredients in blow-dart poisons. Nevertheless, this use is more often applied to centipedes (chilopods) because they are active predators and large species have poisonous bites that can even kill humans. The use of centipede venom on arrow tips has been reported from Mexico, and both the Orang Asli from Peninsular

Malaysia and the Penan from Borneo likewise sometimes add centipede as well as cobra and scorpion venom to blow-dart poison mixtures.

The nutritional value of invertebrates

For many indigenous rainforest-dwellers additional sources of nutrition from invertebrates are locally and seasonally important, often to a much greater extent than is generally thought. Food items are often eaten in the moment of capture and thus may not be noticed by observers. For example, the Tukano people of Colombia collect more than 20 species of arthropod that provide 12% of the crude protein for men and 26% for women and perhaps up to 20% of all animal fat consumed during the collecting season. Analysis of caterpillars of the genus *Bombycomorpha* by the FAO showed that they possess greater food value than rats, zebras, and wildebeests and only slightly less than beef and chicken. Termites have also been shown to be very rich in proteins (36%) and fats (44%).

Insects normally accumulate fat in their larval stages when they are approaching maturity or, in the case of termites, just prior to a major reproductive effort. It seems that humans select the most nutritious insects, since random samples of locusts and termites have much lower fat contents (between 3% and 8%) than those consumed by

163 Eating insects and their larvae is common among many rainforest people, like this Sepik man from New Guinea. Many of the factors conditioning human diet are cultural in origin. Consequently, humans are not fully omnivorous, and human groups can also be classified according to their dietary preferences.
[Photo: Jean-Paul Ferrero / Auscape International]

humans (28% in some species, about 22% in *Rhynchophorus*). It is said that the grubs of one of the most consumed insects, the rhinoceros beetle *Oryctes*, have a similar chemical composition to beef, whereas other species contain fats resembling fish oils or seed oils.

Within the hunting territory of one rainforest-dweller there are thousands of invertebrate species, principally insects, of which the majority are too small or too disperse to be nutritionally useful. Gleaners of the forest have to be very wary of toxic invertebrates; many, nevertheless, including locusts, worms, caterpillars, larvae, pupae, ants, termites, and spiders are relatively abundant and edible.

The most eaten species

It is a common sight in Thailand to see stick-loads of barbecued short-horned grasshoppers (acridid orthopterans). The nymphs of the common locust (*Locusta migratoria*) are eaten as a substitute for prawns in curries at various places in the Far East, including the Philippines and, at least formerly, in Malaysia. Meanwhile, on the other side of the Old World, African children eagerly gather the winged termites that flock and fall beneath street lights, eagerly eating their fatty bodies. Similar scenes can be observed in Java (Indonesia), where fried winged termites are sold ready-mixed with grated coconut or chili sambal.

A notable example concerns the larvae of the beetles of the genus *Rhynchophorus*. In the Mentawai islands off the west coast of Sumatra, the Mentawaians relish the protein-rich masses of beetle larvae and culture them in cracks in the trunks of swamp sago palms (*Metroxylon sagu*). This habit of using beetles to turn the starch of the sago palm into animal protein is extremely efficient and explains why sago is such a useful crop in marginal, swampy rainforest areas. Grubs of the beetles *Rhynchophorus ferrugineus* and *Oryctes rhinoceros*, as well as various cockchafers (large beetles), are eaten throughout Indochina, Borneo, eastern Indonesia, the Philippines, and many other places. Since many beetle larvae rely on concealment rather than on chemical defense to avoid predation, it is possible that these animals are used as food wherever humans coincide with their rainforest

habitats. The same could be said of bee-grubs, which are widely collected with honeycombs and are eaten enthusiastically by forest-dwelling people.

Giant snails (*Achatina achatina*) are an important food item in west Africa. Bundles of shells up to about 8 in (20 cm) in length are sold by the roadside in forest areas from Guinea to Cameroon. About 8,000 t were sold in the Ivory Coast in 1986 (almost 25 oz [700 g] per person for the population as a whole), and they are collected at a similar rate in other places in their range. The bodies of these snails each provide 3.5-10.6 oz (100-300 g) of meat with no waste and contain about 16% protein by dry weight, a figure that is in the same range as beef. Snail proteins contain higher proportions of the essential animo acids arginine and lysine than chicken eggs do.

Many of the food sources obtained from invertebrates are much prized and sought after and are not only gleaned in times of need or hunger. They are delicacies or food products, used as flavorings or condiments, but are not important sources of proteins or fats. For example, in India, Myanmar, and Thailand a condiment is made from ground red weaver ants (*Oecophylla*), while in Indochina the secretion of an abdominal gland of an aquatic bug, *Belostoma*, is used to flavor food.

Many rainforest-dwellers also consume large quantities of honey and pollen. The Aka Pygmies, for example, eat a large amounts of honey and are especially adept at finding bee nests. They climb trees and smoke out the bees to obtain honey and to trade with neighboring agricultural people. Most Amazonian peoples are fond of honey, above all that produced by *Melipona* bees; some groups even use honey to produce a fermented drink.

3.3 Subsistence hunting

Hunting is an essential part of life in the rainforest. It provides all kinds of indispensable elements such as food and ornamental and domestic products (skins, feathers, and teeth and bones for making tools), as well as serving important ritual functions. Yet hunting is most important as a source of food.

164 Preparation of wild meat inside a Waorami dwelling in the rainforest on the Pacific coast of Ecuador. Preparing the meat is the responsibility of the women; in the photo a woman is quartering a monkey.
[Photo: The Hutchison Library]

The importance of hunting

Subsistence hunters take impressive numbers of animals, although hunting intensity may vary from one region to another. The following figures are a good example: the 230 inhabitants of three Waorani villages in Ecuador took in less than one year 3,165 mammals, birds, and reptiles. A third of this total comprised three species: 562 woolly monkeys (*Lagothrix lagothrica*), 313 Cuvier's toucans (*Ramphastos cuvieri*), and 152 white-lipped peccaries (*Tayassu pecari*). In 1980 there were an estimated 2,847,000 rural inhabitants in the Brazilian Amazon, occupying 1,382,695 mi² (3,581,180 km²) (not including urban areas). Yearly per capita consumption values taken from studies of colonist hunting practices indicate that approximately 14 million mammals were killed in that year. The addition of birds and reptiles to this figure brings the total to a staggering 19 million individual animals. Even if a wide margin of error is allowed for, the magnitude of subsistence hunting is obviously enormous.

Hunting for food

Much more hunted meat is normally consumed in remote areas than in urban areas. For this reason, average national figures tend to underestimate the importance of hunting for some sectors of the population, normally those sectors least able to afford alternative foods. Wildmeat or bushmeat consumption in parts of the Peruvian Amazon reaches 352.4 lb (160 kg) per person per year and in parts of West Africa up to 165.2 lb (75 kg), whereas the inland agricultural communities of Baram in Sarawak, consume only 72.7 lb (33 kg), although this figure may well be far higher for the Penan hunter-gatherers.

In the interior of Sarawak on the island of Borneo, records of locally obtained and consumed food from 63 rural schools showed the consumption of 203 t of meat and fish in 1984 and 1985. The largest single component was wild bearded pig (*Sus barbatus*) with 32% of total consumption. Other wild meat contributed about 7%, fish around 18%, and domestic pork, beef, and chicken each contributed 13-16%. The staple foodstuff of all these communities was rice and other farmed crops, although all were taking more than half of the animal matter in their diets from the wild. This pattern gave an estimated harvest of about 18,000 t of wild meat per year in the mid-1980s for Sarawak as a whole, an average of about 26.4 lb (12 kg) per person per year for the whole population. This consumption rate is close to the normal range calculated in various countries in sub-Saharan Africa.

Hunting for cultural purposes

Hunting of animals for food is very important in the ecology of the rainforest. Yet it is by no means the only use made of terrestrial vertebrates and in many traditional societies, hunting has an additional social and religious significance.

Throughout southeast Asia pangolin scales, bear paws and gallbladders, rhinoceros parts, and tiger bones are commonly used in magic and medicine. Wild cat skins are used for similar purposes in west Africa. Another important component of traditional medicine are bezoar stones; these concretions of tannins and hairs found in the guts of herbivores, such as porcupines, were first found in the pasang (*Capra aegagrus*). They are a physiological response to the presence of a foreign body. They have been exported from southeast Asia for millennia for use in China, the Middle East, and Europe.

Hunting features strongly in the folklore of rainforest-dwelling people. The Iban people of Borneo, for example, took their tiger legends with them in the form of innumerable dances and songs when they left Sumatra. The indigenous people of the Mentawai Islands believe that wild animals are the domestic pets of people living in another dimension and that rituals are necessary to placate the owners of animals hunted in the wild. The skins and feathers of wild vertebrates are widely used for decoration and for trade. The larger cats are particularly vulnerable: Leopard-skin (*Panthera pardus*) robes are a popular sign of chiefhood in West Africa, and clouded leopard-skin robes (*Neofelis nebulosa*) are used in an identical fashion in Borneo. Also in Borneo, hornbill feathers are used in headdresses and in dancing and bird of paradise feathers are used for the same purpose in New Guinea. This almost endless list of examples indicates how imaginative and acquisitive humans have found diverse ways to use the rainforest environment they live in.

And then there is feather trade. The whims of fashion have historically stimulated an incredible amount of trade in a great diversity of animal products. The ceremonial and decorative use of feathers has a very long and widespread tradition among rainforest people. Elaborate feather art reached its zenith in the capes worn by Aztec emperors. Macaw (*Ara*), quetzal (*Pharomachrus mocinno*), and roseate spoonbill (*Platalea* [=*Ajaia*] *ajaja*) feathers were especially valued by the Aztecs. Feathers from tropical species adorn Inca artifacts such as the *suntur paucar*, the emblem of leadership in Inca armies. Evidence shows that Native Americans of present-day southwestern United States raised young scarlet macaws (*Ara macao*), brought from the Mexican forests 620 mi (1,000 km) to the south, for their feathers.

Game animals

The species that are the biggest, commonest, and easiest to catch are considered the best game. In the Amazon, for example, these include deer (*Mazama* and *Odocoileus*); peccaries (*Tayassu*); large rodents such as capybaras (*Hydrochaeris hydrochaeris*), agoutis (*Agouti*) and pacas (*Dasyprocta*); armadillos (dasypodoids) and various monkeys. Large carnivores, including large cats such as the ocelot (*Felis pardalis*), the margay cat (*F. wiedii*), and the jaguar (*Panthera onca*) are taken only for their skins, and this true of the giant otter (*Lutra longicaudis*) and the river otter (*Pteronura brasiliensis*).

In Sarawak, ungulates are the most important prey and contribute 60-90% of the harvest. This category comprises sambar deer (*Cervus unicolor*), barking deer (*Muntiacus muntjak*), chevrotains, or mouse deer (*Tragulus napu* and *T. javanicus*), and the most hunted of all, the bearded pig (*Sus barbatus*). The bearded pig's ecology is adapted to that of the exceptional forests of the Bornean interior. Its populations are very mobile and herds move hundreds of kilometers (1 km=0.6 mi) in search of ripe dipterocarp seeds and display "boom and bust" population cycles linked to food supply. Their abundance in any one location therefore varies greatly and extensive damage to the forest (especially the felling of mature dipterocarp trees) can virtually eliminate them from some areas. When this happens, rainforest-dwellers tend to start hunting other ungulates as well as a greater variety of smaller and, in particular, often nocturnal or arboreal prey that has to be taken with firearms. When ungulate populations decline, other species such as civets (*Viverra*, *Viverricula*), monkeys (*Macaca*, *Presbytis*), pangolins (*Manis*), squirrels (*Callosciurus*, *Lariscus*, etc.), porcupines (*Hystrix*, *Trichys*, and *Thecurus*), otters (*Lutra*) and wildcats (*Felis*) are successively overexploited by rural people in a relentless search for meat. This change is evident from the proportion of shotgun cartridges loaded with birdshot or buckshot sold at shops in different locations: in western Sabah, North Borneo, where large ungulates are rare, more birdshot is sold; in less-disturbed eastern Sabah, the opposite is true.

In west Africa there is a strong accent on the capture of large rodents—especially the grasscutter (*Thryonomys*), porcupines (*Atherurus*), and giant rats (*Cricetomys*)—small ungulates such as duikers (*Sylvicapra* and *Cephalophus*), other antelopes (*Tragelaphus* and *Neotragus*), the bush-

165 Hunting with nets is a Pygmy specialty, and trapped animals are killed with a spear. The photo was taken in the central African rainforest and shows a woman and child returning to a village with their net and a duiker (*Cephalophus*).
[Photo: Georges Merillon / Gamma]

pig (*Potamochoerus*) and monkeys (especially guenons *Cercopithecus*). Normal hunting does not generally affect very large animals such as the buffalo (*Syncerus caffer*) or the elephant (*Loxodonta africana*), although individuals with special equipment such as automatic rifles are often available to take on these targets.

In some rainforests birds are also regularly hunted. In southeast Asia hornbills (Bucerotidae), peacock-pheasants (*Polypectron*), pheasants (*Lophura*), and doves and pigeons (*Columba* and *Treron*) and in New Guinea cassowaries (*Casuarius*) are all consumed regularly as supplementary sources of protein. Many birds are also hunted in the Amazon: guans (*Penelope*), chachalacas (*Ortalis*), toucans (ramphastids), trumpeters (*Psophia*), and various species of parrots and macaws (Psittacidae) are the commonest targets. Large wading birds and raptors are not commonly hunted for food.

Reptiles and amphibians are also consumed on a local scale. In southern Asia and in New Guinea, monitor lizards (*Varanus*), pythons (*Python*), and giant frogs are hunted. Meat from crocodilians traditionally provides an important source of protein for many indigenous groups. *Caiman* species are the most common targets, although distinctions between species are not usually made. Eggs are also frequently harvested. Inhabitants of the basin of the Tocatins river consume 21,500 to 32,000 caiman a year. Although customs vary from place to place, colonists of European extraction often regard caimans as a marginal food source, and they are one of the first food items to be rejected as acceptable game species. The situation changes during Lent when the consumption of the flesh of aquatic animals such as caimans, turtles and even capybara is authorized by the Roman Catholic Church, as though they were fish. The capybara (*Hydrochaeris hydrochaeris*) is often present in high densities and can be an important species for subsistence hunters. However, European settlers find its taste bitter, possibly due to secondary compounds ingested from the vegetation it consumes in the forests. It seems that the capybara that live in the open savannah of the Llanos taste better, although no comparative quality analysis has been carried out. In some areas of Brazil and Bolivia, cattle ranchers believe that they carry disease and shoot them as vermin.

Preferences ensure that most animals taken belong to a small number of key species, although there are groups that will hunt a great variety of species. In all societies with close access to the rainforest and strong hunting traditions, almost any animal constituting a mouthful of meat or more is liable to be captured and eaten. Prey lists in Borneo, Palawan, New Guinea, Ghana, Cameroon, and Nigeria are all long and comprehensive inventories of the local fauna. In Surinam, the *djuka*, the descendants of escaped black slaves who adopted the Guyanan Amerindian way of life, have been recorded to hunt 27 species of mammal, 24 of

166 Hunting with bows and arrows or with spears used to be practiced everywhere and is still common in some rainforest areas. Arrows need not always be pointed as they might damage delicate prey. These Nambicuara indians from the Juruena Basin in the Amazon (above) are hunting with blunt-tipped arrows. Spears are still used by the Penan from Borneo on their hunting expeditions (below).
[Photos: Jesco von Puttkamer / The Hutchison Library and Nigel Dickinson / Still Pictures]

bird, and five of reptile. The Maracá natives of Colombia hunt 51 species of bird, including 10 species of hummingbird. The fact that certain animals may be poisonous at certain times of year because of the fruits they eat excludes temporarily some species from being hunted. For example, in Borneo porcupines (*Hystrix*, *Trichys*, and *Thecurus*) and the great argus pheasant (*Argusianus argus*) are widely believed to be poisonous in some seasons.

Traditional hunting techniques

Little evidence of hunting artifacts used by prehistoric rainforest settlers remain, although use of the bow, the most universal traditional technology, was undoubtedly common. Early European explorers of the Amazon greatly feared the forest archers; not only did they put up greater resistance than their Andean counterparts, but they also used poison-tipped arrows, and this brought some parity with firearms. The design and materials used vary considerably among forest groups. Some have many arrow styles designed for specific prey, whereas others have basic, generalized patterns. Groups cannot be categorized according to these patterns because much trade between peoples exists and technology is shared. Proficiency in use appears to be related to the social importance placed on bow hunting and to the degree that a given group has been acculturated to western society. An increasing reliance on firearms has led to a loss of archery skills, given the need for continual bow practice.

Within the Americas, blowpipes, widespread throughout southeast Asia, are only used in the Orinoco and northern Amazon Basins. Construction requires time and skill but results in a silent weapon of great accuracy using simple projectiles that can be easily made in large quantities. Use of fast-acting neurotoxic poisons, mostly of plant origin, makes this a very effective weapon. Some people of Venezuela and Colombia use a poison extracted from small frogs (Dendrobatidae) and rely exclusively on blowpipes, despite being well acquainted with the bow and arrow.

The use of spears in the Amazon is irregular but widespread. Among certain groups use is restricted to intertribal conflicts, whereas for others such as the Borôbô, the Guato, and the Karajá of the central and western Amazon, it is an important hunting tool. Spear-throwers were reported by early chroniclers, but they are not seen today. A.R. Wallace wrote that the Paumari people of the Purus River "have a surprising dexterity in the use of this weapon, and with it readily kill game, birds and fish."

The use of traps and nets for terrestrial game is found sporadically and is suitable only for a limited number of species. At times, fire or beaters are employed to drive game towards waiting hunters, a practice requiring cooperation and coordination of large groups of people and which is a departure from usual hunting strategies.

Modern hunting techniques

The introduction of firearms has given the forest hunter a powerful new weapon. The .22 caliber rifle is commonly used and is accurate at greater distances than are traditional arms. Shotguns are also used and do not require as much skill, although both tend to be employed with great discretion owing to the price of shells. As great prestige is attached to the use of firearms, traditional methods are beginning to disappear.

The introduction of a new hunting technique can upset the human-prey balance just as effectively as improvements in transport, which bring hunters into new areas and allow wild meat to be sold in greater quantity. During the last two or three decades, the hunters of southeast Nigeria have begun making extensive use of trained hunting dogs. Dogs greatly

facilitate the capture of drill monkeys (*Mandrillus leucophaeus*) and have provoked such a rapid decline in their numbers that they are now one of the most endangered primates in Africa. The use of dogs forces the drills to seek refuge in the tree canopy, where they are easy targets for firearms.

Both shotguns and hunting dogs are relatively recent additions to the widespread hunting repertoires found in Sarawak. Premodern hunting patterns similar to those of the Paleolithic were still in use until quite recently, as the primate, pig, and porcupine remains found at Niah Cave, inhabited for 40,000 years, demonstrate. Currently the most hunted species are pigs, deer, and chevrotain (mouse deer). If records of prey caught by gunfire and dogs are eliminated, hunter-gathers in this area capture prey from a pseudoarchaic spectrum that corresponds to the species found at Niah Cave. The same pattern was also found in the Mentawai Islands in the 1970s before the use of firearms became widespread there, too.

Nevertheless, the use of firearms is not yet generalized among indigenous peoples. The example of Sarawak is atypical: The average family is well equipped, and in the mid-1980s there was an average of approximately two spears and two dogs per family, one firearm for every two families (60,000 in the whole of Sarawak), and one blowpipe per four families. In the two thirds of Borneo in Indonesian territory, however, firearms are illegal, and there is a much stronger reliance on trapping and the use of dogs, spears, and blowpipes.

3.4 Commercial hunting

Hunting supplies necessary proteins as well as providing a cash income in more developed societies. Many subsistence hunting groups in rainforests are being drawn further into the market, and hunting is becoming ever less a subsistence activity with associated religious values and ever more an economic activity linked to exchanges with other extracommunity groups.

Meat

Game meat has a high market value compared with other forest products and the incentives to commercialize subsistence hunting sometimes prove irresistible. Historically, meat remained

167 The sale of excess bushmeat is not unusual in rainforests. The photo was taken in a market in Pointe-Noire in Democratic Republic of Congo, where meat from sitatungas (*Tragelaphus spekei*), an antelope of marshy areas, is on sale. The situation is very different in Brazil, as most hunters of larger prey are "game hunters," generally business men on weekend trips from large cities. These rainforests do not have sufficient numbers of large mammals to attract international hunters and so the big draw, especially in Latin America, tends to be bird hunting. In Brazil, there is no control at all of the shooting of hundreds of thousands of eared doves (*Zenaida* [=*Enaidura*] *auriculata*). Hunting of the tasty game bird the solitary tinamou (*Tinamus solitarius*) is regulated. The active management for sport hunting of three species of whistling ducks (*Dendrocygna*) is also an effective tool for reducing damage to the rice crop. [*Photo: Michel Gunther / Bios / Still Pictures*]

within the community or was traded in small quantities. However, as reliance increases on goods from the external market, so do incentives to sell game meat, very often to the detriment of community nutrition. Cash obtained is often spent on food of low nutritional value such as sugar, coffee, or alcohol or on manufactured goods such as ammunition or batteries. The balance between transport links, storage techniques, and market demand may substantially influence the amount of meat eaten in urban areas.

In west Africa both fresh and smoked "bushmeat" is commonly marketed, both informally by the roadside and also as a large-scale, organized traffic that may involve crossing frontiers (for example, between Nigeria and Cameroon). Bushmeat usually commands a higher price than beef or chicken and it is often the most important cash crop of villages located near intact rainforests. Without road access, goods must be taken to market by being carried by hand or on the head, and it is often more economically viable to carry bushmeat than bulkier materials of lower value.

A well-established traffic in wild meat exists throughout the basin of the Rajang river in Sarawak. It involves using cold stores located in longhouses, boats and towns as well as low-cost river transport to downstream markets. In 1984 this trade involved many thousands of bearded

pig and deer carcasses, valued in excess of 2 million U.S. dollars. During sample periods in 1984 and 1985, one single trader exported meat worth about 500 U.S. dollars per day, and in one month in 1985 dispatched downriver nearly 8.5 t of gutted and headless bearded pig carcasses.

The sale of wildlife for consumption has a long history in the Americas. Despite being prohibited in most countries, it can be readily found in markets and on restaurant menus. Quite frequently wild meat is sold for less than domestic beef unless local game supplies are depleted. Quantities are sometimes staggering, as records from Iquitos in Peru demonstrate. It was estimated from statistics gathered in 1975-1976 that 11,000 primates of six species were sold. Inhabitants of the surrounding department killed an estimated 370,000 primates each year. Before the arrival of Europeans, trade in bushmeat was limited, probably by transportation and storage problems.

Trade in manatee meat (*Trichechus manatus* and *T. inunguis*) began in the 17th century and caused a population crash from which these species have never recovered. These aquatic mammals may attain weights over of 1,321.6 lb (600 kg) and their meat is highly valued. The flesh was sold either salted or fried in its own abundant fat and then stored in oil. This *mixira* would keep for many months and could be commercialized. Although no accurate records were kept, at least several thousand animals were being caught annually until the mid-20th century.

The commercial importance of capybara (*Hydrochaeris hydrochaeris*) is limited, and there is only a small market for its fresh and salted meat. It is not much appreciated, but it continues to be eaten because it is an aquatic animal, and so the Catholic church tolerates its consumption during Lent, in the same way as it allows consumption of fish. In Venezuela in 1981 over 90,000 animals were processed, and a successful wild harvest has been developed for meat and skins in open areas of the Llanos, although annual production levels are very variable.

Venezuela has developed the only legal, large-scale commercial system for wild-harvesting of caiman. Animals are taken principally for their hide value, although substantial income is also generated from the sale of salted meat. The 1985 harvest registered meat from 110,357 animals and retail sales were estimated at over U.S. $400,000.

Skins

Before the first contacts with Europeans, the use of wild animal skins for clothing, armor, decorations, and many other utilitarian purposes was widespread. These customs persist today to varying degrees, although among forest people manufactured items and synthetic materials are replacing traditional products.

Skins were the first nonfood product to be traded with the pioneer European visitors to the rainforests. However, the first large-scale exploitation did not begin to get underway until the end of the 19th century. In 1898, 75 t of deer hides representing approximately 54,000 animals, probably largely brocket deer (*Mazama americana* and perhaps *M. gouazoubira*), another small Amazonian deer, were shipped from Belém in Brazil. Between 1900 and 1950, approximately 832,000 white-tailed deer (*Odocoileus virginianus*) were exported from Costa Rica. In Brazil, a short-lived but intense manatee (*Trichechus manatus* and *T. inunguis*) leather industry evolved during the 1930s and lasted until the early 1950s. During this period, at least 19,000 manatees were killed in the Brazilian state of Amazonas. Re-

cords show that between 1938 and 1942 a single firm in Manaus shipped 6,549 hides to Rio de Janeiro. The hides, measuring about 0.8 in (2 cm) thick, are very durable and had very specialized purposes: machine belts, gaskets, steam engine hoses, and glue production.

Other wild animals have also been exploited for leather in large numbers, and, for example, Europe and Japan have been important markets for peccary hides. Export records from Iquitos show that 848,364 white-lipped peccary (*Tayassu pecari*) and 2,013,006 collared peccary (*T. tajacu*) hides were exported between 1946 and 1966. Trade is still active today, although exports have declined greatly. Exports of capybara (*Hydrochaeris hydrochaeris*) hides from Brazil exceeded 497,000 between 1960 and 1969. Current laws forbidding export of Brazilian wildlife products have curtailed such intense exploitation.

Reptilian quality hides

Trade in wild animal skins also includes reptile hides from snakes, lizards, and above all crocodiles. The skins of the larger boid snakes (*Boa*, *Epicrates*, and *Eunectes*) are used in large quantities to produce handbags, wallets, shoes, and belts. Lizards such as the iguana (*Iguana iguana*) and the caiman lizard (*Dracaena guianensis*) are also exploited, but to a lesser extent.

In terms of the number of skins and their economic value, crocodilian species dominate world trade. Intense exploitation began in the 1930s with the true crocodiles (*Crocodylus*). At one point, one hide buyer in Venezuela was receiving 3,000-4,000 Orinoco crocodile skins daily! As stocks of the larger species were depleted, hunters turned to the smaller, less valuable caimans. Commerce peaked in the 1950s and 1960s, with 5-10 million skins traded annually. Export records from Colombia, which represent only part of the actual total, show that 11,649,655 *Caiman crocodilus* hides were shipped abroad legally between 1951 and 1980. International controls, such as CITES and legislation in Latin American countries, have somewhat reduced these figures. Nevertheless, numbers remain impressive and 2,593,834 crocodilian skins were exported from South America between 1980 and 1984. *Caiman* skins represent approximately 75% of the world crocodilian trade, much of it passing

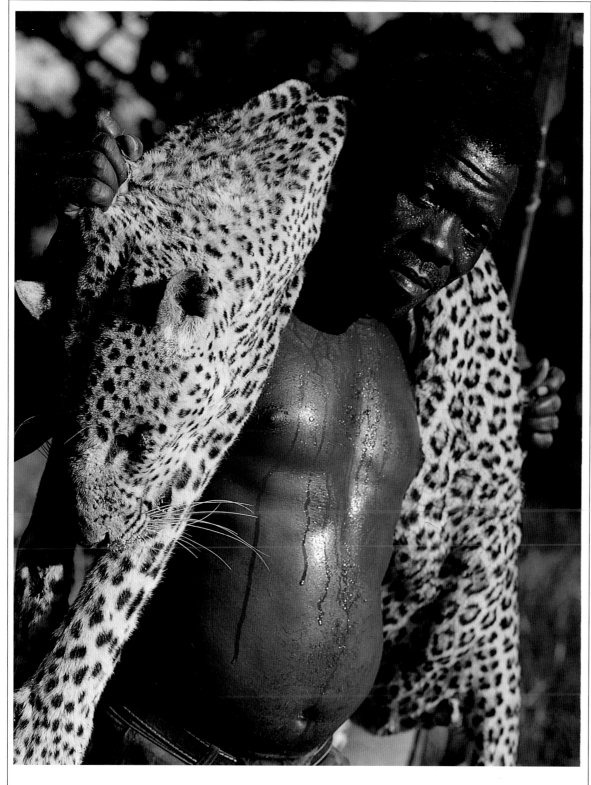

3. HUMANS IN THE RAINFORESTS

168 The fur industry's demand for high-quality furs made the hunting of large felines very financially rewarding, severely reducing their populations. As these species are at the top of the trophic chain, they are naturally scarce. The photo shows a poacher in the African rainforest carrying a recently killed leopard (*Panthera pardus*), a legally protected species in danger of extinction. [*Photo: Laboureur Mathieu / Bios / Still Pictures*]

through clandestine channels. As with other wildlife products, the hunters receive little for their efforts, and the profits generated from the manufacture and sale of finished products remain in the consumer nation.

Luxury markets in Europe, North America, and Japan have stimulated the commerce in quality furs and hides from the rainforests, as well as from other biomes. The big dappled or striped cats, such as the leopard (*Panthera pardus*) in Africa, the tiger (*P. tigris*) and the clouded leopard (*Neofelis nebulosa*) in southern Asia, and the jaguar (*Panthera onca*) in tropical America, have always been the most sought after species.

Fur exports from the Amazon greatly increased in the 1940s and continued into the 1970s, although the trade in jaguar (*Panthera onca*) hides had in fact begun

169 The high prices paid for crocodile skins has caused their populations to crash, although the situation has stabilized as a result of the creation of crocodile farms. The hunter in the photo from the basin of Madre de Dios River (Peru), is drying the head and skin of a black caiman (*Melanosuchus niger*), a threatened Amazon and Orinoco species.
[Photo: André Bärtschi / Planet Earth Pictures]

the period 1959-1972, exports from Peru totaled 113,718 hides.

Feathers, oils, and other animal products

In 1886, a North American ornithologist identified no less than 40 species of bird as possible sources of feathers for ladies' hats. Although the majority of trade involved egrets and herons (ardeids) from temperate wetlands, there were also many rainforest species, including even hummingbirds. Most of the commercial material originated from Argentina (thus from outside rainforests), Venezuela, and Brazil (from rainforests and more open environments). The global ornamental feather trade collapsed after the First World War and currently is of little significance. However, items for the tourist trade are found in markets throughout the tropics, and in many South American countries colorful parrot and macaw feathers are used to adorn objects sold as "authentic Indian products" (see also "Remarkable feathers and beaks," pages 134-137).

The giant river turtle (*Podocnemis expansa*) was exploited by natives before contact with Europeans. Early explorers reported that hundreds of turtles were held captive in village pens along the Amazon.

The indigenous peoples ate the flesh of the turtles and their eggs as well as extracted a fine oil from the eggs. The giant river turtle once nested in huge colonies on certain beaches and were plentiful enough to impede river travel. Traveling in Venezuela in 1800, Alexander von Humboldt observed abundant turtles along the Orinoco River and estimated that they had laid 33 million eggs on a single beach. A turtle oil industry was eventually set up in Brazil in the 18th century and was even regulated by royal decree. In 1719, 190,000 pounds (around 87 t) of oil were derived from an estimated 24 million eggs. Demand and then production increased so much that in the 1860s the annual harvest was calculated at around 48 million eggs. Today the turtle is absent from much of its former range.

Most species of freshwater turtle in the neotropics are taken for eggs and meat, although none have suffered as much from human action as the giant river turtle.

at the turn of the century. This species occurs naturally in low densities and overexploitation caused a severe decline in numbers. Hunters then turned increasingly to smaller felines, mainly the ocelot (*Felis pardalis*) and, to a lesser extent, the margay (*F. wiedii*) and the little spotted cat (*F. tigrina*). Peruvian registers from 1946-1967 show exports of 12,704 jaguar and 138,102 ocelot skins. This trade was not confined to South America. Data are scarce, but figures compiled for the period 1966-1971, for example, show that 1,751 jaguar skins, 17,157 ocelot skins and 21,473 margay skins were exported from Nicaragua.

Pressure on the giant otter (*Pteronura brasiliensis*) has been equally intense, and it is now locally extinct over much of its original range. Over 23,000 skins were taken from the Peruvian Amazon between 1946 and 1970, while nearly 20,000 skins were reported taken from the Brazilian Amazon between 1960 and 1969. The smaller river otter (*Lutra longicaudis*) was also persecuted heavily and, like *Pteronura*, has been exterminated in some areas of its former range. In

Owing to the demand for fuel, caimans (*Caiman*) were also exploited for oil. When oil lamps became common at the turn of the century, caiman oil began to be used mixed with kerosene in household lamps. The fat of the manatee (*Trichechus*) was also exploited, and a single carcass could yield up to 220 lb (100 kg) of fat. This was melted down to oil to be used for cooking, in lamps, or mixed with pitch to caulk boats. On a much smaller scale, nestlings of the oil bird (*Steatornis caripensis*) have sometimes been collected from the caves and crevices they live in for their fine oil.

The hard skeletal parts of wild animals provide materials for many tools, utensils, and ceremonial and decorative objects. Arrow tips are frequently fashioned from the split bones of various species, and in the Amazon some are tipped with the spine of the freshwater stingray (*Potamotrygon*). Rodent incisors, frequently from the agouti (*Dasyprocta*), are used to fashion arrows and for other carving tasks. Necklaces and ornaments may include the teeth of various species, small bones, bird beaks, claws, tree porcupine quills (*Coendou prehensilis*), or other animal body parts. Although manufactured items may have replaced commonly used natural animal body parts, owing to increasing tourism and related trade, they are often still quite an important source of income.

Many wildlife products continue to be used for medicinal purposes in accordance with the traditional values ascribed to them. In markets in Belém, Brazil, several species of dried lizard, dolphin genitalia, fox fur, and other assorted wildlife parts can be seen for sale. In many areas of the Americas, caiman oil is used topically or ingested as a cure for flu, asthma, and other pulmonary complaints. In the market in Trinidad (Bolivia), jaguar, caiman, stingray, and tapir oils are commonly sold to cure a variety of ailments. Rattlesnake oil (*Crotalus durissus*) is available for cataracts and other eye problems.

Many other uses, such as amphibian and snake venoms for blowpipe darts, are known for a wide variety of species, but there are few data on their use and diffusion. Attention is now being paid to the importance of the orally transmitted traditional knowledge, known as ethnoscience, that is being lost as more and more indigenous people are being integrated into modern society. Currently, efforts are expanding to gather this

information from older group members and other people who have been taught the ancient ways.

The trade in live animals

Some uses of rainforest fauna are more recent and reflect the interaction of traditional hunting societies with the world economy within the international marketplace. For example, animals are caught for sale to zoos, on for biomedical research or are simply kept as pets, a well-established tradition among rainforest dwellers.

Trade in live animals destined for experimental use in the biomedical industry was very important up to a few years ago. Research laboratories, mostly in Europe, the United States, and Japan, were able to import primates easily and relatively inexpensively. In the quest for a polio vaccine in the 1950s, about 1.5 million primates were traded annually, 200,000 of them sent to the United States.

Many of these primates originated in the American rainforests. Records from the Iquitos

170 Feathers are of great ritual value among Amazonian peoples. This Kayapó child from the Xingu Basin is proudly showing off a headdress made from feathers. In fact, feathers are also popular among the indigenous peoples of New Guinea and North America, as well as in western society (see insert "Remarkable feathers and beaks," pages 134-137). Between 1899 and 1920, the United States imported approximately 33,069 lb (15,000 kg) of feathers from South America. This would represent about 12 to 15 million smaller birds, or 3 to 4.5 million larger birds. It is estimated that imports to France between 1890 and 1929 reached an incredible 110,231 lb (50,000 kg), mostly from tropical America. [Photo: Jesco von Puttkamer / The Hutchison Library]

171 The capture and trade of live animals, in particular of birds, reptiles, and small mammals, for zoos and for private collectors has increased all but unchecked since the 1980s. These parrot chicks (left), captured in the Lacandon rainforest in Mexico, present a particularly pathetic image. Most parrots and macaws live in rainforests. Habitat modification and transformation has reduced wild populations, and now many species are in danger of extinction, like many other animals and plants. Around a hundred species of parrot and macaw, roughly a third of all species in the group, are in danger of extinction. One threatened macaw is the handsome hyacinth macaw (*Anodorrhynchus hyacinthinus*) from the Amazon Basin (right). The forests of the Brazilian Atlantic coastline are one of the planet's most threatened forest habitats and are home to 22 endangered species of parrot. Indonesia is one of the world centers of bird biodiversity and has 76 species of parrot, 21 of them considered to be in danger of extinction. In some cases, the sudden and brutal pressure exerted by trappers and traders is beyond belief: 700 of the last 2,000 blue and red lories (*Eos histrio*), endemic to the Sangihe, Talaud, and Nanusa islands, were captured in 1992, and 200 died before being put on sale. The province of Irian Jaya in New Guinea puts tens of thousands of parrots on the market every year. Some are trapped to satisfy local demand for pets, but most form part of the large and well-organized trade in protected species destined for Jakarta or even further afield. [Photos: Adalberto Rios & Maria Lourdes Alonso and J. Cancalosi / Bruce Coleman Limited]

(Peru) show 139,000 live primates exported between the years 1961 and 1965 and over 91,500 in 1973. National and international legislation and breeding in captivity reduced world trade to about 65,000 live exports annually during the 1980s.

Commerce continues today at approximately this level. The most commonly exported primates are the crab-eating macaque (*Macaca fascicularis*) from southeast Asia; squirrel monkeys (*Saimiri*), widely used for research into malaria and other diseases, and night monkeys (*Aotus*). Many marmosets (*Saguinus*) and capuchin monkeys (*Cebus*) also reach the world market.

Commerce in animals for zoos is lower in volume but may also have a significant impact. Zoos frequently have large sums to offer, and unscrupulous buyers may deal in protected or endangered species. For every animal caught and put on sale, a significant number inevitably die during the hunt. Additional mortality occurs during shipment and in the adjustment period at the final destination, which varies greatly in accordance with the needs of the species in question.

3.5 Freshwater fishing

Freshwater fishing is a common activity in the rainforest, and in some areas fish are the main source of protein. A considerable part of fish captures are consumed by the actual fishermen, although commercial fisheries are becoming more frequent.

The role of fishing

The importance of fishing varies greatly from one community to another and depends on the accessibility of streams, rivers, and lakes as well as on the community's knowledge of appropriate fishing techniques, on local preferences, and on the impact of the consumption of meat from domesticated species. For example, in the Oban forest of Cross River State in southeast Nigeria, fishing is generally a minor activity carried out by children with hooks, lines and small nets. It is more significant, however, at an isolated riverine community (a community situated on the banks of a river) in the same forest block; while in the Okwangwo forest in the same state, it is much more important on an overall level because of the greater number of large streams and rivers. At the other end of the scale, in the local markets of Itacoatiara in Brazil, at least 86 species of fish can be found and in Manaus 64 species are on sale. In contrast, in the Bolivian lowlands where part of the forest has been felled for grazing for cattle, only six species are commercialized. For most forest-dwellers fishing is a subsistence activity, and for some it represents nearly 100% of their animal protein intake. When catches are good, they may occasionally sell their excess to generate money for manufactured goods. They are very knowledgeable about fish species and their feeding habits, migration, and seasonal changes. The traditional myths, taboos, and prohibitions that govern fishing sites, seasons, and consumption are rooted in ancient beliefs and often have certain protective effects on fish stocks. These practices are slowly breaking down as commercial fishermen extend farther and farther from urban centers and recent immigrants, unfamiliar with local customs, colonize new areas.

173 A table showing the principal species of fish caught in the rivers of the central Amazon Basin, in particular in the areas of Itacoatiara (confluence of the Amazon and Madeira) and of Porto Velho (upper and mid-course of the Madeira), with the food value marked for some species. Fish that are considered *reimosos* or inedible, by the local population are indicated. Some commonly eaten fish are considered inedible during certain periods of the year, during pregnancy or when suffering from certain illnesses. The sheer number of species caught is remarkable (the final total could be extended to more than 80), and all are present in the great fish markets such as Itacoatiara. [Source: N.J.H. Smith, 1979, and M. Goulding, 1979]

(FAMILY AND SPECIES) CAPTURED SPECIES	LOCALITY		COMPOSITION %			EDIBILITY
	IT	PV	lipids	proteins	minerals	*reimosos*
ANOSTOMIDAE						
Leporinus fasciatus and L. friderici (aracu)	■	+	15.8	18.0	2.6	-
CHARACIDAE						
Brycon melanopterus and others (matrinchão)	+	■	22.8	16.0	3.0	●
Colossoma bidens (pirapitinga)	+	+	-	-	-	●
Colossoma macropomum (tambaqui)	■	■	-	-	-	●
Metynnis (pacu mafura)	+	*	-	-	-	●
Myleus (pacu galo)	+	+	-	-	-	●
Mylossoma (common pacu)	+	■	24.8	13.8	2.8	●
Serrasalmus serratus, S. elongatus and others (piranha)	*	+	8.2	15.0	4.4	●
Triportheus elongatus and T. angulatus (sardinha)	+	■	21.6	15.2	2.4	-
CICHLIDAE						
Astronotus ocellatus (carauaçu)	*	+	3.6	17.0	5.2	●
Cichla ocellaris (tucunaré)	■	■	2.0	17.6	3.0	●
Cichlasoma severum (cará roxo)	*	*	3.6	17.2	4.8	-
CYNODONTIDAE						
Hydrolycus pectoralis (peixe cachorro)	*	*	18.2	16.6	1.2	-
CLUPEIDAE						
Pellona flavipinnis and P. castelnaeana (acapá)	*	*	12.4	17.6	3.0	-
CURIMATIDAE						
Gasterotomus latior (braquinha)	*	■	-	-	-	-
DORADIDAE						
Oxydoras niger (cuiú-cuiú)	*	*	0.2	15.8	1.0	-
SCIAENIDAE						
Plagioscion squamosissimus (pescada)	+	+	5.8	19.4	2.8	-
ERYTHRINIDAE						
Hoplias malabaricus (traíra)	*	*	-	-	-	-
HYPOPHTHALMIDAE						
Hypophthalmus edentatus (maparà)	*	+	28.8	12.4	2.6	-
LORICARIIDAE						
Plecostomus plecostomus (acarí)	*	*	-	-	-	-
Pterygoplichthys pardalis (acarí)	*	*	-	-	-	●
OSTEOGLOSSIDAE						
Arapaima gigas (pirarucú)	+	+	-	-	-	-
Osteoglossum bicirrosum (aruanã)	*	+	2.6	20.0	2.0	-
PIMELODIDAE						
Brachyplatystoma filamentosum (piraíba)	■	■	0.6	17.4	1.4	-
Brachyplatystoma flavicans (dourado)	■	■	-	-	-	-
Brachyplatystoma vaillanti (piramutaba)	+	*	-	-	-	-
Calophysus macropterus (piracatinga)	■	*	-	-	-	-
Paulicea luetkeni (pacamum)	■	*	-	-	-	-
Phractocephalus hemiliopterus (pirirara)	■	*	-	-	-	-
Pimelodus blochii (mandí)	*	+	-	-	-	-
Pinirampus pirinampu (piranambu)	*	*	-	-	-	-
Pseudoplatystoma fasciatum (surubim)	■	*	2.0	17.0	1.2	●
Sorubim lima (bico de pato)	*	*	-	-	-	-
Surubimichthys planiceps (peixe lenha)	+	*	-	-	-	-
PROCHILODONTIDAE						
Prochilodus nigricans (curimatà)	■	■	17.4	15.4	2.6	●
Semaprochilodus insignis and S. taeniurus (jaraquí)	*	■	9.4	15.4	3.0	●

range of captures: ■ from 1 to 10
+ from 11 to 20
* more than 20

IT: Itacoatiara area (Amazon)
PV: Porto Velho area (Madeira)

Fish species

As at sea, owing to a combination of factors such as size, habitats, fishing techniques, consumer income, and preferences, a small number of key genera and species account for the great majority of the freshwater catch. In rainforest rivers the availability of fish may fluctuate during the year, and seasonal exploitation of migrating or spawning shoals may often be most appropriate. The fish fauna appears to be more influenced by short-term changes in habitat and the surrounding landscape than by the color or the transparency of the water (white or clear), despite the differences in the suspended material transported by these rivers. In the Amazon, for example, as riverine forests flood seasonally during high water, fish move

174 The biggest Amazonian fish, the arapaima, or pirarucú (*Arapaima gigas*), is also one of the biggest river fishes in the world. Some specimens can reach 8.2 ft (2.5 m) in length and their scales are so long and rough that they are sold as nail files. The photo shows a fisherman in the Upper Amazon skinning a recently caught fish. [*Photo: Mark Edwards / Still Pictures*]

into the *várzea* to feed and to accumulate the fat that they need to survive the dry season when food is scarcer. Likewise, runoff during the rainy season affects the water quality of the *terra firme* waterways, and the fish respond to this stimulus.

The ease or difficulty of catching the fish and therefore the amount of fish protein available to rainforest-dwellers depends on water depth, rate of flow, and water transparency. An example of variation in capturability is shown by the river turtles (*Trionyx*) caught in six small communities on the upper Baram river in Sarawak. Turtle meat was absent from the diet of the villages of the area in 1982 and 1985, but it was a major item of their diet during the long droughts of 1983 and 1984. These records correlate with reports that spoke of falling water levels in the main river that concentrated turtles in pools where they could be easily caught.

No river basin on Earth has more freshwater species than the Amazon: Almost 1,400 species have been described, in contrast to the 560 known species in the Zaire Basin. It is easy to see why fish have traditionally been the most important source of animal protein for the inhabitants of the Amazon. Fish still provide a significant portion of daily animal protein intake in many areas and may in fact be the most important source among some native groups. Even the colonists of the terra firme forests never settle too far from rivers and often make use of this resource. Some of the most caught species, such as the pirarucú (*Arapaima gigas*) and the piraiba (*Brachyplatystoma filamentosum*), reach huge dimensions and weights (some individuals reach 3.3 ft [1 m] in length and 220.3 lb

[100 kg] in weight). The tambaquí (*Colossoma macropomum*) and other common characins easily weigh 6.6-11 lb (3-5 kg).

Traditional fishing techniques

A great variety of traditional methods have been devised and are still in use today. Fishermen generally use a wide range of techniques to suit season, water clarity, depth and volume, target species, and other factors such as migrations (see chapter 2.4.1). Hooks, projectiles, nets (fixed, hung from boats or thrown), traps (of varying size and degrees of intricacy), and poisons are used.

Hooks were once commonly made from bone and used with lines of vegetable or animal fiber (with the possible exception of the American rainforests, where there is no evidence of the use of hooks before the arrival of Europeans). Later, nylon fishing lines and metal hooks became part of fishing habits.

Projectile weapons, including arrows and harpoons, are widely used, especially in shallow water. Harpoons, often with detachable shafts, are reserved for larger prey such as the pirarucú or arapaima (*Arapaima gigas*), species that have now almost been wiped out in their natural range. Traditionally, arrows and harpoons had a wide range of different types of pointed tips for use against different target species; the great range of arrow designs seen in New Guinea is a good example of the options available.

A variety of net types, including castnets, seines (vertical nets), and weirs (trap nets), are employed. Crude traditional nets made from vegetable fibers may not last for long but they are very efficient. They are especially effective when combined with techniques involving damming or herding to concentrate the fish or involving the use of poison to stun them. Today, larger synthetic-fiber nets are increasingly seen, although there are groups, above all in the Americas, that still use fish traps and baskets, usually constructed of natural fibers. Large fencelike enclosures, or weirs, that interrupt fish migration are also very efficient, often to such a degree that they capture indiscriminately any fish that happens to be passing.

Using poisons in fishing is widespread among rainforest-dwelling humans and is probably the main way fish are captured for human consumption. Poison is very effective in small streams for a short time. It is usually carried out communally, and as the stunned fish are generally gathered by hand as a group effort it is a technique for occasional rather than continual use. Most fishing and hunting is performed by men, but women and children often assist in this activity. Plant poisons containing rotenone (a pentacyclic ketone lethal to fish but harmless to warm-blooded mammals), principally extracted from the roots of tuba (*Derris elliptica*) and from the bark and seeds of gyamkawa (*Mundulea sericea*) and other plants (*Phyllanthus brasiliensis, Ryania speciosa, Euphorbia cotinifolia*), are highly effective but rather destructive. Many dead fish sink and remain uncollected if the water is too deep or cloudy for them to be seen.

In southeast Nigeria large groups of people collaborate to poison stretches of river and to then collect the fruits of their labor. They use traditional toxic preparations of the fruits of genus *Omphalocarpum* (Sapotaceae), the stems of *Adenia lobata* (Passifloraceae), the twigs of *Olax gambecola* (Olacaceae), or the bark of the genus *Erythropleum* (Leguminosae). Similar techniques are used in southeast Asia, where the most widespread poison is manufactured from pounded tuba (*Derris elliptica*) roots. This species is used from Indochina throughout the Malay Archipelago to Australia and Fiji as well as in South America. Plants of the genera *Paullinia pinnata* (Sapindaceae) or *Serjania* (Sapindaceae), *Hura crepitans* (Euphorbiaceae), and *Tephrosia toxicaria* (Leguminosae) are also used.

Traditional vegetable-based poisons like *Derris* are biodegradable and nonpersistent. However, poisoning is now often used to satisfy the commercial fish market, and modern chemical poisons, including pesticides and the contents of old batteries, are increasingly being employed. This poses a health risk to those eating the fish as well as a serious threat to the ecology of the river. Large amounts of commercial insecticides are needed to disable fish, yet highly diluted doses can wipe out the whole arthropod community in a long section of a river. This is the opposite of the effect of *Derris*, which is much less toxic to arthropods than to fish.

Introduced fishing technologies are gradually taking over in neotropical forest systems. The use of metal hooks by forest river-dwellers is probably the most widely used fishing technique. Bait varies according to target species and may include seeds, fruit, and other fish. Very productive trawl lines with many hooks are also used. Gillnets have also been introduced into fishing cultures, often with destructive effects. Their use is particularly effective in flooded forest environments during high water and can have a strong

175 Fishing with bow and arrows has long been practiced in many rainforest rivers. In the photo, two Kayapó are fishing in the Xingu river in the Amazon. The target is relatively close, but hitting it is not easy. An optical illusion of the fish's real position is caused by the refraction of light, and the arrow changes in speed and trajectory as it enters the water.
[Photo: Bill Leimbach / South American Pictures]

176 The practice of fishing in rapids is very widespread. Rapids are normally shallow areas where fish find their movements hampered and often do not notice the presence of fishermen. Conventional lightweight methods are used (rods, bows, etc.) or batteries of fixed traps are set up, as in the photo. Here, a system of enormous basket traps has been installed on the Wagenia or Boyoma rapids on the Zaire near Kisangani. These rapids prevent navigation further upstream.
[Photo: The Hutchison Library]

impact on stocks of certain key species such as the tambaquí (*Colossoma*) and others of the same genus. These species were previously caught one by one on single hooks; today they are taken out in large numbers. The new practice of using submerged, drifting nets in deep river channels allows the exploitation of areas previously beyond the capabilities of traditional fishermen. Finally, the use of explosives to fish is an enormously destructive method, because fish are killed indiscriminately yet only the desired species are collected. Although this type of fishing is illegal in all countries, explosives are easy to obtain for legitimate purposes and can simply be used for fishing in rivers.

Commercial fishing

Fishing in rainforest rivers and lakes has been progressively affected by regional trading patterns. As mentioned above, many forest-dwellers sell their excess catch in small quantities. Few, however, are employed fulltime as fishermen. As urban centers grew so did the demand for fish. Salted fish was not particularly appreciated, and so fishermen were obliged to supply fresh fish and hence to fish near urban centers. However, as motors became available and in particular outboards, distant areas were opened up to exploitation by the increasing numbers of fishermen. This

also increased operating costs and more fish were needed to make a profit. Boat owners increasingly adopted more efficient methods and equipment, thereby increasing production but also raising their overheads.

As ice-making facilities are built, the area and range of fishing boats are extended. In Sarawak during the 1970s, commercial speedboat routes penetrated the interior, allowing traders to invest in cold-storage facilities for collecting fish and game for sale downstream. During one month in 1985, for example, one trader dispatched nearly 3.5 t of frozen river fish down the Rajang river, earning the equivalent of about U.S. $1,000 per day. Most of the fish in these river basins are from three genera of cyprinids, *Tor*, *Puntius*, and *Pangasius*. Curiously, in 1935, an official report from the Malayan Fisheries Department described one of these genera (*Pangasius*) as "not sufficiently abundant to rank as of any great economic importance except in so far as it helps keep the Malays in the interior supplied with food." The contrast between 1935 and 1985 is a good example of how modern trade has changed the ecological significance of human harvesting of fish stocks.

However, many fishermen can barely keep ahead of these spiraling costs and find it hard to stay in business. As more boats enter the commercial

STATE	1970	1971	1972	1973	1974	1975
Pará	25,347	30,651	26,985	31,603	45,215	58,202
Amazon	20,420	18,919	19,364	19,426	25,823	59,767
Acre	358	295	343	377	3,243	595
Rondônia	490	603	603	951	1,546	1,223
Amapá	638	710	715	744	741	815
Roraima	120	96	96	139	171	199
	47,373	51,274	48,106	53,240	76,730	120,801

fleet, fish size and production per boat decline. The demands of trade may have impacts well beyond the simple selective overharvesting of certain species. At the beginning of this century 10 exotic fish species were introduced into the lakes of Celebes (Sulawesi), Indonesia, to encourage commercial fish production. The result was the nearly complete replacement of the poorly known indigenous fish fauna, which had never been systematically assessed for its fishery potential.

As market demand is for a limited number of species, commercial fishers discard large numbers of fish. These huge quantities of rejected fish often contain prey species or juveniles of commercial species. As preferred fish decline in number, prices rise and the urban poor are forced to purchase less acceptable species. This uncontrolled intensification of commercial fisheries, especially in the Amazon, has provoked a decline in captures in many areas.

3.6 Domesticated fauna

Few domesticated animal species are specifically of rainforest origin, although the forests of tropical Asia in particular are home to many relatives of domesticated animals.

Domesticated animals

Various wild forms of pig (*Sus*) living in Asian rainforests often hybridize with domesticated animals. The Eurasian wild boar (*Sus scrofa*) is native to the southeast Asian rainforest, and there are other indigenous species on all the other major islands: the bearded pig (*S. barbatus*) on Borneo, Malacca, and Sumatra; the Javan warty pig (*S. verrucosus*) on Java; and the Sulawesi warty pig (*S. celebensis*) on Sulawesi in Indonesia. Another case is the water buffalo (*Bubalus bubalis*) and its wild relatives the tamarao (*B. mindorensis*) of Mindoro in the Philippines and the anoas (*B. [=Anoa] depressicornis* and *B. [=Anoa] quarlesi*) of Sulawesi. The water buffalo is one of the most important domesticated species in southeast Asia. The rainforests of southeast Asia are also the center of origin of another important domesticate, the chicken, whose wild ancestor the jungle fowl (*Gallus gallus*) is one of the many Asian pheasants.

Such connections have raised the question of which other species might possibly be domesticated, or which genes might be used to improve the stock of existing domesticates. Considerable

178 The ancestor of the domestic chicken is the jungle fowl (*Gallus gallus*), an inhabitant of the monsoon and rain forests in southeast Asia. This magnificent forest bird, shown here in Java, has to be seen in its natural habitat, away from commonplace chicken runs, for its full beauty to become apparent. [Photo: Gunter Ziesler / Jacana]

research has been done, in particular in west and central Africa where wild meat is much appreciated and where high rates of rainforest destruction are closely linked to poverty and malnutrition. The feeling is that few African animals have been truly domesticated (perhaps only the donkey, *Equus asinus*), in part because of the abundance of wild meat and relatively low human densities. This equation has changed in recent decades, and particular attention has been paid to species that are simple to raise, productive, and acceptable to local people.

One example is the African giant snail (*Achatina*), a major invertebrate source of protein as described previously. It is a quick-growing species producing up to 200 eggs a year that can be fed upon vegetable kitchen waste. Another wild animal that has been studied is the grass-cutter (*Thryonomys*), whose virtues include fast growth and acceptability as a food item by local people. Nevertheless, neither species has yet proved itself as a domesticate in practice, since both are vulnerable to disease in captivity, and in the case of the snails, to predation by ants. These problems may be resolved eventually by redesigning enclosures, but this is proving to be a long process of trial and error, and both species are so abundant and productive in the wild that collection rather than domestication may ultimately be the more effective option.

Pets

Rainforest-dwellers have probably kept wild animals as pets for thousands of years. This practice continues today, with virtually every village having captive fauna from its own biome. The modern Kayapó people of Brazil keep 31 species of animals, including 16 species of parrots and macaws, 5 turtle species, a lizard, and a spider. Young animals such as peccaries and agoutis may be encountered or orphaned during hunting forays and brought back to the village and kept until they reach a sufficient size and weight to be slaughtered.

Many animals sold as pets in local markets or exported to other areas, in particular to the developed nations, originate in rainforests. Macaws, parrots, monkeys, and hundreds of small songbirds are taken from the rainforest and shipped off to the world's pet markets. The inhabitants of tropical cities are normally very fond of pets, above all

179 Keeping pets is not, as might be thought, a western habit to replace the absence of nature. It is, in many cultures, a highly significant ancestral practice. Many rainforest people surround themselves with more-or-less domesticated birds and small mammals. This Yanomami woman is holding a small monkey that is so integrated into the family circle that she is breast-feeding it alongside her young child.
[Photo: Mark Edwards / Still Pictures]

birds and monkeys, and in the cities and towns of tropical Latin America parrots and macaws and various songbirds are common. Hundreds of thousands of finches are sold in Brazil, and value increases by song quality.

It is hardly necessary to remark on the interest in exotic animals shown by the inhabitants of the most developed countries outside the tropics. Exports for the pet trade can be very lucrative. Parrots and macaws fetch very high prices, and large numbers of these and other birds are exported from Indonesia every year to satisfy demand. In west Africa the story is repeated. Prices vary according to location, species, and legal situation. A relatively common species like the scarlet macaw (*Ara macao*) may sell legally for U.S. $2,000, while a black-market smuggled Spix's macaw (*Cyanopsitta spixii*) could fetch as much as U.S. $40,000 or more indeed. Retail sales in the United States of both wild and captive-bred birds are estimated currently at more than U.S. $300 million annually. Between 1981 and 1986, the United States imported 703,000 parrots from the neotropics. New laws enacted in 1992 curbed legal importation into the United States, but Europe and Japan remain major markets. These long-lived birds reproduce slowly, and trade has been responsible for serious declines in the wild populations of a number of species. The same type of continual demand means continual exports, often illegal, of orangutans (*Pongo pygmaeus*), chimpanzees (*Pan troglodytes*), and other animals from the southeast Asian and west African rainforests.

4. Management problems and environmental conflicts

4.1 Human impact

Colonization of an adverse environment like the rainforest has historically been a challenge that human beings have never completely resolved. In the face of the intricate complexity of the planet's most diverse biome, humans have tended to apply simplistic solutions that are often incompatible with the conditions necessary for the forest's survival. Itinerant farmers and ambitious politicians, ranchers and timber companies, landless peasants and petroleum prospectors have only too often chosen the same solution: getting rid of the trees that stand in their way. It is probably because human beings are so poorly adapted to life in the forest that the first thing to be done when settling in the forest is to make a clearing. This is true not only of the equatorial rainforest, but of temperate forests, which have also suffered similar or worse aggressions in the past.

The difficulties and types of colonization

The reproductive mechanisms of the rainforest plants are very well adapted to resist biological competition but are not well adapted to dealing with large changes in the environment, such as those caused by human exploitation, compared with simpler and more resilient ecosystems, such as those in temperate regions, which are more resistant and show a greater ability to regenerate. Other terrestrial ecosystems contain most of their available nutrients in the soil, but in the rainforest almost all the nutrients are in the biomass, and the small part that returns to the environment is recycled almost immediately. Deforestation in the rainforest is not just the loss of the trees and lianas, as well as their associated microflora and micro- and macrofauna, but above all a major loss of nutrients. If large areas of rainforest are destroyed in well-drained areas, the material that formerly supported the rainforest, often hardly deserving to be called soil, rapidly breaks down to form eroded, desolate landscapes. Not only are rainforest ecosystems highly vulnerable, but in addition, it is often difficult if not impossible to recover lost nutrients.

Yet there are many different ways of clearing the rainforest and establishing settlements in it or exploiting it. In terms of the impact of human activity in the rainforest, two types of colonization can be distinguished.

180 Using fire to clear land has long been common practice in the rainforest. Since the 1950s, these fires have become more common in the Amazon in sites like the one in the photo, in the basin of the river Branco. They have now reached such alarming proportions that on any day of the year there is a fire burning in the region. This beautiful photo hides a very serious environmental management problem, as the characteristics of the local soils mean that most of the grazing and crop lands created by this burning becomes unproductive after a few years. [Photo: Mark Edwards / Still Pictures]

181 New highways through the rainforest are becoming more and more common, bringing civilization and exporting problems. One famous case is the BR-364 road, which joins Cuiabá with Porto Velho, the capitals of the states of Mato Grosso and Rondônia, near Brazil's western border with Bolivia. Initial plans to asphalt the highway were expanded to include the development of the area influenced by the road, resulting in the "Polonoreste" resettlement scheme, which was funded by the World Bank. The intention was to ensure the demarcation of tribal lands, to provide social services for the native peoples, to protect the biological and forest reserves and to promote sustainable agriculture, but this is not what happened. The improvements to the BR-364 in 1984 tripled the number of immigrants to 150,000 in 1986. They were attracted by easier access and government propaganda. In Rondônia more than, 4,942,087.4 acres (2 million ha) of forest were burnt or cleared. The limits of the native reserves and forest reserves were not respected, and illegal logging was accompanied by the displacement of indigenous peoples and violent conflicts. The price of land rose dramatically, encouraging forest clearance to establish land claims. Almost 80% of the new colonists could not maintain their farms because of the soil's infertility, high agricultural costs, and the fall in crop prices. Many smallholdings were abandoned to ranchers. The failure of the Polonoreste scheme provoked widespread international criticism. In 1985 the World Bank briefly withheld financing for the project to force the Brazilian government to set aside lands for the Uru-Eu-Wau-Wau people and to remove settlers from several native and forest reserves. This shows that roads as a means of communication are not always a way to progress. [Photo: Mark Edwards / Still Pictures]

The first type of colonist, few in number, clear only a small space in the rainforest to settle, around which they try to find the food and other resources they need; they are integrated into their environment. If they do not find all they need in their environment, they move to a new site and start the cycle again. Over centuries of repetitions and learning from their mistakes, many of the descendants of the first colonists have adapted to the rainforest environment and manage it in such a way that it is conserved yet also a source of useful products. This type of colonization was practiced by the first human populations to reach the rainforest and to be capable of learning to live in it. An estimated 50 million of their descendants now live in the rainforest, still living in traditional tribal societies. These peoples have developed environmentally harmonious lifestyles that do not subject their resources to excessive pressure.

A different type of colonization was carried out by the later waves of human settlement, especially modern ones, although there were also invasions in the distant past by populations adapted to very different environments, such as the Indo-European populations in India and the Bantu in Africa. This is a spreading form of colonization, *frontier colonization*. This second type of colonization is currently associated with the landless peasants or the cattle ranchers now felling and burning the Amazon rainforest to establish unsustainable crops and grazing land, but they have had notable predecessors, especially in the expansion of the peoples of western and central Europe over the last five centuries. These new arrivals normally do not possess the knowledge to use the resources and goods provided by the rainforest or adequate techniques to sustain them and thus they contribute to its destruction.

The retreat of the rainforest

The area occupied by rainforest is declining throughout the world. This rate varies from continent to continent and from region to region within a single continent, but it is estimated that 49.4-74 acres (20-30 ha) of rainforest are deforested every minute. Just three countries (Brazil, Indonesia, and Democratic Republic of Congo) account for 44% of total deforestation, and together with Myanmar, Colombia, Malaysia, Mexico, Nigeria, and Thailand they account for 76% of total deforestation. It is very difficult to produce accurate global estimates of the rate and area of this deforestation. The U.N. Food and Agricultural Organization (FAO) has undertaken a thorough assessment combining national figures for deforestation from the different tropical countries. According to this assessment, the rate of tropical deforestation increased from an estimated 27,922,793.7 acres (11.3 million ha) per year in the period 1981-1985 to 37,806,968.5 acres (15.3 million ha) per year for the decade 1981-1990 as a whole.

The direct causes of this deforestation vary greatly: logging, clearing for agriculture or for ranching, mining, the construction of roads and reservoirs, urban growth, and so on. Yet the remote causes are even

182 **Rates of deforestation in the tropical rainforest in the different continents between 1981 and 1990**, with an indication of the relative percentage loss of species and the density of the human population.

[Drawing: Editrònica, with data from FAO and UNEP]

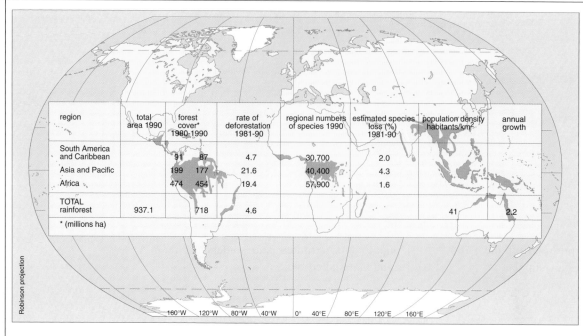

region	total area 1990	forest cover* 1980-1990		rate of deforestation 1981-90	regional numbers of species 1990	estimated species loss (%) 1981-90	population density habitants/km²	annual growth
South America and Caribbean		91	87	4.7	30,700	2.0		
Asia and Pacific		199	177	21.6	40,400	4.3		
Africa		474	454	19.4	57,900	1.6		
TOTAL rainforest	937.1		718	4.6			41	2.2

* (millions ha)

Robinson projection

160°W   120°W   80°W   40°W   0°   40°E   80°E   120°E   160°E

more complex, as many interests are involved, from those of a peasant family that needs to cut a patch of forest for their survival to the interests of a multinational company in search of large and quick profits. These indirect causes also include the public interest of corrupt local administrations and dictatorial governments in countries with rainforest, and the interests of democratic governments in developed countries that unthinkingly exploit the resources of third world countries.

Poverty, social inequality, and unrestrained population growth are the most important basic causes of deforestation in all tropical regions. Land-ownership systems that concentrate large areas of productive land in the hands of a minority (in Brazil, for example, less than 1% of the landowners control almost half the country's cultivable land, and in Colombia 80% of the cultivable land is in the hands of 10% of the land-holders) tend to increase the problem, by increasing the demand for land and the need to cut the forest, whether the soil is suitable for agriculture or not. These major imbalances in the distribution of wealth stimulate many of the dispossessed to try colonizing the supposedly virgin land apparently within their grasp. Unfortunately, they do not possess the same knowledge of the rainforest environment as the rainforest's traditional inhabitants, and they thus endanger its future without obtaining the benefits they had hoped for. On the other hand, the number of the dispossessed continues to grow, and an estimated 140 million people now live in or near the rainforest biome, most of them below the poverty line. At the end of the 21st century, four out of every five people will live in the countries that now possess rainforest, and most of them, unless something is done, will live in the most abject poverty.

On a different scale, national policies and the unequal relations between rich and poor countries usually reinforce these basic causes. The governments of the tropical countries often consider their forests as unproductive areas that ought to be transformed to provide land for the poor and to provide economic benefits through the sale of wood, other forest products, and the harvests from the new crops grown on land cleared from the rainforest. These countries, faced with the problems of enormous foreign debt and rapidly growing populations, generally consider the forests as their most important potential economic asset, often without realizing that this is a limited and short-lived resource unless measures are taken to ensure exploitation is sustainable. Almost half the total debt (1.3 billion American dollars in 1993) of poor countries with the governments and banks of rich countries and international financial agencies corresponds to the 27 countries that have the most rainforest in their territory.

Many pressures on tropical rainforests originate elsewhere: in international trade, banks, and political advantage. Foreign debt problems force many tropical countries to exploit their forest resources to obtain the foreign exchange they need and often to destroy the rainforest through inappropriate aid-financed development projects that then have to be paid back in foreign currency. Responsibility for preserving the tropical forests goes beyond national

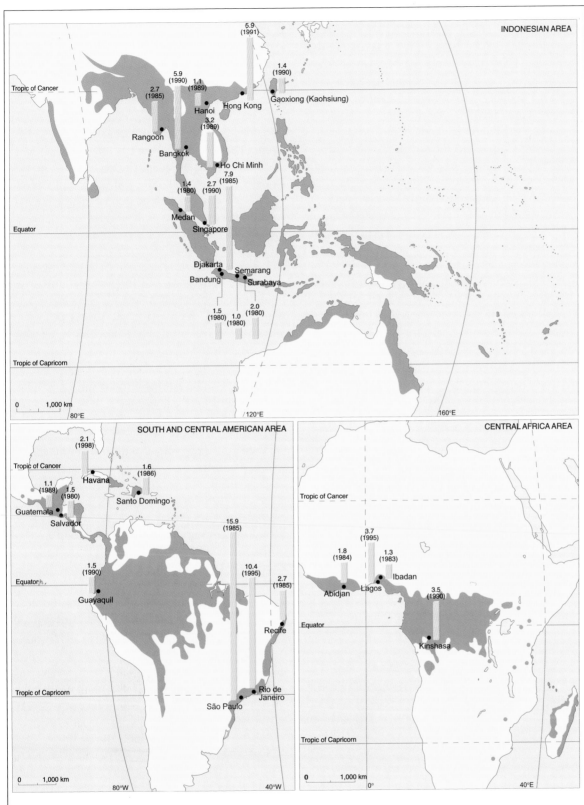

INDONESIAN AREA

5.9 (1991)
5.9 (1990)
1.1 (1989)
1.4 (1990)
2.7 (1985)
Gaoxiong (Kaohsiung)
Hanoi
Hong Kong
Rangoon
3.2 (1989)
Bangkok
Ho Chi Minh
7.9 (1985)
1.4 (1980)
2.7 (1990)
Medan
Singapore
Djakarta
Semarang
Bandung
Surabaya
1.5 (1980)
1.0 (1980)
2.0 (1980)

Tropic of Cancer
Equator
Tropic of Capricorn

0 — 1,000 km
80°E / 120°E / 160°E

SOUTH AND CENTRAL AMERICAN AREA

2.1 (1998)
1.6 (1986)
Havana
1.1 (1989)
1.5 (1980)
Guatemala
Salvador
Santo Domingo
15.9 (1985)
1.5 (1990)
10.4 (1995)
2.7 (1985)
Guayaquil
Recife
Rio de Janeiro
São Paulo

Tropic of Cancer
Equator
Tropic of Capricorn

0 — 1,000 km
80°W / 40°W

CENTRAL AFRICA AREA

3.7 (1995)
1.8 (1984)
1.3 (1983)
Ibadan
Abidjan
Lagos
3.5 (1990)
Kinshasa

Tropic of Cancer
Equator
Tropic of Capricorn

0 — 1,000 km
0° / 40°E

183 Urban areas with more than a million inhabitants in rainforest areas. Each of the 24 areas shows the number of inhabitants and the year the census was taken. *[Drawing: Editrònica, from several sources]*

frontiers, and global measures are needed to strengthen local conservation programs.

Protected areas reserved for conservation only cover 5% of the tropical rainforest biome, and in recent years the establishment of new national parks and other protected areas has been greatly delayed. Management of the remaining forests is increasingly important as destruction and fragmentation continue without any effective control.

The exploitation and decline of the American rainforest

Of the 2,300,000 sq mi (6 million sq km) of tropical rainforest distributed between the nine countries of the

Amazon Basin, 60% is in Brazil. According to estimates of the FAO 9,770 sq mi (25,300 sq km) were deforested every year between 1981 and 1985, and according to the Brazilian national research institute, in 1987 and 1988 the rate of deforestation was 13,500 sq mi (35,000 sq km) a year, 1.5 sq mi (4 sq km) per hour! But the situation of the forest cover is not uniform throughout the region. In some parts of Amazonia the forest has been largely destroyed, whereas in other areas it is almost intact. The states of Amapá and Amazonas are relatively intact, but the state of Maranhão is largely deforested. Outside Brazil, in the rest of the Amazon Basin, deforestation also varies from country to country. In Colombia the annual rate over the period 1981-1990 was 849 sq mi (2,200 sq km) a year. In Ecuador, 540 sq mi (1,400 sq km); and in Peru, 425 sq mi (1,100 sq km). In the Amazon as a whole, between 5 and 12% of the original forest appears to have been lost, although in some cases it is regenerating to relatively species-poor secondary forest.

During the 1980s transformation of the Amazon speeded up as planning projects allowed people to enter formerly inaccessible areas. In the state of Rondônia in the southeastern Amazon, the Brazilian government built a highway (the BR-364) that allowed large-scale migration of landless farmers into the region, resulting in the destruction of a large part of the state's primary forest. Other Brazilian government projects have led to large-scale logging to supply fuel for iron smelters, such as the Grande Carajás region in northeast Brazil, and the flooding of large areas of forest by the construction of hydroelectric dams on several tributaries of the Amazon.

Yet Surinam, which is also in South America, has one of the lowest rates of deforestation of any tropical country, as most of its forests are still intact. It has also created an extensive network of reserves with samples of most ecosystems. In Guyana and French Guyana the rainforest is also little exploited. In Venezuela, deforestation continues at a slow rate, as the government has issued a decree protecting 60% of the forested area.

On the other hand, on the western side of the Andes the exceptionally species-rich forests of Peru, Ecuador, and Colombia are being cleared very quickly, mainly to cultivate opium poppy (*Papaver somniferum*) and coca (*Erythroxylum coca*). There are also plans by foreign timber companies for large-scale exploitation of these forests for chipboard production. In Ecuador, most of the lowland forests west of the Andes (among the richest in the world in terms of biodiversity, and among the most threatened) have been destroyed in the last 30 years.

The Brazilian Mata Atlântica is an extreme example of deforestation. It formerly occupied about 38,610 sq mi (100,000 sq km), but has now been cut back to 5% of its former area. The region now houses Brazil's most agriculturally and industrially developed areas and 148 million people. There are still some isolated remnants of the former forests, one of the world's most diverse ecosystems.

In Panama, forest loss near the Canal Zone owing to shifting cultivation and illegal logging has led to an increase in erosion and a significant reduction in rainfall. As a result, the Panama Canal is silting up and its water level has fallen, causing difficulties for shipping.

Central America's lowland rainforest was virtually intact until 1950. By the early 1960s the area of forest had declined to 80%, and by the end of the 1980s to 40%. If this rate of deforestation continues, most of the tropical rainforest in the region will be cut in the next 20 years, and all that will remain will be a few impoverished fragments in reserves and national parks. No primary rainforest remains in San Salvador, and in Costa Rica the area of primary forest has declined from 67% of the forest cover in 1940 to only 17% in 1983. Except for Belize, all the other countries are losing between 193 and 386 sq mi (500 and 1,000 sq km) a year. The situation is much worse because of the doubling of population over the last 30 years and the political instability of most countries in Central America.

The Caribbean's islands were almost all totally covered in rainforest until the 16th century. Most have now disappeared as a result of high population pressure. Cuba still had 90% of its original forest cover in 1890, but now has only 14%. In Puerto Rico, before 1770 only 6% of the territory had been deforested, but in 1903 only 0.4% of the forest was left. In 1978, 32% of the island was once more covered by rainforest, although it was mostly secondary forest.

The exploitation and regression of the African and Madagascan rainforests

The Zaire Basin contains more than 80% of Africa's rainforest and, due to the region's inhos-

184 Madagascar is rapidly being deforested, as the rainforest is lost through fires and clearing. This would not be environmentally serious (except in terms of rainforest conservation) if stable and productive agriculture and ranching maintained the area's viability, but unfortunately, this does not occur. These recently deforested slopes in Ranomafana will be used for temporary crops and then abandoned. The heavy rainfall and steep slope will probably lead to intense erosion before the rainforest can reestablish. This increases the already tragic spread of the *lavaka*, or erosion gullies, in Madagascar.
[Photo: Paul Harrison / Still Pictures]

pitable nature and the difficult access, it is almost intact. Western and eastern Africa's rainforest areas have, however, suffered greater impacts because conditions are more favorable for human settlement.

Africa's population is growing extremely quickly, doubling every 20 years. In 1880, there were still 162,000 sq mi (420,000 sq km) of rainforest, but only 67,000 sq mi (173,000 sq km) were left in 1980, and now there is little more than 60,000 sq mi (160,000 sq km). The rate of forest loss is about 4% a year. In some countries like Sierra Leone, Ivory Coast, and Nigeria, only about 10% of the original forest is left, and in Ghana about 22%. Over the next 10-15 years Gabon plans to fell most of the forest now occupying 70% of the country for timber. Democratic Republic of Congo and the Central African Republic have already built highways throughout the rainforest; although the population levels are low, they are growing rapidly, and this will speed up the destruction of the forests.

Madagascar's rainforest is suffering more from human population pressure than anywhere else. In 1985 only 61,776 sq mi (30,000 sq km) was left, only half of the area that was forested in 1950 and only one third of the original forest cover. It is estimated that in 35 years only the remotest and most inaccessible areas of the Madagascar forest will survive. Since their arrival 1,500 years ago, humans have eliminated countless populations of giant flightless birds and large bearlike lemurs by hunting or habitat destruction. The human population is growing explosively. The 12 million inhabitants in 1990 will reach an estimated 28 million before 2025. Forest fragmentation is occurring so fast that more extinctions will soon occur. Many unique and potentially valuable species are only hanging on in a few patches of forest that shrink year after year as land is invaded by settlers to feed their families.

The exploitation and decline of the Asian and Indo-Pacific rainforest

The destruction of the forests of southern Asia over the last 50 years has been exceptionally rapid. Large areas of primary rainforest have been altered by timber extraction, and in other areas the forest cover has been totally lost.

For example, in 1943 45% of Vietnam was covered by forests, but this number had declined to 20% by the mid-1980s. The pressure of the population in search of agricultural land seems to have been the main factor behind this loss of forest, but during the war in the 1960s and 1970s, bombing and deliberate spraying of defoliant agents also played an important role. Many affected areas show little sign of natural regeneration of forest cover, although reforestation programs are under way. Cambodia is still suffering the environmental aftereffects of the Vietnam War and its own civil wars. During the Vietnam War, eastern Cambodia was as heavily bombed and extensively defoliated as Vietnam. In Laos all that is left of the rainforest are very small fragments in the mountainous central regions and in the plain of the Mekong.

Thailand is one of the richest and most stable countries in the area, but now only 15% of its territory is covered by forest. Most of this is exploited, and in the 1980s deforestation was nearly 579 sq mi (1,500 sq km) a year. This is not far behind Myanmar's estimated annual loss of 618 sq mi (1,600 sq km) a year, one of the world's highest rates of deforestation (2% a year). This is the result of the increasing population's growing need for agricultural land, extraction of wood for markets in neighboring countries, and excessive logging quotas, which are rapidly exhausting the most productive areas. In Peninsular Malaysia from 1986-1990, an average of 367 sq mi (950 sq km) were deforested a year, about 1.6% of the area forested in 1985.

The forests of India, Bangladesh, and Sri Lanka have also suffered greatly as a consequence of population growth and the uncontrolled logging of the last decades. Sri Lanka's civil war has led to uncontrolled deforestation of part of the island and the probable extinction of several endemic species with localized distributions on the island, precisely in areas that are now totally deforested. Only 1% of the original vegetation is left, in the southwestern tip.

Considering 15% of the world's population, more than 800 million people, live in India, with a population density of 250 inhabitants/ sq km (1 sq km=0.4 sq mi), it is surprising that there is still any rainforest left. Between 1950 and 1980 India lost large areas of forest, but vigorous reafforestation policies due to strong pressure from the population slowed down this loss. In the western Ghats there are still 8,494 sq mi (22,000 sq km) of rainforest. Yet in northeastern India the forest that used to occupy large areas has been destroyed by population growth. Bangladesh was formerly covered by forest, especially monsoon forest, from the delta of the Ganges to the mountains. Only 5% of this original forest survives due to the enormous pressure on natural resources, as Bangladesh is one of the poorest countries in the world and one of the most densely populated (more than 600 inhabitants/ sq km).

The Indonesian archipelago consists of more than 13,000 islands and is one of the richest areas in the world in term of biodiversity. Indonesia contains 10% of the world's area of rainforest, 424,711 sq mi (1.1 million sq km). However, the amount of forest lost every year between 2,700 and 4,633 sq mi (7,000 and 12,000 sq km), is the highest in the world after Brazil. The worst affected is the island of Java, which has lost 90% of its original vegeta-

tion; the only primary forest left is in remote areas above 4,593 ft (1,400 m). Sumatra, the most westerly island of Indonesia, has extensive areas of rainforest and is losing them at almost the same rate as its population is growing (3.3% a year). The island of Borneo, shared between Malaysia, Brunei, and Indonesia, still retains a large area of primary rainforest, one of the largest in southeast Asia, although forest exploitation and agriculture are increasing greatly, mainly in the Malaysian states of Sabah and Sarawak. In Sarawak, according to 1987 data, 741,300 acres (300,000 ha) of forest were lost every year, giving it the sad privilege of the highest rate of deforestation in the world in relative terms. Large areas of rainforest have also been degraded in the Indonesian part of the island, and between September 1982 and July 1983 drought and fire destroyed more than 15,444 sq mi (40,000 sq km).

When the Philippines changed from Spanish sovereignty to the American sphere of influence in the early 20th century, it was almost totally covered by rainforest and monsoon forest. In 1945 only two thirds was left, and now only less than one fifth of the original 154,400 sq mi (400,000 sq km) is left.

Large-scale forest exploitation and agriculture have affected only a small part of the forest in New Guinea, in spite of its long settlement by people practicing shifting agriculture. In fact, the island of New Guinea, whose western half is occupied by Indonesia and eastern half by Papua New Guinea, contains the largest area of rainforest in the south Asia and Pacific region. Between 80 and 85% of the area of Irian Jaya (the Indonesian western part of island of New Guinea) and between 75 and 80% of that of Papua New Guinea are still intact.

The situation is different in Australia, almost the only developed country with rainforest on its territory. The rainforest in Australia now covers 90% of the area it occupied when the Europeans arrived (about 4,000 mi^2 [10,500 km^2]) and is mostly protected. Even so, the native fauna and flora are to some extent under threat from the introduction of non-native species, such as the cane toad (*Bufo marinus*, which is toxic to the marsupial native cat, the spotted tailed quoll (*Dasyrus maculatus*).

4.2 Timber mining

The rainforest is full of a wide diversity of trees, many of which provide useful products for local

185 The large trees of the rainforest are being felled one after another, in an apparently endless process. But it will certainly come to an end. This timber capital, ceaselessly extracted without any replacement, is being exhausted and will take centuries to replace. The photo shows a recently felled specimen of *Cedrelinga catenaeformis* (Leguminosae) in the basin of the river Madre de Dios (Peru).
[Photo: André Bärtschi / Planet Earth Pictures]

people or for export to other regions or countries. Timber is the economically most important product from the rainforest, and has a value on the world market estimated at 7,000 million U.S. dollars a year. The problem is that timber exploitation is performed as though it were a mineral resource to be mined, that is to say, extraction without replacement.

Forest devastation

Together with the clearing of new land for agriculture and ranching, timber exploitation without later replanting is one of the most important causes of rainforest loss throughout the world. In 1988, according to the World Resources Institute, 11 million acres (4.4 million ha) were cut for timber extraction. Two years later, in 1990, according to data from the U.N. Food and Agricultural Organization (FAO), this figure had almost doubled to 21,003,871 acres (8.5 million ha). About 83% of the wood felled is used only as fuel, and this proportion is increasing. Only 13% is commercially used locally, and 4% is exported. Although timber exportation accounts for only a small percentage, it causes the most damage, as the trees exported are large trees that are extracted with heavy machinery.

Japan is the largest consumer of tropical hardwoods, accounting for 35% of the world trade, followed by the other countries of the Far East with 25%, and Europe with 13%.

Logging systems

Almost all the tropical hardwoods arriving on the world market are extracted from natural forests, and only a small part comes from plantations. Natural forests, if sustainably managed, can produce timber in economically important quantities without being exhausted in the short or medium term. Unfortunately, however, less than 1% of the world's tropical forests are managed for sustainable timber production.

Some people support the establishment of plantations as a measure to avoid felling the rainforest. Managed and unmanaged forests show similar productivity, but managed ones have more useful species, and in this sense plantations may be much more productive than the original forest. Several studies on fast-growing species of equatorial conifers, or similar groups (*Agathis*, *Podocarpus*, *Dacrydium*, *Pinus merkusii*, *P. kesiya*, *P. caribaea*, *Casuarina junghuhniana*, etc.) suggest they are potentially useful forestry species. If the tropical hardwoods needed were obtained from plantations, it would not be necessary to extract timber from the primary or secondary forest. Forest exploitation in tropical rainforests generally uses techniques closer to mining than to agriculture. Only useful trees are extracted, and this requires opening tracks, earthworks, and the use of heavy machinery in poorly accessible areas.

Selective felling cuts only a small percentage of the trees to benefit the useful species. If these are slow-growing and shade-tolerant species, a polycyclic logging regime must be followed, that is to say, several fellings during the average life of a tree. This avoids creating excessive gaps in the canopy and the growth of the sun-loving species of secondary forest, and at the same time benefits desirable shade-loving, slow-growing species. If, however, what is sought are fast-growing, light-tolerant species, it would be better to follow a monocyclic felling regime, which consists of making a single cut during the average life of a tree, taking all the trees from the forest sector being logged. This favors the formations of gaps in the canopy and the entry of the light that will promote the growth of new trees of this type.

Selective felling of forest trees, although it is not as destructive as clear cutting, can also be damaging, because nearby trees are also damaged. The ones felled are usually the tallest specimens and their fall damages neighboring trees. Furthermore, the populations of the species felled are genetically impoverished, as the best trees are taken and the next harvest will be from the seeds produced by the less vigorous surviving trees.

Penetration routes
Commercialization of timber and other rainforest products depends on transport systems. In Amazonia trunks used to be transported down the rivers for export. The building of new roads through the region is leading to a massive expansion of the timber trade and the resulting environmental problems.

The development of the road network in the tropical rainforest is often the beginning of deforestation, as it irreversibly opens the forest to exploitation and settlement. The construction of roads and tracks to transport trunks and the use of heavy machinery cause erosion and soil compaction. The heavy machinery used to extract the trunks from the forest may destroy up to 55% of

the selectively felled site. Erosion, the downward movement of sediments and nutrients, leads to soil impoverishment. Suitable location, design, construction, and maintenance of road access are very important for good forest management. The damage to the soil and the extent of erosion depend on the characteristics of the site, on what and how much is felled, and on the methods used to extract the wood; the rest depends on the skill of the operator.

In Africa, the coastal forests of the equatorial region, with easy access to ports, were the first forests to be exploited. The valuable timber resources of the countries of western Africa, such as Ivory Coast, Ghana, and Nigeria, are severely depleted. Many of the accessible forest areas have also been exploited in Cameroon, Equatorial Guinea, and Gabon. Historically, the exploitation of the rainforest in Cameroon for timber concentrated on the coastal areas and only a few species were exported, mainly African oak or azobe (*Lophira alata*, Ochnaceae) and ilomba (*Pycnanthus angolensis*, Myristicaceae). Azobe is still the most important timber exported from Cameroon, but other species are now coming onto the market. Diversification has been accompanied by the expansion of timber exploitation towards the interior. The completion of the longest railway line in Gabon, joining the coastal capital of Libreville to Franceville, has opened up remote areas of forest for logging. Foreign companies have been quick to see this economic potential, and at the end of the century most forests in the country will have been logged for the increasingly valuable wood of okoume (*Aucoumea klaineana*, Burseraceae).

As timber resources decline in western Africa, commercial interest is concentrating on central African countries such as Congo and Democratic Republic of Congo.

Commercial exploitation of timber in the Congo began in the 1920s with the construction of the railway between Brazzaville and Point-Noire. The Mayombe forest zone was the first to be exploited, as it is accessible from the coast. The forests of this area are now highly degraded. The forests in the north of the country are still, however, considered by European timber merchants as a major unexploited reserve of quality hardwoods. These forests remain almost intact because there are few means of transport. Even so, some timber has begun to be extracted from

186 The extraction of timber from the rainforest was initially performed by using watercourses. This method is still used, as shown by the upper photograph, taken in Nigeria. Later, the construction of highways and the availability of large lorries opened up new possibilities, shown in the lower photo of the transport of large trunks along a central African road showing the typical red color of plinthitic (lateritic) soil, under the gaze of two Pygmies.
[Photos: Mark Edwards / Still Pictures and Georges Merillon / Gamma]

two tree members of the Meliaceae, sapele (*Entandrophragma cylindricum*) and utile (*E. utile*).

In the 1980s however, logging companies started to buy areas of accessible forest, near the River Zaire and its tributaries. By 1984, extraction from the country's forests was about 17,700,000 ft³ (500,000 m³), 5,300,000 ft³ (150,000 m³) of them for export, and 10 years later about 20% of the area of rainforest was held under one of the three forms of exploitation licence. The government intended to increase production by the end of the century to 22 million ft³ (6 million m³), 177 million ft³ (5 million m³) of them for export. But the

management plans and strategies recommending division into zones and the sustainable management of resources have not yet been put into effect because of the war that broke out in 1997, which has not, however, stopped the logging.

The effects on the flora and fauna

The range of timber species on the market has always been very narrow. Almost all tropical hardwood exporting countries are now trying to introduce less well-known species to the international market, in order to reduce pressure on the hardwood species traditionally preferred by the market and now on the brink of extinction.

However, the timber trade is very conservative in its choice of raw materials and sticks to species of proven value. It may be difficult to find alternatives for certain woods for very specific uses, but it is possible to replace some species for more general uses.

In any case, the highly selective pressure on some species is threatening them with extinction. An extreme example is the Brazilian rosewood (*Dalbergia nigra*, Leguminosae), which is on the brink of extinction in the last areas of the Mata Atlântica. "Timber cruisers," or *madeireros* locate the last few specimens and fell them regardless of size. The trade and export of this wood has been banned in Brazil since the 1970s, in accordance with the Convention on International Trade in Endangered Species (CITES). In fact, everywhere any species of rosewood grows, its valuable wood is exploited for international trade. All the populations in accessible areas have been felled, and this has turned these trees into a very scarce natural resource. The only species grown in plantations is the Indian rosewood (*D. latifolia*), a savanna tree cultivated in India and Java.

The fauna also suffers the effects of deforestation. The opening of sectors of forest by logging companies leads to the invasion of the deforested areas by new farmers and to greater hunting pressure. This may lead to the local extinction of some species. Not only does hunting directly reduce the richness of the fauna, but when clearings are opened in the forest many animals cannot survive in the new environment. One of the worst affected groups is the primates, especially those living in the tallest trees, normally those that the logging companies are searching for.

The pillaging of the forests for timber

Commercial logging of dipterocarp forests has played a major role in the deforestation of the Philippines. They were very well conserved until the Second World War, but since then they have been subject to large-scale logging to extract the timber of different species of lauan and meranti (*Shorea* and *Parashorea*, Dipterocarpáceae), sold as "Philippine mahogany." Initially, demand was from the United States market but by the 1960s Japan was also a major consumer of Philippine timber. The Philippine timber boom of the 1960s made enormous profits for the logging companies as regulations were scarcely enforced by the government of the dictator Ferdinand Marcos. Almost all the forests of dipterocarps have been felled and almost 30 species of dipterocarp are in danger of extinction in the Philippines. A ban on log exports was introduced in 1975, but this ban did little to stop forest destruction.

Since 1989, logging has been banned in all the provinces of the Philippines with less than 40% forest cover. It was also necessary to introduce legal protection for other hardwood species, such as Amboyna wood or Burmese rosewood (*Pterocarpus indica*), one of the best hardwood species in the archipelago, supa (*Sindora supa*); Philippines ebony (*Diospyros philipinensis*); and New Guinea walnut or paldao (*Dracontomelon dao*). Philippine kaori (*Agathis philipinensis*), a source of Manila copal, is also declining due to logging and resin extraction.

187 Inept removal of tree trunks is usually the common denominator of logging in the rainforest. This adds a further problem, alteration to the soil structure, to the problems of forest management. The photo shows logging of dipterocarps, the Borneo camphorwood (*Dryobalanops*), and sal (*Shorea*) in Sarawak, Borneo. [*Photo: Nigel Dickson / Still Pictures*]

188 The volume of planks leaving sawmills in tropical countries every year is enormous, often far greater than the year's biological production. This means that logging exceeds capacity, and is at the cost of the timber capital accumulated over centuries. The photo shows planks are Honduran mahogany (*Swietenia macrophylla*) in a Brazilian workshop.
[Photo: Tony Morrison / South American Pictures]

The best resin comes from Palawan and Quezón, and extraction is probably the cause of its increasing rareness in Palawan.

In the Dutch East Indies (now Indonesia), from the 19th century onward growing demand for another copal, extracted from the white kaori (*Agathis alba*), led to destructive exploitation and to the disappearance of many trees from the forests of the central islands of the Indonesian archipelago. When Indonesia became independent, 1,000 tons a year of Macassar ebony (*Diospyros celebica*) were exported from the north of Sulawesi, mainly to Japan. Felling of this species has had to be regulated by a quota system, which is often broken by smugglers dealing in this valuable wood.

Most of the Caribbean's rainforest was soon destroyed by uncontrolled logging of species such as mahogany (*Swietenia mahagoni*), and yellowwood, or West Indies satinwood (*Zanthoxylum flavum*). The islands of the tropical Indian Ocean suffered the same fate. Perhaps nowhere in the world has deforestation been as severe as on the tropical island of Saint Helena, where trees are now very rare. Two hardwood species, the Saint Helena redwood (*Trochetia erythroxylon*, Sterculiaceae) and Saint Helena ebony (*Trochetia melanoxylon*) were already rare at the end of the 17th century as a result of intense logging. Their sale for private use was banned, but both species continued to decline and are now on the brink of extinction. There is now only a single known wild specimen of the St. Helena redwood.

"Mining" of valuable hardwood trees is a major cause of the current destruction of the Amazon rainforest. Honduran, or Mexican, mahogany (*Swietenia macrophylla*) is the wood most in demand on the international market. This species used to be widespread in South America but is now endangered in several areas of its range. In Brazil, the most important producer country, it was included in the list of endangered species published by the Brazilian Institute of the Environment (IBAMA). Logging roads are penetrating increasingly remote areas in search of mahogany. A recent study has shown that each of the major sawmills in Brazil is constructing 310 mi (500 km) of new roads to reach stands of mahogany. Once the valuable timber has been extracted, the land is frequently cleared for agriculture or it is turned into pasture for cattle ranching. Illegal logging that does not respect the limits of native reservations or wildlife reserves felling is widespread. Between 1985 and 1988, more than one third of all mahogany extraction in Brazil was the result of illegal logging in reserves, set aside for indigenous peoples. The best quality wood is exported to the United Kingdom to make reproduction furniture and carved doors and windows, as well as to Germany and Spain. The medium-quality wood is exported to the United States, and the lowest-quality wood is consumed in the local and Argentinean markets. The rosewood (*Aniba rosaeodora*, Lauraceae), from whose wood bois-de-rose oil is extracted, is now almost extinct.

Until recently, mobile distilling factories were set up in the forest to extract the valuable essential oil, but as the forests have been opened up, increasingly remote stands of rosewood have been located and destroyed. Sadly, this destruction was totally unnecessary, as the leaves are a better source of the essential oil and plantations can be established to produce a sustainable supply of this valuable product.

Ghana's equatorial forests have been devastated during the 20th century, especially during the last 40 years when more than 90% of the country's primary rainforest has been felled. Ghana's timber industry is very important to the national economy, as it is the country's third largest source of foreign exchange after cocoa and gold. So little rainforest is now left in Ghana that logging is a relatively small factor in overall deforestation. Yet logging continues to degrade the remaining rainforest, and some timber species, such as afrormosia (*Pericopsis elata*, Leguminosae), have been taken with little thought for future regeneration. Afrormosia is now one of the world's most valuable hardwoods for furniture production. It is an African legume tree whose wood came onto the international market around 1950 as a substitute for teak. Unfortunately, wild stocks have declined dramatically, the tree's regeneration is insufficient, and the development of plantations has been very limited. Felling and habitat destruction threatens it not only in Ghana but also in Nigeria and the Democratic Republic of Congo. In Democratic Republic of Congo, afrormosia wood is used very little locally but is appreciated in traditional medicine.

4.3 From shifting cultivators to planters and herders

Traditionally, rainforest dwellers survived by combining shifting agriculture with harvesting forest products, making use of their thorough knowledge of their environment. Shifting agriculture, however, is viable only with low population densities that exert limited pressure on the rainforest. When populations were relatively small, clearing the forest had little impact on the forest cover, and the fallow periods between crops were long enough for the natural vegetation to regenerate. During the 20th century, however, the rapid growth of the local native population and the arrival of new colonists has increased the pressure from shifting agriculture on most rainforests. The reduction of the fallow period

between cultivation, less attention to maintenance operations, and the social and political pressures on the people practicing this agricultural system all tend to reduce yields. Even so, 250 million people still support themselves through shifting agriculture.

Shifting agriculture: destroying the rainforest or sustainable exploitation?

Opinions on the suitability of shifting agriculture as a sustainable method of land use in the rainforest biome is split between those who consider that it destroys the rainforest, impoverishing and deteriorating the soil, and those who consider this form of exploitation is ecologically well adapted to rainforest conditions. Paradoxically, both positions can be justified. In traditional conditions of low population density and insignificant population growth, with long fallow periods between cultivation of the same plot, shifting agriculture is an excellent way of making use of the natural resources of the rainforest. However, rapid population growth, shortening fallow periods, and intensification of cultivation without respecting the restrictions agreed by the traditional community leads inevitably to soil degradation and the destruction of large areas of forest.

In Madagascar, for example, primitive agricultural systems still predominate, and the pressure of the rural population is the main factor causing rapid destruction of the remaining rainforests. The island currently has a population of 11.2 million inhabitants, more than twice the population in 1960. To feed this growing population the rainforest is cleared and burned to plant rice, cassava, maize and other crops. Only a single crop is harvested, and then a new *tavy*, or forest plot, is cleared. The soils, which have low fertility, deteriorate rapidly and support only a degraded vegetation that is often invaded by rampant weeds. In many sites in the Americas, however, *chamiceras* (burned woodland), *milpas* (corn fields) and *conucos* (small farms) have been able to maintain significant population densities by multiple cropping. They have also been very important in the conservation of countless cultivated varieties of plant of great interest to geneticists and may provide genetic material to many globally important crop species such as maize, beans, cocoa, and avocadoes.

The problem is to find alternatives to shifting agriculture in the nutrient-poor soils of the rainforest environment. In some conditions yields can be improved. Corridor cultivation systems practiced in preindependence Belgian Congo (now

Democratic Republic of Congo) minimize nutrient losses and promote natural regeneration of the forest, if carried out correctly. The introduction of more productive varieties or species, the more intensive use of space, and some fertilizer input allow slight improvements in yields. In the last few years, satisfactory results have been given by the introduction of crops to enrich the soil and to promote forest regeneration at the beginning of the fallow period, such as the Nepal alder (*Alnus nepalensis*) in northeastern India or *Erythrina peoppigiana* (Leguminosae) in Central America.

Yet these agricultural systems are much more satisfactory than the permanent cultivation of land along the routes crossing the forests in different areas of western Africa, some Indonesian islands, and especially the Amazon. This is also, to some extent, a form of shifting agriculture, although it is totally unlike the agriculture practiced by the rainforest's traditional inhabitants. Generally, these new agricultural systems have not been planned to meet the needs of expanding populations or to deal with the decreasing soil fertility and the soil loss caused by the techniques employed. This normally begins with clearing a large area of forest using heavy machinery.

Unless this is done carefully, it may cause soil compaction, loss of the surface horizons, and general erosion. As a result, after two or three years the site becomes so poor that another patch of forest must be found and felled to repeat the process.

Large plantations: from slavery to enslavement by the market

Permanent plantations of tree, or at least perennial, crops are a special case. They are similar to the forest in many ways, except in their diversity. Plantation crops include rubber, cocoa, and other trees whose crowns protect the soil from the sun and rain and also supply it with organic material. Yet their intensive exploitation requires the use of fertilizers and intense and permanent maintenance—weeding and dealing with pests, and so forth.

The origin of plantations lie in European expansion over the last 500 years and the creation in the Americas of large estates for the cultivation of a single high-value crop for export to the metropolis (sugar, tobacco, spices, etc.). The abundance

189 Plantation agriculture became the model of colonial agriculture for the European powers with overseas territories until decolonization in the mid-20th century. Plantations still in many cases reveal the former colonial power's economic control over countries that are now politically independent. Almost all the crop is exported to the developed countries that most of the capital invested also comes from, and it is these countries that benefit most. Large stakes are held by American, European, and Japanese multinational companies in many of the companies nationalized by the governments of the new states, as well as in the establishment of new exploitations. The early American plantations led to the shipping from 1500-1870 of more than 10 million Africans to the Americas as slaves. In the last two centuries plantations in southern Asia and Africa have also led to major population movements of Chinese to Malaysia, Singapore, and the former Dutch East Indies (mainly Java); Biharis to Assam; Tamils to Sri Lanka; Indians from several areas to Eastern Africa and Malaysia, and so on. Islands like Mauritius and Réunion were not settled until their colonization and have since then been dedicated to plantation agriculture. They now have populations from the most varied origins who were brought by the successive colonizers or attracted by the chance of finding work. The photo shows a banana plantation on the island of Dominica.
[Photo: Philip Wolmuth / The Hutchison Library]

of land and cheap, generally slave, labor formed the basis of the plantation system, which established the extreme social inequalities that still exist in many American countries. The plantation system was not introduced into other tropical regions until the 19th century. In Africa this was because the lack of good ports and the unhealthiness of the coasts made exploitation through slavery more profitable than the establishment of colonies and plantations. Plantation agriculture was not introduced into Asia because the first Europeans colonists, the Portuguese and Dutch, were more interested in trade than in production and because they were dealing with much more advanced civilizations in much more densely populated regions than in the Americas.

The size of the plantations are very variable and depend on the type of crop, on the country, and on the history of each plantation. The Harbel plantation in Liberia, the property of the Firestone company, covers more than 135,907 acres (55,000 ha) (roughly half of Los Angeles), whereas in Malaysia there are many rubber plantations of about 98 acres (40 ha). All plantations, whether large or small, require a great amount of work, performed either by hand or by mechanization. It is also very common to use fertilizers and pesticides, with the predictable effects on the environment. Not all the typical products of plantation agriculture that reach the international marketplace come from plantations. Many small producers try to combine subsistence agriculture to feed themselves and their families with a high-added-value plantation crop for sale on the export market, generally through intermediaries who take a

large part of the profits. This places many domestic, and some national, economies at the mercy of oscillations of the prices of one or a few products in the international marketplace.

Herds against the jungle

The conversion of tropical forest ecosystems into pasture for cattle for meat production has by far the greatest impact on the ecological balance of the wet American tropics. Almost everybody agrees that ranching is the main cause of rainforest loss in tropical America, although in comparable areas of Africa and Asia rainforest loss is due to logging and shifting agriculture. Studies performed by the U.N. Food and Agricultural Organization (FAO) and the United Nations Environment Programme (UNEP) showed that the highest rates of deforestation were in Latin America and the Caribbean (13,8 million acres [5.6 million ha] a year in 1980-1985, and 20,5 million acres [8.3 million ha] in 1990). This is much greater than in Africa and Asia, the other two regions of the world with rainforest, where cattle ranching is only important in a few rainforest countries (Nigeria, Bangladesh, and Madagascar), where ranching tends to take place on land belonging to

190 The spread of ranching in the rainforest has at least three kinds of environmental impact: biological, economic, and climatic. The biological impact refers to the number of species of plant, animal, and microorganism lost in each hectare (1 hectare=2.47 acres) of rainforest converted into grazing land, with a great loss of biodiversity. The economic impact affects the productive potential of these displaced species, as it is now known that the rainforests contain many species that produce foodstuffs, medicinal drugs, wood, textile fibers, various chemical compounds (gums, resins, colorings, etc.) and other products with known or probable value. The climatic impact of the unrestrained deforestation of tropical areas for ranching results in regional climatic changes and contributes to other global changes by increasing the amount of carbon dioxide emitted into the atmosphere, contributing to global warming as a result of the greenhouse effect. Furthermore, when cattle digest the cellulose of the plants they eat, they emit considerable quantities of methane into the atmosphere, further contributing to the greenhouse effect. The photo was taken in the Brazilian Amazon.
[Photo: Dave Brinicombe / The Hutchison Library]

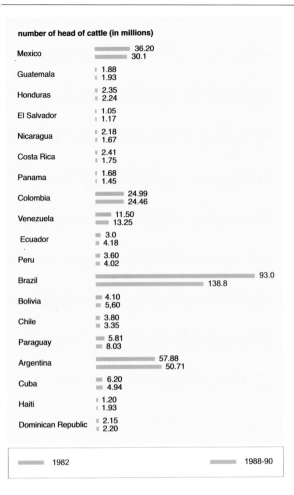

number of head of cattle (in millions)

Mexico	36.20 / 30.1
Guatemala	1.88 / 1.93
Honduras	2.35 / 2.24
El Salvador	1.05 / 1.17
Nicaragua	2.18 / 1.67
Costa Rica	2.41 / 1.75
Panama	1.68 / 1.45
Colombia	24.99 / 24.46
Venezuela	11.50 / 13.25
Ecuador	3.0 / 4.18
Peru	3.60 / 4.02
Brazil	93.0 / 138.8
Bolivia	4.10 / 5,60
Chile	3.80 / 3.35
Paraguay	5.81 / 8.03
Argentina	57.88 / 50.71
Cuba	6.20 / 4.94
Haiti	1.20 / 1.93
Dominican Republic	2.15 / 2.20

1982   1988-90

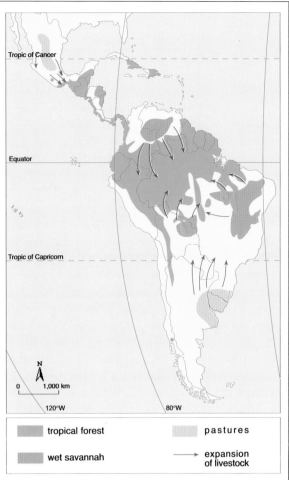

tropical forest   pastures

wet savannah   expansion of livestock

191 The increase in the number of head of cattle in the rainforest biome between 1982 and 1990. There is a general tendency to stability or decline, except in Brazil, where the cattle population is increasing spectacularly. The map shows the main direction of the expansion of ranching. Increased ranching in Latin America has mainly been at the cost of lowland rainforest, especially in the Amazon. In Central America, however, much of the forest that was felled was seasonal monsoon forest.

[Drawing: Editrònica, from data provided by the authors]

other biomes. Statistics show that between 1960 and 1980 two types of "quadruped" underwent showed explosive growth in the American tropics—cars in urban areas and cattle in rural ones. The number of cars increased from 2.77 to almost 20 million, while the number of head of cattle increased from 177 million to 266 million. In some countries, like Costa Rica, Honduras, Guatemala, and Nicaragua, the number of cattle doubled. In others, the cattle population grew to equal (Venezuela) or exceed (Costa Rica) the human population.

The reasons for the spread of ranching

Although some authors have tried to give a single simplistic explanation for the spread of ranching in these tropical areas (such as the increase in international demand for meat or the increase in the rural population), the fact is that the phenomenon is the result of a complex set of factors. In the mid-1980s some authors saw this as the result of the so-called "hamburger connection": the spread of ranching (especially in Central America) was, they argued, stimulated by the increase in demand for beef for hamburgers in the United States, and environmentalists boycotted major hamburger chains in America and western Europe. Statistics, however, show that in Latin America beef only represents 5% of the total raw materials exported.

The fact is that the number of head of cattle has not increased so fast for a single reason. One of the most important factors has been the growth of Latin America's urban population, as beef forms a substantial part of their diet (and regional supply covers only 50% of demand). Other factors behind this increase in cattle have been large national and international credits (mostly from the World Bank and the Inter-American Development Bank) to boost livestock production in tropical countries, financial incentives, and of course the fact that ranching is highly profitable. (This profitability is the result of the aforementioned factors, and is not because of the high productivity of ranching.) Without these financial incentives, subsidies, and aid, these spaces could not be used for cattle ranching, as it is economically inviable. Thus, the spread of cattle ranching has been the result of a deliberate policy of rural modernization with a total lack of concern for the ecological consequences. Although this policy has mainly been carried out by medium and large landholders, it has also been practiced by many peasants (especially in Mexico and the Amazon).

The spread of cattle ranching in Latin America has followed a clearly defined pattern of colonization. As might be expected, European livestock was introduced during the 16th century into the landscapes that were most similar to those used for raising livestock in Mediterranean Europe.

The first ranches were in temperate and semiarid areas with natural grazing, such as the central plateau of Mexico, the Andean altiplano, and logically the huge pampas grasslands of Argentina and Uruguay. Once ranching had taken root in several areas of the Americas, it gradually spread into new spaces at lower altitudes and latitudes. The second Latin American spaces colonized by cattle ranchers were the semihumid tropical areas with different types of savanna (or tropical grasslands), such as the *llanos* in Venezuela, the *mojo* in Bolivia, and the *cerrado* in Brazil. Finally, ranching spread to the lowland tropical areas, the world's greatest forest reserve.

Ranching has spread into these rainforest reserves owing to the introduction of different pasture grasses of African origin, including Guinea grass (*Panicum maximum*, Poaceae), whose tropical origin meant they could adapt to the climatic conditions of the Latin American lowlands. Some authors have referred to this as the "Africanization" of Latin America. At the other end of the scale, native wild plants are not good grazing, and many are even poisonous. This is true, in the Amazon Basin, for *Palicourea marcgravii* (Rubiaceae), *P. grandiflora* and *P. juruana*, and *Arrabidaea bilabiata* (Bignoniaceae) and *A. jupurensis*.

A revised assessment of Latin American and Caribbean livestock resources, which in 1988-1990 reached a total of 312 million head of cattle (10% of the world total), showed in 1994 that most cattle ranching took place in countries dominated by rainforest (such as the Amazon region and Central America), and that Brazil is at the head. No precise calculations exist of the area of forest converted into grazing for cattle, but estimates made in 1994 in Mexico, Central America, and the Amazon region suggested that 80 million acres (32.4 million ha) have been deforested, 55,8 million acres (22.6 million ha) of them corre-

sponding to rainforest and 24,2 million acres (9.8 million ha) to seasonal deciduous forests.

The consequences of ranching

The conversion of the rainforest into grazing for cattle is a genuine ecological catastrophe. The replacement of the rainforest's intricate structure by the much simpler structure of pastureland is an intrinsically negative process of biological simplification. The rainforest's biomass of maybe 350 to 400 t/ha is usually reduced to less than 20 t. Yet the main problem is not the drastic reduction of biomass but the fact that it is impossible for the ranching agroecosystem ever to become a self-sustaining productive system like the rainforest it replaced. Unless the pastureland is chemically fertilized and treated with pesticides and herbicides against pests and weeds, production will tend to decrease with time.

The ecological degradation of these "created" pastures is explained by the major biological and physicochemical limitations of tropical soils, an obstacle that the forest ecosystem avoids by recycling its nutrients; this takes place, however, in the biomass and not in the soil. If the forest is eliminated, the soil is rapidly degraded to an almost inert substrate. The microclimatic changes resulting from deforestation, such as the high temperatures (which destroy the bacterial life in the soil) and the torrential rains that cause leaching (the migration of surface materials to deeper layers), eventually lead to degradation of the already poor soils. In these conditions, soil nutrients (and in the Amazon, especially phosphorus) tend to diminish rapidly below the levels necessary to maintain the pasture. In addition to these chemical limitations there are also problems derived from soil compaction in pastures as a result of trampling.

For all these reasons, pasture rarely lasts more than 10 years. This forces the rancher to move on to another site, thus requiring the clearing of new areas of forest and thus furthering forest loss. It is estimated that now more than 50% of the areas in Latin America formerly dedicated to tropical ranching have already been abandoned, and these degraded areas can only be recovered with great difficulty.

In short, two and a half acres (a hectare) of rainforest (which may contain a biomass of 400 t and a high biological diversity) converted to grazing land feeds an average of less than one animal, which after eight years of grazing will reach a weight of about 881 lb (400 kg) and will be made into, at most, 1,600 individual 4.4 oz (125 g steaks)!

4.4 Mineral exploitation

Mining and industrial development have been relatively unimportant causes of deforestation in the rainforest biome as a whole, but in some areas they have caused major devastation. The threat from mining activities will probably increase, as investigation reveals the full potential of mineral-rich areas such as the Amazon Basin and some parts of Indonesia, Papua New Guinea, and the Philippines.

Gold and iron in the Amazon

Gold was discovered for the first time in the Brazilian state of Minas Gerais in the 1690s, and the discovery led to the first gold rush at a time when Portugal signed a trade agreement with Britain. Gold from Brazil underwrote Britain's early industrial development and later paid for its wars against Napoleon. In the 20th century, the discovery of gold and other valuable minerals in Amazonia has led to another wave of immigration into the rainforest.

The largest current mining operation in the rainforest, the Grande Carajas Program in the eastern Amazon, is ongoing. This program envisages a large industrial complex of iron ore mines and smelting plants, aluminium plants, and hydroelectric dams. An area of rainforest in the state of Pará as large as England and France combined is being transformed. Originally conceived as the answer to Brazil's lack of foreign exchange, unemployment, and land shortage, the Grande Carajas Program has been severely criticized for its major environmental and social impact. In 1982, the Japanese government and the World Bank helped to launch the scheme by lending the state mining company, Companhia Vale do Rio Doce, 804 million U.S. dollars to construct the Carajás iron mine and a 558-mi (900-km) railway line to the coast and to develop a port at Ponta de Madeira.

The European Community also provided additional funding for this enormous project. The first pig iron smelting plant started production in 1988 in Marabá and another 20 are now operational. These smelting plants are fueled by charcoal extracted from primary rainforest. It is estimated that when all the smelters are operational they will consume the charcoal produced by 880 mi^2 (2,300 km^2) of forest every year.

The Carajás mining project was accompanied by plans for colonization, agriculture, and cattle ranching that have not been successful. The Companhia Vale do Rio Doce built a new city, Parauapebas, for settlers attracted by the industrial development, with housing, a hospital, and school, but the city was overwhelmed as immigration was much greater than expected. Slum settlements grew up around Carajás that did not satisfy people's requirements. Cities like Marabá and Açailândia have grown by at least 50% in size, which implies hundreds of thousands of immigrants. The life of the indigenous peoples has been ruined. More than 20 groups that lived in an area within a radius of 62 mi (100 km) of the mine have been displaced from their communities. Until the 1980s, the 300 members of the Guajá hunter-gatherer tribe lived in extreme isolation; now their survival is precarious.

Copper in Papua New Guinea

Mining is also of great importance to the economy of Papua New Guinea. Almost 40% of the country's national product comes from the mining sector. A single project, the Panguna mine on the island of Bougainville, once provided 17% of the country's entire income. The Panguna copper mine, in the south of the island, is one of the largest in the world and is also a source of silver and gold. Lax environmental regulations at the Panguna mine have led to heavy pollution of the river Jaba and its tributary the Kawerong. In 1989 the mine was forced to close by local landowners angered by the deforestation and pollution caused by mining and the unfair distribution of the mine's profits. The unresolved conflict has acquired a political aspect as some of the inhabitants favor separation from Papua New Guinea, as Bougainville is one of the northern Solomon Islands and has few traditional links with New Guinea, from which it is separated by 497 mi (800 km) of high seas.

On the Papua New Guinea mainland, the development of other mines has also led to destruction of the rainforest. The OK Tedi mine is the fifth largest mine in the world and a major source of river pollution. It is located in the headwaters of the river Strickland, the most important tributary of the river Fly, in the Star mountains on the fron-

192 The Brazilian rainforest is in the grip of a new gold rush and is now full of exploitations, such as this one in Pará. Brazil is now the world's fifth largest gold producer. Gold-mining is performed on a small scale and often illegally. Gold was discovered in the state of Pará in 1967, but was kept secret for 10 years, until small-scale prospectors began to move in. The largest mine, Serra Pelada, attracted hundreds of thousands of miners who toiled in appalling conditions. By 1986 more than 33,000 t of gold had been mined from this single mine. Yet most of Brazil's gold production is by the quarter of a million small-scale miners, the *garimpeiros*. One of the worst problems of gold mining in the Amazon is the indiscriminate use of mercury to separate the gold from the ore. Sediment dredged from the riverbed is filtered through sieves containing mercury to separate and concentrate the gold. The gold-mercury amalgam is then heated to drive off the mercury. It is estimated that in the Amazon more than 1,100 t of mercury are burned or discharged into the river every year. The extraction process not only affects mining sites but also the entire watershed and all the people living downstream. The lives of indigenous peoples have been greatly disrupted by gold extraction. The Yanomami, who entered contact with western civilization for the first time in 1950, have been badly affected. Road-building and mining for gold, uranium and cassiterite have brought them deforestation, pollution, disease, hunger, and alcohol problems. The Yanomami's territories have been invaded by more than 45,000 *garimpeiros* since 1986. In November 1991, a law was passed creating a permanent indigenous territory for the Yanomami and the goldmines were closed. The *garimpeiros* have now moved across the northernmost Amazon into the lands of the Macuxi people and from there across the border to Guyana.

[Photo: Herbert Giradet / Still Pictures]

tier with Irian Jaya, a region that was unexplored and isolated from the rest of the world until 1963.

4.5 Wildlife in agony

The fauna of the world's much-abused rainforests suffers as much as if not more than the plantlife from bad management. The direct impact of hunting and overfishing is important, although no more so than the indirect impact of the destruction of habitats. Hunting and fishing affect only the relatively small number of species of interest to hunters and fishermen, but habitat destruction affects practically all species.

Hunting and the destruction of habitats

Overhunted species cannot fulfill their ecological role within forest communities. Hunters tend to pursue the largest species of animal and so the impact of extraction by hunting has great repercussions on the biomass of animal communities. For example, in the parts of the Amazon that are not hunted, large primates weighing over 9 lb (4 kg) represent 61% of the total primate biomass. Yet in areas where primates are actively hunted, large primates only represent 16% of the total primate biomass. Although there is little detailed information from any area concerning the effects of hunting on animal species, it is clear that the tendency is towards a direct loss of fauna as a result of selective hunting.

The indirect loss of fauna is less obvious, yet in the long term its effects may be more serious. Indirect losses as a result of activities that are not directly focused on animals may, in fact, involve more people and a greater range of activities.

Deforestation logically leads to the total destruction of a habitat. Nevertheless, for some species the destruction of smaller, more delicate habitats can be equally devastating. The establishment of a new agricultural community in the path of a traditional peccary (*Tayassu pecari*) migration route may exclude these animals from a large area of highly suitable habitat. In the case of river turtles (*Podocnemis*) that breed in colonies on beaches, the loss of traditional egg-laying sites may lead to a breeding failure.

Extractivist activities in jungles also have many serious side effects. Logging damages and alters habitats; nest sites are destroyed, important fruit-

193 Oil is Ecuador's main source of foreign exchange. Oil was discovered in the east of the country in the mid-1960s. From then to 1993, more than 2,432 sq mi (6,300 sq km) of forest have been destroyed and further large areas are being explored for new oil reserves. The Cuyabeno Wildlife Reserve was invaded by settlers following the construction of an oil pipeline, and the Yasuni National Park is also threatened. The Yasuni protected area was established by the Ecuadorian government in 1979, but in 1990 its limits were changed so that the oil exploration was outside the park. In early 1994 a further problem arose, the risk of certain annihilation of the last 2,000 Huaoranis people in the Ecuadorian Amazon by oil production. The photo shows an Ecuadorian pipeline through the Amazon, in the foothills of the Andes. [Photo: Edward Parker / Still Pictures]

194 Many zoologically important, or even endangered, species are actively hunted as food. The photo shows a clearing in the Congo rainforest in the early morning, when the animals caught that night are for sale. The animals are a white-faced cercopithecan (*Cercopithecus nictitans*) and two bay duikers (*Cephalophus dorsalis*). [Photo: Michel Gunther / Bios / Still Pictures]

bearing trees are eliminated, and commercial harvesting of wild fruits competes with wild frugivore species. Subsistence and commercial hunting eradicates the potential prey of many carnivores and carrion-eaters: the jaguar (*Panthera onca*) in particular suffers as it tends to compete with humans for the same prey. Developmental activities, generally financed by banks and international institutions, are often responsible for the destruction of rainforests. Intensive agriculture provokes sedimentation and pollution problems. The proliferation of mining operations, especially gold mining, has caused increasing sedimentation and contamination by heavy metals. The gold mines cause serious mercury pollution. Mining is also destroying riverbank and beach habitats.

The decline in the fish fauna

River fish are very sensitive to the deterioration in water quality caused by changes in surrounding land. The extensive exploitation of the forests of the interior of Borneo is leading to increasing erosion of the topsoil, muddying river waters for a long time. Motor oils from logging machinery are also an important contaminant. Although the exact details of the ecological mechanisms at work are unknown, the inhabitants of lower stretches of rivers say there has been a clear decline in fish catches. This is just one of the many environmental changes facing rural communities as nearby forests are commercially exploited for the first time. Hunting and fishing diminish and people increasingly depend on alternative sources of proteins that have to be paid for in cash. As these communities rarely have money to spare, there is a decline in the quality of food consumed that has led recently to malnutrition.

Fishing in the Amazon has suffered from the indirect effects of the large-scale development and deforestation of the jungles of the "terra firme," where the mines, hydroelectric dams, roads, and agriculture that have caused erosion, sedimentation, and, in general, habitat destruction tend to be concentrated. All these development policies have negative effects on the health of rivers and fish production. The long-term consequences are as yet unknown, and it precisely for this reason that it is essential for studies to be carried out now. In 1993 in Itaituba in the headwaters of the river Tapajoz cases of degenerative diseases with symptoms resembling Minamata disease (mer-

cury poisoning) were detected. These cases have been related to high concentrations of mercury in the people affected and in the fish that form the base of their diet, due to pollution of local rivers by illegal gold miners, known as *garimpeiros*, who use mercury to extract gold.

The transformation of the *várzea* for agriculture and intensive stock-raising is probably even more significant in terms of fish stocks than the changes affecting the *terra firme*. Logging eliminates many areas of flooded jungle used by fish to spawn. Flood waters are increasingly contaminated by chemical processes, and fish mortality is high. The effects of these large-scale projects, normally sponsored by governments, on subsistence and commercial fisheries must be studied.

4.6 The green reserve

Tropical rainforests cover about 6% of the planet's land surface and contain over half the world's species. These fragile habitats are thus extraordinarily rich in biodiversity. A single hectare (one hectare=2.5 acres) of rainforest in Peru has been shown to contain 300 species of tree, and a hectare of rainforest in Malaysia may contain 180 species, a fantastic quantity in comparison with the 700 species in the whole of continental North America. The same high levels of diversity are shown by other groups of flowering plants and spore plants, as well as by plant-eating animals such as insects. Scientists at the Smithsonian Institution have shown that in Panama a single tree species may host more than 1,200 species of beetle (coleopterans), 163 of which are found on no other tree species. About 80% of all known insect species live in tropical rainforests. The greatest species diversity is probably found in Latin America, followed by southeast Asia. The Amazon contains 20% of all known species of bird, and Indonesia contains another 16%.

Biodiversity is not uniform throughout the tropical rainforests. Historical and environmental influences, such as altitude, soil type, rainfall, humidity, and temperature, have led to the concentration of biodiversity in several areas, sometimes known as "hot-spots." Ten were identified that are characterized by their high concentration of endemic plant species and high rates of forest modification or conversion to other uses.

These ten areas cover less than 1% of the world's surface and represent 3.5% of the primary forest cover, yet they contain 34,400 species of endemic plants, that is to say, 27% of all tropical forest species and 13% of all known plant species.

One of these hot spots is the Colombian Chocó district, whose rainforests run along the Pacific coastline of Colombia. This region is biologically underexplored, but it is already known to be the botanically richest area in the world. There are an estimated 9,000 species of plant in its lowland rainforests, about a quarter of them endemic. The rate of endemism among birds is also estimated to be higher than anywhere else, with more than 100 endemic taxa. There are also many endemic reptiles (137 taxa) and amphibians (111 taxa). The Chocó is clearly a priority in international biodiversity conservation, and ways must be found to prevent its deforestation.

The value of biodiversity

The potential economic value of biodiversity may be one of the most potent arguments for conserving the rainforests. Yet it is very difficult to put a price on a species that has no clear resource value, or that is only used locally and does not enter the marketplace. It is even more difficult to estimate the financial value of rainforest biodiversity, that is to say, the total diversity of the species and their genetic resources in different habitats. In any case, the value of diversity is generally divided into consumptive values and nonconsumptive values.

Consumptive values are related to the biological resources of known use to humans. Resources of this type in the rainforest include timber and medicinal species, and wild relatives of cultivated species with potential value in crop-breeding programs.

Nonconsumptive values are related to the indirect uses of biodiversity, and these are normally very hard to quantify. They include ecological services, such as the maintenance of water supplies, flood prevention, energy and nutrient recycling, and climate control. The rainforest's capacity to grow productively on poor soils, where human systems usually fail, is partly due to the numerous interactions between species. Without this capacity these ecological services cannot be provided.

Another type of nonconsumptive value is *existence value*, the appreciation people have for wildlife that they may never see. This can be measured to some extent by the quantity of money people will give to conserve wild species or habitats even though they have no direct experience of them. The interest aroused by the rainforest throughout the world and the success of fund-raising for conservation initiatives suggests that rainforest has a considerable existence value, although it should not be expected that this alone will compensate for the development pressures exerted on the rainforest. Therefore, of all the possible systems for the evaluation of biodiversity, the hardest to quantify is what is known as the *option value*, the insurance premium that people are willing to pay to keep the option of using biodiversity directly and indirectly in the future. There is much yet to be discovered about the rainforest's diversity, especially in the underexplored and species-rich rainforest systems. Yet in a rapidly changing world the needs of future generations are not taken into account. The genetic resources of the forest may provide solutions to the expected climatic changes linked to deforestation and global warming.

Sustainable use

The rainforest cannot be kept apart from the dynamics of the world economy, and this is probably not desirable anyway. As elsewhere, but to a greater extent, the protection of the equatorial rainforest depends on adequate management, that is to say, the application of ecologically rational and socially equitable measures. This is the basis of the concept of *sustainable development*, easier to state than to put into practice in an environment that is disjointed and subject to all sorts of pressures. Yet some initiatives are trying to bring sustainable-use programs into operation. These are intrinsically useful and serve as a reference for later experiences. There are many lessons to be learned from the behavior of the local populations with centuries of experience of life in the forest, especially those with some degree of economic development.

The experience of the indigenous populations: the Kuna
The Kuna people of Panama have responsibility for one of the few remaining equatorial rainforests in Central America. Their rights to the land were recognized 60 years ago, and they have devised a strategy for the wise use of their forest resources. The idea of a protected area came from the Kuna belief in "spirit sanctuaries," places where spiritual plants,

195 Kuna woman preparing cassava. The Study Project for the Management of the Forested Area of the Kuna Territory (PEMASKY) is designed to preserve 148,263 acres (60,000 ha) of the western part of the Kuna Yala Reserve from settlers. The land is divided into four categories of protected area. In the core area of forest only tourism and scientific research are allowed. Tourists and scientists have to pay to visit this area. Each scientist has to be accompanied by a Kuna assistant and must leave a record of the results of the scientific work performed. The other categories of protected area are land reserved for agriculture; a cultural area where the Kuna villages are located, together with their fisheries and coastal farming sites; and an external park buffer zone that protects the park from outside disturbances.
[Photo: A. Kerstitch / Planet Earth Pictures]

animals, and "demons" reside. Their project is now considered as a model of good tropical rainforest management, and other native groups consult the Kuna on the development of similar plans.

About 40,000 Kuna live on the madrepore coral reef islands off the eastern coast of Panama and in 12 coastal villages. They rely on fishing and multiple-crop subsistence agriculture. Their land's rainforest vegetation is almost intact, although some farming and gathering of forest products takes place. Construction of a major new road near the Kuna territory in the 1970s provided an important communication link but also brought the risk of illegal colonists. To prevent problems arising, the Kuna obtained the support of national and international organizations to draw up a management regime for their lands. The Kuna decided to utilize their forests for ecotourism, scientific research, and habitat conservation.

The traditional lifestyle of the Kuna is changing; some communities remain staunchly traditional, but others are now highly westernized. The rituals and historical chants by which the Kuna traditionally learned about the natural world are less important to young people, and knowledge about the forest is being lost. Yet the Kuna have managed to adapt, and they retain many of their ancestral values within a changing world. With control over their lands and a conservation program that they devised and manage, they have at least the basis for continuing to live in harmony with their environment.

Agroforestry

Another interesting experience in the field of sustainable land use is *agroforestry*, as exemplified by some traditional forms of permanent cultivation practiced in tropical forests to make the best use of native species and local ecological conditions. Agroforestry is increasingly seen as a more sustainable form of land use than the shifting agriculture that is contributing to deforestation throughout the tropics. In areas near to natural parks, for example, development of agroforestry may prevent farmers from encroaching into the park. The retention of trees within the agricultural system provides shelter for crop species, helping to maintain soil fertility, climatic conditions, and biodiversity. Agroforestry has traditionally been practiced in the forests of the western Ghats in Mysore, in India. The natural forests were enriched by planting native species, such as the jackfruit (mainly *Artocarpus heterophyllus*, known in Hindi as *kathal*), sago palm (*Metroxylon sagu*), and sugar palm (*Arenga pinnata*), in a system developed more than a century ago.

Agroforestry systems may use different combinations of crops and may modify the original tree cover to a greater or lesser extent. The Chinese island of Hainan had been extensively deforested by shifting agriculture, the establishment of rubber plantations and timber exploitation. Bawangling Nature Reserve is one of the best remaining fragments of forest. The areas around the reserve are managed in several ways, as part of an integrated research program into the ecosystem that forms part of UNESCO's MAB Programme. As part of this integrated program,

experimental agroforestry plantations are being created to meet the needs of local people and to stabilize the environment. The most widely planted tree is teak (*Tectona grandis*), which is underplanted with camphor laurel (*Cinnamomum camphora*), cardamons of the genus *Ammomum* and other trees, including *Lannea grandis* (Anacardiaceae), which is used for mushroom production. Annual and perennial herbaceous crops are also included in the cultivation system. Agroforestry development in Bawangling basically uses economically valuable nonnative species to restore the environment and prevent further forest loss.

Where the rainforest has been less modified, agroforestry may conserve and use more native species. The riverside inhabitants of the Amazon estuary, the *ribeirinhos* practice a similar form of extensive agroforestry in the floodplain forests. The ribeirinhos cultivate vegetable plots on a permanent basis and also use some areas of managed and unmanaged forest. Managed areas are selectively cleared to promote the regeneration and growth of economically worthwhile species such as the assai palm, or palmiche (*Euterpe oleracea*). Limited cultivation of trees crops takes place, mainly understory plantations of cocoa (*Theobroma cacao*). The unmanaged forest is used for collection of natural forest products.

Ecotourism

The best land-use systems for tropical forest ecosystems combine different forms and intensities of forest management to satisfy the needs of local people. As in the extractive reserve system, agroforestry and the sustainable use of natural resources are two basic elements in forest management. There is, however, a third component that is becoming increasingly important, the development of ecotourism.

Rainforests have captured the imagination of people throughout the world. Experiencing the rainforest environment has become a popular goal and tourism companies offer rainforest holidays in different continents. Carefully controlled tourism may provide essential income for rainforest countries without exerting excessive pressure on the environment. Some projects ensure that the local people benefit from tourism and that profits are used to improve conservation management. Yet ecotourism is not without problems, as the increasing number of visitors alters the forest ecosystem.

196 Fauna is one of the main ecotourism attractions, as shown by the fascinating beauty of this margay (*Felis wiedii*) in the Cockscomb Basin Jaguar Reserve in Belize. This reserve, covering 3,500 acres (1,417 ha) in the basin of the River Cockscomb is prime jaguar (*Panthera onca*) habitat and also contains large populations of species like margay, ocelot (*F. pardalis*), peccary (*Tayassu*), deer (*Odocoileus*), anteater (*Cyclopes*), and armadillos (*Dasypus*). There is a center for visitors, cabins, marked trails, and an administrative center. Indigenous women have set up a cooperative gift shop, and several young eople are being trained as tourist guides. This small-scale economic activity has encouraged local people to protect the area's natural resources.
[Photo: Carol Farneti / Natural Science Photos]

In spite of this, ecotourism is increasingly seen as one way of obtaining economic benefits from the rainforest without transforming their ecosystems.

Ecotourism for wildlife observation grew throughout the 1980s, almost certainly related to growing environmental concern among the citizens of developed countries. More and more people want to see the tropical areas they have only seen in television documentaries and read about in the press. Tourism in the New World tropics has not reached the levels of the African savannah, but it has great potential. Initially bird-watchers went to see the neotropical rainforest's unequaled bird fauna. As the number of ecotourists increased, wildlife enthusiasts traveled increasingly to Latin America to see the beautiful landscapes and the wildlife. This development gave national governments a chance to develop ecotourism and to promote wildlife conservation. It has been shown, especially in Africa, that local people in rural areas are willing to protect wildlife resources that produce clear economic benefits for their community. The creation of jobs for these people and infrastructure will lead to new attitudes towards these crucial wildlife resources. Government commitment can also achieve a wide range of objectives, such as school visits and ensuring access for a wide range of the country's citizens.

Two small Central American countries, Belize and Costa Rica, have taken the lead in promoting ecotourism. Belize established a number of bird and wildlife reserves 30 years ago, and several ecotourism projects are now under way. The government's national tourism policy gives high priority to conservation. The country's attractions include the Cockscomb Basin Jaguar Reserve and the lands acquired by the *Programme for Belize*. This program, launched in 1989, has bought a 111,197 acre (45,000 ha) plot of rainforest, now known as the Río Bravo Conservation and Management Area, with the aim of managing it sustainably for conservation purposes. It is now promoting carefully controlled ecotourism. A million dollars a year are needed to finance the conservation project, and much of this is to be obtained from tourism, together with scientific and archaeological expeditions.

Costa Rica's tourism is a major source of foreign exchange, and is the third largest source of foreign income. Tourism was traditionally concentrated in the capital San José in the central highlands, but in the last few years the country's interesting natural history has been promoted. Despite its small size, Costa Rica has a wide variety of landscapes and ecological zones. As a result of this and its location as a bridge between North and South America, the country also has a spectacularly diverse wildlife. Furthermore, Costa Rica has a well-developed national parks system covering almost 20% of the country; the most visited parks are the Poás Volcano National Park, Cahuita, Manuel Antonio, Irazú Volcano, Santa Rosa, Tortuguero, Corcovado, and Carara.

Research and scientific tourism have been the main activities promoted in Costa Rica's La Selva Reserve, an area of rainforest in the Atlantic lowlands. About 90% of this reserve is virgin forest, and the 3,375 acre (1,366 ha) site contains more than 1800 species of plant, 388 species of bird, and 143 species of butterfly. The research installations include a modern laboratory with a library

197 One of the trees helped by the creation of **extractive reserves** is the Brazil nut tree (*Bertholletia excelsa*, Lecythidaceae), the source of the Brazil nut, or Pará nut. The nuts are the seeds (lower photo) borne within the dark globose fruit, which may weigh up to 7 lb (3 kg) (upper photo). Each fruit may contain up to trigonous 20 nuts (seeds with a hard woody testa). The seed itself is very rich in fats (60%) and proteins (18%) and can be eaten raw or pressed for oil for cooking, lighting, or making soap. Attempts at large-scale cultivation have been unsuccessful because of its complicated pollination, which depends on female euglossine bees (*Euglossa*). Male euglossine bees require scent from a particular rainforest orchid to attract females for mating. About 50,000 t of Brazil nuts are harvested every year, all produced by wild trees in natural rainforest and collected manually after falling from the tree. Each tree produces 100 to 300 nuts a year. The main importers of Brazil nuts are the United Kingdom, the United States, and Germany. [Photos: André Bärtschi / Planet Earth Pictures and Rudolf König / Jacana]

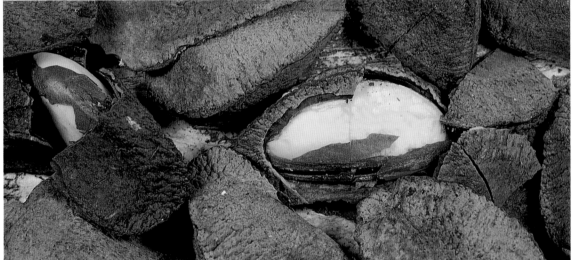

and taxonomic reference collections, as well as four permanent forest research plots. Computerized data are available on all trees with a trunk diameter over 4 in (10 cm) growing in these plots.

Extractive reserves

Extractive reserves are another interesting idea. The Brazilian ministry of agricultural reform and development defines extractive reserves as "forest areas inhabited by extractive populations granted long-term usufruct rights [legal rights to use and enjoy] to forest resources they collectively exploit and manage." The first Brazilian extractive reserve was created in 1989. This was the Upper Jurua Extractive Reserve, which covers an area of 123,600 acres (50,000 ha) in the upper watersheds of the river Jurua. This was followed by the Cachoeira reserve, also in the state of Acre, which occupies almost 61,776 acres (25,000 ha). In 1994 the Brazilian government had already recognized 16 of these reserves. Each extractive reserve is different, and their effectiveness in preventing deforestation is not yet proven. Adequate marketing techniques need urgently to be developed for the products of these rainforest reserves. One promising example is the trade agreement signed between the Kayapo people of the Amazon and a British company selling cosmetic and hygiene products.

Extractive reserves have the necessary pre-existing local population skilled in these activities. In the interior of the Brazilian rainforest, the caboclos, descendants of the first European colonists and Africans, possess detailed knowledge of forest resources. They typically live by combining small-scale agriculture, fishing, and hunting with the collection of forest products, such as rubber and Brazil nuts, for sale. The caboclos have always led a very harsh life, controlled by the landowners (*patrões*).

When the collecting season begins, the landowner advances tools, food, and other goods to the rubber collectors and tappers, the *seringueiros*, who have to work to repay the landowner with products collected from the rainforest. The prices of these goods are manipulated so that the caboclos remain in debt. These harsh conditions force them to abandon the forest and move to cities or mining communities, a move that often leads to an even more miserable life. Those who have remained, however, are becoming increasingly organized to resist both the brutality of the patrões and rainforest destruction for cattle ranching.

International management and protection initiatives

Growing general concern for the rainforest's future has led to a series of initiatives to slow down deforestation and to promote more rational use of tropical forest resources. There have been some small successes, but there are no easy solutions, and the rainforest is disappearing increasingly quickly. International initiatives play an essential role in saving the rainforest because they reinforce and financially support national conservation programs and they also eliminate some incentives for deforestation. Yet they will not be successful unless they develop new, locally appropriate, models for the use of the rainforest ecosystems and their resources.

The Rio Conference on the Environment and Development (UNCED)

The 1992 United Nations Conference on the Environment and Development (UNCED) in Rio de Janeiro, Brazil, focused the attention of governments and the entire planet's communication media on environmental issues. Expectations were great in the run-up to the conference, as it led people to think that international solutions would at last be found to the problem of tropical deforestation. A new Forest Convention was hoped for, but agreement was not reached. The compromise solution was the formulation of the "Non-legally Binding Authoritative Statement of Principles for a Global Consensus on the Management, Conservation and Sustainable Development of all Types of Forest."

Other results of the UNCED included the Convention on Climate Change and the Convention on Biological Diversity, two international treaties that when fully implemented will have major implications for forest preservation. The Rio Conference also agreed on a comprehensive action plan, generally known as "Agenda 21." This plan aims to reverse the effects of environmental degradation and promote environmentally sound and sustainable development in all countries. The stated objectives for forests are to maintain the multiple roles and functions of all types of forest, to strengthen their protection, to manage them sustainably, to conserve them by rehabilitation, to promote efficient usage of forest goods and services by full valuation of the resources, and to strengthen capacities for the planning, assessment, and systematic monitoring of forests.

The Tropical Forestry Action Plan

Most of the world's rainforests are in less developed countries, whose main aim is to increase living standards above mere subsistence. Thus, at a national scale there is only limited financial support for conservation. National policies tend to favor logging the rainforests and converting them to more intensive uses, but in the long term this is unsustainable. The Tropical Forestry Action Plan (TFAP) was drawn up to help overcome these problems. Its intention was to channel aid money from donor governments to tropical forestry to help reverse the process of forest loss.

The TFAP was published in 1985 by the Committee for Forest Development in the Tropics (CFDT) of the United Nations Food and Agriculture Organization (FAO). Five priority areas for action were identified for the development and conservation of tropical forest resources: forestry in land-use, forest-based industrial development, fuelwood and energy, conservation of tropical forest ecosystems, and strengthening institutions for research, training, and education.

The World Resources Institute, the United Nations Development Program, and the World Bank jointly drew up an forestry investment program for 53 tropical countries for the period 1987-1991. The funding necessary to meet the program's aims was estimated at 8,000 million U.S. dollars, with 8% allocated to tropical forest conservation.

Under the TFAP process, national forestry action plans were drawn up for tropical countries. The procedure followed is that each country requests assistance from the TFAP coordination unit, and then a donor agency is identified to fund and take responsibility for preparing the national plan.

198 Measures and campaigns to protect the rainforest fauna vary in scope and effectiveness, but they always respond to a growing outcry to stop the senseless destruction now taking place. The poster in the photo is a warning by the government of the Caribbean island of St. Lucia.
[Photo: Alan Colclough / Planet Earth Pictures]

An issues paper is drawn up using background information to identify the main forestry problems in the country in question and to guide preparation of the plan. The document is discussed and reviewed, and a forestry review commission is formed to carry out a forestry sector review within the country. This normally takes two or three months. Then, on the basis of this review, the national forestry action plan is prepared. This plan is presented to the countries and international agencies that provide development aid to guide future financial aid to the country concerned. The TFAP has been supported by all the main donor governments and 70 tropical countries, which contain about 60% of the remaining tropical forests. However, not a single national TFAP plan has yet been fully developed.

The TFAP has helped to channel financial aid into tropical forest conservation. It is not clear, however, that this program has stimulated the provision of extra revenue to conserve the forests. Furthermore, it is hard to tell if the TFAP has had any impact on reducing the rate of deforestation. It is difficult to see how this can occur without resolving the underlying problems of population growth, land distribution, and international debt. Nongovernmental Organizations (NGOs) have severely criticized the TFAP because they feel it puts too much emphasis on the commercial and industrial aspects of forestry, thus perpetuating

some of the causes of deforestation. It is also widely felt that participation by local inhabitants in the development of national plans has not been strong enough. Several reforms have taken place in the administration of the TFAP. Its future direction, within the everchanging setting of the international agencies, is unclear. Coordinated planning of international aid projects for the preservation and development of the forests remains important, and the TFAP will probably continue in a slightly modified form.

The International Tropical Timber Agreement

The International Tropical Timber Agreement (ITTA) came into force in 1985, the same year as the Tropical Forestry Action Plan was published. Their content and manner of operation are very different, but the roles of the TFAP and ITTA in addressing tropical deforestation are often directly compared. They have similar aims—promoting sustainable use of tropical rainforests—but they have very different means of achieving them. The fundamental difference between the two conventions is that ITTA is an international legal instrument, whereas TFAP is an international policy or process that has no legal content.

The ITTA was developed as a commodity agreement and, as such, is unique because it includes environmental provisions. One of its objectives is to "encourage the development of national policies aimed at the sustainable utilization and conservation of tropical forests and their genetic resources, and at maintaining the ecological balance in the regions concerned." The International Tropical Timber Organization (ITTO), based in Yokohama, Japan, was established under the terms of the ITTA to administer the agreement and to promote its objectives. In 1990, the 46 member governments of ITTO agreed to ensure that by the year 2000 all internationally traded tropical timber should come from sustainably managed forests. In general, it is accepted that "sustainable" management should relate not only to timber production but also to the maintenance of the forest's ecological functions and biodiversity. Transforming the international timber market from an agent of deforestation into a force for conservation is not a simple task, and it is difficult to see how the ITTO can play an important role. The Organization's Secretariat is small, and conservation is only one of the ITTA's eight overall objectives.

So far, the ITTO's successes in conservation have been modest. It has given support to a few pilot projects related, for example, to sustainable timber production and the development of extractive reserves in Brazil and Bolivia. Guidelines for a sustainable management have been produced together with guidelines for conserving biodiversity in the exploitable forests. Yet the ITTO has not been able to obtain the implementation of these policies at a national level or show any progress towards sustainable exploitation ("Target 2000"). In 1994, the ITTA was being renegotiated and its future direction was still unclear. Many nongovernmental organizations, like the countries producing tropical hardwoods, feel that ITTA should cover all timbers, both temperate and tropical, and that its mandate should be more focused on trade-related policies that have an impact on limiting deforestation.

Redeeming foreign debt for nature

"Debt-for-nature" swaps were pioneered in the 1980s as a way of releasing money for tropical forest conservation. The first swap was negotiated in 1987 by the organization Conservation International, a U.S. environmental NGO, that paid U.S. $100,000 to a Swiss bank to buy Bolivian debt with a face value of U.S. $650,000. The bank lost money, but it received cash payment for a debt that could not be paid back. The conservation organization paid off the debt and in exchange the Bolivian government spent Bolivian pesos to establish a buffer zone around the Beni Biological Reserve.

199 **The differences in culture and purchasing power** between westerners and the rainforest peoples are immense. Any European can, without great economic effort and simply by arranging it through a travel agency, be comfortably taken in hours to remote places, like the one in New Guinea shown in the photo, that just a few decades ago were accessible only to explorers or adventurers. Their limited comprehension of the cultural and environmental context to which they are suddenly transferred, the destructuring this will unintentionally provoke in the receptor community, and the enormous comparative affront this represents are aspects of the social and ecological conflicts occurring in the modern world. Unless these problems are overcome, the sustainable use and conservation of the tropical rainforests seem difficult objectives to achieve. [Photo: Manuel de Sostoa & Adolf de Sostoa]

In Ecuador, the Fundación Natura, the country's main conservation NGO, reached an agreement with the government to exchange up to U.S. $10 million of debt for local currency bonds. The debt was purchased with national and international donations, and the bonds are being used to finance the conservation and improvement of Ecuador's national parks.

Debt-for-nature swaps of this kind are an imaginative way of funding conservation activities without having to use a country's foreign currency reserves. They have only been used in a small number of occasions and do little to solve the overall debt crisis or the problems related to the contemporary inadequate development model. What is needed is a major international undertaking by governments to resolve the debt problem and to work towards a new international economic era based on sustainable development and conservation.

From Henry Wickham to Chico Mendes

In mid-May of 1876 the steamer *Amazonas*, originally from Manaus, weighed anchor and left the port of Belém with a cargo of "extremely delicate botanical specimens," to quote the customs declaration. Immediately on docking in Liverpool, the shipment was transferred to a special train destined for the Royal Botanic Gardens at Kew near London. The cargo consisted of 70,000 seeds of a species of Brazilian tree, and the staff of Kew Gardens gave them as much care and attention as Henry Wickham, an eminent British plantation owner living in Santarém, had already given them during the long sea voyage. Wickham had patiently collected and packaged the seeds and gone to the trouble of chartering the steamer and dealing with all the customs requirements with, one imagines, more than a few headaches in the process. The first steps towards the large-scale cultivation of the main rubber-producing plant had been taken. As a result of Charles Goodyear's invention of the vulcanization process in 1839, latex could be made into a valuable industrial material, rubber.

Of the 70,000 seeds planted in the Kew greenhouses, only 2,800 germinated. Nevertheless, the operation was a success as all previous attempts had failed, largely because of the terrible conditions experienced on the long sea crossing. The young seedlings of *Hevea brasiliensis* were carefully sent to various botanic gardens throughout the British colonies in southeast Asia. The Henaratgoda Botanical Gardens in Ceylon (Sri Lanka) succeeded in growing viable trees but failed to standardize either production or exploitation techniques. However, once Henry Nicholas Ridley (1855-1956) assumed charge of the Singapore Botanic Gardens things began to change. He succeeded in domesticating the rubber plant and thereby opened the door to systematic commercial exploitation: The Brazilian monopoly had been broken.

The development of rubber plantations in southeast Asia undoubtedly contributed to the decline in production in the Amazon. Many rubber producers abandoned their concessions for other more profitable activities. The case illustrates perfectly two differing concepts of economic activity: on the one hand, the exploitation of a natural resource based on cheap and abundant labor with no investment or attempts at rationalization or improvements, and on the other hand, the concept of "industrial production." It must be said that the failure to establish rubber plantations in the Amazon was also due to the spread of a fungus (*Mycrocyclus* [=*Dothidella*] *ulei*) that attacks the leaves of the *Hevea* when too many are planted together. Wickham was incredibly lucky that none of his seeds carried the disease and today it is unknown in both Asia and Africa. Nowadays, 97% of the world's rubber production (about 6 million t a year) is from southeast Asia, although extraction does continue in the Amazon jungle and in 1986 the Brazilian Amazon produced 26,880 tons of raw rubber.

Compared with the output from plantations, spontaneous production is negligible. The first plantations produced around 496 lb (225 kg) of latex per hectare (1 hectare=2.5 acres) per year, although by the beginning of the 20th century this figure had risen to 660 lb (300 kg). By 1930 it had reached 880 lb (400 kg) and in the 1980s over 6,600 lb/ha (3,000 kg /ha) were being produced. The problem is that all Asiatic and African plants originate from the first few seedlings obtained in Singapore, leading to genetic deterioration. Attempts are being made to improve the clones of the original stock by crossing with strains from Sri Lanka, Java, and Sumatra, as well as with wild Brazilian specimens of *Hevea brasiliensis* and *H. benthamiana*. Meanwhile, the destruction of the Amazonian jungle is continuing, increasingly threatening the wild rubber trees that remain.

European explorers in the late 18th and early 19th centuries, such as Charles Marie La Condamine (1701-1774) and Alexander von Humboldt (1769-1859), realized the rubber plant's potential when the Amazonian indigenous peoples showed them that latex could be used to make things waterproof. In 1827 Brazil produced 36 t, but by 1857, at the height of the euphoria following Goodyear's discovery of vulcanization, 2,600 t were produced. By 1865 production could no longer keep up with demand: The rubber boom was underway. Iquitos and Manaus became flourishing cities as traders recklessly spent their profits on ostentatious palaces and on world-famous attractions: In 1896, for example, Enrico Caruso sang at the opening night of the luxurious Amazonas Theatre in Manaus.

This new-found wealth was based on a monopoly on production and the inhuman working conditions of the *seringueiros*, or rubber tappers, forced by poverty to come from all over the country to work on the concessions. The rubber barons or, *seringalistas*, controlled concessions extending over vast areas of jungle in which they rarely, if ever, set foot (the Suárez brothers, for example, controlled over 24,000 sq mi [62 000 sq km] in Bolivia). Interest in developing rubber plantations in other areas of the tropics increased, though in the Amazon narrow-minded, short-sighted exploitation of the jungle continued as before. In 1900, 4 t of rubber (see insert "Tires and chewing gum," pp. 218-221) reached the world market from southeast Asia, but by 1914 this figure had reached 70,000 t: In face of such competition, the Brazilian market collapsed like a house of cards.

Nevertheless, Amazonian rubber production continued (in 1920 it covered only 12% of world demand and by 1990 barely 1%), increasingly in the hands of semi-independent rubber tappers, the seringueiros. Rubber tappers were seriously threatened by the opening up of roads, as happened in the state of Acre in the 1960s and 1970s and by the increase in cattle-ranching. Many were expelled by ranchers and ended up in the slums of the big cities, though a few began to assert their right to use the jungle. A seringueiros movement began in the mid-1970s in

Acre, but even by the mid-eighties they were still subject to exploitation by the rubber barons, who controlled all aspects of the trade, as well as claiming ownership of land and demanding rent from the seringueiros.

In 1985 more than a hundred rubber tappers from the whole of the Brazilian Amazon met to create the "Conselho Nacional dos Seringueiros" (CNS, or National Council of Rubber Tappers). This meeting formulated a series of demands for economic and social reforms, including the creation of rubber extraction reserves. The first was established in 1989, covering 1.2 million acres (500,000 ha) of the headwaters of the River Jurua. However, the price paid was high: the movement's leader, the rubber tapper Chico Mendes, was murdered in 1988. The well-to-do Henry Wickham and his rational agroforestry plans, and humble Chico Mendes defending traditional systems of production to benefit the local population, symbolize the human face of rubber production and the struggle for a rational use of this jungle resource.

4
Protected areas
and biosphere reserves
in the rainforest

1. The world's protected rainforests

1.1 General considerations

Until recently the main reasons for protecting the equatorial rainforests were to preserve its landscape and to try to prevent the extinction of its wildlife. Yet the rainforests also play a major role in the planet's water cycle, a further reason for concern about their preservation on a world scale.

Most of the world's rainforest is at risk of being plundered by the local population's exploitation of its resources. Thus, the solutions required must be transnational.

The problem is very complex. The rainforest's distribution is almost entirely within countries with weak economies and serious problems of underdevelopment, and this makes it difficult—difficult, but very necessary—to set up and implement effective protection plans, even if only for the distribution of information.

Yet it is a fact that reductionist proposals ignoring the need to associate rainforest protection with improving the living conditions of the human populations concerned were socially unjust and ecologically inviable.

Nor can the problem be reduced just to the need for measures to ensure a decent life for local people. Many rainforest areas contain plentiful biological or mineral resources, and this often leads to outside economic groups taking possession of areas and abusively exploiting them. They exert very strong pressure on weak, or simply corrupt, governments when it comes to protecting—that is, managing rationally—the forests, and private interests usually prevail over public ones.

The reader should note that the rainforest, the cloud forest, and the monsoon forest are often in direct contact, and so to comprehend this section fully it should be read in conjunction with the corresponding sections in this volume on the rainforest and monsoon forest.

1.2 Protected parks and areas

The protected areas of rainforest are distributed throughout almost all the equatorial regions and in many southern hemisphere countries. In the neotropical region there are a hundred protected areas containing some rainforest. Some of the most representative ones are in Brazil, which has 49,420,874 acres (20 million ha) of protected land, mainly forest, that is divided between parks, biological reserves and federal and state environmental protection areas. The largest are the National Parks of Pico de Neblina and Jau, which cover almost 4,942,087 acres (2 million ha). The African tropics have many important protected areas, including the Africa's first national park, Virunga (Albert) National Park, which was created in 1925 during Belgian colonization of present-day Democratic Republic of Congo and covers 1,927,415 acres (780,000 ha). The Salonga National Park, also in Democratic Republic of Congo, covers more than 8,648,653 acres (3.5 million ha) and is the largest in the African rainforest. Some of the most important protected areas in the Indomalaysian region are in Peninsular Malaysia, including the Taman Negara Natural Park in Malaysia, where about 200 endemic species of animal are dependent on the park for their survival. The Doi Suthep-Pui National Park in Thailand is another major protected area, covering 64,509 acres (26,106 ha) and home to 250 species of orchid. Great efforts have been made to assess the minimum size a forest reserve must be for it to survive, and there is still no clear answer. First, the reserve's plant and animal species must be identified and the dynamics of their recovery after stressful situations must be studied. Obviously, this has a lot to do with the population density of each species (the case of a tree species with one specimen per hectare is different from that of a species with 20 specimens per hectare), and their pollination and seed dispersal mechanisms as well as with the distribution ranges of the animals and their movement through the rainforest. An area of 2.5 acres (1 ha) may be sufficiently large to watch a species, especially a plant species, gradually become extinct. This is a slow process, and it is often hard to realize that it is occurring.

200 The establishment of areas of rainforest completely protected from all forms of exploitation is essential to guarantee the survival of many species, in fact most of the species now in existence. The titis of the Brazilian Mata Atlântica, such as this specimen of *Callithrix jacchus*, are a good example of species whose survival is inseparable from the protection of the rainforest.
[*Photo: Jany Sauvenet / Auscape International*]

2. The UNESCO biosphere reserves in the rainforest

2.1 The biosphere reserves in the rainforest

In 1998 there were 46 biosphere reserves containing tropical rainforest in 29 countries, mainly in South America, Africa, and Asia, together with some in the Caribbean, to protect more than 39,535,000 acres (16 million ha) of forest. The size of the reserves is variable: 1,140 acres (460 ha) has the Omo Nature Reserve in Nigeria, almost 12 million acres (5 million ha) the Brazilian Mata Atlântica Reserve, in fact a series of linked reserves, etc. Anyway, the area of rainforest in each reserve is variable, and a single reserve may contain several types of ecosystems, such as cloud forest, monsoon forest, and other types.

The first biosphere reserves created were in the Caribbean, in 1976: the Luquillo Experimental Forest in Puerto Rico and the Virgin Islands National Park in the American part of the archipelago. Later in 1977 a further 15 biosphere reserves throughout the southern hemisphere were approved. The most recently created ones are the Mata Atlântica in Brazil, the Guadalupe Archipelago in the Lesser Antilles, the Sierra de las Minas in Guatemala, the Alto Orinoco-Casiquiare in Venezuela, the Xishuangbanna in China, the Bosawas in Nicaragua and the Tonle Sap in Cambodia. Some are unique and irreplaceable blocks of intact rainforest, such as the Montes Azules Biosphere Reserve in the Lacandón mountains of the Mexican state of Chiapas.

2.2 Biosphere reserves in the American rainforest

The different biosphere reserves in the American rainforest are in very different situations with respect to their state of conservation and former management. These countries' social and political situation often mean that the commitments acquired by the authorities when promoting the reserve often cannot be fulfilled, or are only partially fulfilled.

The case of the Mata Atlântica Biosphere Reserve in Brazil is unusual. Established in 1992 and ratified in 1993, it was formed from two biosphere reserves that had previously been established in 1991 (Phase I), the Vale do Ribeira-Sera da Graciosa Reserve, covering 4,433,000 acres (1,794,000 ha), and the Tijuca-Tingua-Orgâos Reserve, which covers 166,000 acres (67,000 ha). The new reserve runs along the entire Serra do Mar on the Atlantic coastline and includes within its perimeters two of Brazil's largest cities, Rio de Janeiro and Sâo Paulo. So much of the Atlantic coastline is privately owned that only 0.1% of the original forest is protected. The vegetation includes tropical rainforest with typical species such as the Brazil nut (*Bertholletia excelsa*), whose nuts are one of Brazil's most important rainforest products; the brazilwood, or *pau rosado* (*Caesalpinia echinata*), a now-endangered species that was formerly used as a dye; and the black Brazilian rosewood (*Dalbergia nigra*), a timber tree that is in danger of extinction. The fauna includes 2,000 species of butterflies and 6 genera of primates, including 13 species now in danger of extinction. The reserve is remarkable for the broad scope of the research and management undertaken, and particularly for its reforestation efforts, which include bombing denuded areas with gelatin "bombs" containing the seeds of at least 10 tropical trees.

The La Amistad Biosphere Reserve

The La Amistad Biosphere Reserve covers more than 1.2 million acres (half a million ha) in the southern part of the Talamanca Range between Costa Rica and Panama (and more than 2,471,043 acres [a million ha] including the Panamanian section of the La Amistad International Park). One of the reserve's special features is its position on the border; it includes parts of the Costa Rican provinces of San José, Cartago, Limón, and Puntarenas and of the Panamanian provinces of Chiriquí and Bocas del Toro.

201 Biosphere reserves in rainforest areas (1998), showing the year each one was declared and its area. The area (in hectares) corresponds to the total area of the reserve, although other formations may be present, especially montane cloud forest and monsoon forest. Remember that many biosphere reserves were previously protected under other forms of protection, such as a national park, a flora reserve, or a forest reserve, and these may or may not coincide in surface area. The largest are the Mata Atlântica Biosphere Reserve, which conserves the remains of Brazil's tropical lowland rainforest ecosystem; the Manu Biosphere Reserve, the second largest, which also includes a large area of cloud forest; the Palawan Biosphere Reserve (Philippines), which also has cloud forest and monsoon forest; the Maya Biosphere Reserve (Guatemala) is of great importance in the preservation of the world's cultural, as well as natural, heritage.
[Drawing: Editrònica, from several sources]

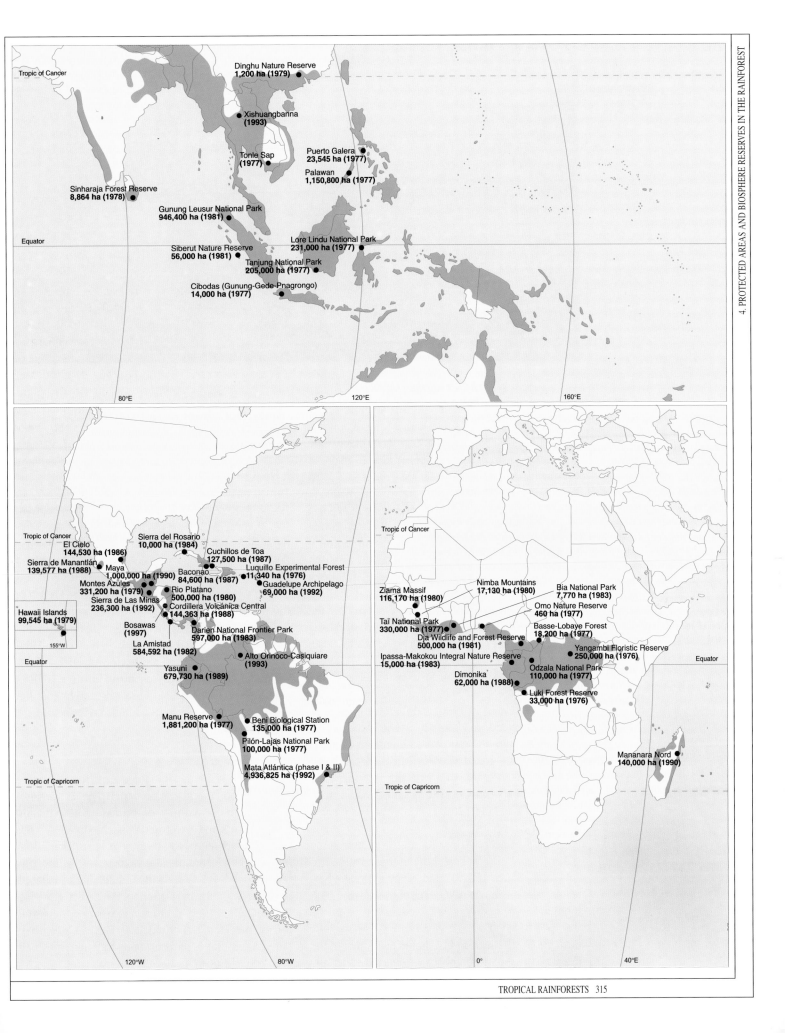

Dinghu Nature Reserve
1,200 ha (1979)

Xishuangbanna
(1993)

Tonle Sap
(1977)

Puerto Galera
23,545 ha (1977)

Palawan
1,150,800 ha (1977)

Sinharaja Forest Reserve
8,864 ha (1978)

Gunung Leusur National Park
946,400 ha (1981)

Lore Lindu National Park
231,000 ha (1977)

Siberut Nature Reserve
56,000 ha (1981)

Tanjung National Park
205,000 ha (1977)

Cibodas (Gunung-Gede-Pnagrongo)
14,000 ha (1977)

Tropic of Cancer

Equator

80°E

120°E

160°E

El Cielo
144,530 ha (1986)

Sierra del Rosario
10,000 ha (1984)

Cuchillos de Toa
127,500 ha (1987)

Luquillo Experimental Forest
11,340 ha (1976)

Sierra de Manantlán
139,577 ha (1988)

Maya
1,000,000 ha (1990)

Baconao
84,600 ha (1987)

Guadelupe Archipelago
69,000 ha (1992)

Montes Azules
331,200 ha (1979)

Rio Platano
500,000 ha (1980)

Sierra de Las Minas
236,300 ha (1992)

Cordillera Volcánica Central
144,363 ha (1988)

Hawaii Islands
99,545 ha (1979)

Bosawas
(1997)

La Amistad
584,592 ha (1982)

Darien National Frontier Park
597,000 ha (1983)

Alto Orinoco-Casiquiare
(1993)

155°W

Yasuni
679,730 ha (1989)

Manu Reserve
1,881,200 ha (1977)

Beni Biological Station
135,000 ha (1977)

Pilón-Lajas National Park
100,000 ha (1977)

Mata Atlántica (phase I & II)
4,936,825 ha (1992)

Tropic of Cancer

Equator

Tropic of Capricorn

120°W

80°W

Ziama Massif
116,170 ha (1980)

Nimba Mountains
17,130 ha (1980)

Bia National Park
7,770 ha (1983)

Omo Nature Reserve
460 ha (1977)

Taï National Park
330,000 ha (1977)

Basse-Lobaye Forest
18,200 ha (1977)

Dja Wildlife and Forest Reserve
500,000 ha (1981)

Yangambi Floristic Reserve
250,000 ha (1976)

Ipassa-Makokou Integral Nature Reserve
15,000 ha (1983)

Odzala National Park
110,000 ha (1977)

Dimonika
62,000 ha (1988)

Luki Forest Reserve
33,000 ha (1976)

Mananara Nord
140,000 ha (1990)

Tropic of Cancer

Equator

Tropic of Capricorn

0°

40°E

The reserve establishes mechanisms to ensure protection of the region's rich wildlife and culture, and also has great potential for sustainable development. To fulfill these objectives the two governments are committed to strengthening cooperation to improve the quality of life of its inhabitants and to safeguard its biodiversity in the long term. La Amistad Biosphere Reserve is a further argument in support of the idea that human-made state frontiers should not prevent continuity of natural and cultural processes. Bilateral conventions and cooperation agreements have helped to improve relations between the two countries and have led to joint efforts towards common goals. The process of the creation of the La Amistad Biosphere Reserve was different in the two countries. The sector in Costa Rica was declared a biosphere reserve by UNESCO in 1982, and in 1983 UNESCO included it on the World Heritage List. The Panamanian sector was included in the list in 1990, and then the two countries both agreed, in accordance with UNESCO's World Heritage Program, to administer the two areas in an integrated way. In May 1992 the two governments signed the Frontier Cooperation Agreement between Costa Rica and Panama, with the aim of ensuring permanent and active mechanisms for cooperation in the biosphere reserve and its area of influence. It is a joint effort between the government of Panama, the Organization of American States (OAS), and several nongovernmental organizations (NGOs), both national and foreign.

Both the Costa Rican and Panamanian sectors of the reserve consist of different areas protected under different categories, based on national laws and administered by widely varying institutions. In the Costa Rican sector, for example, the National Parks Service administers the national parks of Tapantí, Chirripó, the La Amistad International Park, and the biological reserves of Barbilla and Hitoy Cerere; the Directorate General for Forestry runs the Rio Macho Forest Reserve and the Las Tablas Protective Area; indigenous communal development associations run the indigenous reserves of Tayní, Telire, Ujarrás, Salitre, Cabagra, and Chirripó; and the Robert and Catherine Wilson Botanical Garden is administered by the Organization of Tropical Studies (OTS). In the Panamanian sector the Renewable Natural Resources Institute (INRENARE) administers the La Amistad International Park, the Volcán Berú National Park, and the Palo Seco Protective Forest, while the Hydroelectric Resources Institute (IHRE) administers the Fortuna Forest Reserve and the Local Indigenous Councils administer Teribe, Bribri, and Guayamí.

Natural features and values

The reserve is divided into three areas to make management and administration easier. The central area consists almost entirely of primary forest that is strictly protected to preserve its biodiversity (the national park and biological reserves). There is a buffer zone where the indigenous people follow traditional land-use systems that maintain the balance of the ecosystems in relation to human activity. The third area is a zone of influence, where agricultural use of the land is permitted as well as extensive ranching, tourism, and agroindustrial activities that organize and make use of the environment.

203 Howler monkeys (*Alouatta*) are among the most remarkable rainforest primates. In need of protection, these monkeys and especially the adult males are able to produce deep and very loud howls that can be heard from a kilometer away or more (1 km=0.6 mi). This is because they amplify the sound by means of a special adaptation of the larynx. The morning chorus of howler monkeys is one of the most typical sounds of the American rainforest. There are six species of howler monkeys; the one in the photo is the red howler (*A. seniculus*). [Photo: Xavier Ferrer & Adolf de Sostoa]

The Cordillera de Talamanca separating Costa Rica from Panama is the largest and most species-diverse ecosystem in Central America. The range runs northwest-southeast and divides the Central American isthmus into two clearly defined sides. The Atlantic side runs down to the coast, which is swept by the wet trade winds from the Caribbean and crossed by rivers with large flows draining a basin that receives the abundant orogenic rainfall. The Pacific side is less rugged and is subject to strong wet winds from the ocean, and there are large coalescent cones of dejection (alluvial cones) at the base of the slope. During the Miocene and especially Pliocene orogenies the cordillera was affected by intense andesitic-basaltic volcanic activity and by the rising of plutonic rocks. The Caribbean slope consists of ridges of folded sedimentary rocks, the result of the violent Pliocene uprising, when crustal forces raised the sedimentary strata (especially limestones and sandstones). The Pacific slope is the result of intense cracking caused by regional tectonic activity and has a system of stepped horst-type faults. The tallest sites show traces of the last glaciation, such as deep U-shaped valleys that reveal the passing of glaciers thousands of years ago, well-developed glacial cirques separated by sharp peaks or horns carved by the ice, as well as lakes, or tarns, formed during the melting, moraines, hanging valleys, etc. The area's natural richness is impressive, the result of its location as a bridge between two continents, its temperature, rainfall, and altitude; the steep slopes and the physical exposure of the mountainsides. The reserve contains many habitats, from the rainforest in the coastal lowlands to the cloud forests and the subalpine meadows of the highest peaks (almost 13,123 ft [4,000 m]). In the lower parts there is highly diverse wet and hyper-humid tropical and premontane forest. The temperature, humidity, and rainfall conditions ensure that it has a diverse and complex flora, with a high number of species per unit area, and trees with broad crowns and full of epiphytes. In the higher areas there are premontane, low montane, and montane forests, dominated by communities of oaks (*Quercus*). In the higher areas, above 9,800 ft (3,000 m), with a subalpine climate, there are associations of meadows and marshes, some of which are restricted to small and specialized habitats. High levels of endemism and biodiversity make this area one of the richest in the western hemisphere. The area contains more than 10,000 species of flowering plants (including more than 1,000 orchids), more than 4,000 nonvascular plants, nearly 900 lichens, and more than 1,000 ferns. The fauna is also very diverse. The mammals include the tapir (*Tapirus*); six species of cat, including the jaguar (*Panthera onca*); and three species of primate, Geoffrey's spider monkey (*Ateles geoffroyi*), the howler monkey locally known as *congo* (*Alouatta palliata*), and the Central American squirrel monkey (*Cebus capucinus*). The giant anteater (*Myrmecophaga tridactyla*) lives in the mountain meadows. There are many birds, including abundant quetzal (*Pharomachrus mocinno*) and harpy eagle (*Harpia harpyja*), whose distribution is now very restricted owing to the disappearance of large areas of forest. There are also many species of reptiles, amphibians, and insects. The butterfly population gives Costa Rica second position on a global scale.

Management and problems

The Talamanca Range and its area of influence have one of the richest, most varied, and most complex models of human settlement in Central America. Within the region there are three indigenous groups; the *Bribi* and *Guayami* who live in both Costa Rica and Panama, the *Cabécar* in the Costa Rican sector, and the *Teribe* in the Panamanian sector.

These groups, found on both sides of the Talamanca Range, form part of the South American "macro-Chibchan" linguistic group. About 85% of Costa Rica's total indigenous population lives in the Costa Rican sector, and about 65% of all Panama's indigenous peoples live in the Panamanian sector. These groups maintain lifestyles deeply rooted in their cultures and territories, with highly dispersed family groups. The course of history has led to a social organization based on two very different sociopolitical factors: traditional internal social structures (the *awapa*, or elders), and externally influenced ones (indigenous associations). The most important subsistence and self-sufficiency activities are based on shifting agriculture of crops like banana, cocoa, wheat, rice and beans, complemented by hunting, fishing, and other forest products.

The Afro-Caribbean group on the Atlantic coastal area maintains its character and customs and mainly supports itself by cultivating banana and cocoa. Their presence has often contributed to spontaneous colonization and they often settle in legally protected areas.

The groups formed by whites who have come from the interior are settled in small villages or urban-rural centers around the biosphere reserve and exert great pressure on the protected areas. At the same time their work situation is highly precarious, accentuated by the presence of large multinational agroindustrial companies that cultivate banana and pineapple. The settlers living near the reserve have one of the lowest socioeconomic levels in either country. They also suffer from inadequate health, education, and transport services, as well as unemployment. Their economy is based on traditional agriculture and extensive stockraising.

In 1970 cooperation negotiations started between Costa Rica and Panama's Ministers of Economic Policy Planning. Studies began in the same year on organization of frontier development and two years later the two bodies presented their governments with a study explaining the need for joint promotion, on the basis of mutual cooperation, of the integrated development of the common frontier. It also pointed out the need to establish a legal framework to make this cooperation easier. In 1979 the two countries signed a convention to perform short-, medium-, and long-term joint investment and technical assistance projects. This agreement was renewed in 1992 and incorporated as a priority factor the drafting of conservation and binational management plans for the La Amistad Biosphere Reserve. As a result, there have been joint efforts in the conservation and administration of the protected frontier areas, including the creation of a binational technical commission, the formulation of joint financing proposals, integrated operational plans, administrative strategies, scientific research projects, and intersectoral agreements.

The Manu Biosphere Reserve

The Manu National Park (Peru) was created in 1973 and declared a biosphere reserve in 1974. It covers a huge area of 4,648,527 acres (1,881,200 ha), making it the largest area of protected rainforest in the world, except for the Brazilian Mata Atlántica Biosphere Reserve. The Manu Biosphere Reserve is in the provinces of Manu and Paucartambo and includes the entire basin of the Manu River from the eastern slopes of the Andes to the Peruvian Amazon. It includes hundreds of river meanders that run through stretches of protected virgin rainforest whose fauna includes species such as the jaguar, 13 species of primate and more than 1,000 species of bird, such as parrots, kingfishers, chajas (horned screamers), hoatzin, sun bitterns, and nightjars, all in large numbers, and populations of giant otters that play around in the small pools in the forest.

Wildlife studies in the Manu National Park began in the 1950s and led to the establishment in 1969 of the Cocha Cashu Reserve Biological Station, 5 mi (8 km) within the reserve. Since then, research into the black caiman, giant otter, and puma, to mention a few species, have produced very good results. The flora has also been studied with the hope of discovering new medicinal products, as has happened in forests in other parts of the world.

Natural characteristics and values
The topography of this immense park ranges from high areas that are over 12,800 ft (3,900 m) and

descends to lowlands of 1,200 ft (365 m). The Andean condor (*Vultur gryphus*) soars above the highest rocky peaks where temperatures hardly exceed zero. There is a sudden change from the arid vegetation of the Andean *puna*, dominated by tufted grasses and alpine cushion plants, to dense montane forest on the steep, often mist-covered slopes, where annual rainfall may reach 354 in (9,000 mm).

The clear water flows down cascades and converges into the meandering river Manu, the origin of the park's name, in the lowland plains. Here, the water picks up red clays and flows more slowly through wet evergreen forest with an average annual rainfall of 79 in (2,000 mm) and an incredible diversity of plants.

Near the Cocha Cashu Research Station 200 species of tree have been catalogued in a single 2.5 acre (1 ha) plot, including kapok (*Ceiba pentandra*) with trunks 47.2 in (120 cm) in diameter. The commonest tree is the otoba (*Otoba parviflora*), and there are also abundant palms belonging to the genera *Astrocaryum*, *Iriartea*, and *Scheelea*. Another characteristic of these forests is the abundance of the genus *Ficus*, with 18 known species inside the biosphere reserve.

Honduran mahogany (*Swietenia macrophylla*) and cedrela, or false cedar (*Cedrela odorata*), form almost pure stands in the park and produce the best and most profitable timber, while cocoa (*Theobroma cacao*) and chupa-chupa (*Matisia cordata*, Malvaceae) are cultivated for their fruit.

The biosphere reserve houses an apparently unlimited variety of wildlife, and new species are continually being discovered. The park area is estimated to contain about a thousand different species of birds, 25% of the known avifauna of South America and 10% of all the bird species in the world. One reason for this high speciation might be that the Manu Biosphere Reserve is one of the known Pleistocene refugia, an area that retained its forest cover throughout the last ice age, when the surrounding areas dried up and were covered by herbaceous savanna. This continuity gave the flora and fauna enough time to evolve into their current diversity and their current abundance.

The reserve is especially rich in primates. It houses 13 species of primate, including the black spider monkey (*Ateles paniscus*), Humboldt's woolly monkey (*Lagothrix lagotricha*), the emperor

204 **From the lowland rainforest to the desolate highlands of the Andes,** rising from the lowest areas (1,200 ft [365 m]) to the highest areas (13,000 ft [almost 4,000 m]), the Manu Biosphere Reserve is a marvel of biodiversity. The photo shows meanders in the small Pinquén River, a tributary of the Madre de Dios, in the lower part of the plain.
[Photo: André Bärstchi / Planet Earth Pictures]

205 One of the commonest trees in the lowland rainforest of the Manu Biosphere Reserve is the ceiba, or kapok (*Ceiba pentandra*), originally from Central America and now spread throughout the world's tropical rainforests and seasonally wet forests. The ancient inhabitants of Guatemala and Honduras held religious ceremonies in its shade, and in the Yucatan peninsula it is still considered the most sacred of trees by the descendants of the Maya. A light-loving species, the umbrella-shaped crown rises above the canopy to a height of 98-164 ft (30-50 m), while the base of the trunk, surrounded by buttress roots, reaches a diameter of 7 ft (2 m). The branches have a typical horizontal arrangement. The entire bark is rough with spiny conical protuberances. The leaves usually fall at the beginning of the dry season, when the pinkish white flowers are produced. They have many stamens and are wind pollinated. The fruit is a capsule like that of the cocoa and contains many dark, round seeds surrounded by cottony, yellowish white hairs. These fibers, which occupy almost one fifth of the capsule, contain a lot of cellulose and hemicellulose and are smooth, waterproof, and highly elastic. They are ideal as insulating material and for filling cushions and life jackets. Over a year, a tree produces about 44 lb (20 kg) of these fibers. The main producers are Indonesia, Cambodia, Madagascar and Central and South America, with a total world production of about 30,000 t. In the international market, however, the name *kapok* is often used for fibers from other tree members of the Bombacaceae, mainly from southeast Asia.
[Photo: Xavier Ferrer & Adolf de Sostoa]

tamarin (*Saguinus imperator*), the red uakary (*Cacajao calvus* subsp. *rubicundus*), and Goeldi's marmoset (*Callimico goeldii*), which are all considered to be endangered due to excessive hunting pressure. It is very encouraging to see that the black spider monkey, which is generally eliminated by humans when they settle an area, is now very abundant in the biosphere reserve and can be seen everywhere, even near the park's limits, where the most poaching takes place. Other important species of forest monkey in the rainforest include the douroucouli, or night monkey (*Aotus trivirgatus*), the dusky titi (*Callicebus moloch*), the monk saki (*Pithecia monachus*), the brown capuchin (*Cebus apella*), the spider monkey (*Saimari sciureus*), and the red howler monkey (*Alouatta seniculus*), whose cry is amplified by a special adaptation of the larynx that acts as a resonator.

All the large mammals of the reserve are catalogued as endangered owing to intense hunting and habitat destruction. The most important large mammals include the Andean cat (*Felis jacobita*), the ocelot (*F. pardalis*), the margay (*F. wiedii*), the jaguarundi (*F. yagouaroundi*), and the jaguar (*Panthera onca*). The puma (*F. concolor*) also lives at almost all the altitudes, and a study is now being carried out on its habitat within the park's limits. A similar program developed for the jaguar suggested that within the forest it needs an area of 61,776 acres (25,000 ha), which indicates that the Manu National Park might support about 50 jaguars, although it is not known if this figure is correct. The giant otter (*Pteronura brasiliensis*) lives along the peaty lakes, pools, and ponds connecting the streams and tributaries crossing the reserve. Other mammals in the reserve that are also endangered are the giant anteater (*Myrmecophaga tridactyla*), the giant armadillo (*Priodontes max-*

imus), the short-eared fox (*Atelocynus microtis*), the bush dog (*Speothos venaticus*), the three-toed sloth (*Bradypus infuscatus*), and the two-toed sloth (*Choloepus hoffmanni*). In the highest part of the range there are some huemul (*Hippocamelus antisensis*), now eliminated from almost all the lower areas of its former distribution and still widely hunted. The huemul is rather a stupid animal and easily caught if the group's leader is wounded or killed. The endangered spectacled bear (*Tremarctos ornatus*) is also found in the high area of the park where it has now taken refuge.

The birds of open spaces and waterfowl move along the riverbanks. Anhingas (*Anhinga anhinga*) and king-fishers (Alcedinidae) nest high up in the treetops, while the African skimmer (*Rynchops flavirostris*) and gulls (Laridae) nest on the sandbanks. Both feed in the water, *Rynchops* skimming the top of the water with the lower edge of its bill, while the terns dive into the water to hunt their prey. Small scolopacids run along the shores of the river catching insects without disturbing the nests of the nightjars (caprimulgids). The horned screamer (*Anhima cornuta*), a fat black bird with a loud, trumpetlike cry, nests on the banks, together with the noisy hoatzin (*Opisthocomus hoazin*). The sun bittern (*Eurypyga helias*) and the fasciated tiger-heron (*Tigrisoma fasciatum*) perch on the branches near the water watching the movement of the fish. Many other species of heron are common in the reserve, such as the capped heron (*Pilherodius pileatus*), found mainly in lakes formed by the remains of former meanders. The reserve also protects beautiful

macaws, such as the red-bellied macaw (*Ara manilata*), the blue-and-yellow macaw (*A. ararauna*), and the red-and-green macaw (*A. chloropterus*), which are all endangered by habitat loss and their capture for the pet trade. The spectacular Andean condor (*Vultur gryphus*), with its enormous 10 foot (3 m) wingspread, dominates the air in the high mountains, while the harpy eagle (*Harpia harpyja*), one of the largest eagles in South America, eats macaws and other birds.

Many reptiles and amphibians also occur, including 12 different species of reptile belonging to seven families and one of the world's last three wild populations of the black caiman (*Melanosuchus niger*). It can reach a length of 13 ft (4 m) and has been hunted almost to extinction for its hide. The national park contains the only protected population of the species, with an estimated 150 individuals. The spectacled caiman (*Caiman crocodilus*) also occurs in the reserve, and it too has been intensely hunted for its hide, though not as intensely as the black caiman. The Manu forest also contains one of the most feared of all snakes, the bushmaster (*Lachesis muta*), a nocturnal species that can reach a length of 11.5 ft (3.5 m). So far 77 amphibian species belonging to 5 different families have been identified near the Cocha Cashu Research Station. Little progress has yet been made in the study of the reserve's estimated 500,000 species of arthropods, belonging to many groups. The research under way has focused on collecting information from the lowland forest; data from the montainous areas are much scarcer.

206 **A pitiless predator of other birds**, the harpy eagle (*Harpia harpyja*) is the most spectacular eagle in the Manu Biosphere Reserve. [Photo: Xavier Ferrer & Adolf de Sostoa]

207 The immense diversity of insect species is one of the reasons for the Manu Biosphere Reserve's status as a major center of biodiversity. The photo shows one example, the defensive pose of a tetrigid groundhopper. [Photo: André Bärtschi / WWF / Still Pictures]

Management and problems

The park is home to at least four different human cultures, the Machiguenga, the Mashco-piro, the Yaminahua, and the Amahuaca, who are feared even by the park guards. There is no reliable census data for the native population living within the park. The Machiguenga, the best known and most widespread, live in the entire area, except for the upper part of the Manu River and the highlands, and are said to have a population of 12,000 individuals. Much less is known about the Amahuaca and Yaminahua, except that they are much less numerous: Some studies suggest that within the park there are about 2,000 Yaminahua (in the Carija Basin and along the Piedra River) and almost 4,000 Amahuaca (along the Curanga, Inuya, and Sepanua rivers). The park authorities, however, indicate that only 300-500 natives live within the confines of the park. Underlying the indigenous people's isolation, and the reason why there is no reliable census, is the persecution they suffered in the late 19th century by European rubber collectors, who captured and exploited them. Though it did little damage to the forest, it was highly prejudicial to these people. Many tribes were wiped out or decimated by contagious illnesses brought by the Europeans and were displaced from the rivers to the least accessible areas of the forest. The incidents are still remembered, and the natives tend to avoid all contact with white people. The population density is low, as in most tropical rainforest, because this system can hardly sustain people living traditionally by hunting and gathering, as these people do. The nomadic natives of the forest live by fishing in the park's many rivers and streams and by hunting in the forest. Freshwater turtle eggs are also highly appreciated. They practice low-intensity shifting agriculture along the banks of the rivers and lakes.

Because of its complexity and the needs of the indigenous peoples, the park is divided into four different zones. The central area includes most of the national park, is strictly preserved in its natural state, and is accessible only to authorized researchers, official visitors, and scientific tourism groups. The experimental, or buffer, zone is an area for supervised research and tourism, while in the transition, or recovery area, in the Andean meadows stockraising and burning of the forest are strictly controlled. The cultural zone, the area of transition between permanent human settlements, promotes and investigates the sustainable use of the forest and its soil. The native population of the Manu rainforest is considered as part of the protected system and can use the park as it chooses, as its existence does not endanger the park's aims. Great efforts have been made to integrate local inhabitants into the park management team, and the staff training, health, education and rural development programs will surely contribute greatly to the park's rational, well-organized long-term protection.

The Manu Biosphere Reserve seems now to be well defended against the forces that have already destroyed rainforests throughout the world, but it is suffering some aggressions. The plan to construct a highway at the edge of the reserve along the river Manu to connect Urubamba to the Madre de Dios area could bring colonists to Manu and would surely endanger the protection of species that are already threatened. Thus, attempts are being made to change the route so that it goes outside the park, and there are great hopes this will happen. A steady stream of colonists is settling on the park's edges or within it; the eastern edge along the rivers Palatoa and Pinipini is under the most threat, and these families must be moved outside the park if the biosphere reserve is to be properly protected. Furthermore, the Peruvian government has segregated two sectors from the park for oil prospection, in violation of the country's own forestry laws.

Another threat facing the reserve is gold prospecting. An American company has already bought the right to install gold mining operations on the river Palatoa, and it is thought that within the concession there may be a lot of gold. If it is found in large quantities, it will probably lead to a gold rush, inevitably leading to human presence in the area and further settlement. Poaching is also worrying, as poachers still enter the park along the river Sipituali, and although a new guardpost is being built to control poaching, the project lacks funding and expectations are not high.

The main invasion of the park is the result of logging. Most logging is not mechanized, but is carried out on a small scale mainly for local use. Illegal logging on the park's edge, mainly on the eastern and southern banks of the river, does not yet pose any great threat as the forest is inaccessible but could become serious unless a good management plan for the park and its surroundings is made effective. Since the beginning of the 1980s, the illegal extraction of timber along the river Manu has declined, thanks to government pressure.

2.3 Biosphere reserves in the African and Madagascar rainforest

The 13 African biosphere reserved contain some tropical wet forest, covering a total of 40 million acres (1,600,000 ha), approximately 10% of the world total. Congo, Equatorial Guinea, Gabon, and Democratic Republic of Congo are the only countries with more than half their forest cover left, in the other 32 countries only about a fifth is left. Gabon has one of the richest and best known forests in Africa. The African equatorial forest's biodiversity is very high, especially its flora, which contains about 4,000 known species, including many endemics.

One notable case in Nigeria is the Omo Biosphere Reserve, covering 1,137 acres (460 ha) of rainforest and meadows. Although it is the smallest of the African reserves, it is quite an important reserve because only 19,305 sq mi (50,000 sq km) of rainforest are left in the entire country. It was declared a reserve in 1977, but only recently has a real protection plan come into force. Its vegetation contains many typically African species, such as African rubber (*Landolphia*), the widely exploited African mahogany (*Khaya ivorensis*), limba (*Terminalia superba*), and several species of lianas, orchids, and ferns. Nigeria has not put a great deal of effort into research on endemic species in protected areas, but like other countries in western Africa it is becoming increasingly aware of the great value of its forests and the value of saving them.

The Ipassa-Makokou Biosphere Reserve

The Ipassa-Makokou Biosphere Reserve (Gabon) is a representative example of the equatorial rainforest. It has been protected by decree since 1970, and it was approved as a biosphere reserve in 1983, covering a total area of 37,066 acres (15,000 ha), all lying within Gabon. It is divided into a central area covering 2,471 acres (1,000 ha), where scientific research is performed, and several transition zones, in accordance with the management guidelines proposed by the UNESCO's MAB Program.

Natural characteristics and values

The biosphere reserve is located on the northern banks of the river Ivondo in northeastern Gabon, 375 mi (600 km) from the river's mouth and 6 mi (10 km) southeast of the city of Makokou, on the Makokou plateau. It has a rolling relief with low hills (between 1,475 and 1,800 ft [450 m and 550 m]) covered in rainforest. The site is on the pre-Cambrian peneplain of Ivindo, with crystalline formations of leptinite, basic lava, granites, and gneiss and other sedimentary formations of loams, clays, and conglomerates. The valley base has filled up with successive inputs of alluvial clay. Small streams drain the plateau

208 Biosphere reserves have stimulated ecological research in their surroundings. These recent publications are a good example of topics about which there was formerly very little information. [Photo: Jordi Vidal]

towards Ivindo on the reserve's southern limit, and several areas with hydromorphic soils experience seasonal flooding. The climate is equatorial, with four seasons and an average annual temperature of 75°F (23.9°C). The relative humidity is around 80%, and rainfall, which is the dominant feature, has an annual average of 69 in (1,755 mm) that falls mainly in the two rainy seasons, from mid-September to mid-December and from mid-March to mid-June. Between June and September there is a long dry season when the area is continually under cloud cover and a second, shorter dry season from mid-December to mid-March.

The reserve's vegetation, the lowland rainforest of the Guinea-Congo phytogeographic region, varies locally with distance from the river (where the force of the wind is most evident, and clearings are formed more often than in areas farther from the river) and with the type of soil (for example, the rainforest is distinct on seasonally flooded hydromorphic soils). Fifteen hundred plant species have been recorded in the reserve, although there is an estimated total of 4,000 species. There are no reliable data on the level of endemism, but it is believed that there are 243 species endemic to the Congo-Guinean area, 85% of which are threatened, 12 of them in danger of extinction. The diversity of trees and lianas is about 200 species per hectare (1 ha=2.5 acres). Lianas are a major component of the rainforest and have been thoroughly studied. In this region of the eastern Gabon highlands *álep* (*Desbordesia*) is rare, but *sorro* (*Scyphocephalium ochocoa*) and *beli* (*Paraberlinia* [=*Julbernardia*] *bifoliata*) are abundant. Within the area of the reserve there is no oukume (*Aucoumea klaineana*), but *engena* (*Celtis*) occurs, and *limbali* (*Gilbertiodendron dewevrei*) forms pure stands in shallow valley bot-

toms. A typical feature of the old secondary forest is the presence of *ilomba* (*Pycnanthus angolensis*).

Gabon's vertebrate fauna is relatively rich, especially in the biosphere reserve. One hundred and thirty species of mammal live near the city of Makokou, although few are left in the reserve because it is so close to the city. There are 12 species of insectivores; 34 species of chiropterans (bats); 17 species of primates; 3 species of pholidotes (pangolins); 34 species of tubulidentates (aardvarks), proboscideans (elephants) and hydrochoerids; and 12 species of artiodactyls (ungulates such as camel or pig); including 2 species of rodent and 3 species of insectivore that were first described in the 1960s. There is great interest in the primates, mainly related to their evolutionary diversification. The species present include drill (*Mandrillus* [=*Papio*] *sphinx*), bush pig (*Potamochoerus porcus*), and water chevrotain (*Hyemoschus aquaticus*), which has disappeared locally although it is not in danger of extinction. There are also several species of duiker, or duikerbok (*Cephalophus monticola, C. leucogaster, C. nigrifrons, C. callipygus, C. dorsalis*), as well as sitatunga (*Tragelaphus spekei*), bongo (*T.* [= *Boocercus*] *euryceros*), and Cape buffalo (*Syncerus caffer*). A current census of the elephant population in an area of 21,000 sq mi (55,000 sq km) including part of the reserve, confirms that the distribution of elephants depends on the location of human settlements. The density of elephants increases with distance from human settlements. The abundance and diversity of birds in the Ivindo Basin is probably greater than anywhere else in Africa. There are about 424 species, 356 of them found in a single area of just 500 acres (200 ha), although most are migratory species from Europe and northwest Asia. The level of endemism among the birds is low, but Gabon's forests are a sanctuary for relatively unknown birds, such as the tern (*Sterna balaenarum*), the bald crow *Picathartes oreas*, the african river martin (*Pseudochelidon eurystomina*), and the bush warbler (*Bradypterus grandis*). The area of Makokou contains 65 catalogued species of reptile and 47 of amphibian. The rivers in the reserve contain a new family of fish, the Grasseichthyidae.

The invertebrate fauna contains many parasites (nematodes, trematodes, ciliates), some of which have been found in the Makokou region. New species found in the reserve include 50 species of Coleoptera, 120 of Lepidoptera, and 40 more species of other groups of insects. Termites, one of the rainforest's most typical features, are obviously well represented, although they have not been studied much in the reserve.

Management and problems

The rainforest provides many people with shelter, food, fuel, medicines, building materials, and many other products. There are many small settlements around the biosphere reserve along the southern bank of the Ivindo, although there has been no anthropological research into their population and little is known about their traditional lifestyles. Agricultural production is based on shifting agriculture. Hunting, fishing, and agriculture are banned within the reserve, where nothing can be killed or collected except for scientific research, although there are some coffee plantations. Setting traps has been banned, as in most of Gabon's reserves, but trapping is widespread owing to the lack of effective surveillance. Poaching is known to occur in the reserve and is increasing because the territory's only marked limit, apart from the natural limit formed by the Ivindo river, is 1.2 mi (2 km) of logged forest on the eastern edge.

The Ipassa-Makokou Reserve is the only protected area in Gabon where logging is not practiced, although the national government's opinion that total protection of the reserves is unnecessary endangers the future of the entire country's system of nature protection. The main problem in all Gabon's reserves is deforestation, mainly because there is no legislation at all to protect them from selective logging, which affects four out of every five reserves. This is so intense that the forest is being replaced by savanna. In this reserve, however, there are two adjacent blocks of almost virgin rainforest and some areas that are completely intact, except for traditional subsistence hunting. They have been naturally protected by several factors, mainly by the fact that it is impossible to transport logs down the Ivindo River (wide, but

with many rapids and high waterfalls in the area of the reserve), the absence of Gabon's main timber tree, oukume (*Aucoumea klaineana*), from the reserve, and the general difficulty of access.

The biosphere reserve is managed by the National Center for Scientific and Techinical Research (CENAREST), which has set up a field research station with a primate and an equatorial ecology laboratory. Access to the reserve is open to all wishing to carry out research and for groups of visitors for educational purposes. The installations include a network of paths in the 500 acres (200 ha) of the research station's grounds, and infrastructure to house 12 scientists, a library, a laboratory, an herbarium with specimens of all the plants identified in the reserve, and a small collection of insects, ungulates, and other animals for the use of the researchers. In spite of its legal status, the management has so far been totally ineffective and inadequate, and there do not appear to be any plans for the future.

Research, mostly performed and funded by foreign institutions, has focused mainly on the dynamic relation between the rainforest and its diversity, interactions between plants and animals, and ecology and animal behavior. Zoological research has concentrated on primates, small ungulates, pangolins, rodents, fish, and insects. Current studies of rainforest biodiversity in the reserve; mainly in the central area, are among the first to be carried out in the Gabon rainforest. Most studies are performed in a 500 acres (200 ha) plot near the research station. There are also monitoring programs, and a species list has been compiled for the reserve and the Makokou region.

The Mananara Nord Biosphere Reserve

The Mananara Nord Biosphere Reserve on the eastern coast of Madagascar is a good example of the country's lowland rainforest. It has a wet tropical climate and contains wet forest vegetation with high biodiversity. Many different plant communities are present, many of them of great importance to the local human population and for the native animal species, such as the aye-aye (*Daubentonia madagascariensis*).

The biosphere reserve occupies a total of 345,946 acres (140,000 ha) divided into three different parts: a terrestrial national park, a marine national park, and a multiple development area. The terrestrial natural park contains three areas of classified forests, Ivontaka Nord, Ivontaka Sud, and Verezanantsoro. The

209 The oddest and shiest of all Madagascar's Prosimii is the aye-aye (*Daubentonia madagascariensis*), found in the Mananara Nord Biosphere Reserve. This nocturnal animal has an unusual diet that it obtains by even more surprisingly unusual means. It eats various fruits and also eats wood-boring larvae that it locates by listening for the noises they make when they gnaw the wood. When the aye-aye detects a larva, it tears a hole in the wood with its powerful incisors, and it then introduces the middle finger of its hand. This middle finger has become modified into a sort of long articulated nail and serves to extract the larvae or to mush it up and smear it on the finger, which it then licks (see also figure 24).
[Photo: Michel Loup / Jacana]

forested areas belong mainly to the government, and most of the cultivated areas are privately owned. The central area of the reserve consists of the terrestrial national park, which covers 59,305 acres (24,000 ha), whereas the marine national park occupies 2,471 acres (1,000 ha) on the isle of Nosy Atafana.

Natural characteristics and values

The Mananara Nord Biosphere Reserve is in a coastal area with hills consisting of crystalline materials (Antongil granites and Mananara magnetites) that rise to a height of about 1,640 ft (500 m) above sea level (the highest is 1,870 ft [570 m]) and go down to a depth of 164 ft (50 m) below sea level in the marine part of the park. The soils are ferralitic, with a narrow band of sand between Anove and Antanambe. The coast is a series of beaches but to the north of Antanambe is more rugged. About 656 ft (200 m) offshore, a partly submerged coral barrier reef rises above sea level, although in some places it reaches farther out. There are also reefs around the island of Nosy Atafana. The granitic rock is deeply cut into valleys formed by fast-flowing rivers that then meander over coastal plain and through alluvial valleys on their way to the coast.

The reserve has a wet tropical climate with an annual rainfall of 110-126 in (2,800-3,200 mm). There is a monsoon period of 180 days with greater rainfall, but it rains almost throughout the entire year and so there is almost no dry season. Even October, the driest month of the year in Madagascar, has an average of 4 in (101 mm) of rain. The average monthly temperature varies between 66 and 79°F (19 and 26°), although it is hotter from November to March, with minima and maxima of 75 and 86°F (24 and 30°C), respectively.

The Mananara Nord Biosphere Reserve is representative of Madagascar's lowland rainforest. The island separated from Africa million of years ago (human colonization only began 1,500-2,000 years ago), and so the flora and fauna have evolved independently, and many of the species are endemic. In fact, current data suggest there are 10,000 species of plants, of which 80% are endemic.

Approximately 20% of Madagascar is covered by forest. The biosphere reserve's natural vegetation is dense and highly diverse rainforest, with a canopy 82-98 ft (25-30 m) above the ground and few if any emergent trees. The forests of the region surrounding the reserve are rich in species, and none can be said to be dominant, although within the natural vegetation types there are at least two different communities associated with different soil types. On lateritic soils, the trees are typically species of *Weinmannia*, *Tambourissa*, *Diospyros* (with two good timber species, *D. perrieri* and *D. microrhombus*), *Ravensara*, and *Oncostemon*, together with palms of the genera *Dypsis* and *Chrysalidocarpus*. The ebonies (*Diospyros*) and rosewoods (*Dalbergia*) have been so intensely logged that few large, well-formed specimens remain. The natural vegetation of the sandy coastal plain contains trees like the Indian almond (*Terminalia cattapa*) and others belonging to the genera *Calophyllum*, *Canarium*, and *Heritiera*. The mangrove formations are dominated by white mangrove (*Rhizophora mucronata*) and black mangrove (*Avicennia marina*). Less than 3% of the mangrove area in Madagascar is on the eastern coast. Mangroves are important for coastal fisheries, as they are the breeding sites for many species of fish and crustaceans. They are also an important breeding area for several birds, including the Madagascar fishing eagle (*Haliaeetus vociferoides*), an endemic species in harsh danger of extinction, and the tern (*Sterna bergii*).

The best represented plant families are the Rubiaceae, Ebenaceae (including the genus *Diospyros*), Monimiaceae (the genus *Tambourissa*), Apocynaceae, Burseraceae (the genus *Canarium*), and the Euphorbiaceae. In the middle tree layer, the low trees and tall herbaceous plants, the best represented families are the Orchidaceae, Araliaceae, Violaceae, Arecaceae (Palmae), Tiliaceae, and the endemic Sarcolaenaceae. Epiphytic plants, especially ferns and orchids, grow on many species of tree. A very rich flora grows along the reserve's watercourses, with an especial abundance of aquatic plants of the genera *Aponogeton* and *Hydrostachis*.

The fauna of the Mananara Biosphere Reserve's rainforest and coral reef communities has not yet been thoroughly studied, although the value of the island's endemic species is now recognized, as is the reserve's importance as their last refuge. Great efforts have already been made to learn more about some of the rarer species, such as the lemurs and the aye-aye (*Daubentonia madagascariensis*). Among the mammals there are also some noteworthy threatened species, such as the Madagascar mongoose (*Galidictis fasciata*) and the salano (*Salanoia concolor*), as well as others about which there is little information, such as the greater sifaka or simpona (*Propithecus diadema diadema*), the indri (*Indri indri*), and the aye-aye (*Daubentonia madagascariensis*). Madagascar has almost 30 species of lemurs that occur nowhere else, many of which are vulnerable, rare, or threatened. The most characteristic lemurs of the reserve are the ruffed lemur (*Varecia variegata*), the rare dwarf hairy-eared lemur (*Allocebus trichotis*), and the very rare bokombol (*Hapalemur simus*), which was rediscovered in 1972, a century after its first and only previous sighting.

Birds are especially abundant in the central area of the reserve, and according to a 1989 study, 60 different species nest there. Some are important, such as the groundrollers *Brachypteracias squamigera* and *B. leptosomus*; both are restricted to Madagascar, like the entire family of the Brachypteraciidae, and both, but especially *B. squamigera*, are endangered. Another important bird is the vanga (*Eurycerus prevostii*) of the Vangidae family, which is endemic to Madagascar and the Comoros. The reserve is one of the few regions where it is possible to find the hawk owl (*Ninox superciliaris*).

The most important reptiles in the reserve are the Nile crocodile (*Crocodylus niloticus*), which is in danger of extinction; the fandrefriala (*Ithycyphus perineti*), a long, slender tree snake with a bright red tip to its tail; and the chameleon *Chamaeleo cucullatus*), one of the 30 species of this genus that occurs in Madagascar. The area of the marine reserve is now a refuge for the dugong (*Dugong dugon*).

Management and problems

The reserve is very important for the local population, which considers Mananara as its lands and obtains several resources from it, including honey and medicinal and edible plants. About 40,000 people live in settlements within the reserve, with a few dozen living in the cental area and the rest in the area of influence. Continuity in the studies of the life, culture, traditions, and lifestyles of the settlers is very important in order to try to ensure their compatibility with the biosphere reserve's management. The local population lives basically from subsistence agriculture, mainly the cultivation of rice, taro, bananas, mangos, and lychees (*Litchi chinensis*), and also by traditional stockraising—mainly the rearing of zebus, pigs, chicken, geese, and ducks—and by fishing, limited to a few river species. This subsistence agriculture is practiced in areas subject to traditional "slash and burn" known as *tavy*, now the main cause of deforestation in Madagascar's rainforest and other biomes. Yet most of the forests at higher altitudes have remained intact for many years owing to ancient superstitions based on the belief that they are shelters for the souls of the dead, whose reprisals are feared by the living. A small part of the mangrove forest is being logged for fuelwood and timber, but most is still intact. The zone of influence includes large estates with plantations of clove, vanilla, coffee, and pepper for sale in Madagascar and export, although production is controlled by those in charge of the biosphere reserve.

210 The lemurids and indrids are large prosimians that contrast with the tiny size of some members of the cheirogaleids (see also figures 24, 83, and 277). The lemurids and indrids are represented in the Mananara Nord Biosphere Reserve by this female ruffed lemur (*Varecia variegata*, on the left) and this male Verreaux's sifaka (*Propithecus verreauxi*, on the right).
[Photo: Rod Williams / Bruce Coleman Limited and Nick Gardner / Planet Pictures]

So far, little research has been carried out in the reserve. The Muséum National d'Histoire Naturelle of Paris carried out a study on the aye-aye in the island (1978-1988), and in 1989 there were 30 local researchers working in the area and about 10 foreign scientists studying a wide range of species.

The legal protection of Madagascar's forests began 200 years ago in the reign of Andrianapoinimerina (1787-1810) with a decree fining those felling the region's forests. Years later, under the former Hova monarchy, those caught felling trees were sent to prison. Punishments are not now so severe, and the Direction des Forêts, which is responsible for their management, generally applies less drastic sanctions. According to the Direction des Eaux et Forêts, there are a dozen guards, four of them responsible for the biosphere reserve's administration and management.

The law creating the Mananara Nord Biosphere Reserve was approved in 1989, and the nomination was accepted by UNESCO's MAB Program in 1990. The legislative developments referred to have introduced into Madagascar's legislation the subject of the biosphere reserve as defined by the MAB Program. The area of the terrestrial national park was established in accordance with the African Convention, and all types of fishing or aquiculture activities are prohibited in the marine park. Industrial and economic development is only permitted inside the biosphere reserve if it is in accord with the reserve's management plan. Even so, there is still no definitive management plan, although attempts are being made to improve agricultural land, especially by small-scale irrigation, to increase rice production. The World Wide Fund for Nature (WWF) and the Ministry of Animal Production and Forests started a study project, finished in 1989, to establish management criteria.

Illegal timber exploitation is increasing throughout Madagascar, especially in the eastern part, in the areas of classified forest of Mananara Nord, especially in Ivontaka Nord and in Ivontaka Sud, and to a lesser extent in the northern sector of Verezanantsoro. The trees logged are mainly ebonies (*Diospyros*), rosewood (*Dalbergia*), and *Ravensara*. The inhabitants of the settlements immediately around the classified forests cut the trees for unirrigated rice crops and also for firewood and building materials. There is also poaching, mainly of lemurs, but also of dugongs.

A new danger facing the reserve is the project to build a road to join Sandrakatsy to Antanambe through Verezanantsoro forest. Roads abandoned 20 years ago by the Societé des Moulins de Dakar have been reopened by loggers, encouraging tavy in a larger area. Between 1950 and 1985 the deforestation of these eastern forests reached an estimated average of 430 sq mi (1,110 sq km) a year, mainly due to increased tavy agriculture caused by the growth of Madagascar's population.

2.4 The biosphere reserves in the south Asian and Indo-Pacific forests

Of the nine Asiatic biosphere reserves in the biome, only Sinharaja in Sri Lanka has a significant percentage of tropical forest. The Palawan Biosphere Reserve in the Philippines also lies within the biome, although it is of greater interest because it is an island and because the management relations that have been established.

The Palawan Biosphere Reserve occupies the entire island, a large area 264 mi (425 km) long and with an average width of 19 mi (30 km). It was established in 1990 and covers a total area of 3,906,226 acres (1,580,800 ha). The island's central backbone is now almost completely deforested, and near the coast the forest blends into mangrove. The forest is very well conserved, although there are some incursions by loggers, mining, and uncontrolled agriculture. Much of the Palawan forest is occupied by mature formations of dipterocarps, including lauan or Philippine mahogany *Shorea polysperma*). There are also many rattans of the genera *Daemonorops*, climbing palms that provide the raw material for "Manila style furniture" as well as produce edible, tender young shoots and provide a liquid (obtained from the fruit) that is used as a coloring agent and for medicinal purposes. Around one third of the birds in the Philippines are endemic, most of them forest-dwellers that are very sensitive to alterations of the forest. Many birds are also endangered by hunting, as they eaten or sold as caged birds, for example, the red-tailed cockatoo (*Cacatua haematuropygia*), whose main populations have been decimated. The main threat to the Palawan forest is deforestation by shifting agriculture, logging and mining. The island as a whole is ecologically fragile and needs careful planning. It is thought that unless measures are taken, by the year 2000 the last remnants of rainforest will disappear. Recently plans for research into the protected area have been developed, and a management system has been proposed for the entire island that includes all aspects of the activity of the human population.

The Sinharaja Biosphere Reserve

The Sinharaja Biosphere Reserve includes the last large area of lowland tropical rainforest in Sri Lanka. It is in a region that features in the island's legends, and its name literally means lion (*sinha*) king (*raja*), which might refer to the original royal forest of the Sinhalese, the legendary "lion race" of Sri Lanka, or the territory of a lion famous in the island. The reserve is very valuable because it contains many endemic species of plants (60% of the trees) and animals (21 species of bird and many insects, amphibians and reptiles) and a wide range of useful plants.

Natural characteristics and values
The reserve is in the wet lowland area of southwestern Sri Lanka, surrounded by the rivers Napola Dola and Koskulana Ganga to the north, by the rivers the Maha Dola and the Gin Ganga to the south and southwest, by the rivers the Kalukandawa Ela and the Kudawa Ganga to the west, and by the former road near the Beverly tea plantation and the Denuwa Kanda to the east. The Sinharaja Biosphere Reserve, also a UNESCO World Heritage Site, covers an area of 21,903 acres (8,864 ha), 14,286 (6,000 ha) of them forest reserve. This narrow strip of rolling land consists of a series of ridges and valleys that rise from 984-3,839 ft (300-1,170 m) above sea level (the peak of Hinipitigala). The site is crossed by an intricate network of watercourses that flow into the Gin Ganga on the southern edge and into the Kalu Ganga, via the Napola Dola, Koskulana Ganga and Kudawa Ganga, on the northern edge.

211 A typical plant of wet, nutrient-poor spots, the carnivorous plant *Nepenthes distillatoria* is one of the most representative plants of the Sinharaja Biosphere Reserve. It is locally known as *bandura*. [Photo: Xavier Ferrer & Adolf de Sostoa]

The soils are mainly red-yellow podzols and are well-drained with little accumulation of organic matter, owing to the combination of favorable climatic conditions, a rich and varied soil microflora that rapidly decomposes organic matter, and rapid nutrient uptake and recycling by the trees.

According to meteorological data avalaible (more than 60 years of registers), annual rainfall is between 142 and 197 in (3,614 and 5,006 mm) and the temperature ranges from 66-93°F (19-34°C). Most of the rain falls during the May-June monsoons from the southwest and during the November-January monsoons from the northeast; in February there is a relatively dry period.

The reserve houses two types of forest. There are the remains of the dipterocarp forest (*Dipterocarpus*, etc.) covering the valleys and gentle slopes, mainly *D. zeylanicus* and *D. hispidus*, which forms almost pure stands. Secondary forests form where the original forest has been eliminated by shifting agriculture, and in other sites it has been replaced by tea and rubber plantations. The *Shorea* forest, the climax vegetation of most of the reserve, covers gentle slopes above 1,640 ft (500 m) and steep slopes above 1,099 ft (335 m); garcinia (*Garcinia hermonii*) and to a lesser extent *Xylopia championii* (Annonaceae) invariably dominate the lower tree layer, while several species dominate the second layer and the upper canopy layer is normally dominated by the ironwood (*Mesua nagassarium*).

Sri Lanka has 830 species of endemic plants, 217 of them, trees and woody lianas, occur in the wet lowland area. One hundred and thirty-nine of these, (64%) occur within the reserve, and 16 species are considered very rare on a global scale. Other rare endemic species include the palms

Loxococcus rupicola and *Atalantia rotundifolia*, which is restricted to a single site in Singhagala at 2,434 ft (742 m) above sea level. Of the 217 species of tree and woody liana, 40% have low population densities (10 specimens per 62 acres [25 ha]), and 43% have a restricted distribution that makes them very vulnerable. Within the reserve the large variety of plants traditionally used by humans includes the kitul palm (*Caryota urens*), the source of jaggery, a sweetener used as a sugar substitute; wewal (*Calamus*), rattans that are used for wickerwork; Ceylon cardamon (*Elettaria ensal*), a spice and flavoring; *dun* (*Shorea*), a source of varnishes and aromatic wood for incense; and *weniwal* (*Coscinium fenestratum*), the source of a yellowing coloring agent and active principles with tonic and digestive properties.

The biosphere reserve's fauna, especially the bird fauna, contains a very high percentage of endemic species, including 19 of Sri Lanka's 20 endemic bird species, and more than 50% of the island's endemic mammals and butterflies. Some mammals that occur in the reserve, such as the leopard (*Panthera pardus*), are globally threatened species, and others, such as the Indian elephant (*Elephas maximus*), are in real danger of extinction. The reserve also contains langur (*Trachypithecus* [= *Presbytis*] *retulus*). Rare or endangered birds include the Ceylon wood pigeon *Columba torringtonii*), the green-billed coucal (*Centropus chlororhynchus*), the white-headed starling (*Sturnus senex*), the Ceylon blue magpie (*Cissa ornata*), and the laughing thrush (*Garrulax cinereifrons*), all of which are endemic. Although it is not an endemic, the red-faced malkoha (*Phaenicophaeus pyrrocephalus*) is rare and in danger of extinction. Other important endemic species include the broad-billed roller

(*Eurystomus orientalis irisi*), whose population has declined notably in the last five years. The reptiles and amphibians include the vulnerable Indian python (*Python molurus*); several threatened endemic species, such as the lizard *Calotes liolepis*, the island's rarest agamid, and the lizard *Ceratophora aspera*, now restricted to the wet areas of Sri Lanka; and the small endemic frog *Ramella palmata*. Endangered freshwater fish include gourami (*Belontia signata*, polyacanthids), smooth-billed snakeshead (*Channa orientalis*, channids), ruby-black barb (*Barbus nigrofasciatus*), cherry barb (*B. titeya*), and red-tailed goby (*Sicydium halei*). Of the 21 species of endemic butterflies, the Sri Lanka endemic *Atrophaneura jophon* is vulnerable, while the very rare Sri Lanka endemic *Grophium antipathes ceylonicus* is very common within the reserve at certain times of year.

Management and problems

The southwestern area of the reserve contains two villages, Warukandeniya and Kolonthotuwa, and about 52 families live in the northwestern sector. There are at least 20 human settlements on the periphery, some of them squatters on state-owned land. The total population is about 5,000. Part of the land adjoining the reserve is privately owned, including some small rubber and tea plantations. Local dependence on rainforest resources varies, but about 8% of all households must be totally economically dependent on the rainforest.

Sinharaja was recognized in 1936, as the island's only remaining large patch of undisturbed tropical rainforest. Inaccessible because of the steep hilly terrain, the reserve remained untouched until 1968, when a government decree was issued to extract timber for the plywood sawmill and chipwood complex

212 Outside the core area of Sinharaja, as is common of most biosphere reserves, traditional agricultural activities continue, including rice cultivation (upper photo). The local people also manufacture *jaggery* using the inflorescence of the kiyul palm (*Caryota urens*). Jaggery (lower photo) is a sugary substance that is the main resource of many small villages in the reserve.
[Photos: Lucas Abreu / Incafo and Christine & Myriam Masson]

in Kosgama. From 1971-1977, when logging was banned as a result of public pressure from the Wildlife and Nature Protection Society, about 34,600 acres (1,400 ha) of forest in the western sector were selectively logged. Intact forest now covers from 16,062-17,297 acres (6,500-7,000 ha). Since 1977, the Forest Department has given high priority to protecting the reserve. In 1978, it started to plant *Pinus caribaea* along the periphery to establish a live boundary. More recently, betelnut palm (*Areca catechu*) has been used for the same purpose. Sinharaja Forest was declared a biosphere reserve in 1978 and was included on the World Heritage List in 1988, although the biosphere reserve continues to be the property of the state. The reserve is now managed by the Forest Department.

An officially approved conservation plan is being applied on the basis of an agreement between the IUCN and the Sri Lanka government, with additional funding from the Norwegian government. To ensure the reserve's strict protection for aesthetic and scientific reasons, a zoning and management scheme has been proposed for the neighboring areas. The reserve has three wardens and four forestry officials. The intention is to produce and distribute essential products in the areas outside the reserve to satisfy local needs and thus diminish dependence on resources from within the reserve. One strategy is to establish a 2 mi (3.2 km) wide zone of influence around the protected area or, alternatively, to extend the reserve to cover 117,000 acres (47,380 ha), so that the reserve forms a strictly protected area and the surrounding areas act as buffer zones. Kitul (*Caryota urens*) is the only resource still legally extracted but only by permitholders. The favored approach is to freeze resource use in the reserve at the 1985 level and to decrease use by transferring the villages to external areas.

Some of the main difficulties that stem from protecting the reserve are social and economic, related to peoples and the organizations that neighbor the reserve. Encroaching cultivation, especially on the southern edge, is perhaps the greatest problem. Roads are opened to facilitate logging operations; although logging is not permitted within 1 mi (1.6 km) of the reserve's boundaries, these new roads may create easy access for future illegal logging. The cultivation of Honduran mahogany (*Swietenia macrophylla*) along the abandoned logging trails to enrich these sites may displace native species, as it is a prolific seed-producer. Alleged malpractice by the State Timber Corporation is a source of con-

cern for the Forestry Department. Private landowners along the periphery may be making illegal use of the timber resources within the reserve; after felling all the merchandisable timber on their land, they still request permits for further logging. The most important extractive activity, however, is firewood collection, as significant quantities are used in jaggery production. The traditional use of minor forest products, the most important of which are kitul (*Caryota urens*) and wewal (*Calamus*) for weaving baskets, is now restricted to the forested areas around the reserve. Illegal gem mining is also considered to be a serious problem in the eastern parts of the reserve; it is organized mainly by wealthy merchants from outside the Sinharaja region and needs to be stopped. The lack of a uniform land-use policy and the multiplicity of governmental and semigovernmental agencies involved in land-use planning in Sri Lanka are the main administrative constraints on reaching an effective protection plan. All land transactions around the reserve have now been suspended by presidential order, until the conservation plan is ready for application.

The first studies performed in the reserve, based on field work and aerial surveys, recommended selective logging. One of the first inventories of the Sri Lanka flora was made here in 1937, and the first lists of the fauna (mammals, birds, reptiles, amphibians, fish, and butterflies) were compiled in 1985 for inclusion in the Forestry Department's 1985 draft conservation plan. The floristic and phytosociological compositions of the woody vegetation have been studied recently (1980-1985) and some work on its conservation. The World Wide Fund for Nature (WWF) has also carried out research into the reserve's endemic fauna, together with the IUCN and other organizations, such as Natural Resources and March for Conservation. There have also been studies of the conflicts over local use of forest resources (1985, 1986), and a map of the reserve's soil use and vegetation has been drawn up (1:40,000 scale). The Natural Resources, Energy, and Science Authority of Sri Lanka has supplied a field research station, and the Forestry Department has a residential center in Kudawa, near the entrance to the reserve, where visitors and scientists can stay for a time.

Few people visit the biosphere reserve, most of them naturalists. Entry is by permit, which must be obtained from the Forestry Department in Colombo. There are paths leading to the peaks of Moulawella and Sinhagala, and a special guide was recently published.

The montane equatorial cloud forests

Behind the houses there rose to the heavens a promontory of scarped mountains with a cornice of iron sculpted in the form of a crag. The river port awoke transformed into a Sunday fair, with Indians selling ivory palm amulets and love potions, wrapped in rope ready for the six-day climb to the orchid forests of the central mountain range.

Gabriel García Marquez
Love in the time of cholera (1985)

1
The realm of the epiphytes

1. The kingdom in the clouds

1.1 The permanent mist

Hidden among the clouds at mid to high elevations of tropical mountains there are special forests with a distinct fauna and flora, adapted to an ever-wet and low-light environment—the montane cloud forests. Thick mist and fog blanket the landscape, giving it a surreal, mystical appearance. The trees are often stunted, gnarled, and twisted and covered with mosses, liverworts, bromeliads, and other epiphytes. There is a constant background "drip, drip, drip" noise of the water dripping from the mist. The varied vegetation, the preponderance of epiphytes, and the colorful bird and other animal life all distinguish montane cloud forests from lowland forests in the same region.

In the humid tropics, increase in altitude is typically accompanied by a decrease in temperatures and increases in rainfall and cloud cover, and sometimes with increased wind frequency and intensity. These factors influence the species composition and development of the vegetation. The frequency of cloud cover is the most important single climatic factor affecting the cloud forest. This cloud cover increases precipitation and nutrient input through interception by the vegetation and reduces solar radiation, temperature, and transpiration.

The available water

Cloud forest vegetation is a physical link between the atmosphere and the terrestrial environment because of to its ability to catch and retain cloud moisture and associated nutrients. The nutrient-laden moisture is then channeled down through the complex forms and structures of the forest and is used by epiphytes, by canopy aerial roots, and by other organisms on its way.

The plants adapted to this high-humidity environment exploit the atmosphere in a way recalling lowland forest's exploitation of soil resources, as if it were a "substrate," and have developed many mechanisms to catch and use atmospheric nutrients. Cloud forests can thus be considered as a sort of wetland ecosystem where nutrient acquisition by the vegetation is focused above ground level, as a result of the cloud inundation, waterlogged soils and low soil oxygen levels.

There have been many studies of interception of cloud moisture by vegetation, and there are several different methods to measure fog interception, the symbiotic and ecological relationships of cloud moisture in forest ecosystems, and the physiological implications for plants exposed to frequent cloud cover. It has been suggested that the smaller size of fog and mist droplets when compared with raindrops increases the wetting of the leaf surface.

The amount of precipitation captured by the vegetation varies with leaf shape and total surface area. Water intercepted from clouds is a major source of moisture for montane forests, especially those that have a dry season, that is a season in which there is no rainfall. For example, in a montane forest in Mexico, during the 32 weeks of the dry season, cloud moisture accounted for 100% of the precipitation received by the vegetation. The tree canopy captures the moisture from the clouds and channels it so effectively that soil below isolated trees remains wet even when it has not rained for days.

Some authors have called these forests "ever-wet" forests, because the moisture from the clouds keeps the plant tissues effectively hydrated throughout the year. A study of elfin forests in Colombia and Venezuela showed that the additional precipitation obtained by cloud moisture interception represented 2.8-30 in (72-769 mm) a year, and that it decreased along a gradient from west to east. Rainfall also increased along the same gradient, and in mountains, fog interception increased with elevation and exposure (i.e., interception is greater on windward slopes than on leeward slopes). This study led to the conclusion that fog interception is an important source of humidity for the elfin forests, which do not experience a dry season, unlike the dry vegetation of their surrounding.

213 **Persistent mist** gives the montane cloud forest a fantastic appearance that is emphasized by the abundant presence of epiphytes, like ragged shreds falling from the trees. This is the feeling conveyed by this photo of the Monteverde Reserve in the mountains of Costa Rica, with tree ferns, lichens hanging from the branches, and climbing plants growing up the trunks.
[Photo: Michael & Patricia Fogden]

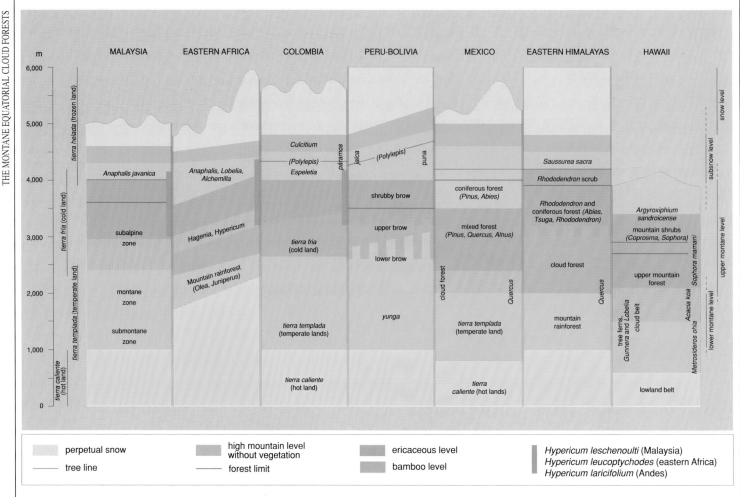

| | MALAYSIA | EASTERN AFRICA | COLOMBIA | PERU-BOLIVIA | MEXICO | EASTERN HIMALAYAS | HAWAII |

Legend:
- perpetual snow
- tree line
- high mountain level without vegetation
- forest limit
- ericaceous level
- bamboo level
- *Hypericum leschenoulti* (Malaysia)
- *Hypericum leucoptychodes* (eastern Africa)
- *Hypericum laricifolium* (Andes)

214 Altitudinal zoning in tropical montane vegetation. With increasing altitude, the forest diminishes in height, becoming less complex and less diverse. The typical progression goes from the lowland forest to submontane forest to montane forest and subalpine forest, and finally to a low herbaceous or shrub vegetation, before reaching the perpetual snow. The most typical montane forest is called *cloud forest* (shown in the diagram in shades of green), which grows in the subalpine or montane zone between 3,281 and 9,840 ft (1,000 and 3,000 m), and follows the same progression with increasing altitude in Malaysia, Africa, and South America. In the tropical Andes the cloud forest is known as *ceja de monte*, (the brow of the mountain), although the species composition varies in the different regions. On islands, like Hawaii, the zones are the same but displaced to lower altitudes.

[Drawing: Jordi Corbera, original by C. Troll]

To sum up, cloud moisture may be high, accounting for 13-37 in (325-941 mm) in cloud forests in Puerto Rico and Mexico and up to 122 in (3,100 mm) in a cloud forest in Venezuela, with respective annual rainfalls of 138 in (3,500 mm), 177 in (4,500 mm) and a mere 2.8 in (72 mm). In areas with a clear wet season, cloud moisture input may seem excessive and not especially beneficial. The epiphytic vegetation, however, depends on this frequent cloud inundation for its water and nutrients.

Filters of radiation

In addition to adding moisture, cloud cover reduces the amount of solar radiation reaching the vegetation. In Puerto Rico, the clouds reduced annual solar radiation by 40-60%. This drastic reduction naturally limits photosynthesis and means the forest has low rates of growth. Reduction of solar radiation also leads to lower temperatures. In most tropical mountains the average annual temperatures tend to decrease with increasing height, by about 0.9 and 1.1°F per 328 ft (0.5 and 0.6°C per 100 m), and this is known as the mean lapse rate or the vertical tem-

perature gradient. In the cloud forests, temperatures of 59-66°F (15-19°C) have been measured in Venezuela, 63°F (17°C) in Fiji, 66.2°F (19°C) in Puerto Rico and 54-73°F (12-23°C) in Ecuador. In comparison, lowland tropical forests normally have average annual temperatures between 68-86°F (20-30°C).

1.2 Orography and wind

Locally, the distribution of cloud forest is associated with the occurrence of cloud cover, as already mentioned. Cloud cover is the result of large-scale climate patterns and of local orographic and convectional phenomena. Orographic condensation or rainfall occurs when masses of warm, humid air move up a mountain and condense against a landmass. Convection is the process by which warm, moist rises due to warming of the earth's surface.

The clouds formed by orographic and convection processes tend to follow daily cycles related to temperature and airflow; clouds formed by these

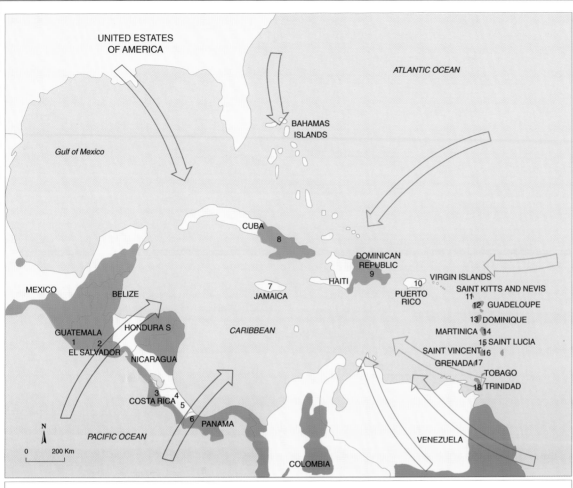

215 **The winds that converge on the Caribbean and their origins**. On the green patch showing the distribution of the forest, the main points of cloud forest are marked. They could form a network of research centers to clarify the relationship between the climate and the biota.

[Drawing: Editrònica, from data supplied by the authors]

1 Quetzal Reserve
2 Montecristo National Park
3 Monteverde Reserve
4 Poas Volcano National Park
5 Chirripo Volcano National Park
6 Baru Volcano National Park
7 Blue Mountain Peak
8 Pico Turquino
9 Armando J. Bermúdez National Park
⟹ polar front (masses of polar air)
⟹ trade winds
⟹ winds from the southwest

10 National Caribbean Forest and Commonwealth Forests
11 Mount Misery
12 La Soufrière Volcano
13 Morne Trois Pitons National Park
14 Montagne Pelée
15 Mont Gimie
16 La Soufrière
17 Mont St. Catherine
18 El Aripo
⟹ winds from the south
⟹ hurricanes

process are most likely to create the frequency of cloud cover necessary for typical cloud forest to develop.

The Massenerhebung effect

As cloud cover depends on local conditions, the lowest altitude at which cloud forest grows varies greatly. For example, on coastal mountain ranges, such as in the Caribbean, cloud forests occur at altitudes of 3,281 ft (1,000 m) or less, or even much less in some islands. In the Andes, the lower limit of the cloud forest may be as high as 7,546 ft (2,300 m), with an upper limit above 9,840 ft (3,000 m).

The phenomenon of the difference in the altitude at which the cloud layer forms is known as the *Massenerhebung* effect (or of the mass of the elevation, that is to say, of the mountain or cordillera in question). These differences allow cloud forest to prosper as a function of local differences: They reach higher altitudes on larger mountains or mountain systems. In temperate zones, where the effect was first described in relation to the tree line, it was assumed to be related to temperature differences associated with local geography and topography. In the tropics, its causes and consequences have given rise to considerable, but as yet unresolved, scientific debate focused on the specific characteristics of

216 The devastating effect of a tropical hurricane on a cloud forest. The photo shows an area of cloud forest after a cyclone, on the island of Dominica.
[Photo: Adolf de Sostoa]

climate, geology, soils, and ecological processes in cloud forest ecosystems.

The action of the wind

Wind is another factor that may well contribute to the distinctive appearance of the different kinds of cloud forest vegetation. Strong, sustained winds in montane environments may damage fine branches, leaves, and buds. Wind may also desiccate leaf surfaces, although the generally high humidity tends to reduce this effect. In reality, wind increases the rate of respiration by removing excess water from leaf surfaces, thus accelerating evaporation and leading to a favorable saturation deficit.

As wind and topography interact, ridge-top forests are most susceptible to wind damage.

Some authors suggest that some growth forms found in the cloud forest on ridges on some mountains may be a response by the trees to mechanical stress, known as (*thigmomorphosis*). Ridge-top forests in Costa Rica show reduced height growth and branch length in relation to the main stem diameter, an effect that does not occur in species in other very windy environments, such as some coastal areas.

Many cloud forests are exposed to infrequent but recurring cyclones and hurricanes. The strong winds associated with these storms cause major defoliation, damage to branches and trunks and uproot trees, and thus probably have a significant effect on the cloud forest's carbon balance. It has recently been suggested that special plant adaptations to cyclones and hurricanes may provide useful insights into the cloud forest's structure and function.

2. Soils on the ground and among the branches

2.1 Substrates and topography

The cloud forest's soils, like its vegetation, are clearly distinct from lowland rainforest. These soils are derived from a great variety of parent materials, indicating that rock type alone does not determine the presence or distribution of cloud forest. In addition to the parent material, soil formation processes depend on factors such as topography, climate, time, and biotic processes.

High amounts of organic matter and low levels of cations

Cloud forest soils often show accumulation of organic matter. Climate and time, two important factors in soil formation, interact with the biota to determine the amount of organic matter that accumulates. High humidity, low soil oxygen availability, and cooler temperatures tend to slow down the activity of the soil microbial decomposer. If the soil is stable, as in most ridge-top soils, over time deep organic horizons may form. In extreme cases, peat formation occurs, and as peat requires a long time and stable conditions to form, its depth may provide considerable information on soil age. Limited oxygen availability in peat means organic remains are preserved for a long time, and so pollen analysis may provide information about the forest's earlier species composition or its dynamics. The characteristics of the vegetation may also influence the accumulation of organic material; thick, abundant root mats, the coriaceous (leatherlike) leaves common in the cloud forest and the high levels in leaves and roots of complex chemicals that may slow the rate and degree of the decomposition that leads to humus formation.

The montane nature of cloud forest environments suggests they are greatly influenced by topography. Extensive studies of soils in cloud forests in different topographical areas in mountains in Jamaica indicate that the area's geology is very complex (including granodiorites, shales, volcanic materials, and limestone), but that few differences in soil types could be interpreted as the direct result of differences between parent materials. Different soil types correlate well with the

217 **Leaflitter accumulates on the soil of the cloud forest**, unlike what is found in lowland rainforest. The photo shows the leaflitter lying on the soil of the El Triunfo Reserve in Mexico, with a conspicuous millipede (diplopods).
[Photo: Xavier Ferrer & Adolf de Sostoa]

218 High humidity favors rapid decomposition of the stumps of cloud forest trees whose stems have fallen, mainly owing to the combined action of fungi and arthropods. This stump in Monteverde, Costa Rica, will not last for long.
[Photo: Xavier Ferrer & Adolf de Sostoa]

topographic and altitudinal zoning and lead to the development of distinct vegetation types. Two types of ridge soil have been identified (mull and mor), together a wet slope soil and gully soil. Mor-type ridge soils are different from mull-type ridge soils, as they have a thick humic layer (up to 20 in [50 cm] thick) and a lower pH. The wet slope soil has a discontinuous litter layer, low organic matter, and more stones. The gully forest soils also have a discontinuous litter layer, slightly more organic matter, and a higher pH.

The differences in organic material accumulation between sites cannot be explained by differences in rates of litterfall. Decomposition is a little faster in a high-altitude gully site, but in general rates of decomposition are also not an adequate explanation for differences in the amount of organic matter. These observed differences are probably the result of the interaction of the topography and the climate on the landscape. Weather systems have a different impact on mountain masses depending on their aspect (leeward or windward), altitude, and vegetation. The amount and intensity of rainfall, cloud moisture, and wind energy will thus probably differ in the different topographic zones (e.g., between north-facing ridges and valleys), and thus affect the rate of ecosystem processes. Large-scale global research is needed to clarify the combined effects of these different parameters.

The soils of the cloud forest tend to be very acidic (pH less than 4.5), even those derived from limestone materials. They are probably nutrient poor, although there are few data available. In Jamaica, for example, tree growth in cloud forests increased after application of nitrogen and phosphorus fertilizers, but not all species responded to fertilization. Low nutrient availability due to leaching, the fixation of phosphorus, and limited nitrogen mineralization may be one factor contributing to reduced height growth in cloud forest trees, but data on total nutrient pools and their dynamics do not confirm this hypothesis.

The case of andosols

The tropical mountain soils that form on volcanic materials have special features and are mainly found in the Andes, in the mountains of southeast Asia (Borneo, Sumatra, Java), in the Hawaii Islands, locally in the mountainous regions of central and eastern Africa, in Cameroon and on the island of Bioko (Equatorial Guinea). Andosols have a thick, dark surface horizon that is formed by the accumulation of organic material and subsurface horizons that are a lighter yellowish brown color.

Soils on volcanic ash are normally well aerated and drained because of their high porosity. They have a high water retention capacity, due to the enormous surface area of one of its components, the clay mineral allophane. As a result, these andosols are very prone to slide down slopes with steep gradients, especially in seismically active areas.

The high allophane content also means that the soil has a high capacity for phosphorus fixation, limiting its availability to plants. Agricultural use requires fertilization every year with phosphate.

The pH values of tropical mountain andosols are usually between 5.5 and 6.5. Most have a large quantity of basic cations, and their potassium content is high.

2.2 Arboreal soils

Low nutrient availability at soil level may not limit growth in a forest adapted to obtaining nutri-

219 Taking root on an almost soilless branch is one of the skills an epiphyte must develop, as this bromeliad shows in this photo of a cloud forest in Ecuador. The small amount of soil that allows them to establish is in fact a thin layer of semimineralized organic material. Yet the possibility of obtaining water directly from the atmosphere, which is always cloudy and humid, makes things easier. This water-catching function, and the general function of linking the cloud forest ecosystem to the atmospheric system, is one of the most important roles played by the epiphytes in the cloud forest.
[Photo: Xavier Ferrer & Adolf de Sostoa]

ents from aboveground sources by using unusual soil resources. Unlike other forest ecosystems, the soil in the cloud forest is not restricted to ground level. On the branches and adhering to the tree trunks is a brown mucky material with a soil-like appearance and texture that is thought to nourish epiphytes and roots.

Soils in the canopy

Arboreal "soil" consists mainly of leaflitter, excrement, and other animal remains as well as small quantities of mineral soil blown in as dust in the wind, rain, or mist. About 45% of the epiphytic cover of cloud forest trees in Costa Rica was found to be dead plant material and organic matter. It has been found that the mineral soil on the plants in the cloud forest of Puerto Rico is dust from the Sahara, blown from Africa by the trade winds.

The roots that exploit the arboreal soil may come from two sources. Some cloud forest tree species can produce adventitious roots in their crowns. Others produce ageotropic roots that grow upwards from the soil. In a cloud forest in Puerto Rico a study estimated that on the branches and the trunks there was about 1 t/ac (2.7 t/ha) of live plant material, 0.5 t/ac (1.3 t/ha) of roots and 0.4 t/ac (1.1 t/ha) of arboreal soil. A study in Venezuela estimated there was about 0.4 t/ac (0.1 t/ha) of arboreal soil. This quantity is low compared with the 100 t/ac (250 t/ha) of soil and leaf litter present in the top 4 in (10 cm) of the terrestrial soil. Yet the arboreal soil, associated with epiphyte biomass, has higher nutrient levels than terrestrial soil. In Puerto Rico, the tree soil associated with the epiphytes has a phosphorus concentration 7.8 times higher than the upper 8 in (20 cm) of terrestrial mineral soil, explainable by the theory that epiphytes increase the ecosystem's nutrient content by intercepting and retaining nutrients from the mist.

The soil formation activity of earthworms

The most conspicuous soil fauna in most cloud forest ecosystems are earthworms. Several authors have mentioned the abundance of large earthworms in cloud forests. Earthworms increase the mixing and aeration of the soil; the bright orange trails left by earthworms clearly show they aerate the poorly oxygenated cloud forest soils.

Earthworms also increase soil respiration. Soil respiration in a Colombian cloud forest is higher than that of other tropical montane and lowland forests and may be due to the high density of the earthworm population in the soil. As might be expected, earthworms and other soil fauna occur in both the terrestrial and the arboreal soils. In a cloud forest in Venezuela, earthworms have in fact been collected in the canopy at a height of 131 ft (40 m). The soil fauna in arboreal soils can be as diverse as in terrestrial ones, and the concentration of individuals tends to be greater in the arboreal environments.

3. The ecological functioning of the cloud forest

3.1 Covered by clouds

The montane cloud forest is located in areas of great mist and humidity rather than great rainfall and, like the lowland rainforest dominated by evergreen vegetation, is characterized by a wide diversity of wildlife and great taxonomic diversity. The main feature visually distinguishing it from lowland rainforest is the much simpler structure of the tree canopy and the dominance of epiphytes.

Despite the many species in common with the lowland rainforest, many organisms live exclusively in the cloud forest. Cloud forests are well known for their diversity of plants and many species of brightly colored amphibians and birds. Their flora typically shows high levels of endemism and diversity. This is partly attributable to the epiphytes, which are also of great importance to the ecological functioning of the cloud forests through their key role in the nutrient and water cycles.

As already mentioned, the many environmental factors affecting the cloud forest all influence its structure and function. Yet atmospheric conditions, especially frequent cloud cover, have the greatest impact on its ecological processes.

Trophic cycles

The trophic cycles that develop in the cloud forest are very special. The epiphytes covering almost every available surface, together with the canopy roots, absorb nutrients from the cloud and from rain. They also export nutrients, but these are recovered by other organisms, forming a relatively closed nutrient cycle. Lichens, mosses, and algae cover trunks and branches, filtering the nutrients channeled down the bark, known as *stem flow*.

The wet, low-light, and windy conditions in the cloud forest are relatively stressful to the plants, and lead to low rates of growth and biomass accumulation. In a cloud forest in Puerto Rico, the net primary production, the measure of the ecosystem's net carbon gain, was estimated to be only 1.6 t/ac/yr (4 t/ha/yr), very low in comparison with sites lower down the same mountain, where it was between 3.2 and 4.8 t/ac/yr (8 and 12 t/ha/yr). These low growth rates are shown even more clearly in the low annual diameter increment. A 9 mi (15 km) long transect in Puerto Rico rising 3,281 ft (1,000 m) in altitude—the transect runs from a young mangrove swamp through early successional lowland rainforest to a montane cloud forest—showed a general decrease in the annual diameter increment from 0.2 in (0.45 cm/yr) in mangrove and young rainforest to 0.01 in (0.03 cm/yr) in the cloud forest.

Leaf litter inputs give a measure of the extent of nutrient recycling in an ecosystem. In cloud forest, nutrient recycling by normal means appears to be slower, although there are data on only a few sites.

In general, litterfall rates are low, and nutrient input from litterfall is typically low, but nutrient-use efficiency is relatively high. In a cloud forest in Puerto Rico, the ratio of leaf litter dry mass to phosphorus concentration, an estimate of the efficiency of phosphorus use, is one of the highest recorded for a tropical forest, whereas the values for nitrogen are only slightly higher than average. The nutrient-use efficiency shown by cloud forest in Jamaica ranges from average to very high. Warm, wet ecosystems are at greater risk of losing nutrients by leaching. High nutrient-use efficiency implies that nutrients are recycled within the biomass of the plants, thus reducing losses by soil leaching. There are other alternative strategies for nutrient access and uptake that also facilitate nutrient conservation and retention.

1. THE REALM OF THE EPIPHYTES

220 The cloud forest is less dense than might be expected, considering the abundance of water. As shown by these images of the cloud forest of the Torricelli Mountains in New Guinea (upper photo) and the high montane forest of Ecuador, at an altitude of over 8,200 ft (2,500 m) (lower photo), the vegetation is relatively open, and there are many palms, together with tree ferns and bamboos, although one might expect to find bamboos in less humid conditions.
[Photos: Jean-Paul Ferrero / Auscape International and Gunter Ziesler / Bruce Coleman Limited]

Low rates of transpiration

The lack of penetration by the sun's rays and the low saturation deficit reduce the rate of transpiration by plants. Transpiration is the water lost by evaporation from leaf surfaces. Transpirational pull is the main process controlling the movement of water and nutrients from the roots to the leaves. In an elfin forest in Puerto Rico transpiration rates were 9×10^{-4} g of water / sq cm / hr; in a nearby site, the rates of transpiration measured were only between 0.9 and 11.4×10^{-4} g of water / sq cm / hr, which is very little in comparison with the rates of transpiration of lower sites in the same forest, between 7 and 29×10^{-2} g of water / sq cm / hr.

There has been much discussion about the effect of low transpiration rates on vegetation. Some authors suggest that the cloud cover and the low transpiration rates reduce nutrient uptake by

TROPICAL RAINFORESTS 345

221 **Leaf xeromorphism and hygromorphism** in the cloud forest are clearly shown in this photo of part of Monteverde in Costa Rica. The finely divided leaves of the bamboos and the feathery fronds of the tree ferns grow side by side with the broad leaves of a member of the banana family (Musaceae). [Photo: Michael & Patricia Fogden / Bruce Coleman Limited]

plants, possibly influencing the reduced height of trees in cloud forest ecosystems. Other authors argue that in low nutrient conditions water movement in the plant has little effect on nutrient uptake. In other words, if nutrient availability is low, as it generally is in tropical montane soils, absorption appears to be limited by metabolic processes taking place in the roots, not by transpiration. On the other hand, in Fiji it was shown that there is a direct correlation between the low transpiration rates and low canopy height in cloud forests. Resolving this problem will require more data on transpiration rates and nutrient availability from different cloud forest ecosystems.

Slow transpiration also means there is a greater amount of water in the soil, increasing the risk of nutrient loss by leaching and erosion. In waterlogged soils, the toxicity of iron may limit the establishment of some plants. Some cloud forests are in fact temporary wetlands where waterlogging and the low root oxygenation may lead to soil oxygen values of between 0 and 3% for all or part of the year.

Xeromorphism and hygromorphism

Leaf size, shape, and texture vary according to their function, especially with reference to their water balance and light conditions. One of the great paradoxes of cloud forest ecology is the presence in an extremely wet environment of leaves that appear more typical of hot dry environments. These apparently xeromorphic leaves are small, and relatively thick, have larger and less abundant stomata than the leaves of warmer climates, and recall Mediterranean sclerophyllous vegetation (see volume 5, pages 89-90). Closer observation, however, reveals significant anatomical differences. These leaves, called *pachyphylls*, are thicker, have a spongy mesophyll with large air spaces, less of a palisade layer, and often a hypodermis.

It is necessary to distinguish between xeromorphic features apparently adapted to arid conditions and hygromorphic features that have developed as a response to high atmospheric humidity. Xeromorphic leaves are thick and tough, often with sunken stomata and sclerenchyma fibers (sclereids) to give water-stressed leaves mechanical support. Hygromorphic plants, on the other hand, typically have thin cell walls and cuticles, a large mesophyll with large intercellular spaces to facilitate gas exchange, and large, raised stomata.

A single leaf may, however, show a combination of both sets of features, presumably in response to high humidity and reduced water and nutrient uptake by the roots due to waterlogging and low transpiration rates. Desiccation of leaf surfaces by the wind may also lead to water-stress, even if the soil is saturated.

On the other hand, xeromorphic and hygromorphic features in the leaves of the cloud forest are not distributed equally along a vertical section of the vegetation. Hygromorphic features are present in the shade-tolerant plants of the understory, whereas xeromorphic features are more common in the trees of the canopy, and in those plants exposed to high ultraviolet radiation and periods of intense transpiration. The hygromorphic leaves of the understorey plants tend to have very low rates of transpiration per unit leaf area. Yet some understory species have large leaf surfaces, thin cuticles and cell walls, many stomata, and other characters that increase transpiration. The drawback of this type of leaf is lowered ability to regulate respiration, and greater risk of damage by drought and desiccation. Xeromorphic leaves seem to be well adapted to situations of environmental stress, but they also pay a price, as they are usually costly to produce and require greater investment of photosynthetic resources.

Most trees and shrubs of the cloud forest are no more resistant to dry conditions than lowland ones are. Studies of Jamaican and Malaysian cloud forest showed that leaves exposed to a small water deficit close their stomata to limit water loss and are very vulnerable to leaf death, just like the species of the lowland rainforest.

The diversity of leaf size and shape

Cloud forests show not only high species diversity but a great variety of form and function. It has been suggested that leaf-form diversity may provide an alternative yardstick to measure diversity in forest ecosystems, one that directly reflects ecosystem function, because the diversity of biological forms leads to diversity of functions; since leaves show great developmental plasticity, they are one of the most appropriate organs for showing this diversity. Applying a very simple diversity coefficient to a cloud forest in Venezuela, namely multiplying the number of species in a given area by the number of leaf types and comparing it with the equivalent index for other types of forest, led to the conclusion that cloud forests are among the most diverse ecosystems in the world. The favorable temperatures and high humidity within the cloud forest, it has been suggested, provides an almost optimal environment for the expression of diversity, favoring not only the appearance of special adaptations to

periods of environmental stress, but also the "freedom of development" of the species living there.

This system is a novel approach to diversity but has been criticized as subjective in the choice of ecologically important leaf types and for inconsistencies in the classification system. Yet most scientists agree that the diversity of leaf size and shape in cloud forest ecosystems is astonishingly high. Using Raunkiaer's scale for the classification of leaf size, *leptophylls* are leaves have a surface area less than 0.04 sq in (25 sq mm) (the term is also used for the plants that bear them); *nanophylls* are leaves between 0.04 and 0.4 sq in (26 and 225 sq mm); *microphylls* are leaves between 0.4 and 28 sq in (226 and 18,225 sq mm); *macrophylls* are from 28 and 254 sq in (18,226 and 164,025 sq mm); and *megaphylls* are leaves that have a surface area greater than 254 sq in (164,026 sq mm). In a study carried out in a cloud forest in Venezuela, most of the leaves were mesophylls and macrophylls; however, in an elfin forest in Puerto Rico, that included lianas, herbaceous plants, epiphytes, shrubs, and trees, 58% of the leaves were microphylls, 25% mesophylls, only 2% leptophylls, and 12% nanophylls.

Cloud forest dynamics

Little is known about the forest dynamics of the cloud forest ecosystem in comparison with those of the lowland rainforest. Treefall gaps, one of the most common disturbances in rainforests, are known to occur in the cloud forest. The periodic impact of hurricanes and cyclones on the cloud forest leads to a sort of dynamic of destruction and regeneration, like that of the lowland rainforest, although recovery is slower and there are effects on the nutrient cycle. The cloud forests in both the Old and New World tropics are located in the hurricane-cyclone belt, where they are exposed to occasional catastrophic wind events.

One of the few quantitative studies yet performed on the regeneration of treefall gaps in the cloud forest was in a Mexican cloud forest. The area of treefall gaps represented 25% of the 15 acres (6 ha) studied, and the forest's natural recovery time was estimated at 158 years, in contrast to the 90 years taken to recover from human disturbances. Cloud forest is, in effect, slow to recover from disturbances, among the slowest of all tropical forest ecosystems. Regeneration and secondary succession in an elfin forest in Puerto Rico was studied after clearcutting of three small 49 ft x 49 ft (15 m x 15 m) plots, and compared with regeneration in a site disturbed by a plane crash, gave the same result. The dominant pioneer plants of the recolonization included ferns and herbaceous plants, but tree and shrub seedlings were scarce. The study suggested that seedling scarcity might reflect the lack of seed input, washout of the seeds, or the absence of the woody species typical of secondary successions. Eighteen and a half years after the plane crash, almost three quarters of the species were species of primary elfin forest, although it was estimated that the site would take 200 years to recover its original biomass. Sprouting seems to be the most common form of regeneration by many cloud forest trees.

Hurricane winds can defoliate and uproot trees and break branches and stems, but the cloud forest's slow recovery rates make it difficult to predict the extent to which these systems are destroyed by these storms. They have great impact on the nutrient cycle, altering the annual input of leaf litter to the soil. In Puerto Rico, in a single day, Hurricane Hugo added 1.9 times as much leaf litter to the soil as the annual input in a normal year without hurricanes. The leaf litter deposited by the hurricane contained almost twice as much phosphorus and three times as much potassium as normal leaf litter. As nutrient absorption is slow in these soils due to waterlogging, these nutrients added to the forest floor component have an increased chance of being lost by leaching, runoff, or erosion.

It has been suggested that some tropical forests are adapted to recurring catastrophic wind events and take advantage of the associated reorganization of carbon and of nutrients. The cloud forest's structure may also help it to survive strong wind events. The relatively smooth canopy surface might channel wind across the treetops, preventing its entry into the understory where it would do more damage. Interconnected dense root systems might anchor the vegetation, making uprooting even more difficult. Even so, recovery from hurricane damage is slow. The plants in some areas of cloud forest in Puerto Rico had still not recovered their leaves more than three years after Hurricane Hugo. The most striking aspect is the slow recovery of epiphyte biomass: Some epiphytes uprooted from the trees by the winds have survived on the ground, but others were destroyed, leaving branches and trunks devoid of

epiphytes. The loss of epiphyte biomass is likely to feed back on nutrient cycles, further slowing down the ecosystem's recovery. Damage to the Puerto Rico cloud forest was variable. Some sites seemed to have been crushed by spiraling winds, whereas others were almost untouched. The high variability of hurricane damage is probably the result of the interaction of wind direction, wind speed, and topography. It is possible that, given enough time to recover, cloud forests are well adapted to hurricanes, because they can resist relatively intense winds and are able to sprout. However, models of global climate change predict that the frequency and the intensity of catastrophic wind events will probably increase as global temperatures rise.

3.2 Epiphytes and ferns

Perhaps the clearest expression of the cloud forest's functional diversity is its epiphytes. Epiphytic plants grow in both well-lit and shady areas, and show great variation in leaf structure and function. Cloud forest epiphytes use very special nutrient uptake systems.

Epiphytes are perhaps the most conspicuous inhabitants of the cloud forest, covering almost every available surface from ground level up to the canopy. Epiphytes are not restricted to the cloud forest, but it is where they show greatest species diversity and highest biomass, as epiphyte abundance increases with altitude. Epiphytes are particularly important in the American tropics. The difference between the 90,000 species of angiosperm known from the New World tropics and the 60,000 species occurring in the Old World tropics is partly due to the fact that two of the most numerous families, Bromeliaceae and Cactaceae, are essentially endemic to the New World. The study of epiphytes can provide information about the cloud forest, from the fine scale of nutrient circulation to the global scale of planetary models of air circulation. Epiphytes are just one component of cloud forest ecosystems, but they appear to provide a keystone function on which the rest of the ecosystem partly depends.

More epiphytes than supports

In cloud forests as a whole, epiphyte biomass tends to be high, and their green biomass may even

1. *Gongora*

2. *Vriesia*

3. *Platycerium*

4. *Myrmecodia*

5. *Monstera*

6. *Cladonia*

CORBERA

222 **The main types of epiphytes common in the cloud forest**, with different rooting strategies (cracks in trunks, adventitious roots, clasping aerial roots, etc.). The different forms of epiphytes have a characteristic distribution in the canopy of the forest. Ferns are important as epiphytes, and so are the Orchidaceae, Bromeliaceae, and Cactaceae. Orchids shows a great variety of adaptations. Epiphytic lichens, inconspicuous at first glance, are important as they may cover the leaves and significantly reduce the tree's ability to photosynthesize. Fruticose branched lichens form a large proportion of the epiphytic biomass (generally between 0.8-4 t/ac [2 and 10 t per hectare]) in some Central American cloud forests. Epiphytes play a fundamental role in the functioning of the cloud forest ecosystems, both contributing to the forest's physical structure and participating in the flow of energy and materials. Epiphytes act as a bridge between the atmosphere and the terrestrial environment, providing habitat and nesting materials for many animals and helping to form the substrate of the arboreal soil. Furthermore, they capture nutrients and water from the clouds, storing them in their tissues and then supplying them to other components of the ecosystem, transferring carbon and nutrients to the terrestrial and arboreal soil. They are also a primary and a secondary source of food for the fauna.
[Drawing: Jordi Corbera, from several sources]

223 The lush growth of bryophyte mats is very typical of the cloud forest, where they sometimes form a thick layer covering the tree trunk, as in this photo taken in Ruwenzori, Democratic Republic of Congo.
[Photo: C. Jones / Natural Science Photos]

exceed that of the plants supporting them. For example, epiphyte biomass reaches 1.9 t/ac (4.7 t/ha) in a cloud forest in Costa Rica, and 5.6 t/ac (14.0 t/ha) in one in Tanzania. This high biomass is possible because of the ecosystem's high relative humidity. Epiphytes have been shown to be very sensitive to water stress, so they can thrive in an environment where atmospheric humidity is considerably higher than in forests at lower altitudes. Even so, some species show xeromorphic adaptations, such as thick cuticles and a multilayered epidermis with thickened walls, which reduce losses by evaporation in dry or cloud-free periods. The frequency of cloud cover is probably more important for the occurrence of epiphytes than the rainfall. In a Colombian cloud forest, epiphytes were most abundant in a site covered with clouds for an average of 14 hours a day, although it received negligible rainfall for 10 months of the year. Epiphytes mainly grow on tree trunks and branches, but also grow on the soil surface and on the aboveground roots of other plants.

Bromeliads and orchids are the best-known epiphytes because of their economic value as ornamental plants. Some species of the Bromeliaceae are also known for the special arrangement of their broadened leaf-bases, which form a catchment, called a tank that collects water and catches invertebrates, small vertebrates, and leaf litter. The nutrients released as the trapped material decomposes are taken up by adventitious roots or specialized hairs. The many epiphytic life forms include vascular and nonvascular plants, such as bryophytes and lichens. They share available surfaces with several algae and microepiphytes, or epiphylls, which contribute to nutrient cycling processes. One hundred and twenty-six different species of epiphytic algae were described in a Puerto Rican cloud forest.

Bryophytes—nonflowering plants such as mosses, liverworts, and hornsworts—are abundant at all levels within the cloud forest, often forming cushiony blankets up to 6 in (15 cm) thick on tree trunks. It is well known that bryophytes can intercept and retain large volumes of water, and in the cloud forest they help to maintain moist environmental conditions during dry periods. In an elfin forest in Tanzania, it was estimated that the bryophytes retained an average of 12,356 gal (46,772 liters) of water/ha, while in the submontane forest at lower altitudes in the same region they only retain 3,694 gal/ha (13,983 l/ha), roughly a third. Bryophyte mats also help to protect the soil from torrential rain, as they channel and slow the water, thus reducing the risk of erosion.

Epiphytic plants may occur singly, like many bromeliads, or they may form clumps. Tank bromeliads and bryophyte mats often collect organic matter and nutrients from the leaf litter, in addition to the resources they obtain from the arboreal soil.

Several organisms use the epiphytes as shelter or as a food source. The birds of the cloud forest are known to use them as a source of fruit, nectar, inver-

224 Orchids and bromeliads are among the most representative of the cloud forest epiphytes. This is exemplified by this *Oncidium* (upper photo) in the El Rey National Park (Argentina), from the southernmost cloud forest, and by this *Guzmania nicaraguensis* (lower photo) in the Monteverde Reserve (Costa Rica) in one of the northernmost cloud forests in the Americas. In these formations the total epiphyte biomass is huge: while it may reach 0.8-1.6 t/ac (2-4 t/ha) in lowland rainforest, in the Central American montane cloud forest it is estimated to reach 1.6-2 t/ac (4-5 t/ha) and as much as 5.4 t/ac (13.5 t/ha) in the cloud forest of the African mountains.
[Photos: Adolf de Sostoa & Xavier Ferrer]

tebrates, water and nesting material. The number of invertebrates in bromeliad tanks can be astoundingly high. Invertebrate densities are often 10-100 times greater in the epiphytic canopy than in an equivalent area of soil. Frogs and lizards use epiphytes for shelter and to lay their eggs, taking advantage of the moist environment. It has long been known that ants may form associations with epiphytic plants that are beneficial for both parties. In some cases, ants use epiphytes to cultivate nest-gardens, while in others the ants simply use the epiphytes for protection and shelter; in exchange, the plant may obtain nutrients from decomposing material or benefit from ant patrols that provide protection from some herbivores.

Epiphytes and nutrient cycles

Epiphytes live in the terrestrial-atmosphere interface, exposed to higher inputs of light, water, and nutrients and, at least in the cloud forests, to favorable conditions of temperature and humidity. These interfaces are zones of high metabolic activity in which resources are concentrated from the abiotic components of the ecosystem (atmosphere) and recycled to the biotic components (plants and animals). Thus epiphytes play an important role in the cloud forest, capturing nutrients, water, and organic matter that will benefit both the arboreal and terrestrial communities. Unlike plants rooted in the soil, they obtain their nutrients from aboveground sources and not from soil minerals. Epiphytes filter most of these nutrients from the atmosphere in rainfall, cloud moisture, or from dry deposition. These nutrients are cycled back by the arboreal and terrestrial components of these ecosystems in three pathways: host tree canopy roots or terrestrial roots occurring near or under epiphytic mats; stemflow or throughflow of water enriched in nutrients by leaching from the epiphytes or organic matter associated with epiphytes; and senescence (old age) of the epiphytes or disruptive forces (wind, disturbances caused by birds or other animals, the falling of trees or branches) that cause the epiphytes to fall to the soil, where they decompose.

Nutrient supply to epiphytes is often not regular and often occurs in pulses associated with rainfall or cloudiness. Thus, the plants have to be able to survive periods of resource deprivation. Epiphytic plants also increase the cloud forest's nutrient-use efficiency by concentrating nutrients in their tissues, in the aboveground soil and in the water they store. In a cloud forest in Costa Rica, 45% of the nutrient pool of the leaves was stored in the epiphytes. Some species of epiphyte and micro-epiphyte fix atmospheric nitrogen. In a study undertaken in Colombia, 12.6 lb/ha (5.7 kg/ha; 1 ha=2.5 acres) of cyanobacteria-containing lichens could fix 3.3-17.6 lb (1.58-8 kg) N/ha/yr. The cloud conditions apparently favor the nitrogen-fixing capacity of the microepiphytes and fungi liquefied by cyanobacteria. The cyanobacteria associated with sphagnum moss (*Sphagnum*) also fix nitrogen, and in a cloud forest in Guadalupe, in the Lesser Antilles, they supplied around 8.8 lb (4.02 kg) N/ha/yr.

The nutrients concentrated in epiphyte tissues return to the earth in litterfall. The epiphytic leaf litter, as shown in a study carried out in 1992 in a cloud forest in Costa Rica, falls irregularly in time and space, and represented 5-10% of the fine leaf litter of the forest floor. Its nutrient concentration may account for 8% of the total input from soil-rooted plants. Epiphyte leaf litter decomposes faster than that of rooted plants (an average of 8 months, as opposed to 15 months), but it may retain nutrients in tissues resistant to decomposition, thus helping to conserve them and reducing the risk of losses from leaching and erosion. Bryophytes, however, which contribute about 76% of the epiphytic litterfall, decompose much faster than other epiphytes. One may conclude (1) that epiphytic leaf litter contains a mixture of fast- and slow-decomposing tissues, (2) that

while soil-rooted plants often translocate nutrients before shedding their leaves, epiphytes do not translocate nutrients, as the loss of plant material is unpredictable, and (3) that the epiphytes' nutrient sources differ from those of soil-rooted plants, and thus provide an additional input of nutrients into the ecosystem (as opposed to merely recycling nutrients). This clearly shows the important functional role of epiphytes in the ecology of the cloud forest.

Epiphytes provide a major link between the atmosphere and the terrestrial environment; control significant inputs and flows of nutrients and water; provide habitat, food, and nesting material for the cloud forest fauna; and contribute to the internal cycling of carbon and nutrients.

Epiphytes as environmental indicators

Because they are so closely linked to the atmospheric environment, epiphytes could be used as indicators of change in global climatic conditions. Epiphytes have been used as indicators of other atmospheric phenomena, such as pollution and radioactive fallout from nuclear tests. Similar techniques (the presence or absence of epiphytes and the chemical concentrations in their tissues) could be applied to detect changes in the global air circulation, paying particular attention to the Caribbean. The Caribbean, it is argued, is a major route for climate patterns originating in different parts of the northern hemisphere and even from Africa. The presence of dust from the Sahara Desert in a Puerto Rican cloud forest provides evidence for global airflow patterns. Other cloud forests are located within this area, including previously studied sites in Puerto Rico, Venezuela, Guadeloupe, Haiti, and Jamaica, on which there is already considerable background information.

Tree ferns

Tree ferns (Cyatheaceae, Dicksoniaceae, and members of other families) are another striking feature of the cloud forests. The Cyatheaceae live in the lower and middle strata of the cloud forest, where they occupy a significant percentage of the basal (foundation) area, though they also occur in other types of lowland and montane forest. In a cloud forest site in Jamaica, one species of tree fern, *Cyathea pubens*, occupies 17% of the ground cover, a proportion that is very high considering that tree ferns do not show secondary thickening, that is to say, they are not woody and do not increase their diameter as trees do.

Tree ferns contribute to the functioning of cloud forest in several ways. Like some species of palm, tree ferns form a pocket at the leaf base that acts as an aboveground container for leaf litter and the associated flora and fauna. These pockets trap moisture, nutrients, and organic matter, and provide a suitable habitat for small reptiles and invertebrates. Tree ferns also serve as a site for seedling establishment. In a montane forest in Jamaica, 97 of the 121 tree ferns surveyed had seedlings of other trees rooted in these receptacles.

This seems to be the main regeneration strategy of the most abundant tree species *Clethra occidentalis* (Clethraceae), as 97% of its seedlings root there; the limited reserves in its cotyledons makes survival problematic for seedlings growing directly in the ground leaf litter.

3.3 Animal life

The fauna of cloud forests has been poorly studied, and only a small number of the few existing studies attempt to relate any particular species to the singularity of life in cloud forests. For this reason, the fauna of cloud forests remains relatively unknown. Broadly speaking, there are few large mammals, although the mountain gorilla (*Gorilla gorilla beringei*) of Africa is a notable exception. However, there are groups that, because of their unusual characteristics, warrant a more detailed treatment.

Pollination by birds

The bird communities of the cloud forest have been well studied. Birds help pollinate and disperse the seeds of many cloud forest plants, although some plants rely on more unusual pollinators such as rodents. In a Costa Rican cloud forest, hummingbirds pollinate large numbers of plants. Many plants have evolved morphological and physiological adaptations to attract hummingbirds and ensure pollination.

Some plants encourage hummingbirds to visit more flowers by a "guesswork" strategy as regards nectar supply. To minimize the cost of

225 Tree ferns are one of the most typical components of the cloud forest flora, where they play an important role in biological and nutrient cycles in general. Their enormous fronds are eye-catching both when the large frond is fully spread and before opening. The photo shows a specimen of *Cyathea* from the Monteverde Reserve (Costa Rica).
[Photo: Adolf de Sostoa & Xavier Ferrer]

226 **One of the most attractive cloud forest birds** is the marvellous quetzal (*Pharomachrus mocinno*), the national bird of Guatemala. Its body with its small crest is 14 in (35 cm) long, although the male has, in addition, a tail of up to 3.3 ft (1 m). These long tail feathers were attributes (symbols) representing Quetzalcoatl, or Kukulcan, the Aztec and Maya god and cultural hero, and had great ceremonial and symbolic value in Mayan society. Both males and females are emerald green, although the males also have carmine-red bills. Curiously, when magnified 10,000 times, quetzal feathers are brown and only appear green because of the wavelength of light they reflect. They are very shy birds and spend most of their time in the tree canopy. They nest in holes and will often enlarge holes made by other birds or mammals. They are not widespread and are only found in a few areas of Central America, principally in Costa Rica and Guatemala. Today, they are in danger of extinction: Habitat destruction and the disappearance of the old trees with soft bark they use for nesting is as much to blame as the persecution they have been subject to for their long tail feathers.
[Photo: Michael & Patricia Fogden]

producing nutrient-rich nectar, plants mix a few nectar-rich flowers among others with little or no nectar. Thus, hummingbirds have to visit many flowers to obtain their reward (which is a good reward), pollinating many flowers in the process. Another interesting strategy is the production of staminate flowers (flowers having the pollen-producing male reproductive organ) that do not produce fruit alongside the ordinary hermaphroditic flowers (flowers having both male and female reproductive organs).

In 1992 a cloud forest plant, *Besleria triflora* (Gesneriaceae), has been described that has large, showy staminate flowers for the sole purpose of attracting its pollinator, a hummingbird. These flowers deliver little pollen and remove none from the hummingbird. However, they attract the hummingbird to the nearby genuine hermaphroditic flower. This strategy does not seem very efficient, as the hummingbird has to visit many flowers before collecting enough pollen to be able to fertilize the plant.

Frogs and toads

Cloud forest anurans (frogs and toads) have attracted a lot of attention. Comparative studies of frog species diversity across the New World tropics, including cloud forest sites from Mexico to South America and along an altitude gradient from lowlands to the high mountains, produced interesting results. In Mexico, near the northern limit of the tropics, frog species diversity in cloud forests is similar to, or slightly greater, than in lowland forests. However, further south species diversity tended to decrease with altitude. The same is true of the cloud forests of Costa Rica, despite the generally high levels of endemism among frogs and toads. The frogs of the South American cloud forests do not occur further north and they have probably evolved in isolation. These populations tend to be confined to a small area and do not spread into neighboring forests. The absence of certain taxonomic groups of frogs in cloud forests has been linked to a lack of suitable undisturbed pools to breed in. Nevertheless, species that breed in forests and streams are abundant.

The number of frog and toad species in an area may also be related to the amount of light entering the tree canopy. It has been shown that frog species diversity in Puerto Rican cloud forests is

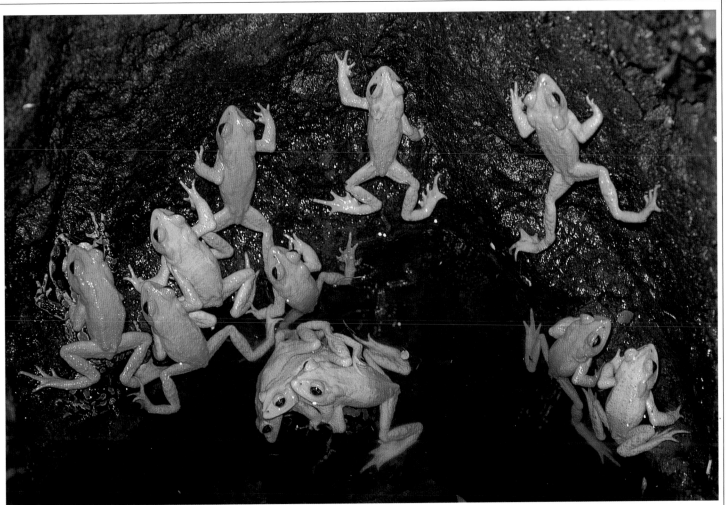

slightly higher than in surrounding forests. This diversity may be linked not only to the favorable moisture conditions but also to the fact that the cloud forest canopy prevents the entry of moonlight. The explanation appears to be that several species of frog in this cloud forest are nocturnal and are more active on moonless nights or when clouds or where the tree canopy intercept the moonlight. One of the most striking features of the misty slopes of the Monteverde cloud forest reserve in Costa Rica is the croaking of the many colorful frogs. The males of the many species of small arrow-poison frogs (*Dendrobates*, Dendrobatidae) seek high perches to croak their courtship calls to the four winds.

However, some species of frog and toad are mute and rely on their conspicuous coloration to attract females. This is the case of the endangered golden toad (*Bufo periglenes*), a species discovered in 1965 and found only in the Monteverde cloud forest reserve in Costa Rica. It has very bright coloration and marked sexual dichromatism (differences in coloration between males and females). This is uncommon in anurans. The male is bright golden yellow, whereas the female is more discretely colored.

The coloration of the males is for breeding purposes, as they are mute and depend on their color to attract the female's attention. Their bright color may also alert potential predators of the toad's distasteful or toxic nature, a further example of *warning coloration*. The golden toad is a synchronized breeder: the entire population mates and spawns within a period of less than one week. During the breeding period, females are in a minority and males may outnumber females by up to eight to one.

After hatching, the tadpole's survival depends on torrential rains providing enough water to maintain small pools. If these dry up, frog and toad mortality is high.

227 Rare and beautiful are perhaps the most fitting adjectives that can be applied to the golden toad (*Bufo periglenes*). Rare, because it is confined to the Monteverde reserve (Costa Rica) and beautiful for the unequalled golden color of the males, which contrasts sharply with the female's brown with red spots. Unfortunately, this fascinating species' rate of reproduction, like so many other amphibians worldwide, has decreased drastically over the last few years and its numbers have, as a result, dropped to worryingly low levels.
[Photo: Michael & Patricia Fogden]

The colors of frogs

"They catch them in the forest and keep them in hollow canes, where they enclose them, feeding them until their poison is needed. Then they spit the poor animals on a twig from its mouth through to one of its legs. This makes the creature sweat greatly, especially on its back, which is covered with a white foam. This is the poison they are after, which they smear on the tips of their arrows, which will keep their power for a year. Under the foam a yellow oil forms, also poisonous, that keeps its deadliness for four or five months.

A single animal provides enough poison to poison about fifty darts." This is the account of the British explorer Charles Stuart Cochrane, who traveled through the Colombian jungle, as described in his book *Journal of a Residence and Travels in Colombia during the years 1823 and 1824.* The account would not be very surprising, except for the fact that he was not referring to poisonous snakes or fearsome arachnids. The animals in question were small and rather attractive creatures, as pretty as a colored toy: the dendrobatid frogs (Dendrobatidae, also known as arrow-poison frogs).

Dendrobatid frog (*Dendrobates pumilio*) in Costa Rica [Alex Kerstitch / Planet Earth Pictures]

Using curare to poison blow darts is widespread among Amazonian indians, but the procedure described by Cochrane is not. This expertise is restricted to the Chocó Indians, who live in the Pacific basins of the rivers San Juan and Saija. The Chocó of the San Juan River use *Phyllobates bicolor* and *P. aurotaenia* in the way described by Cochrane. The Choco of the river Saija merely rub the points of their arrows across the back of a specimen of *P. terribilis*. This is easily understood, because the poison produced by this very bright yellow species is 20 times more active than the other two species, which are both deadly enough. What is this fearsome toxin? And what sort of frogs are the Dendrobatidae?

The Dendrobatidae, a family forming part of the Anura (tailless amphibians), is restricted to Central and South America's cloud forests and lowland rainforests. These frogs are small (0.8-2.0 in [2-5 cm]) and very pretty. Four genera have been described, with more than a hundred species. The most toxic specimens belong the genus *Phyllobates*, which only has five species (*P. aurotaenia*, *P. bicolor*, *P. lugubris*, *P. terribilis*, and *P. vittatus*), restricted to the mountainous arc running from Costa Rica to Colombia. The genus *Dendrobates* has about 50 species that are toxic, with a broader geographical range and, like *Phyllobates*, with bright and contrasting, colors. *Dendrobates lehmanni* is red and black; *D. auratus* is metallic green and black; *D. tricolor* is red and white; *D. tinctorius* is black with yellow and blue patches and stripes; *D. azureus* is completely blue, with a delicate black and white border; and *D. reticulatus*, perhaps the most spectacular of all frogs, has a ventral and lateral black and white network, whereas the head and back are bright red. In contrast, the 60 or so species of the genus *Colostethus* have discrete darkish colors, and most show no toxicity at all.

Dendrobatid frog *(Dendrobates tinctorius)*, with patches of fungus [Jany Sauvanet / Auscape International]

The fact that the brightly colored species are poisonous is no coincidence. This is an example of warning coloration. Possible predators are unmistakably warned by the danger signal and usually refrain from attacking. In fact, being poisonous is not enough, as there is no point in poisoning a predator after being eaten: The important thing is to avoid being eaten. As always happens in these cases, some species take advantage of the situation with colorations that deceive predators. *Eleutherodactylus gaigeae*, for example, is an inoffensive frog belonging to the Leptodactylidae family that looks strikingly like *P. aurotaenia* and *P. lugubris*. Color polymorphism is not uncommon; for example, *Dendrobates pumilio*, a species from Panama, occurs in every imaginable color, from red to blue to black and white.

Dendrobatid frog (Dendrobates) [Francesc Serrat & Angela de Dalmau]

Dendrobatid frog (*Dendrobates pumilio*) in Costa Rica [Kevin Schafer / NHPA]

The poisons produced by dendrobatid frogs are alkaloids, compounds more often found in plants than in animals. They may be piperidinic alkaloids with a ring of five carbon and one nitrogen atoms, which are found throughout the group, or they may be steroid alkaloids, known as batrachotoxins, that are exclusive to *Phyllobates*. Piperidinic alkaloids act on the endplate of the nerve cells blocking the transmission of stimuli to the muscles, as does curare, and producing paralysis. The batrachotoxins, among the most powerful known nonprotein poisons, make the membranes of the nerve cells permeable to sodium, thus depolarizing them and altering the transmission of nerve impulses. This causes cardiac arrhythmia, fibrillations, and failure. Batrachotoxins are highly unpleasant and frequently lethal.

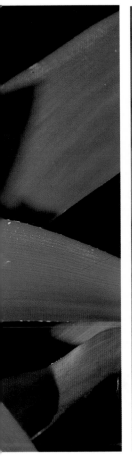

The Dendrobatidae are diurnal animals and defend their territory by whistling and puffing so noisily that they are the permanent background noise of the montane and lowland forests where they occur. They are animals of forests, not of pools and wetlands, like most other anurans. They lay their eggs outside the water, in relatively cool, wet places, often on trees, for example in the tanks of bromeliads. This forces them to take charge of the tadpoles when they hatch. Depending on the species, the male or female is responsible for placing the tadpoles on their moist back, where they adhere in a gelatinous mass. The adult transports them for hours or days until it deposits them in a stream to complete their development. The tadpoles are sometimes nourished by the "mother frog," precisely those of the same species with unfertilized eggs.

This results in unusual behavior that is accentuated in species that live in *inselbergs*, islands of montane forest in other environments, such as the tepuys of the Venezuelan part of the Orinoco Basin, where the dendrobatids are replaced by other equally unusual families of anurans, such as *Centrolenella duideana*, *Dischidodactylus colenolloi*, and several species of *Stefania* and *Oreophrynella*. These frogs show direct development, that is to say, their life cycle does not include the tadpole stage. Tepuys are often isolated worlds with their own flora and fauna, such as the frogs of the genus *Tepuihyla*, and with an endemic species in almost every tepuy. This gives an idea of the fascinating world of the rainforest's tree frogs.

4. The cloud forest in the world

4.1 A small, scattered and diverse biome

Cloud forests are dispersed throughout the wet tropics but occupy only a relatively small area. In 1979 cloud forests were estimated to cover an area of only 193,050 sq mi (500,000 sq km), approximately the area of Thailand, or a little less than the Iberian Peninsula. The cloud forest's world distribution coincides closely with the distribution of the tree ferns (Cyatheaceae), which are very common in these ecosystems. Cloud forest occurs in the America from south Mexico to northwest Argentina, in the Antilles and in mountainous areas of Venezuela. In Asia, it occurs on some foothills of the Himalayas and other mountain systems in India, Myanmar (Burma), and the rest of the Indochina Peninsula and in the mountains of most of the islands of the Indonesian archipelago, in New Guinea, and in many islands with steep relief in the tropical Pacific. In Africa, it occurs on several mountain massifs in eastern Africa, in Cameroon, and on the island of Bioko (Fernando Poo).

The scattered nature of the cloud forest

The great diversity of cloud forest ecosystems makes a precise definition difficult. The feature they share, and reason for their name, is that they occur at a height that is typically cloudy. Cloud forests include all forests in the humid tropics that are frequently covered in clouds or mist, thus receiving additional humidity, other than rainfall, through the capture and/or condensation of water droplets (horizontal precipitation). This additional humidity affects the hydrological regime, radiation balance, and several other climatic, edaphic (relating to soil) and ecological parameters.

The terminology dealing with cloud forests is as diverse as the forests themselves. The presence of these fascinating and special ecosystems in the cloud layer has led some scientists to classify them using more precise terminology based on the vegetation's typical features: *mossy forest*, *montane or upper montane forest*, *elfin woodland*, or *dwarf forest*. The last two terms refer to the low height of the trees in these forests in comparison with those growing in neighboring areas.

Endemism and diversity

The very high level of plant endemism in cloud forests is confirmed by the results of all the studies in different sites in this biome. In the Americas,

228 World distribution of cloud forest (dark green) and of rainforest (light green). As they are montane forests, the cloud forest has a highly dispersed distribution, with small patches corresponding to mountainous areas, meaning that their representation on this map is not to scale. The world's most continuous strip of cloud forest runs north-south along the Andes (the *ceja* in Colombia, Ecuador, and Peru and the *yunga* in Bolivia), and this is why it has been the most studied. The average input of water from the clouds into the cloud forest of South America varies between 11.8 and almost 78.7 in (300 and almost 2,000 mm), while the rainfall is between 3.9 and 137.8 in (100 mm and 3,500 mm).
[Drawing: Editrònica, from data provided by the authors]

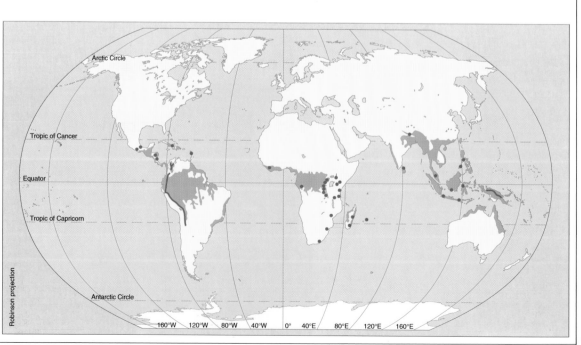

the high number of endemic forms in Panama's cloud forests has led some authors to suggest that they were centers of evolution and that they may have been a refuge for many cloud forest species after the isolation of these mountains from the North American mountain chains. For example, the Rubiaceae, the family that includes coffee (*Coffea*) and quinine (*Cinchona*), has a very high number of endemics in the Panamanian cloud forests. There are also many local or insular endemics in the cloud forests of the Caribbean. Many Caribbean species have discontinuous ranges, suggesting they are able to disperse over long distances and can maintain their community structure from within, without needing a regular input of propagules (propagating pieces, seeds, or spores) from outside. Furthermore, cloud forest on the Caribbean coast of Colombia had very few species that were also present in the neighboring forest ecosystems at lower altitudes. Of the 126 species of vascular plant found in this forest, approximately 41% are adapted to internal dispersal by birds, 39% are wind dispersed, and 5% are probably dispersed by migrating birds or mammals.

In comparison with other plant life forms, tree species account for a low proportion of the endemics and of the total number of species in the cloud forest. In Puerto Rico, a total of 12,864 plants were identified on a 1-acre (0.4-ha) plot, including trees, shrubs, lianas, herbs and epiphytes, from 54 taxa, of which 24 were endemic and only 12 were trees. Seventy percent of the tree canopy consisted of just two species, *Tabebuia rigida* (Bignoniaceae) and *Ocotea spathulata* (Lauraceae). Epiphytes contribute significantly to species diversity in the cloud forest. Epiphytic plants account for 50% of the individual plants and one third of the species in tropical forest, and cloud forests are the richest of all tropical forests in epiphytes.

Dwarf vegetation is common in cloud forests and has been the subject of much research seeking to explain why tree height decreases with increasing altitude. Yet not all cloud forests show reduced height growth. Some differences in the stature and species composition in montane cloud forests may be related to the vertical and temporal distribution of cloud inundation. For example, cloud interception by the tree canopy leads to a saturation deficit that is more favorable for leaves in the lower strata than when vegetation is flooded at ground level. Factors of this type may explain some of the structural and functional differences observed between different cloud forest ecosystems.

4.2 The distribution and types of cloud forest

As a whole, there is little information about the cloud forest: In practice the only information that exists is about forests that have been centers of research. The most studied areas are those in Central and South America, the Caribbean, Malaysia, and New Guinea.

The African cloud forest

Cloud forest occurs in the African continent in two separate blocks. The largest and most important block is in the mountains of eastern Africa, a group of widely separated massifs surrounded at their base by savannah and dry forest, except for those on the eastern edge of the Zaire Basin from Lake Albert to Lake Tanganyika, such as the Rwenzori mountains and others with bases surrounded by the Zaire rainforest. At the northern end of this group are the Ethiopian highlands. Further south, to the east of the great lakes, cloud forest occurs on Mount Elgon, the Kenyan highlands, the Mount Kenya massif, Kilimanjaro, and other smaller mountains. To the west of the great lakes, there is cloud forest in the Rwenzori massif and the highlands of Kivu, Rwanda, and Burundi. Further south, there is a string of small enclaves that run near the coastline of the Indian Ocean, almost to the southern tip of the continent but not including the highest peaks on Madagascar. The second important block of cloud forest in Africa is in the Gulf of Guinea, where there are two high massifs, Mount Cameroon and the island of Bioko, with its summit, Mount Basilé.

In Kilimanjaro (3° south of the equator) the cloud forest occurs between 6,000 and 10,000 ft (1,800 and 3,100 m) on the southwestern faces, and between 9,200 and 9,800 ft (2,800 and 3,000 m) on the northeastern faces. The dominant trees are golden olive (*Olea chrysophylla*), Ethiopian holly (*Ilex mitis*), African juniper (*Juniperus procera*), African podocarp (*Podocarpus milanjianus*), and rosaceous koso (*Hagenia abyssinica*). Most trees are covered in lichens, such as beard lichens (*Usnea*) and other epiphytic lichens, lycopods, ferns—especially filmy ferns (Hymenophyllaceae)—mosses. The soil is carpeted

229 **The African cloud forest**, as shown in this photo of the Ruwenzori mountains in northeastern Democratic Republic of Congo, is very rich in mosses and bearded lichens (*Usnea*) that hang from the branches, especially those of *Hagenia*.
[Photo: C. Jones / Natural Science Photos]

with *Selaginella*, and there are meadows of Bermuda grass (*Cynodon dactylon*) in the clearings. Candelabra euphorbias (*Euphorbia*) also appear.

Mount Kenya is sited on the Equator, although the highest peaks lie to the south of the equator itself. The cloud forest's lower limit is unrecognizable because the mountain rises from a cultivated plateau at an altitude of 4,921 ft (1,500 m) and crops are grown on the northern slopes up to altitudes of more than 6,562 ft (2,000 m). The dominant genera are the same (*Olea, Juniperus, Podocarpus,* and *Hagenia*), but there is a very typical layer of the bamboo *Arundinaria alpina* that is absent on Kilimanjaro and scarce on other mountains in eastern Africa.

The American cloud forest

The largest areas of cloud forest occur between the tropics on the long mountain chain running north-south the length of North and South America, and they are probably also the most thoroughly studied.

The northernmost cloud forest in the New World tropics occurs in the Sierra Madre Oriental in Mexico, especially on the Atlantic facing slopes. In Mexico and in the northern part of Central America, the cloud forest also contains Holarctic species, especially pines (*Pinus oocarpa* reaches the mountains of northwestern Nicaragua) and oaks (*Quercus granatensis* and some other oaks reach as far south as central Colombia). Yet from Costa Rica southwards the flora of the cloud forest is predominantly Neotropical, comparable to the northern Andes, although the altitudinal limits, especially in the slopes exposed to the trade winds, are much lower than in Colombia or Venezuela.

In the northern Andes the cloud forests occur between approximately 7,874 and 12,467 ft (2,400 and 3,800 m) (although locally they can reach 13,800 ft [4,200 m]). As in the neighboring lowland rainforest, the variety of trees is immense, although some genera are especially frequent, such as *Weinmannia* (*W. penicillata, W. trianae, W. jahnii,* Cunoniaceae), species of *Brunellia* (*B. rufa, B. macrophylla,* Brunelliaceae), species of *Drimys* (such as *D. granatensis,* Magnoliaceae, known as *ají de Nueva Granada* in Colombia), and species of *Miconia* (*M. salicifolia, M. elaeaoides,* Melastomaceae). In the Cordillera de Mérida in Venezuela, the cloud forest occurs between 7,546 and 10,499 ft (2,300 and 3,200 m), showing a complex composition, frequently including sites domi-

230 The South American **cloud forest** is dominated by flat-leaved epiphytes, especially orchids and bromeliads, and also by small ferns and mosses. In the northeastern Andes, at an altitude of about 10,000 ft (3,000 m) (upper photo), the dominant trees are *Podocarpus*, whereas in the southern Andes, such as this site in Manú (Peru) (lower photo), there are abundant tree ferns and lianiform bamboos of the genus *Chusquea*. [Photos: Tony Morrison / South American Pictures and André Bärtschi / Planet Earth Pictures]

nated by the *pino laso* (*Podocarpus rospigliosi*); other podocarps are typical of the higher layers, such as *P. montanus* and *P. oleifolius*, as well as species of the genera already mentioned (*Weinmannia jahnii*, *W. microphylla*, *Brunellia integrifolia*, etc.). Little is yet known about the cloud forest in eastern Ecuador, where it is known as *ceja* (brow), as in Peru. The upper limit is at about 11,155 ft (3,400 m) (although locally they may reach 12,467 ft [3,800 m]), while their lower limit is known with less precision though it is presumably around 6,562 ft (2,000 m).

The largest and best studied area of ceja is in the central Andes. Its lower height limit is 5,900-6,562 ft (1,800-2,000 m), and its upper limit is 11,155-12,467 ft (3,400-3,800 m) (rarely 12,795 ft

[3,900 m]). Its floristic composition is essentially no different from that of the more northerly Andes, at least in terms of the families and species present. There are podocarps, such as *Podocarpus oleifolius* and *P. glomeratus*, and members of the Cunoniaceae, such as *Weinmannia fagaroides*, and so on. It is also worth mentioning the presence of bamboos, in this case of the genera *Chusquea* and *Guadua*, as happens in other regions of cloud forest with other genera or species of bamboo. Further south, in Bolivia, the lower levels of the cloud forest are known as *yungas* and are very rich in tree ferns (for example, species of *Asplenium* and *Elaphoglossum*) and in species from the lowland rainforest. The yungas occur between 4,291-6,562 ft (1,500-2,000 m) and 7,874-9,186 ft (2,400-2,800 m), and are the sites

231 The Asiatic cloud forest shows a notable diversification of *Rhododendron*, to a greater or lesser extent and depending on the zones and the altitude. In flower they are proverbially beautiful, as shown by this image of *Rhododendron lowii* in the Kinabalu National Park, in Sabah (Borneo).
[Photo: Jacques Jangout / Auscape International]

local farmers prefer for coffee plantations. Above this, the true ceja rises to an altitude of 11,155 ft (3,400 m), with a composition similar to that of the ceja in Peru, including many lianiform bamboos of the genus *Chusquea*.

The southernmost cloud forests are the myrtaceous forests in the Tucumán forest in northwest Argentina, where the abundant mato (*Eugenia pungens*) and pitanga (*E. uniflora*) produce valuable timber.

In the Antilles, the cloud forest occurs at much lower altitudes (the *Massenerhebung* effect), above an altitude of 2,625 or 2,953 ft (800 or 900 m), or even lower on the smaller islands (St. Lucia, Grenada, St. Vincent). In almost all of the Lesser Antilles, below the true cloud forest, there is a layer of secondary vegetation dominated by palms, mainly mountain cabbage palm (*Euterpe lobosa*).

The Asiatic, Insulindian, and Polynesian cloud forest

Cloud forest also occurs on the southern slopes of the Himalayas, between 6,562 and 9,842.5 ft (2,000 and 3,000 m), depending on the orientation of the valley and watershed, and is dominated by oaks, magnolias, members of the Lauraceae, and birches. Unlike the Andes or Africa, the high mountains of southern Asia have forest vegetation in the layers above the cloud forest. These sub-alpine forests are dominated by conifers, because, as in Mexico, in these regions of south Eurasia there have been exchanges between the Holarctic flora and vegetation of the temperate areas of the northern hemisphere and those of tropical areas. The evergreen oaks that dominate this cloud forest include *Quercus lanuginosa*, *Q. semecarpifolia*, *Q. lamellosa*, and others. The understory is rich in beautiful spring-flowering rhododendrons (*Rhododendron*, Ericaceae), *Prunus* (Rosaceae), and *Berberis* (Berberidaceae).

Further south, as in the Malay Peninsula, members of the Fagaceae (the genera *Castanopsis* and *Lithocarpus*, rather than *Quercus*), together with many members of the Lauraceae, form a transition forest (in reality a laurisilva) between the montane rainforest and the true cloud forest. The latter, however, is dominated by conifers (*Pinus*, *Agathis*, *Araucaria*, *Casuarina*) and members of the Ericaceae (mainly *Rhododendron* and *Vaccinium*) and the Myrtaceae (especially, *Eugenia*, *Rhodamnia* and *Tristania*). Open secondary forests form in clearings and are dominated by tree ferns (*Dicranopteris*, *Matonia*), whose growth form recalls that of some of the palms common in similar habitats of the Americas. The Fagaceae-Lauraceae forest is usually between 2,625-3,281 ft and 3,937-4,921 ft (800-1,000 m and 1,200-1,500 m) above sea level, whereas the true cloud forest occupies the levels from 4,921.3 ft (1,500 m) upwards.

In the mountainous islands of Insulindia, the lower limit of the cloud forest may reach 2,300-2,600 ft (700-800 m) in some low mountains, such as

Maquiling on the island of Luzón in the Philippines or up to 4,921-5,905 ft (1,500-1,800 m) in the highlands of central New Guinea. Conifers also dominate the cloud forests of the Insulindian islands. In New Guinea there is a combination of podocarps (*Podocarpus*) and evergreen southern beeches (*Nothofagus brassi, N. grandis*) in the intermediate montane level, where cloud cover is most permanent, from 4,921-6,562 ft to 8,900-9,800 ft (1,500-2,000 m to 2,700-3,000 m). At the upper limit of this layer (from 8,900-9,800 ft to 9,800-10,800 ft [2,700-3,000 to 3,000-3,300 m]), depending on exposure) there is another type of cloud forest dominated by species of *Phyllocladus* (Phyllocladaceae, a small family related to the Podocarpaceae) and species of *Xanthomyrtus* (Myrtaceae). Above these altitudes, in the highlands of New Guinea, cloud forest occurs from here up to the tree line and is dominated by *Amaracarpus caeruleus* and *Pittosporum pullifolium*, with many specimens of the tree fern *Cyathea percrassa* in the lower levels together with members of Ericaceae (*Rhododendron gaultheriifolium, Dimorphanthera microphylla*) and Epacridaceae (*Trochocarpa dispersa, Rapanea vaccinioides*).

In the Pacific, the islands of volcanic origin that are high enough also have a layer of cloud forest, as in the Lesser Antilles. In the highlands of New Caledonia, between 3,600 ft (1,100 m) and the highest peaks (5,325 ft [1,623 m], Mt Panié), there are two variants of cloud forest. The lower levels between 3,600 and 4,265 ft (1,100 m and 1,300 m) are on ultrabasic (very low in silica yet rich in iron and magnesium) substrates and are dominated by members of the Myrtaceae (*Mearnsia, Metrosideros*), Cunoniaceae (*Cunonia*), Epacridaceae, and Podocarpaceae, with some almost pure stands of *Araucaria humboldtiensis* in the southern part of the island. From 3,937 ft (1,200 m) upwards, on mica schists, the forests of the conifer *Agathis montana* with evergreen southern beeches (*Nothofagus*) recall the forests in New Guinea above 4,921 ft (1,500 m), with an understory rich in palms and tree ferns as well as in several families and genera that are endemic to the island. In the smaller islands, such as the southern islands of Vanuatu and most Polynesian volcanic islands, the cloud forest may begin at an altitude below 1,640 ft (500 m), at least on windward slopes. The highest point on Rarotonga, the largest of the Cook Islands, is at an altitude of 2,139 ft (652 m), and the "montane" vegetation begins at an altitude of approximately 984 ft (300 m).

In Hawaii, the cloud belt occurs between 3,937 and 7,218 ft (1,200 and 2,200 m). These cloud forests show great floristic diversity, although in this case perhaps it would be better to call it luxuriant scrub. It is at most 33 ft (10 m) tall with abundant tree ferns, *Gunnera* (Gunneriaceae), *Lobelia* (Lobeliaceae), and many other genera of these families and others endemic to the Hawaiian Archipelago or other Pacific archipelagoes. Among the crowns of the dominant layer, the occasional *ohia* (*Metrosideros*) emerges, which also grows in the lowland forest from an altitude of 1,970 ft (600 m) upwards. *Koa* (*Acacia koa*) is also present in the highest levels of the cloud layers.

232 In addition to its floristic or faunistic interest and botanical and zoological value, the Insulindian cloud forest is enchantingly beautiful. Natural scenes like this view of the slopes of the Merapi Volcano in Java disappearing in the mist can scarcely be equalled for their beauty. It is worth recalling that beauty, seen with human eyes, also has ecological value.
[Photo: Adolf de Sostoa]

2
Humans in the cloud forests

1. Human inhabitants of the cloud forests

1.1 Many people for not very much land

The human occupation of the cloud forests

The human population of the cloud forest can be treated separately from the zones immediately above or below it. Its topographic situation, the discontinuities due to irregular relief, and the fact its resources frequently complement those of other zones mean that its inhabitants often also settle space in other zones or that populations mainly settled in other zones also colonize the cloud forest.

Occupation of the cloud forests generally began late, and little is known about its history in comparison with that of the neighboring lowlands. As already mentioned, in New Guinea the remains of human settlement in coastal areas date to about 50,000 years ago, yet the oldest remains from the highlands are only 26,000 years old. Colonization of the lowland rainforest was late, but settlement in the cloud forest was even later.

Since human occupation, however, cloud forests have played an ambivalent role. On the one hand, their unusual climatic conditions mean that cloud forests are less ecologically unhealthy than the lowlands, and wherever the relief has favored it (small level patches, sheltered valleys), these conditions have allowed very productive farming. On the other hand, difficulty of access to these sites and the readily available hidden defensive positions made them sanctuaries for peoples retreating from invasions by more warlike, technically advanced, and better-armed groups. Thus, the border between the rainforest and cloud forest in northern Thailand contains some of the oldest known remains of the early Neolithic complex in southeast Asia, yet at the same time the high mountains of the center of the Malaysian Peninsula are now the last refuge of the Semang hunter-gatherers.

Diversity and contrasts in the African cloud forest

The cloud forest's human population is very diverse, although its population has much in common with that of the neighboring rainforest. The cloud forests of central-eastern Africa, for example, are home to some of the shortest people in Africa and some of the tallest. Thus, the groups of Twa pygmoids living in the mountains of eastern Democratic Republic of Congo, Rwanda, and Burundi and on the foothills of Mount Kenya (from whose better lands they were displaced by the Kikuyu, Ogiek, and Dorobo) are the result of interbreeding between Pygmy and Bantu populations (especially those from northwestern and central-eastern Africa) and other neighboring populations. Some authors have suggested studying the gradation in average height in Pygmoid populations in order to reveal the extent of interbreeding with the adjoining populations.

The Twa live in the mountainous areas of eastern Democratic Republic of Congo (Kivu), Rwanda and Burundi. Democratic Republic of Congo populations generally maintain lifestyles similar to those of other Pygmies (although they are slightly taller), but those in Rwanda and Burundi have become sedentary and form a small minority (around 1% of the population) mainly dedicated to different crafts, without excluding some hunting, and in some cases raising small livestock, especially sheep, an animal that no other social group in these countries eats except in case of extreme necessity. Unlike the Twa, the Tutsi are one of the populations with the highest average height in the world (5 ft 8 in-5 ft 11 in [175-180 cm]). They are also very slender, with a body weight of 132 lb (60 kg) for the heights mentioned. Like other populations of Nilotic origin (of the Nile Basin), their head is longer than in other Africans, and they have longer limbs and neck, a narrow nose, and fleshy lips. The Tutsi have formed, for at least 400 or 500 years, most of the upper *ubwooko* (or castes) of Rwanda and

233 The cloud forest is a mountain habitat that is not very suitable for human life. Yet some peoples have made it their home, such as the Moni in the central mountains of Irian Jaya (New Guinea). The photo shows Moni women and children, with their typical baskets hanging from their heads, in Bilogai, a small village at an altitude of 7,050 ft (2,150 m) (see also figure 246).
[Photo: Ron Petocz / WWF / Still Pictures]

234 A small rural village in the African cloud forest in the Kibasha area of Kivu (Democratic Republic of Congo). Many houses are built of traditional materials, that is to say, canes plastered in mud with roofing made from plant material, but note that there are also some covered with corrugated sheeting.
[Photo: Adolf de Sostoa & Xavier Ferrer]

Burundi. The intermediate ubwooko of the two states' traditional societies consisted mainly of the Hutu ethnic group, who formed and still form, the majority (more than 80%) of the population.

This separation into social castes (the ubwooko) on an ethnic basis, with the Twa occupying the lower levels, the mainly agriculturalist Hutu occupying the middle layers, and the mainly pastoralist Tutsi occupying the upper levels, was used and strengthened by the colonizers. Both Burundi and Rwanda were already organized feudal states before European colonization (by Germany, then by Belgium). The Tutsi lineages undeniably occupied a leading role in the former aristocracy, but not all the Tutsi were lords nor were all the Hutu serfs. Although they were not excessively frequent, mixed marriages between Tutsi and Hutu did occur and led to some interbreeding. The Tutsi and Hutu have lived in the same space for more than half a millennium, mixed together in a context of a scattered rural habitat, speaking the same language (Kirundi in

Burundi, and Knyarwanda in Rwanda). Social confrontation between a mainly but not exclusively Tutsi aristocracy and a mainly Hutu peasant population, accentuated by colonial discrimination in favor of the aristocracy (especially in Rwanda), has since independence led to very serious confrontations between the two ethnic groups in both Burundi and Rwanda.

Scattered groups of Twa hunter-gatherers also live in the highlands of eastern Kivu, where small kingdoms arose with a mixed economy based on stockraising and intensive agriculture, but without the sharp social differences found in Rwanda and Burundi. From north to south, these kingdoms were Hunde, Haava (which gave its name to the city of Bukvu), Nyabungu, Fuliiro, and Bembe (at the northwestern tip of Lake Tanganyika). Further south, the highlands of the Katanga shores of the lake are exploited by the same shepherd peoples as the lowlands (Holoholo and Taabwa). All these peoples, even the members of their aristocratic lineages, are more like the Congolose peoples of the Zaire forest and the Hutu than the Tutsi.

To the east of the African great lakes, in the Kenyan and Tanzanian highlands and in those of southwest Ethiopia, the human populations are highly varied. Some groups, such as the natives of eastern Sudan, have very dark skins, while the other Bantu-speaking groups in the Zambezi Basin have lighter pigmentation. There are also Nilotic-looking individuals, similar to the Tutsi, often settled in the lowlands. There are also some individuals of Ethiopian origin, who show a mixture of the typical features of the Melanoafricans (dark skin, sparse, frizzy hair, and thick lips) with other features typical of leucoderms (thin nose, strong chin, and non-protruding eyes), who also mainly live in the lowlands.

Racial mixtures in the Americas

The cloud forest's human population in both the Antilles and Central America is highly mixed and is generally indistinguishable from that of neighboring lowlands. The Antilles has cloud forest in the Sierra Maestra and other areas of southeast Cuba, the mountains in the center of the Dominican Republic, northeast Trinidad, Jamaica, and other smaller islands. This was the first area in the Americas to be colonized by Europeans, and there are almost no traces of the Native American populations. The current inhabitants are mainly of African origin, with some from Europe or the Indian subcontinent. In Central America the native component is greater, but the population is essentially *mestizo*, that is, mixed with other American populations or with Mediterranean Europeans.

In Colombia, the Kogi and Ika of the Sierra Nevada de Santa Marta, the Bari of the Sierra de Perijá and the Pijao or the Páez of the inner ranges of the Cordillera Central in the Magdalena Valle, still maintain their traditional forms of life in some marginal areas. The cloud forest has almost all been cleared by mestizos or criollos to cultivate coffee, and the area houses some of the country's largest cities. Further south, in the Peruvian and Bolivian *ceja*, the population is essentially indigenous, the descendants of the settlers of the plateau.

Mountain dwellers in India, southeast Asia, and New Guinea

The people living in the cloud forests of the upper levels of the western Ghats and of Sri Lanka are essen-

235 **In the cloud forests of the Sierra Nevada de Santa Marta** in Colombia there are villages of Ika—and also Kogi (see photo 237)—who maintain their traditional lifestyles. Their cultural habitats, dress, and so on, are very different from the peoples of the lowland rainforest. [Photo: Brian Moser / The Hutchison Library]

236 In the mountain range running east-west along New Guinea there are many small villages scattered in the cloud forest, such as this one half hidden by the mist on the slopes of Pegunungang Jayawijaya, in Irian Jaya, the Indonesian part of the island. [Photo: Andy Smith / WWF / Still Pictures]

tially the same as those living in the lowland rainforest. Yet in the northeastern Indian subcontinent, in modern-day Bhutan, the dominant populations are derived from wave of expansion from the southeast Asian Neolithic focal center (see the chapter "Humans in the monsoon forests," pages 449-460). This is also true of the people in Arunachal Pradesh; the mountain dwellers of Myanmar, Thailand, and Indochina; and even the Senoi of inland Malaysia. In the rest of southeast Asia, however, morphologies associated with the descendants of the Neolithic expansion are also frequent and are dominant in the lowlands. In the highlands of New Guinea and of other Melanesian islands—as in the lowlands—the population is almost exclusively Melanesian.

High population densities

A common feature of most of the world's cloud forests is the high population density. Some extreme cases, in comparison with the neighboring lowland areas, occur in New Guinea, where the lowland population is sparse and scattered, but some areas of highlands reach densities of over 500 inhabitants/sq km (1 sq km=0.4 sq mi), although they are fragmented into numerous small communities separated by major linguistic and cultural barriers. Almost a thousand languages are spoken in New Guinea—about 20% of all the world's languages—and they belong to about 50 different linguistic families. This strange phenomenon has occurred in sites where populations have been isolated since remote times.

Several situations occur in the islands of the Malaysian archipelago. Densities as high as those mentioned for New Guinea, or higher, are found in islands like Luzon, Java, and Bali, whereas in others, such as Borneo and Celebes, densities are much lower. In those cases, the neighboring lowlands are often also densely populated (often more densely than the montane areas), unlike the situation in New Guinea. This is also true of many mountainous areas of southeast Asia that are generally highly populated, but not as highly populated as the lowlands.

The states of the lakes region of central-eastern Africa, essentially Burundi and Rwanda, have more than 12 million inhabitants in an area of 21,200 sq mi (55,000 sq km), more than 518 inhabitants/sq mi (200 inhabitants/sq km). In the highlands of Kenya, Tanzania, and southwest Ethiopia, population densities are also high but do not reach those of Burundi and Rwanda. The highlands of the southwestern slopes of Mount Kenya have long been inhabited by the Kikuyu, while the southern and eastern slopes of the same massif were inhabited by the Embu and the Meru. The area was the nucleus of the British colonization of Kenya, when many coffee plantations were established; yet the area is now experiencing problems of overpopulation that are forcing some inhabitants to emigrate.

The majority of the most populated districts of Colombia are in the cloud forest. Further south in Peru and Bolivia, the cloud forest is not densely populated, although population densities are higher than in the neighboring rainforest. Two highly contrasting situations occur in Central America: where the cloud forest has been turned into coffee or other plantations, population densities are usually very high, but where there are large areas of well-preserved forest, they are almost uninhabited, especially in Honduras and Costa Rica.

1.2 Health and illness in the cloud forest

One reason for the high population density in many areas of cloud forest may be that the risk from transmittable diseases is much lower than in the neighboring lowlands. Malaria, the scourge of tropical regions throughout the world, is much less common or totally absent, as are yellow fever and other diseases transmitted by mosquitoes.

Apart from the lower incidence of some of the most common infectious diseases, there are no major differences from the neighboring lowlands in terms of human health. Perhaps the only illness restricted to the cloud forest is *kuru*, a neu-

rological disease caused by a prion. *Prions* are infectious particles and were initially thought to be a virus. They were known as slow viruses because of the features of the diseases caused and the very long incubation periods. Since 1982 it has been known that prions are protein particles, totally lacking nucleic acids and very similar to typical neuron membrane proteins. Prions, using an as yet unknown mechanism, reproduce and occupy the site of the normal proteins of the neuron membranes they resemble, causing degenerative diseases of the central nervous system in some species of mammal, including humans. In humans, in addition to kuru, prions cause Creutzfeldt-Jakob disease, which causes progressive loss of memory, visual disturbances, and loss of motor coordination, and Gertsman-Sträussler-Scheinker disease, which develops more slowly and causes progressive loss of motor coordination and dementia. It is suspected that prions may bear some relation to other more frequent degenerative diseases, such as amyotrophic lateral sclerosis, Parkinson's disease, and Alzheimer's disease.

Kuru is known only in a group of about 30,000 Papuans, the Foré, in the Bismarck Range, in central north Papua New Guinea, a region that no European reached until 1932. Kuru develops after a long incubation that may last 5-25 years, appearing first as a characteristic swaying gait, followed by trembling of the hands, arms, head and trunk (the word *kuru* means "shivers," of cold and fear), accompanied by general malaise, headaches, and muscle and joint pains, but no fever. The trembling increases for one to three months, and then motor coordination is lost, making it almost impossible for the sufferer to stand upright. This is accompanied by further neurological disorders (difficulty in articulating words, sitting down, swallowing, and abnormal eye movements) and the illness leads to death within three to six months, rarely as long as a year, generally as a result of emaciation. It is now very rare. The disease mainly infected women and children, and when discovered it was thought to be a congenital disease.

It was later discovered that kuru transmission was linked to the Foré's ritual cannibalism practice in which the women and children ate the brain of the dead, while the men ate only the flesh. The Foré's abandonment of cannibalism in 1955 has led to the almost total disappearance of this prion-transmitted disease.

The vicereine fever

His excellency the Count of Chinchón, Gerónimo Fernández de Cabrera y Bobadilla, arrived in Lima in January, 1629, to take up his office as Viceroy of Peru. Within 10 years, he and his wife Francisca Henriquéz de Ribera had adapted to the country and had even caught the same illnesses as the natives. In 1638 the viceroy's wife contracted a severe fever that brought her to the edge of death. Fortunately, a royal functionary, the magistrate of Loja, Juan López Cañizares, gave her the healing bark of a medicinal plant that had saved him from the grip of tertian fever, that is, malaria. The vicereine took the medicine and promptly recovered. The fame of the *cascarilla* spread like wildfire.

Loja (now in Ecuador) soon became an active center for the distribution of this marvelous powder, obtained from the bark of trees in the cloud forest of the Andes—the *ceja de monte* facing the Amazon Basin—but nobody bothered to find out exactly which tree: it was *ayac-cava* ("bitter bark") from the *yarachucchu* ("fever tree") and that was that. In 1640 the *cascar-illa* or *quina* reached Rome, where it was immediately recognized as a powerful remedy and spread by the Superior of the Jesuits, Cardinal Juan de Lugo. For reasons of convenience, it was ground into a whitish powder and because of its history, this powder had amusing names like "Countess's powder," "Cardinal's powder," and "Jesuits' bark." The Dauphin of France, the future Louis XIV, caught malaria in 1649 and was treated with the powder that

Cardinal Lugo gave to Jules Mazarin, the French Minister of State. In 1654, the future Charles II of England also caught malaria and was successfully treated with cinchona bark by his own doctor Robert Talbor, and these successes definitively endorsed the product.

Rumors soon spread about cinchona bark. Some European courts, for example, prohibited its use, convinced that it was a Jesuit strategy to poison Protestants. Others thought that it had always been known by the native peoples, which is untrue, as it has been proved that they refused to use it when they fell ill, and there is not a single written record of its virtues in any of the ethnobotanical and pharmacological lists compiled before 1630, the year the magistrate of Loja was cured. In fact, maybe the story of the viceroy's wife was not exactly how it has come down to us…

Furthermore, its apparently random performance depending on which cinchona bark the powder was made from—ignoring falsifications—led to the appearance of all types of ideas and interpretations. People had discovered quina, or cinchona, trees in the cloud forests of New Granada (now Colombia) and later in Upper Peru (now Bolivia), but they belonged to different species, which explains the differences in the quality of the cinchona obtained and the resulting commercial rivalries. This commercial rivalry arose because even by the late 17th century cinchona was an economically important resource and becoming increasingly scarce, as it was necessary to cut the trees down to obtain their bark. In any case, scientific curiosity and commercial interests led to the development of pharmaceutical and botanical research into quinine, "quinology."

Glass containers for cinchona bark [Department of Pharmacology / Faculty of Pharmacy, UCM / courtesy of Editorial Lunwerg, Barcelona]

The first scientific note on cinchona trees, *Sur l'arbre du quinquina*, was published in 1738 by French naturalist Charles Marie de La Condemine, but the first botanical description appeared in 1753 in *Species plantarum*, the celebrated work by Swedish botanist Carl von Linné, Linnaeus. He gave Loja's cinchona the scientific name *Cinchona officinalis*, for its pharmaceutical value (*officinalis*) and in honor of the Viceroy of Peru, the Count of Chinchón (whose name he spelled incorrectly). Before this, French botanist Joseph de Jussieu, a colleague of La Condemine, had made a botanical survey and collection for 25 years (1735-1761) in Peru and New Granada, with many observations on cinchona trees. Unfortunately, all his materials were lost in the port of Buenos Aires when he set sail for Europe; humanity lost much extremely useful information, but Joseph de Jussieu lost his reason, as he never recovered from this calamity.

Knowledge accumulated about cinchona trees as a result of these studies, together with Hipólito Ruiz and José Pavón's expedition to Chile and Peru (1777-1788), José Celestino Mutis' expedition to what are now Ecuador and Colombia (1783), and the later work by Hug Algernon Weddell in Bolivia (*Histoire naturelle des quinquinas*, 1849), following in the footsteps of Tadeus P. Haenke and Rubín de Celis (1776). The four species of pharmacological interest are *Cinchona officinalis* (Loja's quina), the first to be used and native to Peru and Ecuador; *C. succirubra* (red quinine); *C. calisaya* (yellow quinine), from the Yungas of Bolivia; and *C. ledgeriana*, now widely cultivated in the tropics.

Cinchona trees are now in fact cultivated. Their cultivation was attempted without success by Hug A. Weddell in Africa and Malaysia (1845), J.C. Hasskarl in Java (1854-1863), and Clement Markham in India and Ceylon (1859). It was finally accomplished by Charles Ledger in 1865, using the seeds of a new species—which now bears his name—that had been collected for him in 1864 by the Bolivian Manuel Incra Mamani. In fact, the plants introduced to Java by Hasskarl were still alive, but Incra had been lucky enough to find specimens of an especially productive variety of an unusually rich species. In 1876, the Javan cinchona obtained from cultivated *C. ledgeriana* contained 13.25% alkaloids, in comparison with the 5-6% produced by the wild specimens of *C. calisaya*, widely considered to be productive.

The active ingredients of quinine are alkaloids—above all quinine ($C_{20}H_{24}N_2O_2$, 6'-methoxycinchonà-9-ol) and quinidine, its dextrorotatary stereoisomer—which were isolated in 1820 by the French chemists Joseph B. Caventou and Joseph Pelletier. These alkaloids are lethal to many protoctists, the reason for their effectiveness against malaria and dysentery. These alkaloids have a tonic effect on the nervous system and a bitter, acquired taste. They were added to drinking water by British colonists in India as a preventive measure, although the drink later changed from a preventine measure into a drink that could be mixed with other things; tonic water.

Between 8,000 and 10,000 t of cinchona (400-500 t of alkaloids) are still consumed annually, grown in southeast Asia, eastern Africa, and the Andean forests. Synthetic antimalarial drugs such as chloroquine have partially displaced quinine, one of the oldest compounds used to treat an infectious disease as a chemotherapeutic agent. Nowadays, 40% of the natural quinine produced is used in the soft-drinks industry, but 60% continues to be used in the fight against malaria. One hundred million people a year still catch malaria. There are no more viceroys, but malaria is still with us.

Box for storing cinchona [Museo de la Farmacia Hispana / Faculty of Pharmacy/UCM, courtesy of the Lunwerg publishing company, Barcelona]

2. The use of animal and plant resources

2.1 Collecting from the wild

Cloud forests contain many useful plant species that are collected to supply local needs or for international trade. Timber, food, medicinal plants, and many other natural plant resources occur in the world's shrinking montane cloud forests.

237 Some cloud forest plants produce useful fibers, including the fibers obtained from some members of the cactus family, such as these dyed fibers that a Kogi woman in the Sierra Nevada de Santa Marta (Colombia) is placing on the roof of her hut to dry.
[Photo: The Hutchison Library]

Tree ferns and orchids

One group of plants that is especially well represented in the cloud forests of Central America is the tree ferns. The understory of the cloud forest contains many members of Cyatheaceae and Dicksoniaceae, especially in ravines. One of the main uses of tree ferns is the use of the fibrous root material covering the stems as a horticultural growth medium for orchids in gardens and nurseries. The U.S. demand for this product has for a long time been satisfied by exports from some Central American countries, such as Costa Rica and Guatemala, although Costa Rica no longer exports it and has banned internal trade. Guatemala still exports about 2,119 ft³ (60 m³) a year.

The many local uses of tree ferns vary greatly. One unusual example is the apices of the species *Cibotium barometz*, which are covered with large golden hairs. If they are cut before the young leaves have unfolded, they look like a golden chicken. In the Cameron Highlands, on the border between Pahang and Perak in Peninsular Malaysia, these tips are collected and sold as ornaments. A French company has managed to obtain 220 lb (100 kg) a year of the golden fibers from this fern, which also has therapeutic applications. In their natural range, these ferns are also used occasionally as foodstuffs, especially the tender shoots, although they need to be boiled to remove the high sapogenin content.

Epiphytic (growing on other plants and receiving nutrients from the air and rain) orchids, another group of plants that is especially abundant in the cloud forest, are used in many ways. *Diplocaulobium solomonense* is traditionally used in the Solomon Islands and Bougainville as a weaving material. The stem fibers are strong and durable, and turn a bright yellow on drying. They are used to make armbands and small baskets of ritual importance, and to decorate ceremonial lances, clubs, and other weapons. They are tied to decorations that are worn as good luck talismans.

238 Unloading leaves of coca (*Erythroxylum coca*) at a reception point in the heart of the Peruvian cloud forest. This is a traditional and honorable activity, unlike that linked to the drug cartels which involves a preliminary treatment at the plantation in order to obtain cocaine base paste (110 lb [50 kg] of leaves are required to obtain 2 lb [1 kg] of paste). Chewing coca leaves goes back at least 4,500 years, as shown by *coqueros*, small ritual ceramic containers found in archeological excavations. Coca leaf consumed in the traditional manner, however, scarcely accounts for 10% of the current volume of production (in Bolivia in 1985, legal production was 15,000 t while production for the drugs trade was estimated at 145,000 t). The coca shrub (coca ipadu) thrives in its natural habitat, the cloud forest between an altitude of 984 and 3,280 ft (300 and 1,000 m), producing about 1,763 lb (800 kg)/ha (1 hectare=2.47 acres) of leaf per year over its 20-30 year lifespan, but fertilizer use can double this. It can also be cultivated in the warmer lowlands, the reason for the dramatic increase in production. These clandestine lowland crops are less productive, but the high price of the drug makes production worthwhile. Regrettably, coca cultivation moves more money than all the American food crops put together, even including maize, banana, tobacco, cocoa and coffee. Eighty percent of cocaine production is commercialized through Colombia.
[Photo: Liaison / Gamma]

Coca, quinines, and other medicinal plants

Coca (*Erythroxylum coca*, Erythroxylaceae), a shrub 7-10 ft (2-3 m) tall with medicinal properties, is native to highland rainforest and cloud forest. For centuries the native peoples of the Andes and upper Amazon have chewed it in religious rituals, as a stimulant and to alleviate hunger. The Incas held the shrub in high esteem and placed a supply of coca leaves in the tombs of nobles. The plant is widely cultivated in the Andean highlands, and rural people in Peru and Bolivia often stop for a *cocada* (coca break).

The active ingredient of coca, cocaine, is an alkaloid that was first isolated in the 1840s and rapidly became a common ingredient in tonic elixirs and powders. It was later used as a local anaesthetic and is still used in surgery. It has been especially important as the basis for the synthesis of other local anesthetics, such as procaine, novocaine, and lignocaine. Unfortunately, cocaine, like opiate derivatives, has become a drug of abuse, mainly in the form of cocaine hydrochloride, which is sniffed. This concentrated method of consuming cocaine is very different from the modest doses traditionally taken by local people. Coca tea is in fact a widely drunk tonic drink that is no more stimulating than a cup of strong black coffee.

The species of *Cinchona* are also very important medicinal plants from the Andean cloud forests. The bark, known as cinchona bark, is the source of quinine. Quinine has been used for centuries as a medicine to treat malaria and has recently been used to produce a drug to regulate the heartbeat. Until the middle of the 20th century, most quinine was extracted from the bark of wild *Cinchona* trees, but 90% of production of natural quinine now comes from plantations. Quinine is still a major treatment for malaria, although since the 1930s effective synthetic drugs have been discovered (chloroquine, mefloquine, etc.).

The medicinal plants of the African cloud forests include the tree *Prunus africana* (Rosaceae). The Kilum region, in the remote Bamenda Highlands in western Cameroon, is famous for its many medicinal plants, for their skilled used by the Oku and for the production of wooden carvings and honey. The Oku people have always considered their forest as a source of food, medicine, wealth, and cultural and religious objects. The Oku collect the medicinal bark of *P. africana* as a source of income. It is used to produce a drug that helps to control urinary problems derived from inflammation of the prostate gland. Then the bark is processed and marketed by international pharmaceutical companies. Every year Cameroon exports a total of about 200 t of bark to France.

The government controls extraction, but in the Kilum region overexploitation is causing problems. To develop a sustainable utilization program, nursery-grown *P. africana* has been replanted and strict regulation of harvesting techniques introduced.

The cloud forests of Sri Lanka are also very rich in medicinal plants and spices, including red Indian madder (*Rubia cordifolia*), cinnamon (*Cinnamonum ovalifolium)*, *Acronychia pedunculata* (Rutaceae), *Symplocos spicata* (Symplocaceae), *Valeriana moonii* (Valerianaceae), *Gaultheria rudis* (Ericaceae) and *Semecarpus coriaceus* (Anacardiaceae). The cloud forests of Horton Plains National Park also contains wild varieties of cultivated plants, such as pepper (*Piper*), guava (*Psidium*), tobacco (*Nicotiana*), and cardamom (*Amomum*).

Timber trees

Montane forest timber trees include several species of conifer of the genus *Podocarpus* from the highlands of eastern Africa and Cameroon. The montane forests of southeastern Asia also produce valuable timber from conifers of the genera *Podocarpus* and *Dacrydium*. There are also forests of *Podocarpus* in Colombia, Peru and Venezuela, but large areas have been felled.

Sri Lanka has no conifers and thus its montane forests lack the genus *Podocarpus* so typical of the montane rainforests of the islands of southeast

Asia. There are, however, other large timber-producing trees, such as *Michelia nilagirica* (Magnoliaceae), *Calophyllum walkeri* (Guttiferae), *Canthium montanum* (Rubiaceae) and *Vaccinium symplocifolium* (Ericaceae).

The timber species of the cloud forests of Central America include the copey oak (*Quercus copeyensis*, Fagaceae), endemic to Costa Rica and Panama. The original copey forests, restricted to altitudes over 6,562 ft (2,000 m), are said to have covered about 772 sq mi (2,000 sq km), almost 4% of Costa Rica. The construction of the Inter-American Highway through the copey oak forests allowed rapid logging of formerly inaccessible areas. By the mid-20th century, three quarters of the accessible oak trees had been logged. The wood was used mainly for railway construction and general building uses. Logging copey is now banned in Costa Rica and only the wood of naturally fallen trees can be taken; it is used for charcoal production.

2.2. Cultivated plants

Except for coffee plantations, crops are relatively uncommon in cloud forest, due to its climate and relief. They are usually limited to small subsistence plots or cultivated woody plants that are undemanding, such as coca plantations (both legal and clandestine). Yet some of the species most widely cultivated in other areas come from the cloud forest. The most important examples are coffee and maize.

The domestication of the potato (*Solanum tuberosum*, Solanaceae) in the highlands of Peru and Bolivia was Pre-Colombian, and within the different species, Andean peasants now recognize about 5,000 different varieties. It was probably first cultivated in an Andean valley occupied by what is locally known as ceja de monte. The potato is discussed in more detail in volume 9, as it is the basis of agriculture in the Andean altiplano and high mountain, the region where it was most diverse and widespread in the past.

The origin of the tomato (*Lycopersicon esculentum*, Solanaceae) is also controversial. Although the species' center of diversity is in the Andes, there are no traces of its domestication in South America, and it does not even have a name in any South American language. However, there are no known possible wild ancestors in Central America where it is thought to have been domesticated and where the fruit is known by its Nahuatl name (*tomatl*), now used everywhere. Recently a variety of tomato was discovered in Panama that is cultivated by the Choco people (possibly closely related to the wild species *L. humboldtii* found in northern Venezuela) which might be one of the ancestors of the cultivated tomato. Conservation of tomato varieties and wild species is important since they have been very important in breeding new cultivated varieties. Habitat destruction is, however, depleting the wild gene pool.

Centers of diversity and of domestication

Except for coffee, originally from Africa, all the widely cultivated cloud forest crops are from Latin America. The tropical Andean region is an exceptionally important center of genetic diversity for crop plants. Agriculture developed long ago in this region and different cultures developed sophisticated agricultural technologies designed to preserve soil and water resources. When the Spanish first arrived in Peru, the Incas cultivated about 80 different food crops. The Meso-American region, where the cloud forest meets drier temperate biomes, is also a major center of crop domestication and stores a surprising genetic diversity of many crops (maize, beans, amaranth, tomato, etc.).

Since the beginning of agriculture in the Andes and Central America, crops have been exchanged throughout the highlands of Latin America. Colonization led to the introduction first of some important crops from the colonists' homeland, and later other crops for export, most of them from other continents. Coffee, for example, is now the main export of Costa Rica and Colombia.

Along with the tropical Andean region, Ethiopia is one of the world's main centers crop diversity, although many have not spread outside their area of origin. The best known and most widespread is coffee (*Coffea arabica*, Rubiaceae), the first and most important cultivated species, from southwest Ethiopia. Not all the cultivated species from Ethiopia come from the cloud forest in the southwest. Teff (*Eragrostis tef*, Poaceae), the most important cereal crop in Ethiopia, appears to have been domesticated in the northern highlands, probably from *E. pilosa*. It is now cultivated in widely varying ecological conditions up to altitudes of 9,186 ft (2,800 m), but outside Ethiopia it is cultivated only in Yemen. In Ethiopia, teff is mainly used to make a bread known as *injera*, porridge, and alcoholic drinks. The straw is fed to livestock, and mixed with mud to plaster the walls of houses. Noog (*Guizotia abyssinica*) has long been cultivated in Ethiopia and is the country's most important oil crop. It seems to have been domesticated in the central highlands. It is not widely cultivated outside the region, despite the high quality of its oil, known as *ramtil*.

Avocado, legumes, and seeds

The avocado pear (*Persea americana*, Lauraceae) has been an important foodstuff for thousands of years in Central America, where it was first domesticated about 5,000 years ago. The fruit's name comes from the Nahuatl word *ahuacatl* (testicle). The evergreen tree is about 33-49 ft (10-15 m) tall, with an aromatic trunk and bark. The fruit is ovoid or pear-shaped and has a smooth, oily, greenish butter-like pulp. It is not sweet and contains far more fats (20%) and proteins (2%) than any other fruit, and it was considered an aphrodisiac. By the time of Spanish Conquest its cultivation had already spread south as far as Peru. The fame of its delicious taste and belief in its aphrodisiac properties explain why it was planted in many gardens in Mediterranean Europe from the 16th century onwards. The fruit,

240 **A large central seed surrounded by buttery flesh** is found in all varieties of avocado (*Persea americana*), whether the outer skin is green or black, smooth, or rough. Now widespread throughout the world, avocado has long been a traditional accompaniment to Mexican food. One example is the popular dish guacamole (mashed avocado pulp, chile pepper, onion, tomato, and salt). Popular medicine in South America uses the macerated exocarp of the avocado's fruit, either macerated or in powder, as a vermifuge, and the leaves and bark as antihelminthic, emmenagogic and antiperiodic, and the liquid extract of the seed as a remedy for neuralgia and rheumatic pains. The avocado is famous as an aphrodisiac. Joan Salvador, a Catalan botanist who travelled throughout Spain and Portugal in 1716 in the company of the French botanist Antoine de Jussieu, tells the story of the presence of an avocado tree in the garden of a convent in Valencia and its effects on a person who, according to a monk, had thanks to the avocado ceased to be "lazy in the act of love," and had slept with 16 women in one night! The various names, abacate, ahuacate, avocate—the fruit is known by in the west derive from the Nahuatl word, *ahuacatl*. In southern South America, it is known as *palta* the name of an ethnic group from, and a region in, southern Ecuador.
[Photo: Joan Biosca]

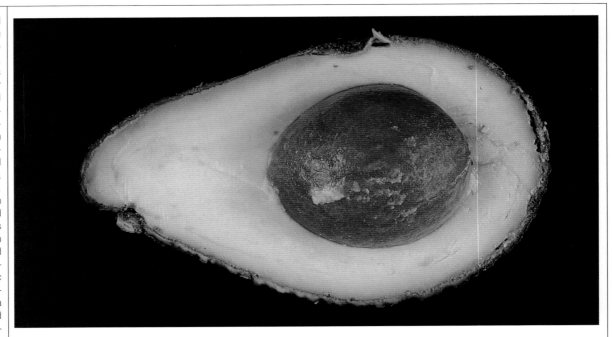

leaves, and bark all have medicinal qualities, and it is widely used in the cosmetic industry for its high content of proteins, fats, minerals and vitamins B and C to make soaps, creams and other products. *P. americana* still grows as a wild plant in small areas of Mexico and Central America, for instance in Costa Rica in the Monteverde Cloud Forest Reserve, Corcovado National Park, and the La Selva Biological Reserve.

Among the less well-known food plants in the tropical Andes are tarwi, amaranths, and quinoa. Tarwi (*Lupinus mutabilis*, Leguminosae) is from western South America, especially the Andean valleys of Peru. Pre-Inca peoples domesticated it over 1,500 years ago, and it is now often grown in rotation with potatoes. The seed has a high protein and oil content, but the plant also contains poisonous alkaloids. This poison is used in traditional native agriculture; it is planted on the edges of fields to repel pests. The crop's toxicity is removed by leaving sacks of seeds to be washed in running water for several days.

Amaranth (*Amaranthus*, Amaranthaceae) produces edible seeds that are ground to prepare a flour used to make porridge, purées, pasta for soup, and omelets; when sweetened, it is very widely used in pastry making. The tender leaves are also eaten in salads or as leaf vegetables. Cultivated for about 6,000 years, species like *A. hypochondriacus* and *A. cruentus* (known as *huautli* in Nahuatl) were as important as maize at the height of the Aztec empire. In addition to its general use as a foodstuff, a sweet biscuit called *tzoalli* was prepared with huautli flour and the sweet juice of the *Agave*. On special occasions, this was made into figures that represented different Aztec gods, and in some ceremonies the figures were broken up, shared, and eaten by those present.

This practice was seen by the Catholic colonizers as a mockery of the Eucharist and a symbol of paganism, and the cultivation of amaranth was persecuted. It never totally disappeared and is now being promoted. Kiwicha (*Amaranthus caudatus*) was a less important crop, but is still cultivated in the Andes, and has the same applications and uses as the Central American amaranths. Its consumption is now being promoted in the form of cereal flakes that have a high protein and amino acid content.

Quinoa, or pigweed (*Chenopodium quinoa*) is, after maize, the most important crop of Andean peasants in the valleys and on the altiplano. The Incas considered it sacred and called it "mother grain." The seed can be boiled like rice; used to make flour for bread, biscuits, and porridge; or fermented to produce one form of the alcoholic drink chicha. The stems are used as livestock feed. Quinoa flour is very nutritious, with a high content of amino acids (for example, it contains twice as much lysine as wheat flour), but the presence of saponin in many varieties gives them a bitter taste.

Despite their historic importance and current use, none of these seeds is as important as maize, the only cereal crop of American origin.

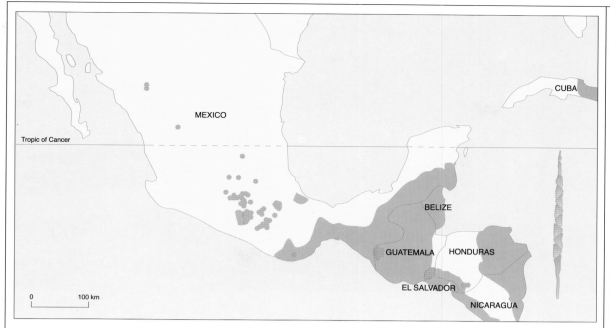

one of the most primitive possible wild parent of cultivated maize (*Zea mays*). For a long time it was thought that teosinte was extinct in the wild, probably because the spikes looked totally different from what was expected of a maize relative, until it was rediscovered in the mountains of southern Guadalajara in Mexico. A new species was also discovered nearby, *Z. diploperennis*, which some think is the real wild ancestor of maize. No other plant has been so changed by cultivation. The side branches of the teosinte end in a spike of male flowers, whereas in maize, these side branches end in a female structure, which will form the ear of corn. This is a hormone-controlled change that may have been initiated by a fungus, a virus or a change in climate. Once they had appeared, the female flowers gave rise to naked grains that probably attracted the attention of gatherers. To protect these wild relatives of cultivated maize, the Mexican government created the Sierra de Manantlán Biosphere Reserve in 1988, whose highest areas are covered in cloud forest. Local communities are closely committed to managing the forests and their natural resources, and ethnobotanical research has rediscovered knowledge of local medicinal plants and at the same time awoken interest in forgotten food plants, so that the collection of wild fruit and plants has restarted (see also figure 242).

[Drawing: Editrònica, from several sources]

Maize

Maize (*Zea mays*) is the most important of all these crops. It is the main cereal crop throughout the Americas and is now widespread throughout the world, from 58°N (Canada, Russia) to 40°S in South America. It is a very common human foodstuff, especially in many rural communities with strictly subsistence economies, and is also used to manufacture animal feeds or other derivatives from the large-scale production in other more suitable locations.

Maize, also known in American English as corn, is a herbaceous annual plant that forms a stem 6.5-13 ft (2-4 m) tall. The stem, or cane, is erect, solid, and cylindrical, and terminates in a plume (tassel), the male inflorescence. The prominent nodes bear dark green lanceolate (lance-like) leaves that sheathe the stem, with a wavy margin and whitish hairs that are rough to the touch. The axil of one or two (occasionally three) of the leaves in the middle of the stem produces a female inflorescences, or ear. The female flowers, with a long, hanging styles (silks), are arranged in parallel rows along a thickened axis. The styles as a whole form the "beard" of the maize, used to treat stomach aches and pains produced by kidney or bile stones. The female flowers on the ear produce the seeds that are one of the basic foodstuffs of much of the human race and have been for many centuries.

The origin and varieties of maize
Maize was originally domesticated in Central America, and the tropical Andean region is an important but later secondary center of diversity.

Columbus found it on Hispaniola on his first voyage and took the first seeds to Europe. It spread rapidly throughout the world, reaching southern China in 1555 as seeds from the Philippines; it was already well known in Egypt by 1560 and Japan in 1565. The earliest herbals of the European Renaissance, such as those by Hieronymus Bock (1539) and Leonard Fuchs (1542), mention maize and include a drawing. Its rapid spread led to the confusion, which still exists, in the plant's common name in several European languages (for example, it is known as "Moorish wheat" [blat de moro] in Catalan and as "Turkish wheat" in Italian). Maize is now widely cultivated throughout the world's temperate and tropical regions, and total production is over 300 million t.

One of the myths of the Mayan cosmogeny says that the ancient gods made several attempts to create earthly servants from different materials. Their efforts failed when they tried to make them from mud or wood. One day, some animals (the ocelot, coyote, deer and parrot) told them that in Paxil (the Mayan pantheon's paradise) there were delicious yellow and white corn cobs. The gods fetched them and made a paste from the seeds and thus managed to create human beings, giving them great strength. This is one of the many maize-related myths of the ancient Central American cultures with maize-based diets (Olmec, Toltec, Teotihuacán, Zapotec, Maya, and Aztec), which they considered sacred, the source of life, the supreme food, and the origin of human flesh itself. Its origin was also mythical: according to the

242 The most probable wild ancestor of maize is teosinte (*Zea diploperennis*). The photo shows a specimen from Manantlán, Mexico. For many years, it was thought that the most primitive known wild relative of cultivated maize was *Zea perennis*. This species was thought to be extinct in the wild, but in 1977 Rafael Guzmán found wild specimens in the mountains of southern Guadalajara, Mexico. Nearby, he also found specimens of a new species, *Zea diploperennis*, probably the true wild ancestor of maize (*Zea mays*). These botanical discoveries in the cloud forests of Mexico are of great importance (see figure 241).

[Photo: Laboratorio Natural de Las Joyas / WWF / Still Pictures]

Maya, Txaak, the god of thunder and rain, cracked the rock the plant was hidden in, thus making it available to humanity as a foodstuff.

It is not surprising that maize's origin was considered a hidden mystery. There are still many questions about maize's origins, as modern-day maize, *Zea mays*, exists only in the cultivated form, and the question of which wild species gave rise to maize is still hotly debated. Maize may have originated from teosinte, or *teocintle* (the Nahuatl name for several grasses of the genera *Euchlaena*, *Tripsacum*, and *Zea*, related to maize; the word is derived from *teotl* which means god and *centli*, which means maize). Several wild species of teosinte may have contributed to the complicated set of hybridizations and mutations that gave rise to cultivated maize, a species that is now unable to reproduce without human intervention. Maize is undeniably a cultural product that is the result of the patient and intelligent labor of many generations of people in the Americas. For at least 7,000 years, the approximate age of the oldest known archeological remains, has been a major foodstuff for the people of Central America, and more recently most of the Americas, from the estuary of the St. Lawrence River to Chiloé.

Modern varieties of maize, developed over centuries of cultivation, are very different from their wild ancestors and cannot survive outside cultivation. Maize has been improved by using the genetic variability of the crop plant, and especially during the 20th century, by the development of hybrid varieties that has resulted in extraordinary increases in yields. Solving the problem of the origin of present-day maize varieties and conserving their genetic variability is thus one of the most pressing questions in contemporary agriculture and genetics.

Traditional uses

Maize is mainly eaten as small tortillas in Mexico and much of South America. A tortilla is a thin, round unleavened bread made from a dough of wet maize flour. They are kneaded by hand and cooked on a flat plate of oven-heated clay. Traditionally, the grains of maize were left to soak overnight in water with saltpeter or lime, and the next day they were peeled, boiled, and ground. They were ground on a *metate* (a rectangular stone with three legs) using a cylindrical pestle (the *metlapil*). This produced the dough to be kneaded into tortillas. This is done by taking a small ball and working it with the palms of the hands into the shape, size, and thickness desired. The process has now been mechanized, and in many cities and sufficiently large villages they are sold in *tortillerías*, tortilla shops. The tortilla has long been consumed as a foodstuff in its own right, also serving as a vehicle to transfer the food to the mouth, or as a base for cooked dishes. In Mexico it is an essential ingredient for about 200 recipes, and a meal without tortillas is unimaginable.

Maize has other applications. The dough, diluted in water and boiled till the liquid is thick enough, is used to make the drink atole. Atole was drunk by the Aztecs and Maya and is used in many preparations, the most appreciated of which is atole champurrado, sweetened atole mixed with chocolate, milk, and cinnamon. Several alcoholic drinks are made from fermented maize grains; for example in Mexico, pozol and tesguino and in some parts of South America, forms of chicha. The hard, toasted and ground grain of maize is also used to make pinole, a sort of biscuit flour that lasts for many days and can be eaten as such or diluted with water. Easily transported and long lasting, in the past it was taken on long journeys on foot and in military campaigns. Another traditional preparation method still in use is to toast and "pop" the grains, making popped corn or popcorn, known to the Aztecs as *momochtli*.

They compared it to hailstones and ate it dry and in soup. Popcorn is now a popular snack throughout the world. In Mexico, even the very common parasitic fungus maize smut (*Ustilago maydis*) was eaten as a delicacy, even though its Nahuatl name, *cuitlacoche*, means "sleeping excrement."

Maize's uses in the food industry

In any case, maize has spread far and wide and is now the world's third most important cereal crop.

Much of the harvest of the large producers goes to the food industry, mainly for the production of animal feeds and also for the extraction of starch, oil, dextrine, dextrose, alcohol, hydrolyzed gluten proteins, and other products.

Maize's uses as a foodstuff are not limited to the traditional uses in the Americas. They include breakfast cereals, long eaten in both Europe and America, made with the coarser fractions of the ground grain, as well as corn flour and other flours that are used to make long-established products, such as *gofio* (roasted maize flour) in the Canary Islands and polenta in Italy.

243 Corn cobs come in a surprisingly wide range of colors and shapes. The picture shows a pile of corn cobs drying in a smallholding in the *ceja de monte* in Peru. [Photo: Tony Morrison / South American Pictures]

From Abyssinia to the heart of Europe

Around the beginning of this century, Vienna was a major creative and intellectual center basking in the sunset of the Austro-Hungarian empire. This period saw the birth of Karl Menger's economics of marginal utility, the logical positivism of Otto Neurath, the 12-tone harmonics of Arnold Schönberg and the psychoanalysis of Sigmund Freud. It was also an artistic capital and home to the Vienna Sezession, where Gustav Klimt's paintings overturned conventions, as did Gustav Mahler's music and Adolf Loos' architecture. Vienna was also a city whose residents drank lots of coffee. Throughout Vienna, unlike any other city ever before, there were tastefully decorated and commodious places to relax and chat: These were permeated by the aromatic and stimulating smell of freshly brewed black coffee. These Viennese coffeehouses were the meeting places of a new epoch, the debating chambers of modern industrial society where conversation and opinions mixed with fresh ideas and thoughts.

However, coffeehouses were not an Austrian invention. In the 15th century they existed in Arabia. The idea spread to Turkey and by the middle of the 17th century, coffeehouses had reached Europe, brought by Venetians who traded with the Ottoman Empire. A Greek, Pas Rosee, opened the first coffeehouse in London in 1652 (apparently by 1675 there were hundreds in the English capital!), and 1674 saw the first coffeehouse open in Leipzig but Paris had to wait until 1702. All became centers of debate and intellectual life. The Pedrocchi coffeehouse in Padua possessed no doors and stayed open permanently, day and night, from the year it opened in 1831 until the Second World War. Coffee, a wonderful stimulant drink, prepared in any one of many different ways, was the reason for these Viennese establishments' existence. Coffee, however, is originally from the mountains of Abyssinia.

Coffee mill from Turkey [M. Daniel / Gamma]

Legend has it that coffee was discovered by an Ethiopian shepherd who noted the effect the wild berries had on his goats. Legends aside, it is a fact that for 2,000 years the peoples of the tropical mountains of Abyssinia have used cakes made with fruits of the coffee plant, mixed with cereals and animal fats, to relieve hunger and fatigue. Even today, the inhabitants of east Africa eat dried coffee berries and also ferment them to make an alcoholic drink. Nevertheless, the Arabs were the first to brew coffee as it is now drunk. Between 600 and 700 years ago, coffee seeds or plants were taken to the mountains of Yemen and plantations established in the area, known as Al-Mukha or Mocha. Despite the prestige of this name still enjoys, the area is in fact fairly unsuitable for the cultivation of coffee and today it contributes nothing to the world market, which is now dominated by Brazilian, Colombian, and Central-American coffee. This is a typical paradox of agriculture that alters the basic ecology: A montane species from tropical Abyssinia that took its name from name from the desert Arabs, and is now cultivated by Colombian creoles and Brazilian negroes and is drunk black or with milk to wake up the western world every morning.

Fragment of the "Coffee Cantata" by Johann Sebastian Bach, c. 1732 [Staatsbibliothek zu Berlin-Preuischer Kulturbesitz - Musikabteilung mit Mendelssohn Archiv]

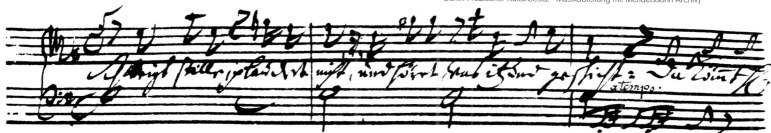

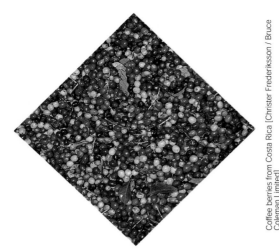

Coffee berries—or drupes—are red, round, fleshy, and sweet when mature and each berry contains two slightly ellipsoidal shapes—the coffee beans—which separate on drying. These "green" coffee beans are roasted to produce roasted coffee or, if sugar is added, sugar-roasted coffee (torrefact) though the actual drink is prepared with roasted beans after they have been ground. Drying out the fruits is not a simple affair. Drying techniques that take advantage of the full heat of the sun or an artificial heat source ensure that the pulp, the endocarp (the parchment) and the silver skin, a paper-like layer that protects the beans, separate from the berry. Wet techniques leave the endocarp stuck to the beans, allowing it to ferment and to alter the resulting aroma. Obviously, the species concerned (*Coffea arabica*, *C. canephora* [=*robusta*] and *C. liberica*), the individual qualities of each plantation, and the different drying and roasting techniques produce a range of different types of coffee, increased even further by blending. Distinct ways of preparing the final drink also add to the vast range of different types of coffee.

There are four basic ways of preparing coffee, all of them using water: boiling, infusion, percolation, and pressure (espresso). Boiling is probably the oldest form and gives rise to "Turkish" or "Greek" coffee. The coffee, finely ground and mixed with sugar, is brought to the boil a number of times and is served with the grounds at the bottom of the cup. Mexican "pot coffee" or "Arabic coffee" are similar and are further aromatized by the addition of cinnamon, and then filtered. Infusion and percolation are the most widespread methods, especially in the Anglo-Saxon world and the result is a light, aromatic drink that can be kept hot and ready to be served for hours or can be reheated as many times as necessary (though each time with a loss of quality). Espresso coffee is an Italian invention widespread throughout the Latin countries. It consists of coffee percolated under pressure and should be drunk freshly brewed and in small doses, as it is very strong and high in caffeine. Caffeine is the active ingredient of coffee. Coffee's stimulant properties are due to this bicyclic alkaloid ($C_8H_{10}N_4O_2$, 1,3,7-trimethylxanthine); coffee beans contain about 1.5% caffeine. As is the case with other alkaloids, caffeine has invigorating and stimulant effects on the nervous system. Some people react badly to caffeine, and so methods have been developed to decaffeinated coffee so these people can drink it without ill effects. These methods can be applied to coffee beans or ground coffee, as well as to instant coffee, prepared coffee that has been dehydrated by one of several methods, and dissolves when water is added.

Caffeine is present, often in greater quantities, in other stimulating drinks, such as tea, an infusion of the leaves of *Camellia sinensis* (1-4.5%); maté, made from the leaves of *Ilex paraguayensis* (0.5-1.5%); cola drinks, zmade from the fruits of *Cola nitida* (2.5-3.5%); guaraná and yoco, made from the fruits of the Amazonian *Paullinia cupana* (2.5-5%) and *P. yoco* (3-4%) respectively; and even cocoa, made from *Theobroma cacao* (less than 0.5%). All are stimulating drinks and can be habit forming. Nevertheless, coffee is the most esteemed drink of all, as half the world's population will vouch: After gasoline, coffee is the world's most important export product. If that Abyssinian shepherd had only known…

244 A specimen of Congolese coffee (*Coffea canephora* [=*C. robusta*]) covered in ripe fruit ready for picking. Harvesting coffee is a delicate operation that has to be done by hand. Only the ripe berries can be picked, and so the coffee pickers have to work their way through the coffee plantations with a bag on their back, into which they throw the gathered berries (see figure 250). The plantations are normally on slopes, and may or may not be shaded by planted trees.
[Photo: Dominique Halleux / Bios / Still Pictures]

Coffee

Coffee is the most widely cultivated stimulant crop plant, due to the very widespread consumption of its fruits in the beverage coffee. In fact, coffee is not a single species but includes about 40 species of the genus *Coffea* (Rubiaceae). *C. arabica* is native to the Ethiopian cloud forest and accounts for about 80% of cultivated coffee plants, but there are also *robusta* coffee (*C. canephora* [= *C. robusta*]), which is originally from central and western Africa and Madagascar, and Liberian coffee, or *abeokuta* (*C. liberica*), from western Africa. All the species of coffee are small trees about 23-26 ft (7-8 m) tall, although in cultivation they are usually trimmed to keep them as shrubs less than 13-16 ft (4-5 m) tall. They have dark green leaves and a shiny upper surface, and prefer warm, wet, half-shaded sites, as corresponds to tropical montane plants.

Coffee cultivation began in the mountains of Yemen, as the Arabs were already fond of coffee. From these mountains it spread east to the Malabar coast, in India, and in the 17th century it was taken to Sri Lanka and Indonesia by the Dutch. When consumption became popular in Europe, the Dutch were not pleased with the monopoly the Arabs enjoyed. Several plants of *Coffea arabica* were transported from Java to Amsterdam Botanical Garden in 1706. Only one plant survived, and this was the origin of all the seedlings that were soon taken to the Caribbean, via Paris and Martinique, and then spread to the rest of the American tropics. Later, there were also some direct introductions from Yemen, passing through the island of Réunion. *Arabica* coffee now accounts for 80% of world production, centerd on the American tropics. *Robusta* coffee, which is mainly cultivated in equatorial Africa together with *C. liberica*, was found by the first Europeans to explore Africa. It was semi-cultivated and then introduced into southeast Asia at the beginning of the 20th century (about 20 plants from the Democratic Republic of Congo were planted in Java in 1900). In southeast Asia it soon became an important replacement for the *arabica* varieties that were destroyed in the late 19th century by several diseases.

Coffee is an understory shrub, so its cultivation requires some shade from taller trees to protect it from the excessive sunshine. Most plantations are established on slopes on high tropical mountains, such as the typical coffee plantations of Central America and Colombia. This difficult relief, together with the need for collection by hand, selecting just the ripe fruit, make its cultivation

245 **Coffee grains are usually dried and sorted** on the plantation so that the coffee fruit's pulp, known as the berry, never reaches the consumer. The photo shows a group of women sorting coffee beans by hand in a plantation in northern Democratic Republic of Congo.
[Photo: Manuel de Sostoa]

2. HUMANS IN THE CLOUD FORESTS

almost a craft activity, despite the enormous area of coffee cultivated, a global total of about 38,610 sq mi (100,000 sq km.) Coffee is now an extremely international commodity, second only to oil in economic terms. The main producers of *arabica* coffee are the Latin American countries, especially Brazil, Colombia, Guatemala, El Salvador, Costa Rica and Mexico. The main producers of *robusta* coffee, mainly used to make instant coffee, are the countries of equatorial Africa, especially Ivory Coast, Cameroon, and Uganda.

2.3 Hunting, fishing, and domestication

The environmental conditions of the cloud forest make it even less hospitable for herbivorous animals than the lowland rainforest, and vertebrate diversity and biomass decrease uniformly with altitude. This decrease is aggravated by the fact that because there are few mammals, there are also few trees that depend on them for seed dispersal, and so there are few trees that produce attractive, nutritious fruit.

Limited hunting and fishing yields

Compared with lowland forests, the low-growing, peaty and mossy forests of tropical plateaux and mountain peaks are home to few birds and mammals, and even fewer reptiles, amphibians, fish and arthropod. Most animals endemic to the cloud forests are so relatively small that they tend not be hunted. Opportunities to exploit the fauna are relatively scarce, but many inhabitants of the cloud forests rely on animal resources to satisfy their daily needs.

The indigenous groups that traditionally live in the cloud forest have developed elaborate strategies to resolve these problems. Generally, hunting and fishing complement foodstuffs derived from shifting agriculture and the different domesticated animals they raise. As the already small populations of the larger game species have declined, there has been a shift towards smaller species. Many inhabitants of mountain regions eat small mammals, such as the *tuco-tuco* (*Ctenomys*) and wild guinea pigs (*Cavia*). The Awa people of

246 Game is not abundant in the cloud forest, but some peoples still practice it as a major source of animal protein. For example, this Dani man from the Pegunungan Jayawijaya mountains in Irian Jaya is pleased with his catch, a specimen of cuscus (*Phalanger*), a small marsupial of the wet forests of Insulindia and the islands of the Strait. Note the phallic sheath he is wearing.
[Photo: Ron Petocz / WWF / Still Pictures]

southern Colombia and northern Ecuador catch all sorts of small rodent, including spiny rats such as *Proechimys semispinosus* and *Hoplomys gymnurus*, and a series of larger mammals, birds and reptiles. They also practice fishing, but it is less important than in the lowlands due to the rugged terrain. Many fishing techniques are used, including traps, palisades, nets, harpoons and fish poisons.

Some examples

In southeastern Asia, the people living in the lowlands rarely enter the cloud forest, and this is reflected in the myths of many hunter-gatherer peoples, such as the Jah Het, who live at the base of Mount Benom, and who believe that the mountain's peak is inhabited by ghosts, pig-tailed macaques and giant squirrels that multiply when killed. As the area of lowland rainforest is diminishing due to agricultural pressure, the montane forests remain as isolated refuges of natural vegetation and are occupied by hunter-gatherer peoples with nowhere else to go. This increases predation pressure on wild animal populations already on the brink of extinction. Examples of intense hunting in cloud forests include the area of Mount Tawu (Taiwan), the Mount Wuzhi and Bawangling areas on Hainan Island (southern China), and the Mount Makiling area on the island of Luzón (the Philippines). In these cases, excessive hunting is stimulated by the demand for meat from restaurants in the towns, which have fewer and fewer alternative supplies. Montane forests are also of great ecological importance to the many mobile mammals and birds present in both montane and lowland habitats that are important for humans in the lowlands. For example, it appears that in Borneo the bearded pig (*Sus barbatus*) uses the high altitude oak forests, which regularly produce great excess of fruit, because they can rely on finding food there. Pig populations feed there seasonally before returning to the lowlands, where many are hunted when crossing rivers or grazing in communal rainforest hunting grounds.

The New World tropical cloud forests, unlike those in southeast Asia, have long been inhabited and were even occupied by some of the most important pre-Colombian civilizations. Today highland areas in the Americas are still densely inhabited and a lot of the forest cover has been destroyed to make way for settlements and agriculture (especially coffee plantations). The most sought after hunting species in the American cloud forests include the mountain coatimundi (*Nasuella olivacea*), the mountain tapir (*Tapirus pinchaque*) and the only member of the bear family to occur in South America, the spectacled bear (*Tremarctos ornatus*). These and some other smaller species such as the northern pudu (*Pudu mephistophiles*), the mountain paca (*Agouti* [= *Stictomys*] *taczanowskii*) and the pacarana (*Dynomis branickii*) are threatened by habitat destruction and overhunting.

In Africa, the mountain gorilla (*Gorilla gorilla beringei*), a subspecies adapted to feeding in clearings in cloud forests, survives in the mountains along the borders of Burundi, Rwanda and Democratic Republic of Congo. These gorillas were formerly regularly hunted, but are now of greater use to lowland residents as a source of

income in the form of an ecotourist attraction. This may be the key to the future conservation of Asian and African cloud forests; despite being highly marginal habitats, they can generate a steady income if the type of human exploitation changes. Another example is the cloud forests of Kaua'i, in the Hawaiian Archipelago, where the last populations of endemic species are more valuable as tourist attractions than for any other type of use.

Domesticated animals

Cloud forests are harsh environments, and it appears that the animals adapted to them have developed specialized feeding techniques, behavior, and physiology. This implies that very few can be used as domesticated animals in tropical lowlands, although their use in temperate areas may be more successful. Useful characters from montane species may also be introduced into the genetic material of domesticated animals, providing greater tolerance of, for example, poor diet and bad weather. Close relatives of several domesticated or semi-domesticated animals live in the tropical cloud forests, often as relict populations on the brink of extinction due to habitat destruction and overhunting.

The Sumatran rabbit (*Nesolagus netscheri*), the Hainan hare (*Lepus peguensis hainanus*), the rare serow (*Capricornis sumatraensis*) from Sumatra and Malaysia and its near relative from Taiwan *C. crispus swinhoei* are examples of high-altitude species of potential use to humans. Finally, other potentially useful species include the highly endangered Visaya spotted deer (Prince Alfred's spotted deer) (*Cervus alfredi*) from the Visaya Islands (Philippines) and the Hainan brown-antlered deer (*C. eldi hainanus*), which is reared in captivity to obtain ingredients for a tonic wine popular in China.

Guinea pigs (*Cavia pocellus*), probably originally from central Peru, have been bred for their meat for 3,000 years in the mountains of South America. It is one of the few animals native to the Americas that has been domesticated, and is still commonly farmed in Ecuador, Peru and Bolivia. It is also bred in temperate areas, not for its meat, but as an animal for laboratory experiments and as a pet.

Gorillas in the mist

Dian Fossey, the American zoologist, at the Karisoke Research Center, Democratic Republic of Congo [Francesc Serrat & Àngela Dalmau]

Young coastal gorilla (Gorilla gorilla gorilla) [Jordi Sabater i Pi]

"He was called Digit but he is no more. His mutilated body, with his head and hands cut off for horrible trophies, lies inanimate amongst the bushes like a sack of blood." These are the opening lines to Dian Fossey's famous 1981 article in National Geographic that was to serve as a platform from which she described to the world her private crusade on behalf of the mountain gorillas. Digit, one of her most-loved gorillas, was killed by poachers in 1977, as much as anything as an act of revenge, but also as a warning. Dian Fossey herself fell foul of the machetes on December 27, 1985, victim of her own intransigent beliefs. Who was Dian Fossey and what was she doing in the jungle?

In 1963, after a first visit to Africa had kindled her enthusiasm, Dian Fossey, a 30-year-old American physiotherapist interested in zoology, decided to dedicate her life to studying the gorillas in the wild. Louis Leakey, her scientific mentor, somewhat doubtful in face of her sudden enthusiasm and in order to dissuade her, suggested that she should have her appendix removed as a precautionary measure before returning to Africa. Dian did not stop to think twice and after the operation, Leakey finally sent her out to the present-day Democratic Republic of Congo. The first few months living on the slopes of the Mikeno Volcano in the Virunga National Park were hard. Poorly housed, unable to communicate with the locals and lacking the material and the methodology (as yet undeveloped) to study the gorilla colonies, Dian was eventually expelled from the country during a war but managed to return immediately. She ended up in the Karisoke Research Center (1967) and settled in what was merely a collection of huts situated at 10,000 ft (3,000 m) on the Rwanda side of the Visoke Volcano, in the heart of the cloud forest of the Volcanoes National Park.

Male mountain gorilla (Gorilla gorilla beringe) in the Virunga National Park [Francesc Serrat & Àngela Dalmau]

Adult male coastal gorilla (*Gorilla gorilla gorilla*) [Jordi Sabater i Pi]

The Mikeno volcano (14,557 ft [4,437 m]) and Visoke (14,787 ft [4,507 m]) which straddles the border, lie side by side, as do the two National Parks (Virunga and Volcanoes), in Democratic Republic of Congo and Rwanda respectively. Virunga, in fact, also forms part of the border with the Sabinyo (11,959 ft [3,645 m]) and Muhavura (13,835 ft [4,217 m]) volcanoes in the southern tip of Uganda. The whole area is theoretically protected but the protection of national resources is, even at the best of times, not always compatible with the existence of human poverty. In this context, the prevention of poaching of mountain gorillas is a complex question as it is a source of income for those most in need. Dian Fossey set herself up as an implacable defender of the gorillas and died in the name of her cause.

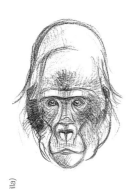

Adult male coastal gorilla (*Gorilla gorilla gorilla*) [Jordi Sabater i Pi]

World awareness of the problematic situation of the mountain gorillas is largely due to Dian Fossey's work. Her book *Gorillas in the Mist* was published in 1983 and was later made into a film. As a follow-up to her work, but against her better wishes, for she was in favor of isolating the gorillas from the humanized world, in 1978 the Mountain Gorilla Project was launched in the Volcanoes National Park in Rwanda. Its aims are to protect the gorillas and their habitat, promote ecotourism and develop education programs. In 1990 the Mountain Gorilla Project was extended to the Democratic Republic of Congo and Uganda borders and became known as the International Gorilla Preservation Project. Likewise, in Uganda, the Bwindi Jungle Conservation Project, an important regional project (124 sq mi [320 sq km]) was set up in the traditional home of the Twa pygmies as a part of the International Gorilla Preservation Project. Although 15 gorillas were poached in this area in the 1980s, since 1986 forest guards have managed to control poaching and a research center has been built. But why so much concern for this particular animal?

A family of mountain gorillas (*Gorilla gorilla beringei*) in the Virunga National Park [Francesc Serrat & Àngela Dalmau]

Young mountain gorilla (*Gorilla gorilla beringei*) in the Virunga National Park [Francesc Serrat & Àngela Dalmau]

There are three subspecies of gorilla: the coastal gorilla (*Gorilla gorilla gorilla*), found in the jungles of the Gulf of Guinea and with an estimated population of 10,000 individuals, the interior gorilla (*G. gorilla graueri*), the typical gorilla of the Zairean rain forest, with a population of only 400 individuals in the wild, and the mountain gorilla (*G. gorilla beringei*). This last subspecies is the rarest of all, because it is found only in the Virunga

tered adults are sold as macabre trophies to collectors.

Fossey fought the poachers and official passivity alone, though she primarily dedicated her time to studying the lives of the gorillas. Around the Karisoke Research Centre she identified four groups of gorillas, each headed by old males who she named Beethoven, Nunkie, Uncle Bert, and Rafiki. They lived in clearings in the forest surrounded by their food plants (*Galium ruwenzoriensis*, *Peucedanum linderi*, *Carduus nyassanus*, *Laportea alatipes*, *Prunus* [= *Pygeum*] *africanum*, etc.) and often descended on food-hunting expeditions to lower altitudes (7,874-8,858 ft [2,400-2,700 m]) for bamboo (*Arundinaria alpina*). Dian gave names to all the members of the groups, in total over 50, much as one would identify the inhabitants of a village. The personalized behavior patterns of each gorilla is one of the ways in which they most resemble humans: each individual has a distinct face and character and plays a particular role within the hierarchies and structures of the group. The gorillas react to the death or capture by poachers of another member of their group much as we would mourn the loss of a loved one. Coco, a young gorilla whose parents and companions were killed by poachers, cried like a baby for hours when she was brought to the Karisoke Research Centre. Perhaps Dian did as well.

cloud forests and had an estimated population of only 250 animals when Dian Fossey began her work, a figure which may have risen to 500 in 1992. The 1994 civil war in Rwanda appears to have affected the mountain gorilla population very badly, and the Karisole population has dispersed.

The mountain gorilla was unknown to science until the early 20th century. It has probably always been fairly scarce, although habitat destruction and persecution have made it even rarer and by the end of the 1970s these factors had pushed it to the

brink of extinction. The destruction of the Virunga cloud forests, dominated by enormous hagenias (*Hagenia abyssinica*) and mountain hypericums (*Hypericum revolutum*) was particularly intense in the 1960s and 1970s when the World Bank was promoting plantations of pyrethrum (*Tanacetum* [=*Chrysanthemum*] *cinerariifolium*), a source of insecticides. These plantations were unsuccessful and only succeeded in reducing local forests. Hunting of the mountain gorilla has also been an major problem—the offspring are sold live to zoos, and the head, hands and feet of the slaugh-

Dian Fossey died a bitter woman, obviously deeply depressed. She understood the mountain gorillas but perhaps failed to come to terms with the people of Virunga. Who was most responsible for the plight of the mountain gorillas, the poor poachers, or the educated western zoologists who paid them to capture young gorillas?

3. Management conflicts and environmental problems

3.1 Human impact on the cloud forests

The cloud forests are subject to pressures and threats that are no different from those affecting the lowland or montane rainforests. As already shown, they were among the first areas to be occupied and exploited by humans due to their relatively favorable climatic and environmental conditions. In many areas, human colonization of the cloud forest has over the centuries had a major impact.

The strategic value of the cloud forests

The cloud forests are an important reserve for the world community. Of all the tropical forests, they interact most directly with the atmosphere, and are probably one of the best indicators of climate change in the wet tropics. The cloud forest may be an important indicator ecosystem for monitoring the effects of global climate change. Due to its direct dependence on atmospheric phenomena, the cloud forest may serve as an early warning system for changes that may in future affect lowland ecosystems. Climate change will affect the cloud forest in several ways. The modification of the seasonal distribution of precipitation and cloud cover might alter the ecosystem's water balance. Observations made in a cloud forest in Natal, South Africa suggest that the increasing dryness of the Africa climate over the last 60 years has reduced the area of cloud forest. The species that now regenerate are those better adapted to arid conditions and are different from those typical of the original cloud forest environment. It is of course difficult to predict the effect of climate change on the structure and function of the cloud forest, but both are obviously closely related to atmospheric phenomena (cloud moisture, precipitation, relatively low temperatures and solar radiation), and thus may well serve as early indicators of the changes associated with global climate change.

The cloud forests are also important to the water cycle: For example, they help to catch and conserve the moisture from the clouds, as it is intercepted by the vegetation, which it channels and retains, avoiding both erosion and waterlogging. They thus provide clean, clear water for the villages and cities, whose supply is often put at risk by destruction of forest cover and silting of reservoirs with sediment borne downstream.

Effects of the pressure caused by overexploitation

Ethiopia, for example, the seat of empires for over 2,300 years, is now almost completely deforested and most of the country's population is now concentrated in the highland montane and cloud forest that occupy about 3% of the highland area. Also in Africa, but further to the south, the montane forests of Rwanda and Burundi are subject to intense pressure. These two states, the smallest countries in central Africa, have the highest population density in the African continent. During the 20th century the development of plantations of crops for export has added to the already intensive land use to support the population, and has greatly increased deforestation.

In the Philippines, almost all the remaining forests are in the highlands, but they too are threatened by the ever-increasing need for land to cultivate. The wave of immigration into these forests gives rise to high population densities, more than 200 people/sq km (1 sq km = 0.4 sq mi), far more than can be supported by the traditional system of shifting agriculture. A rough estimate of deforestation in the Philippines suggests the loss of about 1,000 sq mi (2,700 sq km) of cloud forest, with an estimated total of 19,305 sq mi (50,000 sq km) of rainforest remaining. Protected areas have been created to preserve part of these highland forests, but even these are now threatened by population pressure. Immigrants settled in the highlands and shifting agriculturists have crossed the boundaries into most national parks. As a result, the administrators are now pro-

247 **Destruction of the cloud forest** is not always the result of human activity. The photo shows an area of forest that has been completely destroyed by a volcanic episode, near Goma, in northeastern Democratic Republic of Congo.
[Photo: Xavier Ferrer]

248 The superb agricultural architecture developed by the Incas on the slopes of the Andes, such as these dry-stone terraces and walls still preserved in the area around Machu Picchu (Peru), makes it possible to conserve the soil despite the steep slope and intense rainfall. This strategy has unfortunately not been followed subsequently. [Photo: Francesc Serrat & Angela de Dalmau]

moting the concepts of the pre-park area and community participation. Within the national parks of Canlaon, Arayat, and Bataan, agroforestry development has started and some plantations have been established.

The tropical Andes of South America have been a major center of development since antiquity. The Inca empire, and other empires, such as the Tbitxa, developed agricultural systems that preserved the soil and water resources of the montane environment. From the 16th century onwards, however, European colonists eliminated these systems and started a period of 500 years of disastrous deforestation and soil erosion. Nowadays, the high biodiversity of the Andean cloud forests and other montane forests is threatened by increasing population pressure.

Like rainforests, the ecosystems of the cloud forests are a vanishing resource. They are disappearing even faster than other tropical forests, as these highly fragile ecosystems are threatened from all sides. The trees at the edge of the forest, and some within it, are logged for timber and fuel (firewood and charcoal). In countries like Panama, Guatemala, El Salvador and South Africa, the worst threat is tree felling by shifting agriculturists who only use the soil for a short period of time, as the cloud forest's ability to regenerate is not as great as that of the rainforest. In more densely populated countries, the demand for land from rapidly increasing populations leads even more strongly to the clearance of new

sites. Cattle grazing also has devastating effects within and around the cloud forest, because it leads to increased runoff and erosion, and creates tunnels for the wind to enter the unprotected understory.

The lowland rainforest has received great attention from conservationists and scientists, but the fate of the cloud forest unfortunately appears to interest only its inhabitants and the few scientists and managers who have had a chance to explore this unique and fascinating ecosystem.

3.2 From an extractive economy to ecotourism

The most important cause of deforestation in the world's cloud forests is the clearing of new land for agriculture. Logging and the extraction of other valuable plant resources has historically been less important, although it has also contributed to the cloud forest's decline. There are fewer species worth logging and they are less abundant than those of the lowland rainforest, and they are protected by the difficult access, but in some cases they too have been logged. The tree ferns are felled and shredded for use in as a horticultural medium, and excessive collection of orchids has damaged them and the surrounding vegetation. Yet as a whole these human interven-

249 **The systematic destruction of the cloud forest** has led to scenes as dramatic as this photo taken in the mountains of Chiapas (Mexico). Logging or clearing permits allow clearcutting of huge areas of forest, even in inappropriate mountainous conditions. It is in total contrast to the Inca philosophy exemplified by photo 248. [Photo: Xavier Ferrer & Adolf de Sostoa]

2. HUMANS IN THE CLOUD FORESTS

tions have not affected an area as large as that cleared to cultivate, for example in Central America, large areas of cloud forest, mainly with coffee. In Costa Rica, coffee, together with bananas, is a major export crop grown in both plantations and small plots in the cloud forest. In the mountains of eastern Africa, coffee and tea plantations have also been established mainly in the cloud forest.

Selective harvesting and genetic erosion

In Madagascar, due to the expansion of shifting agriculture and logging, there is now little undisturbed forest in the eastern region of the island, especially above 26,247 ft (8,000 m) where the cloud forests occur with many endemic plants. The last hope for the increasingly scarce remaining patches of cloud forest seems to be protection as reserves and national parks, for example the cloud forest in the Parc National de la Montagne d'Ambre, at the northernmost tip of Madagascar. The vegetation is threatened by the deliberate fires set in the surrounding bush and by the uncontrolled logging of tree species such as *Canarium madagascariense* (Burseraceae), and several species of *Dalbergia* (Leguminosae), as well as by the collection of ornamental plants, mainly epiphytic orchids (*Bulbophyllum, Angraecum,* and *Aeranthes*) and palms and tree ferns from the understory, all of them for sale. Some wild plants of arabica coffee (*Coffea arabica*) still grow in the

highlands of Ethiopia; the genetic base of cultivated coffee is very narrow, as it is based on the very few plants initially introduced direct from the forest. Unfortunately, both the remaining wild populations of the main cultivated species and the related species are disappearing rapidly. They might be as useful in breeding programs as the genes for resistance to coffee-rust (*Hemileia vastatrix*) found in wild varieties of coffee in the Kaffa region of southwest Ethiopia; these genes saved the Brazilian coffee industry from coffee rust in 1970. Ninety percent of the Abyssinian highland forest has already been destroyed. The wild gene pool of *C. arabica* is seriously threatened by deforestation, the replacement of primitive coffee plantations by modern cultivated varieties, and by drought. Madagascar has more than 30 wild species of *Coffea*, most of them now found only in reserves and other protected areas. Some might be of potential commercial importance in breeding programs, as their grains contain little or no caffeine. There has not yet been any research or conservation program.

Agriculture in the American cloud forest

The cool, wet climate of the cloud forest is ideal for the cultivation of many cash crops. They are also ideal for raising livestock, because pasture grows well. This has led to degradation of the soil, with very serious problems for the entire ecosystem. When the first Spanish conquista-

250 Rational agricultural activity is perfectly possible in the cloud forest. This is shown by well-run coffee plantations, such as this one in the central valley of Costa Rica.
[Photo: Francesc Serrat & Angela de Dalmau]

dores reached the Andean valleys of Colombia and Peru some 500 years ago, the skilled native people practiced rotatory cultivation of tubers, legumes and cereals, in accordance with a system that still survives in traditional agriculture. This provided a balanced diet and was a sustainable form of land use. After colonization, the dominant patterns of land use were transformed, resulting in over 500 years of widespread deforestation and soil erosion in the Andes. Very rapid population growth and the need to cultivate new ground or emigrate are further threats to the future of the cloud forests.

In Costa Rica, for example, together with plantation agriculture based on coffee (from Africa) and bananas (from the lowland rainforest of southeast Asia), the country's two main exports and basic source of income, subsistence agriculture is also practiced by farmers who own or rent 12-25 acres (5-10 ha), or even smaller, plots. Maize, beans, and rice are most important foodstuffs cultivated, together with other plants from both tropical and temperate climates. The crops are normally banana, papaya and citrus fruits, with an undercrop of vegetables, such as cabbages, tomatoes, red peppers, carrots, cauliflower, beans, and squashes, and even sometimes wheat. Some small farms also plant a few acres of wheat. Shifting agriculture is now little practiced in Costa Rica, but, as in the lowland, the traditional practice of growing several types of plant together in a single plot has been maintained.

In Peru, Bolivia, and Colombia it is legal to cultivate a limited quantity of coca plants, as it has traditional and practical uses, but illegal production is now a major problem. Thousands of peasants have entered *yungas* and even ridges (*cejas*) in lowland rainforest, to cultivate coca illegally for clandestine export by drug traffickers. It is estimated that this has led to the destruction of about 4,000,000 ac (1,600,000 ha) of rainforest and cloud forest, mainly in the valley of the River Huallaga in Peru. The illegal production of coca is a major source of foreign exchange, equal to roughly half all Peru's legal exports.

Ecotourism, the two sides of the coin

Parks and reserves in the cloud forest attract many tourists. In Costa Rica, Puerto Rico, and Guatemala, the cloud forests are visited by millions of tourists in a nondestructive way. Cloud forests are in these terms an underexploited resource. Before the consequences of the 1994 killings in Rwanda and the consequent civil war threatened its results, the International Mountain Gorilla Project had raised international awareness of the importance of these animals and the factors threatening their survival. Foreign tourists could enjoy themselves and learn by observing the animals in their natural habitat. These visitors were a good source of income in foreign currency for Rwanda, and helped to finance its conservation efforts. Similar centers were opened in Uganda and Democratic Republic of Congo. There was even a major change in the local people's perception of the mountain gorilla. In 1975, more than half of the people of Rwanda were hostile to gorillas, but 10 years later the majority was proud of them. Unfortunately, the consequences of the killings and the war have seriously threatened all the success achieved in the protection of this species, as well as that accomplished in the protection of some of the most important and vulnerable forest habitats in the cloud forests of Africa's Great Lakes region.

3
The protected areas and biosphere reserves in the cloud forest

1. The world's protected cloud forests

1.1 General considerations

Cloud forests are of great importance in the global water cycle and are considered to be the ecosystem most at risk from human pressure and agricultural expansion. Several countries have committed themselves to protecting these systems, although the wide range of forms of legal protection does not always ensure satisfactory regulation. The forms of protection range from strictly protected areas to simple forest reserves, national parks and nature reserves, all managed differently from one country to another. These include areas in the zone known as the Tierra fría ("cold land") in Central America and in the ceja in South America, in the highest peaks of the Caribbean Islands and the Afromontane refugia of East Africa, and in southeast Asia, from the Himalayas, via Malaysia, to New Guinea.

Moreover, some protected areas of rainforest, especially in the mountainous areas of the Americas, also end up with a band of cloud forest (see the section dealing with protected rainforest areas).

1.2 Parks and protected areas

In the New World tropics alone, there are more than 100 protected areas containing some cloud forest. The largest are the Isodoro Secure National Park in Bolivia (3,000,000 ac [1,200,000 ha]), the Pico de Neblina National Park in Brazil (5,400,000 ac [2,200,000 ha]), Cayambe-Coca in Ecuador (1,000,000 ac [400,000 ha]), the Darién National Park in Panama (1,500,000 ac [600,000 ha]), areas within the Peruvian national parks of Manú (3,700,000 ac [1,500,000 ha]) and Huascarán (85,000 ac [34,000 ha]), and the Venezuelan national parks of Canaima (7,400,000 ac [3,000,000 ha]) and Sierra de Neblina (3,360,000 ac [1,360,000 ha]). In the African tropics, the largest protected areas are the Volcanoes National Park in Rwanda (370,000 ac [150,000 ha]) and Ruwenzori National Park in Uganda (54,000 ac [22,000 ha]), Virunga National Park in Democratic Republic of Congo (1,900,000 ac [780,000 ha]) and Kilimanjaro National Park in Tanzania (198,000 ac [80,000 ha]).

The largest areas of protected montane forest in the Indo-Malaysian region are in Indonesia. The largest mountain chain contains large areas of intact montane rainforest, represented by the Gunung Leusur National Park in Sumatra (1,900,000 ac [790,000 ha]) and the national parks of Sungai Mentarang and Sungai Kayan in Kalimantan (3,900,000 ac [1,600,000 ha]) and Pulong Tau in Sarawak (395,000 ac [160,000 ha]). In the eastern Himalayas (India) there is also the Lado National Park (124,000 ac [50,000 ha]).

251 The world's best-known area of protected cloud forest is probably the Monteverde Reserve in Costa Rica. The photograph shows the many tree ferns, epiphytes and bamboos.
[Photo: Michael & Patricia Fogden]

252 The spectacular Angel Falls, a drop of 3,212 ft (979 m), is the highest waterfall in the world and the view most admired by visitors to Canaima National Park (Venezuela). More important than its spectacle is its geological significance: As it emerges from the Auyán tepuy, which reaches an altitude of almost 10,000 ft (3,000 m), as an outflow of the Churún River, an underground river, until it flows over the edge, 197 ft (60 m) below the clifftop. The water flows first into the Carrao, a tributary of the River Caroní, which is in turn a tributary of the Orinoco (see also figure 12).
[Photo: Jaume Altadill]

2. The UNESCO biosphere reserves in the cloud forest

2.1 Biosphere reserves in the cloud forest

There are 29 biosphere reserves in 17 African, Asian and American countries, covering a total of 16, 380,000 ac (6,630,000 ha), that include cloud forest ecosystems. The size of these reserves varies from the small Macchabee/Bel Ombre Biosphere Reserve (8,880,000 ac [3,594 ha]) on Mauritius, and the Sierra de Luquillo Biosphere Reserve in Puerto Rico, to the large spaces of the Sierra Nevada de Santa Marta Biosphere Reserve in Colombia and Manú in Peru (4,648,500 ac [1,881,200 ha], although most of the park is lowland or montane rainforest). In South America, there are six biosphere rainforest reserves that include cloud forest. There are six in Central America; in the Caribbean there are three; and in Africa there are nine and in Asia there are four.

2.2 The biosphere reserves in the American cloud forest

A good example of the New World tropics cloud forest in South America is the biosphere reserve of the Sierra Nevada de Santa Marta, which had previously been established as a national park in 1964, and covers a total area of 1,807,000 ac (731,250 ha). The park runs from the Caribbean coastline, with very well preserved coral reef, up to the high peaks (19,288 ft [5,879 m]) of the Sierra Nevada de Santa Marta (Colombia). At 10,000 ft (3,000 m) there is a native reserve where the Kogi and the Ika practice traditional agriculture in balance with the natural environment. The vegetation includes cloud forest and the *paramos* of the altiplanos, which go up to the snow line. Major forest species include the palms (*Scheelea magdalenica, Sabal mauritiiformis, Caludonica palmata*) and several climbing species of the genus *Desmoncus*. The endemic animals include the *carrikeri* subspecies of the cervid (*Mazama americana*) and the frog *Atelopus carrikeri*. A great deal of research is carried out in the reserve, into questions of socioeconomic organization and forest management and socioeconomic planning and production systems. Research into the hydrography and zooplankton is ongoing in the large Santa Marta wetlands, and archaeological research in the ruins of the Taironan culture, by the Colombian Institute of Archeology, is done as well.

The Sierra de Manantlán Biosphere Reserve

The Sierra de Manantlán Biosphere Reserve (Mexico) is a representative example of the American cloud forest, although it also contains lowland rainforest and monsoon forest. It was established to protect the exceptional natural beauty of the area, to reaffirm its scientific importance, to maintain its high diversity and to protect many species that are not found in any other type of forest. The reserve includes part of the Sierra Madre del Sur and acts as a bridge between two biogeographical kingdoms, the Holarctic and the Neotropical, and this has led to exchanges of species of northern temperate and tropical origins. This, together with the extraordinary range in altitude, climate and soils, is the reason for the area's extraordinary diversity. The importance of the Sierra de Manantlán was reaffirmed by the discovery of *Zea diploperennis*, an endemic wild relative of maize that is resistant to many diseases. The Sierra de Manantlán is one of Mexico's six internationally recognised Biosphere Reserves. It enjoys long-term legal protection and is preserved for its genetic resources and the natural ecosystems it contains.

Natural characteristics and features

The Biosphere Reserve is located on the border of two Mexican states; it includes part of southeastern Jalisco and part of northeastern Colima, and is about 16 mi (170 km) from Guadalajara, 32 mi (52 km) north of Manzanillo and about 31 mi (50 km) from the Pacific coastline. It covers 345,000 ac (139,577 ha), with a central area of 103,500 ac (41,901 ha) and other smaller areas, such as El Tigre and Cerro Grande. The central area is a combination of state-owned land, private communally-farmed land (ejidos), and university research stations, while the zone of influence, covering 241,362 ac (97,676 ha), consists of communal and private lands. The reserve contains

253 **Biosphere reserves (1998) in areas of cloud forest**, indicating the year each one was declared and its area. The area given (in hectares) is for the entire reserve, although it may include other types of formation, especially lowland rainforest. For example, most of the Manu Biosphere Reserve (Peru), one of the largest, is lowland rainforest, whereas the Palawan Biosphere Reserve also includes areas of monsoon forest. It should be borne in mind that in many cases the biosphere reserve was already protected as a national park, wildlife reserve, a forest reserve, and these may or may not coincide in size.
[Drawing: Editrònica, from data provided by the authors]

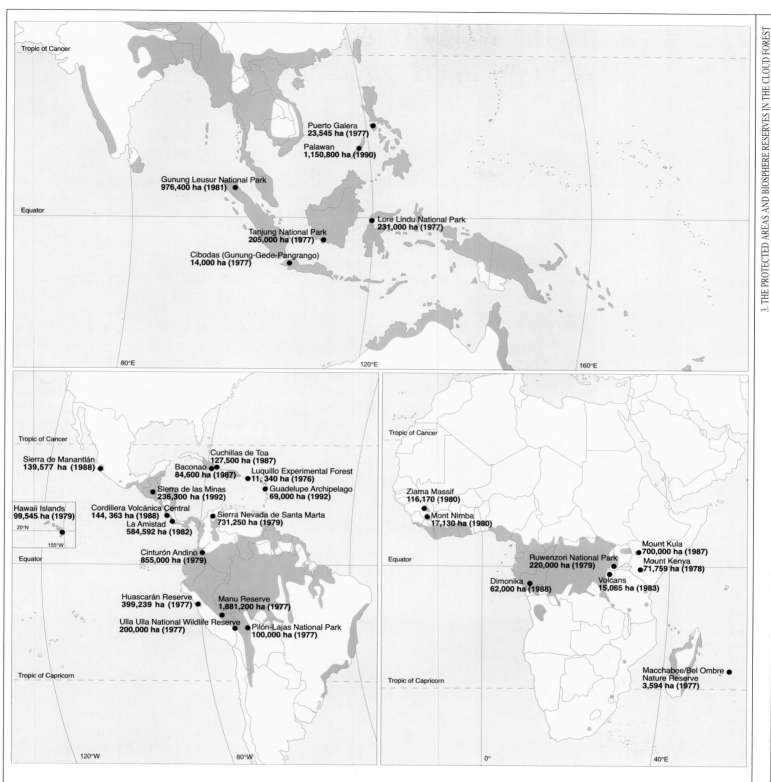

Puerto Galera
23,545 ha (1977)

Palawan
1,150,800 ha (1990)

Gunung Leusur National Park
976,400 ha (1981)

Lore Lindu National Park
231,000 ha (1977)

Tanjung National Park
205,000 ha (1977)

Cibodas (Gunung-Gede-Pangrango)
14,000 ha (1977)

Tropic of Cancer

Equator

80°E

120°E

160°E

Sierra de Manantlán
139,577 ha (1988)

Cuchillas de Toa
127,500 ha (1987)

Baconao
84,600 ha (1987)

Luquillo Experimental Forest
11,340 ha (1976)

Sierra de las Minas
236,300 ha (1992)

Guadelupe Archipelago
69,000 ha (1992)

Cordillera Volcánica Central
144,363 ha (1988)

Hawaii Islands
99,545 ha (1979)

La Amistad
584,592 ha (1982)

Sierra Nevada de Santa Marta
731,250 ha (1979)

Cinturón Andino
855,000 ha (1979)

Huascarán Reserve
399,239 ha (1977)

Manu Reserve
1,881,200 ha (1977)

Ulla Ulla National Wildlife Reserve
200,000 ha (1977)

Pilón-Lajas National Park
100,000 ha (1977)

Tropic of Cancer

Equator

20°N

155°W

Tropic of Capricorn

120°W

80°W

Ziama Massif
116,170 (1980)

Mont Nimba
17,130 ha (1980)

Ruwenzori National Park
220,000 ha (1979)

Mount Kula
700,000 ha (1987)

Mount Kenya
71,759 ha (1978)

Dimonika
62,000 ha (1988)

Volcans
15,065 ha (1983)

Macchabee/Bel Ombre
Nature Reserve
3,594 ha (1977)

Tropic of Cancer

Equator

Tropic of Capricorn

0°

40°E

18 river basins, with the typical landform of highly erosive watersheds. The main rivers are the Ayuquila and Armería Rivers to the north and the Marabasco and Purificación Rivers to the south. The limited absorption of water by the soil and rocky substrate means that runoff accounts for 45% of rainfall, leading to intense soil erosion and sediment accumulation in the valleys, where the rivers flow more slowly and deposit the sediment they bear. Over the course of the year, the Sierra de Manantlán supplies the valleys with a volume of water that is used by the over 4,000 people living in the area of influence. The reserve clearly shows the effects of volcanic and tectonic activity, and there are batholiths (igneous rock below the surface), faults, and volcanic domes formed from ancient seabeds. The dominant landscape features are the

254 There are many rare or noteworthy species in the Manantlán Biosphere Reserve. They include the famous teosinte (see figure 242), and the bird fauna contains interesting species such as Finsch's Amazon (*Amazonia finschi*).
[Photo: Xavier Ferrer & Adolf de Sostoa]

highlands in the northwest, igneous rocks that have formed a volcanic mountain block. There are a large number of rocks of varying chemical compositions; there are also eleven different soil types, none of them very fertile and all subject to erosion.

The climatic conditions in the Sierra de Manantlán range from hot to temperate. The reserve reaches an altitude of 6,398 ft (1,950 m) and its climate is basically cool and wet. Humidity is high due to the sea mist even in the dry season, although at altitudes between 1,312 and 9,711 ft (400 and 2,960 m) the temperatures are relatively cool. The average mean temperature is between 54 and 73°F (12 and 23°C) and the average annual rainfall is about 71 in (1,800 mm), mostly falling in just six months of the year.

255 The collared peccary (*Tayassu tajacu*) is another species in danger of extinction that finds refuge in the Manantlán Biosphere Reserve. It has long been hunted.
[Photo: Carol Farneti / Natural Science Photos]

256 One of the treasures of Manantlán's fauna, and one of its main ecotourist attractions, is the jaguar (*Panthera onca*). Undeniably one of the most impressive felines in the Americas, it is also highly endangered, even though its general range is very large and includes rainforest, dry tropical forest, and savannah.
[Photo: Carol Farneti / Natural Science Photos]

In terms of biodiversity, Mexico ranks fourth in the world after Brazil, Indonesia, and Colombia, and the Manantlán Biosphere Reserve in particular is one of the most important centers of biodiversity in Mexico. This biodiversity is the result of the wide range of ecological habitats and regions. Around 40-50% of the Mexico's plants are endemic, and many occur in the Sierra de Manantlán. The flora is especially rich with 1,958 species of plant, including about 160 species of orchid. Seventeen plants are endemic to the reserve, the most important of which is the wild relative of maize, teosinte or *chapule* (*Zea diploperennis*) discovered in 1977.

The reserve contains eight different types of forest, including mesophytic tropical forest, cloud forest, deciduous forest, and semideciduous forest. The tropical and subtropical vegetation includes tropical rainforest, which originally covered about 6% of the area, but half of this has now been deforested. Mexico has about 173,000 ac (70,000 ha) of mesophytic forest, 50,000 (20,000) of them in the reserve. The cool, moist climate favors the growth of mosses and lichens, together with other epiphytic plants (orchids, ferns and bromeliads), climbing plants and many fungi (including some highly toxic mushrooms and molds). Above 2,953 ft (900 m) the composition of the typical vegetation changes, and cloud forest becomes dominant, with pine-oak and pine-fir forest associations (*Pinus-Quercus* and *Pinus-Abies*), the pine-fir association becoming more abundant with increasing altitude. The ferns of the genus *Trichypteris*, the podocarps (*Podocarpus*) and the genera *Magnolia* and *Talauma* (Magnoliaceae) are very interesting survivors of a very ancient flora. Other interesting representatives include the grasses of the genus *Tripsacum* and a wild maize, *Zea mays* var. *parviglumis*. These wild relatives of cultivated maize are going extinct due to their replacement by cultivated varieties, although in the long-term they may be of great use in responding to changes in environmental conditions. In the past, many of these plants were threatened by large- and local-scale forest exploitation. Since the reserve's creation, a process of regeneration has begun that has mainly benefited the pines, as well as some hardwoods.

Mexico has the highest diversity of reptiles in the world, and the second highest number of mammals. It also has 8.7% of all the world's species of amphibian, 11% of all reptiles and 14% of all fish species. The reserve has more than 20 species of amphibian, 60 species of reptile, 336 species of bird (30% of those found in Mexico), 108 species of mammal (25% of those found in Mexico) and 16 species of fish. The more interesting mammals include the 6 species of feline that occur in Mexico, two of which, the jaguar (*Panthera onca*) and the ocelot (*Felis pardalis*) are in danger of extinction, and a third, the jagouarundi (*F. yagouaroundi*), which may also be endangered. Other species of mammals in danger of extinction include the river otter (*Lutra longicaudis*), the collared peccary (*Tayassu tajacu*), the Mexican shrew (*Megasorex gigas*), squirrel (*Sciurus colliaei*) and the Mexican mole (*Microtus mexicanus naveriae*). The endangered birds include the macaw *Ara militaris*, Finsch's Amazon (*Amazona finschi*), the crested guan (*Penelope purpurascens*) and the golden eagle (*Aquila chrysaetos*).

Management and problems

The reserve's area of influence is sparsely populated and anthropologists call it the "zona de Occidente" (the Western Zone), due to its clear difference from the rest of Central America. Pottery remains, figures and graves have been found and it is thought that before the Spanish Conquest the area was inhabited by the Otomí who built houses with roots, branches and mud, and thus left few remains. They depended on the forest for their food, clothing and shelter, and extracted fibers from the maguey (*Agave*) and cotton (*Gossypium*). The main crops, before and after the Conquest, were maize, chili peppers and fruit trees. The 18th century saw the introduction of ranching, which became important after the 1910 revolution. The Spanish Conquest of Mexico destroyed or modified many of the traditional land-use systems, which in the pre-Hispanic period were based on agroforestry.

About 32,000 people live in the Sierra de Manantlán Biosphere Reserve, about 5,000 of them permanent residents in the inner zone of influence and about 10,000 more in the outer zone of influence. Agriculture is still their main means of support, and they live in poor and marginal conditions as they are one of the most neglected groups in Jalisco, and the local caciques (political bosses) and logging companies often ignore their land rights. Those living in the zone of influence practice subsistence agriculture but also engage in intensive agriculture (maize, beans, tomatoes, sugarcane, watermelon, mango), raise stock, grow timber for construction, and firewood, charcoal production or mineral extraction. Teosinte (*Zea diploperennis*) is considered a potential future crop, as it is the only wild species that is resistant or immune to the seven main viruses that affect cultivated maize. Other activities undertaken in the reserve, in decreasing order of importance, are fishing and mollusc gathering, recreational activities, tourism, agroforestry projects, and aquaculture. Although commercial logging is not permitted in the central area, there are still piles of sawdust several meters tall remaining from logging that began in the 1940s. Between 1961 and 1976, 539,483 yd³ (414,987 m³) of wood were extracted (41,493 yd³ [31,918 m³] a year).

Long-term ecological studies are also being carried out in the reserve and conservation projects are under way for *Zea diploperennis*. Other endemic species are also being studied as is the conservation of animal and bird habitats. There is an integrated project for basic and applied exploitation of the land, sustainable management and conservation aims for the region. Other research activities include a systematic inventory, comparative ecology, ecological succession, restoration of ecosystems, ethnobiology, forest fires and their effects, forestry research, management of genetic resources, limnology and hydrology, pests and diseases, resource mapping, study of soils and their conservation, traditional land-use systems and environmental education. Other research has been planned, such as studies of rural technology, biogeochemical cycles, cultural anthropology, hydrological cycles, grazing land management, rare and/or endangered species, water management and animal population dynamics. The Las Joyas Natural Laboratory has become the most important center in this part of Mexico for research, due to the successful results obtained in the reserve.

The area's management is essentially in line with that of the other biosphere reserves in Mexico. There are a certain number of established objectives, including long-term research and control programs, the promotion of integrated rural development, local participation, environmental education,

257 **Collaboration between different countries** is often desirable when establishing protected areas, as political and administrative frontiers rarely have biogeographical significance. One example of this collaboration is the Mount Nimba Biosphere Reserve, between Guinea and Ivory Coast.
[Photo: Peter Davey / Bruce Coleman Limited]

information exchange and recreational activities. The central area is strictly protected, but berries and fungi are still gathered, river crustaceans are caught and wood is extracted. Approximately 3,088 acres (1,250 ha) has been fenced off to prevent livestock and shifting farmers from entering. The inner zone of influence has a similar status, but there is no information on the activities carried out in it. Legal protection is not so strict in the external zone of influence, where activities include agriculture, grazing, timber production, firewood extraction, mineral extraction, fishing, recreational activities, tourist development, agroforestry projects and aquaculture. Despite the area's management as a biosphere reserve, unauthorized grazing occurs, as does poaching in the central area. Other potentially prejudicial activities are also practiced in the outer area of influence, such as poaching, grazing of cattle, industrial development, and changes in land-use. There are also some settlements. Several of these activities may exceed the limits established by the reserve's regulations.

In general, the most severe restrictions within the reserve apply to matters like the excessive grazing throughout the area, forest fires, logging, soil degradation, loss of genetic resources, poaching and the illegal cultivation of marijuana (*Cannabis sativa*) and opium poppy (*Papaver somniferum*). In the case of grazing, the situation is made worse by the fact that the livestock usually belongs to people who do not live in the area, but rent the land for use as grazing, thus eliminating the cattle deprives the local inhabitants of this income.

2.3 The biosphere reserves in the African cloud forests

In the Afrotropical kingdom there are two adjacent biosphere reserves (one in Ivory Coast and the other in the Republic of Guinea) on Mount Nimba, which has been created from previously protected areas (in 1943 in Ivory Coast, and in 1944 in Guinea) on the frontier between the two countries. Located in an area rising from about 1,476 ft (450 m) to a highest elevation of 5,748 ft (1,752 m), the reserves are covered almost year round by a dense cloud layer above 2,789 ft (850 m).

More than 2,000 plant species have been described and more than 500 new species of animals, more than 200 of them endemic. The more interesting endemic plants include a fern *Asplenium schnelli*, together with *Osbeckia portersi* (Melostomataceae) and *Blaeria nimbana* (Ericaceae). This region has been recognized as a center of plant diversity by the Plant Conservation Programme developed by IUCN and WWF (*Centres of Plant Diversity* project). In addition to the cloud forest, it also includes the highest mountain open areas, with *Loudetia kagarensis*. At higher altitudes, mainly in gullies and gorges, there is a fern, *Cyathula cylindrica*, that is a relict of ancient cloud forests. Above 3,281 ft (1,000 m) the dominant species is the gingerbread plum (*Parinari excelsa*), accompanied by many epiphytes. At altitudes between 3,281 and 5,249 ft (1,000 and 1,600 m), the savannah is criss-crossed by gallery forest. At the base of the mountain there

258 The beauty of rhododendrons, in this photo *Rhododendron javanicum*, is among the attractions of some of the biosphere reserves in the cloud forests of southeast Asia, such as Cibodas Reserve (Indonesia). [Photo: Alain Compost / WWF / Still Pictures]

is primary forest, dominated by obeche (*Triplochiton scleroxylon*), iroko (*Chlorophora regia*), and idigbo (*Terminalia ivorensis*).

Habitat destruction is the main threat facing both these biosphere reserves, mainly as a result of shifting agriculture and mining activity (iron ore extraction) in the south of the range, in Liberia, because this has led to the construction of roads and mining (for iron minerals) and settlement in sites that have been nature reserves for 50 years. In 1989 the authorities in Ivory Coast and Guinea signed a convention with UNESCO and the United Nations Development Program (UNDP) to start a project to study the impact within the reserve of traditional agricultural methods and ion ore extraction.

2.4 Biosphere reserves in the Indo-Pacific cloud forests

The Cibodas Biosphere Reserve is one of the oldest protected areas in the Indo-Malaysian region. The 600 ac (240 ha) site was declared a nature reserve in 1889, the first in what was then the Dutch East Indies, now Indonesia, next to the already existing Cibodas Botanic Garden. The reserve rises from 3,280-9,938 ft (1,000-3,029 m) (the peak of Mount Pangrango), in one of the wettest areas of Java. The annual rainfall varies from 118-158 in (3,000-4,000 mm), and the highest areas have cloud cover throughout almost the entire year. The park contains many types of vegetation, but most is covered by cloud forest. In the wettest areas, between 4,593 and 5,249 ft (1,400 and 1,600 m) in altitude, the forest is characterized by the abundant presence of bryophytes, a canopy more than 131 ft (40 m) high with many epiphytes, such as the bird's-nest fern (*Asplenium nidus*) and 208 species of orchid. The more important canopy species include the highly commercially valuable *Altingia excelsa* (Hamamelidaceae), and several members of the Lauraceae (*Litsea*) and Fagaceae (*Lithocarpus*). Above 5,413 ft (1,650 m), the dominant species are *Leptospermum flavescens* (Myrtaceae) and the conifer *Podocarpus neriifolius*. Above 7,874 ft (2,400 m) there is a subalpine association whose most notable characteristictic is the large number of genera originally from the temperate regions of the northern hemisphere. In the park and surrounding areas, 245 species of bird have been recorded, including a number endemic to Java, especially the pygmy tit (*Psaltria exilis*), known only from this western area of the mountains of Java. The reserve is uninhabited, although the surrounding lowlands are among the most densely populated areas of Java. The park received more than 30,000 visitors a year in the late 1970s, together with another 200,000 visitors to the neighboring Cibodas Botanic Garden. The region has a long history of research going back to the early 19th century when the Botanic Garden was created. A 1978 management plan has divided the reserve into an intensively used area for tourism, a wildlife zone, different strictly protected sanctuary areas, and buffer zone around it. The most important disturbances are agricultural intrusions on the edges, the great impact made by visitors' acts of vandalism and aggression against the natural flora, and the collection of firewood and other forest products by local residents.

Tropical monsoon forest environments

The rains had come, with a force and extravagance which swelled the river and filled the tanks to overflowing in four or five days. In the borders and in the midst of the barren paths tender seedlings sprang up, nourished only by the downpour of warm rain. The old banyan and the huge mango trees appeared in the full dignity (...) So violent were they that, once the hysterical rejoicing at their arrival was over, people began to feel a vague sense of alarm and to talk of the legendary great flood which had happened in the days of the evil Maharajah.

Louis Bromfield
The rains came (1937)

1
Between evergreen
and deciduous leaves

1. The monsoon regime

1.1 Seasonal monsoon changes

Moução or *monção*, the Portuguese word from which the English word "monsoon" and the equivalent term in most European languages are derived, is the name for the seasonal winds that alternately brings rain and dry conditions to several tropical regions, especially southern Asia. The word (and the concept) was used by the Portuguese navigators who began to cross the Indian Ocean in the early 16th century after learning it from the Arabs who had been sailing these waters for several centuries. For them it represented the appropriate season for sailing to India or to return to the coasts of eastern Africa, as in Arabic the word *mawsim* or *mawsam* means the datè or fixed season for carrying out a given activity. In fact, it was necessary to make use of the summer monsoon, which blows from the west or southwest bringing torrential rains to India and the whole of southern Asia, in order to sail from eastern Africa to the Indian subcontinent. To return, it was also necessary to wait for the winter monsoons that blow from the center of the Asian continent towards the Indian Ocean and across the Gulf of Oman from the northeast or east.

The summer and winter monsoons

In reality, the monsoon area has two different types of climatic conditions, giving rise to a relatively long dry season, even though annual rainfall is high. The monsoon, as understood by most climatologists, is a constant flow of winds from the west in the tropical regions between western Africa and the New Hebrides at variable latitudes, depending on the season (further to the north in the northern summer, further south in the southern summer), coinciding with the intertropical convergence zone (ITCZ). It is only noticeable over the oceans, especially the Indian Ocean, where it has long been as important for sailing boats as the trade winds are in other oceans.

In the northern summer, this flow coincides with the depressions that form over the Asian continent,

generating strong moisture-laden winds (summer monsoons) that bring intense rainfall to much of southern Asia from June to September or October. The situation is the opposite in the northern winter, when the flow from the west is situated south of the equator and the high pressures that form over the frozen interior of Asia establish cool winds (winter monsoons) that leave much of southern Asia without rain, except for eastern India and Indochina and many of the islands of Insulindia, which still receive the moisture borne on the trade winds.

Atypical monsoons

A similar phenomenon occurs in western Africa, although on a more local scale, as a result of the alternation of winds from the west of the Gulf of Guinea (monsoon) in summer, and the desiccating wind which blows from the Sahara south-westwards to the Guinea coast (the *harmattan*), in winter. In the southern hemisphere, in northern Australia, a situation occurs that is notably symmetrical to that of southern India, although on a smaller scale, bearing in mind the differences in size and relief between Asia and Australia. When southern Asia is experiencing its summer monsoon, northern Australia is experiencing its winter monsoon, and vice versa.

To the contrary, on eastern-facing coastlines, mainly in southern Asia, but also in Australia and some regions of South America, there is a different type of monsoon climate that is less extreme due to the relatively regular presence of the trade winds. Although rainfall is more evenly distributed over the course of the year, it is also concentrated within a relatively brief period in the autumn (from September to December in the northern hemisphere).

The mechanisms of the monsoon climate

As one travels north or south away from the equator, the sun is lower in the sky and the amount of energy it delivers is less. At latitudes between 10° and 25° (N or S), the solar heating of the land surface is only strong enough to produce a great rising

259 Monsoon forest may be even more lush than true rainforest, with a comparable abundance of epiphytes and climbing plants. The trunk of this specimen of *Geissois benthamii* (Cunnoniaceae) in the monsoon forest of Queensland (Australia) is covered in mosses and small epiphytic ferns. The tree's fork houses a large specimen of *Asplenium australasicum* and there are stems of the liana *Austrosteenisia glabristyla* winding up its trunk. [Photo: Jean-Paul Ferrero / Auscape International]

260 Air movements during the summer monsoon (June to October) in India along the section indicated in the map. The same phenomenon occurs in the north of Australia, the coast of Guinea and coastal areas of Colombia and Panama, although its effects may temporarily reach the edge of the dry areas. The monsoon climate is controlled by the monsoon system, winds whose direction changes seasonally. This climate typically shows a very sharp alternation between a dry season, in the winter, and a rainy season, in the hot season, with the world's highest rainfall. At the summer solstice, in India the intertropical convergence zone is between 10°N and 15°N, and reverses the direction of the dominant winds on its southern front, which change from southeasterly (southern trade winds) to southwesterly (monsoon). The equatorial flow from the west provides the monsoon with its humidity, turning it into a very unstable mass of hot wet air. Due to the convergence of the northern trade winds, the relief, the combination of both phenomena, or irruptions at height of cold air masses from the central Asian plateau, in the summer monsoons large vertically-rising air masses form. They are of greater importance on the windward side of the highest features of the relief, and cause intense rainfall. The monsoon rains, because they coincide with the summer, allow the growth of tropical forest with deciduous species and highly productive agriculture.
[Drawing: Editrònica, from an original published by D.W. Goodall]

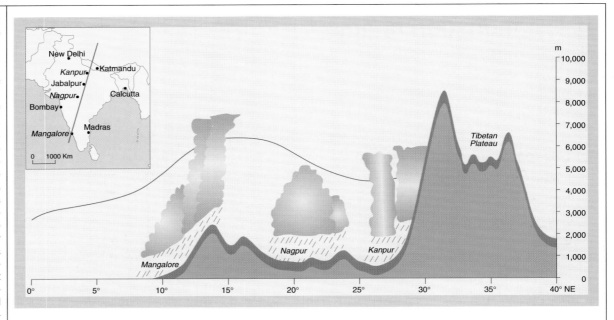

convection zone (a low pressure region) during the months of summer, when the sun its at its highest.

Over southern Asia, this northward meander of the intertropical convergence zone (ITCZ) takes place between June and October, delivering a huge amount of rainfall from the moist air it has absorbed when crossing the Indian Ocean. The south Asian monsoon is the strongest in the world, because the huge Himalayan massif acts as if it were a solar panel that heats up under the summer sun and helps to set off the occlusion of rising air currents. As the moist air is brought in, it rises and cools, and the water condenses out in the form of rain. The latent heat released when the water condenses keeps the air relatively warm, so that it continues rises through the atmosphere maintaining the strength of its upwards flow. The corollary of the summer rains of the monsoon climate is winter dryness, when hardly any rain falls. Plants and animals living in monsoon areas must thus adapt to a climate that delivers water in vast excess during part of the year, followed by months of drought.

Other outer tropical and subtropical areas have weaker monsoon-type climate systems that operate by the same basic model and gradually merge into the ever-wet equatorial climates as one approaches the equator. Other seasonally dry climates, with several wet months, occur in several areas of the tropics close to the equator, where diverse factors block the inflow of moist air during part of the year. For example, in the Far East, a belt of relatively arid climate runs north-south across the central islands of Malesia (Philippines, eastern Sulawesi, Eastern Java, the Lesser Sunda Islands and Bali).

1.2 The advantages and disadvantages of the winds and rains

Rainfall in the area of monsoon or seasonal forest may be greater than in large parts of the rainforest area. The factor distinguishing the monsoon climate, and the one that determines many of the differences between its vegetation and that of the rainforest, is the existence of a relatively long dry season (more than three months in a row with less than 2.4 in [60 mm] of rain). Yet this dry season varies in length and intensity, which explains the variations in monsoon vegetation and the undetectable change into the more open woody formations dealt with in volume 3.

Monsoon rains

In general the monsoons appear suddenly (known as the "bursting of the monsoon" to British colonists) on the western coastline of India and the Bay of Bengal in the first fortnight of June, bringing to an end the very hot, dry spring. For the next three or four months, rain falls irregularly throughout the monsoon forests of southern Asia. However, the monsoons also bring some rain, less widespread and for shorter periods, to the areas of savannah and the open tropical woody formations in the area.

Later, in September or October, and in a less violent manner, although typhoons from the South China Sea cannot be excluded, the rainfalls peaks

261 The proverbial violence of the monsoon rains is clearly shown by this photo of the streets of an Indian city in a seasonal storm, and the relative indifference of the local people, who are accustomed to this type of event. *[Photo: Pillitz / Network / Age Fotostock]*

reach the coastal regions of the China Sea on the Indochina Peninsula. Strictly speaking, most of these areas do not have a long dry season and are more like rainforests.

Something similar occurs in many points of the western shores of the Bay of Bengal, along the eastern coastline of the Indian subcontinent.

The monsoon temperatures

Temperatures also follow a seasonal pattern. Although they do not vary greatly from month to month, there is a peak at the end of spring, immediately before the arrival of the summer monsoon, and in the most typical cases in south Asia, temperatures may oscillate between extremes.

262 The distribution of the world's monsoon forests (shown in dark green) on the total area of rainforest (in light green), and ombrothermic diagrams of four sites representing the different areas of the biome. Each diagram shows altitude and latitude (in black), average temperature (in red) and average annual rainfall (in blue). Annual average temperatures are between 81 and 82°F (27 and 28°C), and average annual rainfall is between 61 and 43 in (1,563 and 1,085 mm). The diagrams show how highly seasonal the biome is. The rainfall curve rises spectacularly every year, approximately between April and November in the northern hemisphere and from September to May in the southern hemisphere. Between December and March in the northern hemisphere and from March to September in the southern hemisphere there is a very dry period (the months when the temperature curve is above the rainfall line). There are never any frosts.

[Photo: Editrònica, from data provided by the authors]

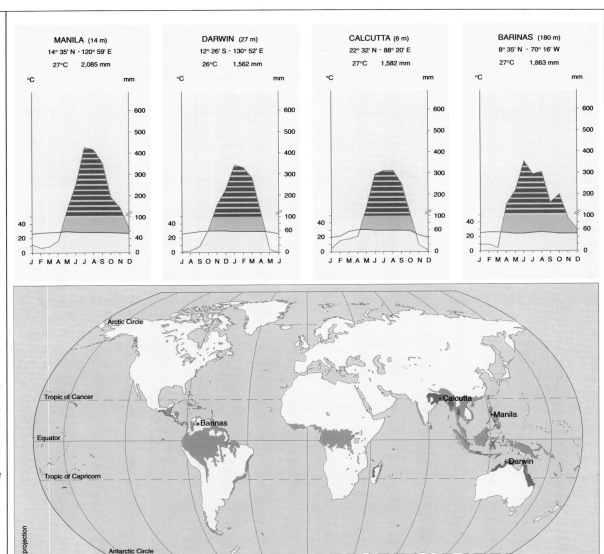

MANILA (14 m)
14° 35' N - 120° 59' E
27°C   2,085 mm

DARWIN (27 m)
12° 26' S - 130° 52' E
26°C   1,562 mm

CALCUTTA (6 m)
22° 32' N - 88° 20' E
27°C   1,582 mm

BARINAS (180 m)
8° 35' N - 70° 16' W
27°C   1,863 mm

Robinson projection

The maximum temperatures during the weeks preceding the summer monsoon may easily exceed 104°F (40°C), although the average remains about 86°F (30°C). In many areas in India, for example, the maximum temperature in the month of May may exceed 113°F (45°C), with low humidity and frequent dust storms in deforested areas. Where the summer monsoon arrives later, effectively in the autumn, the highest temperatures also precede the monsoon, but last longer, virtually the entire summer. The arrival of the rains causes a gradual decrease in peak temperatures and rise of the minimum temperatures, buffering the daily temperature variations. The daily temperature range may, especially in the dry season, be as large as in rainforest gaps or in its upper canopy.

During the dry season, differences of 27°F (15°C) between the minimum and maximum daily temperatures are not uncommon. The suffocating heat of the weeks before the summer monsoon, attenuated only by the relatively cool nights, followed by the torrential rains and cooler temperatures at the beginning of the rainy season, is highly characteristic of the temperature regime of the monsoon forest. In the monsoon regions of southern Asia, the months of January and February are usually the coolest.

The violence of the rains at the beginning of the monsoon summer often causes major flooding in low-lying areas and major erosion of deforested slopes. Yet much of the agricultural production in monsoon regions and the livelihood of huge numbers of peasant farmers in some of the most densely populated areas of southern Asia depends on the punctual arrival and adequate quantity of these rains. When the monsoons arrive late, this has historically been the cause of famine and major disasters for the human population.

2. The range of soils in the monsoon zones

2.1 Soil formation

Knowledge of the soils of the monsoon areas is still partial. Thorough studies have been carried out in India, Thailand, and Indonesia (eastern Java), however, that serve as a basis to extract some basic ideas for the monsoon area as a whole.

In these areas, the soils have formed on a wide range of sedimentary, metamorphic and eruptive rocks and middle and upper Pleistocene alluvial terrace deposits. The soil formation processes are similar to those of the tropical rainforests and may be compared with the type of ferrallitic weathering that is characterized by intense weathering of primary minerals, intensive washing of basic cations (Ca^{2+}, Mg^{2+}, and K^+) and the formation of kaolinitic clay accompanied by the release of free iron oxides (hematites, goethite) and aluminum oxide (gibbsite). As the monsoon area of southern and southeastern Asia is highly dissected, there are the remains of old Tertiary peneplains; the soils have been rejuvenated and most are in the intermediate stages of ferrallitic weathering. Consequently, some soils may develop clay horizons due to the mobility of the clays because of their low cation content, while ferralsols occupy only a small area.

2.2 Soil types

The monsoon area is dominated by vertisols, at least in India. Yet there are also other types of soils, depending on the factors involved in their soil formation.

Peneplain soils

The southern part of the Deccan Peninsula in India is mainly occupied by reddish sandy soils with clay accumulation horizons (argillic) dominated by kaolinites, illites and lesser fractions of montmorillonite, mixed with iron oxides. The soils of the central part of the Deccan Peninsula have formed over a basalt shield; they are vertisols, and typically have a high smectite clay content (40-60%); smectite clays undergo large changes in volume (expanding and contracting) on wetting and on drying out.

Because of the monsoon climate's typical alternation of rainy and dry seasons, the soils alternately crack in the dry season and expand in the wet season, thus mixing together materials in the horizons affected. These soils' scientific name, vertisols, comes from the Latin word vertere (to turn), but they are locally known as regurs ("black cotton soils") because their high content of organic chemicals in the form of gray humic acids, tightly bound to the mineral material and giving the soil a dark gray color. They are argillaceous (clayey) with a well-developed structure (in which there has not been intense washing of basic cations), and thus slightly basic (pH 7 to 8.5). In higher areas, vertisols are shallow and are associated with leptosols where erosive processes on basalt rocks are most active.

Alluvial soils

The river valleys, coastal floodplains, deltas, estuaries, and coastal plains in the monsoon forest area have different types of soils. They are soils that have developed on alluvial recent and subrecent deposits, where the original material was transported in suspension in the water and then deposited. As this material may come from different sources, its mineral composition is often very heterogeneous. Many are temporarily or permanently waterlogged and are at risk of flooding.

In the monsoon forests and in other tropical areas, the micro-relief of the coastal plains and estuaries may have a clear influence on their soil development. The presence of levées (raised sandbanks running along the watercourses) is the result of periodic surges, as most of the coarse sediment is immediately deposited when the velocity of the

263 **Soils suitable for agriculture** are common in the monsoon areas, allowing the cultivation of large areas of land, such as these rice paddies in Sri Lanka.
[Photo: Montserrat Ferrer]

water diminishes. In well-drained *levées* in rivers fluvisols develop, fertile recent alluvial soils, subject to occasional flooding. The subrecent alluvial deposits develop cambisols, more developed soils with some differentiation into different horizons.

Acid soils of coastal plains and flooded environments

Coastal plains in the tropical may develop acid sulfate soils. In these soils, development processes lead to sulfuric acid production, possibly in amounts large enough to affect many of the soil's characteristics. Acid sulfate soils may develop from immature muds with a pH from 7-8 that are almost permanently flooded. If for any reason the level of the water table falls, for example as a result of drainage, the soil is aerated and oxidizes to form an acid clay with sulfates and a pH as low as 2 or 3. The final stage is characterized by the appearance of straw-yellow patches of a double sulfate of iron and potassium, called jarosite. These acid environments also undergo a process known as ferrolysis, the breakdown of the clays

and the washing of iron, which is lost. Ferrolysis occurs when alternating oxidizing and reducing conditions occur over the course of the year in an acid environment in the absence of carbonates.

And finally, in the lower parts of the swamp area, there are peat formations, organic soils—histosols.

2.3 The potential of the soil

A large part of the monsoon area used to be occupied by forests. These forest soils are now occupied by rice paddies and other tropical crops. Yet agricultural use often does not always properly match the soil's potential.

Soils suitable for agriculture

Unlike the highly eroded and leached soils of the rainforest, the monsoon forest's soils are general-

ly much more suitable for continuous agriculture and for supporting large human populations.

The major limitations of these red sandy soils' for plant growth are similar to those of the rainforest, except on slopes, which in the monsoon area are generally steeper. Therefore, land use on these slopes must prevent erosion by adopting conservation measures. The most important factors limiting agricultural use of vertisols are physical ones: insufficient permeability, formation of very hard aggregates on drying, and the irregular microrelief in unworked fields.

The seasonal alteration of cracking and expansion gives rise to undulations in the soil surface, which is known as "gilgai" relief, as well as breaks roots and makes the soil hard to work. Despite this, its high chemical fertility makes it agriculturally important.

In some tropical areas, especially in rice-producing countries, alluvial soils are essential for food production. In coastal plains and the estuaries formed of siliceous materials, and in the absence

of calcium carbonate, flooded soils that produce sulfides may cause many problems if they are naturally drained or are used agriculturally by humans.

Hydromorphic soils, located mainly in marshy areas of coastal plains, are frequently used to grow rice. Other crops experience the problems of poor drainage together with the risk of flooding, which crops and buildings must be protected from.

Marginal soils

Acid sulfate soils show very low structural stability and a limited cation exchange capacity, meaning they are totally unsuitable for agricultural use.

As their recovery or improvement requires flood prevention and drainage works, even for rice cultivation, histosols are generally considered suitable only for agricultural uses in the case of very specific crops.

3. The world's monsoon forests

3.1 Monsoon vegetation

As already pointed out, the alternation of the monsoon season with an intervening dry season does not allow the establishment of equatorial (intertropical) rainforest, as rainforest grows only where the dry season is less than three months long. The monsoon climate favors the establishment of its own distinctive plant cover and associated fauna: the monsoon forest.

Leafloss due to seasonal drought

Where there is enough rainfall in the summer, generally more than 35 in (900 mm), but also an intense dry period lasting several months, the natural vegetation is the monsoon forest. As a consequence, the wildlife's natural rhythm is closely linked to the seasons.

The leaves are shed in the dry months of winter, many trees losing all their leaves. Many deciduous species have soft, damp leaves, closer in texture to the leaves of the temperate deciduous forest trees than to the shiny and thicker leaves of rainforest trees. The leaves are often compound (divided into smaller leaflets) and belong to tree members of the Leguminosae, an important family with many thousands of species throughout the world's temperate and tropical regions. Buttress roots are uncommon in monsoon forests and the trees tend to be shorter (66-82 ft [20-25 m] tall) and have more open crowns. The rainforest has large trees and a whole range of different heights, but monsoon forest generally has a very simple structure, with a single uniform canopy layer. More light reaches the soil in the monsoon forest, and so a grass layer may grow there during the wet season, dying back in the dry season.

As in equatorial rainforests, temperatures in the monsoon forest never reach freezing point, even in winter. Yet the highest temperatures may be far higher than those occurring normally in the rainforests, where the continuous rain cools the air upon evaporating from the leaves of the plants. In the hottest months of the year, just before the beginning of the summer rains, the daily temperatures in monsoonal south Asia may exceed 113°F (45°C). When the cool rains arrive, temperatures fall greatly making life more much pleasant for the human population.

The splendors and limitations of the monsoon forests

Many of the trees of the monsoon forests belong to the same abundant and variable species found in the equatorial rainforests. However, they often differ noticeably from their rainforest relatives in appearance and behavior. The diversity of plants and animals in the monsoon forests is almost always lower than in comparable nearby areas of rainforest and the longer the dry season is, the fewer species there are. Even so, both plant and animal species diversity in these dry forests is generally much greater than in temperate and northern forests.

Drought and the associated fires are the main hazards facing the plants and animals of the monsoon forest. Fires are most frequent during the summer months, but if the rains are late—meaning that summer temperatures may reach their potential peak values—the forest fires may be very severe. Spreading through the dry grass and the litter of the forest floor, fire is most destructive if it reaches the canopy and if the dry twigs of the dormant trees catch fire.

During the dry season, monsoon forest trees shed their leaves gradually, probably as a direct response to drought stress. This is when most trees and herbaceous plants flower, as the open space created by the fall of the canopy's leaves means they are more conspicuous to pollinators. The tree's new foliage tends to appear shortly before the rains begin, perhaps in

265 Seasonal shedding of leaves is the most typical feature of the monsoon forests, distinguishing it from the evergreen rainforest. The vegetation becomes more deciduous as the seasonality of the climate increases, reaching its limit in the transition areas towards drier subtropical forest. This is clearly shown by these two photos of the same forest in Chamela on the Pacific coast of Mexico, the upper one taken in the wet season, and the lower one taken in the dry season.
[Photo: Xavier Ferrer & Adolf de Sostoa]

response to the slight drop in temperatures that marks the arrival of the first moist air.

3.2 The south Asian and Malesian monsoon forests

The monsoon forest in southern Asia would naturally spread from India and Bangladesh east to Thailand and Laos. With a history of civilization stretching back almost 5,000 years, the area is the most densely populated and, in some ways, the most extensively modified of all the world's regions with a monsoon climate.

The floristic components

A botanist familiar with the equatorial rainforest of the Far East would find that the monsoon forests of southern Asia contain some of the same genera of trees, although their lower and less upright growth habit, together with their seasonal leaf-fall behavior, would make it difficult to recognize them at first. Dipterocarps are abundant and diverse, and include the economically important species sal (*Shorea robusta*), a closely relative of the emergent trees that rise above the canopy in the rainforests of the Malayan Peninsula and Borneo.

Other noteworthy trees of the monsoon forest include teak (*Tectona grandis*, Verbenaceae) and pyinkado (*Xylia dolabriformis*, Leguminosae), both valuable timber producers. Teak grows best in the well drained soils that form over igneous rocks, thriving under a regime of occasional ground fires that clear the undergrowth. Tropical pines, such as *Pinus kesiya* from the Philippines, also grow naturally in the monsoon forest, and are a useful source of timber for building. All these trees are encouraged by foresters, who plant them and protect them by selective removal of economically less important species. These forestry resources form a substantial part of the indigenous and national economies of the countries in the monsoon belt.

Many of the tree species of the monsoon forests of southern Asia also occur in the monsoon areas of the central islands of Insulindia. For example, the neem tree (*Azadirachta indica*, Meliaceae), often cultivated for forage, appears to grow wild in Java, as well as in India, Myanmar and Thailand. It is thought that several monsoon forest species managed to spread across the intervening area of rainforest climate during the Ice ages, when the much lower sea levels exposed the continental platform between the islands forming a single landmass known as Sundaland. It is believed that the climates of the Sundaland area were generally much more seasonal than they are now, which made it possible for monsoon forest to spread across areas that are now moist enough for rainforest to grow. When moist climates returned at the beginning of the current warm phase (beginning about 10,000 years ago), the trees of the monsoon forest survived in several pockets with climates dry enough for them to avoid being outcompeted by rainforest.

The effects of human activity on the landscape

Human activity has affected these areas so intensely that it is often difficult to imagine what the original natural vegetation must have been like. Frequent fires and grazing by livestock have in many sites reduced the former monsoon forest to spiny scrub, whereas without human interven-

tion other areas that are now monsoon forest would probably be evergreen rainforest.

In Myanmar (formerly Burma) the monsoon forest tends to grow on shallow poor soils, whereas deep soils with good water supplies support evergreen rainforest. In Thailand, where the climate is drier, there are even more forest types, ranging from open, arid forests with solitary trees up to 66 ft (20 m) tall found on shallower soils to the much taller evergreen rainforests in river valleys. The summer monsoon rains are most marked in India, where some lowland areas may suffer major flooding lasting for 4-8 months, completely drying out only in the winter. The only remaining Indian monsoon forests are in a few areas inaccessible to grazing animals and the plough. In other areas, level sites are covered with vegetation reduced to spiny clumps or are cleared for agriculture.

Finally, most of the areas of monsoon forest in the center of Insulindia have been cleared for agriculture or seriously degraded by fires or grazing.

3.3 The Australian monsoon forests

Wherever there is a change in the bedrock, or perhaps where the local critical rainfall threshold is exceeded, the dense equatorial forest of northeastern Australia suddenly changes (often over only a few meters) to the much more open monsoon forest. The Australian monsoon forests are different from those of southern Asia.

The types of Australian monsoon forest

In Australia there are fundamentally two classes of forests that can be considered monsoon forests. The first group consists of semi-evergreen forests rich in lianas and with a floristic composition, structure and general appearance not unlike those of the neighboring rainforests of northeastern Queensland. The most frequent species, mostly with Indo-Malaysian affinities, include *Gmelina dalrympleana*, Verbenaceae), an Australian endemic reminiscent of Indian gray teak (*G. indica*), *Canarium australianum* (Burseraceae), *Cleistocalix operculata*, (Myrtaceae), several species of *Ficus* (*F. benjamina*, *F. racemosa*) and palms, such as *Livistonia benthami* and *Carpentaria acuminata*.

The second type of monsoon forest is tall *Eucalyptus* forest with a very different floristic composition, struc-

266 Australia's monsoon forests contain many specimens of the genus *Ficus*, often growing in sites with relatively impoverished vegetation and areas of transition towards subtropical dry forests. This magnificent specimen is *F. variegata*, near Cooktown in Queensland. [Photo: Jean-Paul Ferrero / Auscape International]

ture, and general appearance. In the first place, the dominant species are mainly tall evergreen eucalyptus (*Eucalyptus*, *E. acmenoides*, *E. major*), although other tree species are also present, often rainforest trees that are resistant to fire, such as *Tristania conferta* (Myrtaceae) and other species of the same genus, and *Syncarpia glomulifera* (Myrtaceae); slender palms like *Archontophoenix cunninghamiana* are present as well. As a whole, they are evergreen forests, but they are not as dense as the rainforests with which they often compete and are dominated by species of a single genus, *Eucalyptus*, found throughout Australia at all latitudes.

Forests dominated by eucalypts

Their leathery leaves suggest the eucalyptus have adopted a strategy of resistance during drought periods rather than a strategy based on growing thin, soft leaves in the wet season that must be shed in the dry season, and then regrown. The reason for keeping their leaves may be partly due to the need not to waste nutrients, some of which are always lost when a leaf is shed and replaced. Perhaps the mineral deficiency of many Australian soils has led to this feature being so widespread among the eucalyptus. As they have to hold on and protect their leaves from herbivores, eucalyptus tissues are rich in terpenoid oils (eucalyptus oil).

These essential oils make the leaves distasteful, indigestible and toxic, making it difficult for any herbivorous insect or mammal to obtain much from eating them, except for koalas (see pages 173-174, vol. 6), which have a specialized physiology. However, there may be more subtle aspects of these oils that totally modify the ecology of these ecosystems and make the Australian eucalyptus forests really very unusual. The tough, long-lasting leaf litter and the toxic oils may suppress other plants, even the other trees that would otherwise outcompete them.

This phenomenon, known as *allelopathy*, is thought to be widespread throughout the plant kingdom, but is difficult to demonstrate. Even so, careful studies have shown that eucalyptus forests are one of the most convincing cases of allelopathy in the world. The oils drain from the leaf litter into the soil (and probably also evaporate into the surrounding air) and slowly poison other plant species.

The consequences of repeated fires

Eucalypts are literally firebombs (see pages 91-100, vol. 5). Eucalyptus leaf litter is usually abundant (it decomposes very slowly and tends to accumulate on the forest floor) and remains so full of inflammable oils that during the winter dry season fires can start and spread easily. If the fire reaches the canopy it spreads like a wildfire, rapidly burning leaves and twigs. During a canopy fire there are sudden explosions when evaporating oils reach their ignition point, and when trees split because of the intense and pronounced heat.

It is easy to conclude that eucalypts have been designed by evolution to be as inflammable as possible, and this idea is not as absurd as it might appear. It seems that their tendency to burn may be partly responsible for the dominance of eucalypts in the monsoon forest, because when they burn they eliminate the seedlings of other trees and also prepare the soil for a wave of regeneration by their own fire-resistant seeds or by sprouting from their special underground organs. As most fires are in fact restricted to the understory, and as many eucalyptus have an inner fire-resistant bark, the old trees often survive intact with reduced competition.

The sharp boundary between the monsoon forest and rainforests in Australian continent may also be partly due to fires, which die out abruptly when they reach the edge of their fuel supply. In fact, frequent fires help the monsoon forest to spread into areas that would otherwise be rainforest, because at the boundary the soil prevents the rainforest species from recolonizing among the eucalyptus.

Apart from the eucalypts, the Australian monsoon forests contain very few other forest species, and most belong, as already mentioned, to genera found in the Australian rainforests (often to the same species). Only in the highly localized semievergreen forest with lianas are eucalyptus in a minority compared with trees of genera common in other tropical regions, especially the Indo-Malaysian. The spacing of the trees, the lack of a woody understory (or at least it relative scarcity), and the angle at which the leaves and branches are inserted upwards and hang make the eucalyptus forest very open and luminous. There may be abundant grass under the trees, providing good pasture for sheep, but despite its potential as pastureland, the monsoon forest cannot compete with open grassland in agricultural production. This is why much of Australia's monsoon forests has been cleared for farms and ranches.

3.4 Madagascar's dry monsoon forests

In Madagascar, the original dry deciduous forest of the southwest corner of the island has mostly been destroyed by humans burning it and grazing livestock there. The only remaining deciduous forests are some patches within a mosaic of open woodland, scrub and savannah derived from it. One reason why the arid monsoon forests have retreated so much since human arrival on the island may be the susceptibility of many of its tree species to being killed by ground fires, as their relatively thin barks provide little protection.

The remaining arid monsoon forest is dominated by trees like rosewood (*Dalbergia*, Leguminosae), which produce valuable timber, and also several species of *Commiphora* (Burseraceae) with aromatic resins and woods. There are many leafless plants with succulent photosynthetic green stems instead of leaves, including *Euphorbia enteriphara*, a large tree with flattened green branches that from a distance recalls the unmistakeable silhouette of a stone pine (*Pinus pinea*). There is a range of bottle trees and lianas with enormously swollen trunks, such as *Cyphostemma* (Vitaceae). On the African mainland there is only a single species of baobab (*Adansonia digitata*), but the dry forests of Madagascar contain seven (*A. grandidieri*, *A. madagascariensis*, etc.). There is even a species related to the banana, *Ensete perrieri*, that completely loses its leaves in the dry season, leaving a trunk-like structure formed by hardened leaf sheaths. It seems that wherever you look in Madagascar, evolution has taken an unusual turn.

3.5 Central American dry monsoon forests

In Central America, there is still some recognizable typical monsoon forest left in some areas in Panama and on the Pacific faces of the other Central American countries, as far north as Mexico. This monsoon forest, normally referred to as "dry forest" by ecologists working in the region, survives as patches among croplands, burned rangelands and some areas of rainforest.

The relative aridity and the floristic composition

The patches of monsoon forest in northern Costa Rica, for example, are clearly related to the local

267 The repeated forest fires in monsoon forests of *Eucalyptus* leave unmistakable traces. Note the impoverished understory and almost permanent marks of charring on the tree trunks in this photo of a paperbark (*Melaleuca*) formation in the Wasur Reserve in Irian Jaya (New Guinea). *[Photo: John B. Radcliffe / WWF / Still Pictures]*

268 **The attractive tree species** of what is known as the Mexican monsoon dry forest includes *Tabebuia chrysantha* (Bignoniaceae), whose flowering is especially spectacular because it occurs just at the time when the tree has no leaves. The specimen in the photo is growing in Chamela, in southern Mexico. [Photo: Xavier Ferrer & Adolf de Sostoa]

geology. The dry forest tends to occur on limestone hills, thinning out into low species-poor scrub on rocky limestones outcrops. In wet conditions, in the protected patches among the hills, there is an evergreen vegetation reminiscent of rainforest. These patches of evergreen vegetation are probably an important dry season refuge for monkeys, squirrels and many birds.

The climatic pattern under which these dry forests live is typical of the monsoon/dry forest zones found in other parts of the world: about 35-59 in (900-1,500 mm) rainfall per year, with a dry winter season lasting for about six months. Further south it is possible to distinguish two separate dry seasons, one in the middle of the northern hemisphere's summer, and the other in the middle of winter.

The Central American dry forests are deciduous and relatively short (about 66-98 ft [20-30 m]); the canopy trees tend to have short, stout trunks and large, spreading flat-topped crowns that often do not touch one another. Frequent trees include guanacaste (*Enterolobium cyclocarpum*, Leguminosae) and cassie (*Acacia farnesiana*, Leguminosae), with soft, thin, compound leaves that are shed in the dry season; the understory consists of a layer of stunted shrubs and small trees, with crooked, spiny trunks, many of which are members of the Rubiaceae. Underneath the woody vegetation there is normally a sparse herbaceous understory. The trees often have woody lianas and epiphytic bromeliads, making the Central American monsoon forest look rather like the rainforest.

The mystery of the large forest fruits

One particularly interesting aspect of the ecology of Central America's dry forests is that many tree species (such as the guanacaste [*Enterolobium cyclocarpum*]) produce edible fruit that are much too large to be dispersed by the small native mammals and birds. Comparing these fruits with those of other tropical areas, where there are much larger herbivorous animals, such as horses and elephants, the theory has been put forward that Central America's trees are still producing fruit "designed" by evolution for animals that formerly existed in the region but are now extinct.

The fossil record shows there were wild horses, giant ground sloths, giant armadillos, native elephants and other large herbivores that went extinct suddenly and almost simultaneously about 10,000

269 The impression of dryness produced by the peeling bark of the species of *Melaleuca* in monsoonal southeast Asia is also shown by some trees in Mexico's monsoon forests, such as this species of *Bursera* in Chamela.
[Photo: Xavier Ferrer & Adolf de Sostoa]

years ago, perhaps as a result of hunting by the first humans to reach the area. It has been suggested that as trees have such a long life, natural selection has not had long enough to cause them to abandon this menu intended for a clientele that is now extinct.

3.6 The Caribbean dry monsoon forests

On the Caribbean islands, dry forest grows in areas with less than 49 in (1,250 mm) annual rainfall and with 5-7 wet months a year. They cover large areas of lowland in the Greater Antilles, such as Cuba or Jamaica, or on the leeward side of islands, away from the flow of wet air, or where the relief is too low to cause much rain to fall during part of the year. In the driest areas of the Windward Isles in the eastern Caribbean, dry forest occurs further up the slopes covered with dry thorn and succulent woods that grow near sea level.

In general, the trees of these Caribbean arid forests grow to a height of about 33 ft (10 m), forming an open canopy; there are few lianas and epiphytes, and the lichens and mosses that are so abundant in the rainforest are almost absent. In many sites, the arid forest is an almost impenetrable scrub, green and cool in the rainy season, bare and dusty during the winter dry season. Some trees survive the dry season by shedding their leaves, but other species have small, tough leaves that roll up to protect themselves from the dry heat.

Many species, for example *Bursera* (Burseraceae) and *Pisonia* (Nyctaginaceae), are rich in aromatic oils, perhaps to protect them from the mammals and insects that might eat the remaining foliage during the dry season. On limestone, a largely evergreen shrub forest, reminiscent of Mediterranean *garrigue* (see volume 5) might develop; its evergreen habit and abundant aromatic oils are perhaps adaptations to conserve nutrients in these relatively barren soils.

2
Life in monsoon forests

1. Deciduous monsoon forests

1.1 The concept of the monsoon forest

Several tropical regions with abundant rainfall but relatively seasonal climates have dense forests with a cover almost as continuous as the rainforest. They are not the same, however, as the rainforest: the tallest trees are not so gigantic, and many species shed their leaves during the dry months (and the longer the dry season, the greater the number). Yet when the rains arrive, the interior of the forest is as lush as that of the rainforest. They are monsoon forests, subject to the oscillations of the seasonal winds, which impose an annual rhythm on human life and that of all other organisms in southern Asia and in other tropical spaces on other continents.

The effects of leaf seasonality

The absence, at least partial, of leaves during the dry season means that the monsoon forest's internal microclimate is very different from the rainforest's, although during the rainy season the canopy may look very similar. In the dry season, light reaches all the layers of the understory, partly because there is an almost total absence of epiphytes and climbing plants. The interior of the forest is thus, during this season, as dry and bright as the exterior; there is no permanent shade and moisture at any level of the forest, not even at ground level, where the full force of the sunshine dries out the leaf litter and even the top soil horizons.

The microclimate in the rainy season is very different, however, because the trees and shrubs are covered in leaves, and is then much more like the rainforest's, although the less complex understory and the general absence of lianas and epiphytes means that the shade is less dense and the humidity is lower. This has major repercussions on the soils, which experience an alternating regime as regards the input of organic matter and the direction of flow of water, nutrients, and other components.

Arrangement in space

Not all the area with a monsoon climate is covered in monsoon forest, however. The boundary between seasonal tropical forests—here conventionally referred to as monsoon forest, although this denomination has traditionally been reserved for those in southern Asia and Australia—and the open woody formations dealt within the volume on savannahs is a subtle matter. Conventionally, they are considered to be forests when they have a dense tree layer and an understory dominated by woody plants, and to be open woody formations when the tree layer has gaps, or the trees are scattered, and there is a herbaceous layer dominated by grasses. Depending on the strength of the local rains and the length of the dry season, under the monsoon climate, as in the Indian subcontinent, the vegetation may range from savannah to rainforest, passing through the range of monsoon forests and open tropical woody formations, and the limits between these respective ecosystems may be masked by the long history of often very dense human population.

In the Amazon region of South America and on mainland Africa there is a sudden change from the rainforest to savannah or open forest, without any intermediate deciduous vegetation. Confusingly, much of the forest vegetation that in Asia or Australia would be known as open forest is known as dry forest in South America and Africa, although its tree layer is much more open. It seems that the combination of soil types and a long history of fires have eliminated any true monsoon forests there might have been. Even so, there is still identifiable monsoon forest in Madagascar and some areas of Central America, in the Caribbean islands, and on the northern coast of Venezuela, outside the Amazonian area.

270 Despite its terrifying appearance, this arthropod from Mexico's monsoon forests is not dangerous to humans; it is, however, highly dangerous to its normal prey, insects. It is an ambyplygid arachnid of the *Acanthophrynus* group; note its powerful prehensile pedipalps and the long fine structure of the first pair of legs, which have a sensory function. It has four pairs of legs like all arachnids.
[Photo: Adolf de Sostoa & Xavier Ferrer]

1.2 The ecology of the monsoon forests

In sites where rainfall is scarce or irregular, the typical evergreen rainforest species that need plentiful water all year round are replaced by more-or-less deciduous species better adapted to regular water stress. Even so, abrupt changes are not frequent. It is, after all, hard to indicate the precise point at which the change takes place and the exact nature of the factors causing it. There is usually a wide range of transitional forest between the evergreen forest and the seasonal forest, showing a gradual change in floristic composition, a decrease in the number of species and a transition from the dominance of evergreen trees to more-or-less deciduous ones.

Seasonal water availability

The general features of the tropical rainforest are well known and precise maps can be, and have been, made of its potential distribution. This is not, however, true of the forest types that replace the rainforest where there is a seasonal drought. The German botanist A.F.W. Schimper, who almost a century ago was the first to use the term *rainforest* (*tropische Regenswald*), was also the first to use the term *monsoon forest* to describe the dense forest formations of drier and more seasonal areas. Since then, later works have generally restricted the term monsoon forest to the communities of this type in south and southeast Asia, the area to which

it was originally applied. On other continents, these forests are known by various names, *seasonal forests*, *semi-evergreen seasonal forests*, *deciduous forests* or *dry deciduous forests*. This wide range of terminology clearly reflects reality, as no two monsoon forests are similar, let alone identical, in composition or vegetation structure. As a result, it is only possible to generalize about this type of forest's ecological characteristics.

Even the rainforests are to some extent seasonal in terms of rainfall, but these differences are very small, especially when compared with the extremes observed in the southeast Asian monsoon forests, where monthly rainfall may vary from 0-98 in (0-2,500 mm). Dry season timing and length depend largely on latitude, with the shortest and least severe dry seasons occurring nearest the equator. With increasing distance from the equator, there is a clearer pattern of a short dry season (up to two months) in the summer and a long dry period (from two to six months) in the winter. Near the tropics of Cancer and Capricorn, there may be only a single dry season, but it may last for up to eight months. Other factors, such as the exposure to monsoon or monsoon-type air movements, or nearby warm or cold ocean currents, may also greatly influence seasonality.

The timing of biological activities such as growth and reproduction may be synchronized with water availability. Seasonality is the ecologically dominant force in the monsoon forests. Furthermore, the geographical distribution of plant and animal taxa may be restricted due to the lack of water in the dry seasons. It seems that the different types of seasonal vegetation are largely determined by the amount of annual rainfall and by its distribution over the course of the year. In India, for example, the differences between the moister types of forest depend on the length of the dry period, whereas differences between more arid ecosystems (such as shrub savannah and desert) depend more on the total amount of rainfall. In general, it seems that just two or three dry months a year are enough to cause a clear change in the composition and structure from a typical rainforest into a typical seasonal forest. It also seems that the most extreme years, not those closest to average conditions, exert the greatest pressure on the general structure, composition, and function of the drier forests.

Seasonal forests growing where there are several months every year with a rainfall of 2 in (60 mm) or less are generally lower than the typical rainforest and the taller trees of the canopy tend to be deciduous, although they may only shed their leaves for a short period. The longer or more intense the seasonal drought is, the lower the vegetation, and its structure is simplified to just one or two layers, in contrast with the three or more layers of rainforest. Seasonal shedding of leaves becomes more frequent, beginning at the topmost layer and working down to the lowest one. The lower levels keep their leaves longer than the canopy because they are growing in a moister microclimate. There is also a tendency to reduce leaf size: small leaves, microphylls, which are rare in tropical rainforests become more common as rainfall decreases. Furthermore, the enormous buttress roots of some rainforest trees are less common, perhaps simply because large trees are uncommon. Some trees in the drier areas have thorny or spiny trunks, which are not at all common in rainforests. Seasonal forests contain some lianas, but epiphytes are rare, as the humus materials they depend on dry out much faster than the soil when there is no rain or atmospheric humidity. The understory, which is normally inversely proportional to the canopy cover, is normally higher in dry forests.

Phenology and production

The phenology of seasonal forests is not well understood. There is great variation in most aspects of phenology between species and between individuals of the same species, including trunk growth, the growth and shedding of leaves, fruiting and flowering. The available information suggests there is no single factor responsible for the type or initiation of these phenomena, although stress due to water shortage is often cited as a main factor. Some studies of leaf-fall patterns in several seasonal forests show significative correlation with the rainfall or lack of rain.

In a Puerto Rican forest, peak leaf-litter production coincides with the longer and shorter dry seasons; in a deciduous forest in Mexico, leaf-fall was also greater in the dry season. In an abnormally dry season, the seasonal forest may even look just like a deciduous temperate forest in autumn. The ground is covered by a thick layer of leaf litter that rustles and crackles when walked on, and the light passes through the partially defoliated canopy and reaches the soil in a way that never occurs in rainforest.

Yet not all species show leaf-fall in the dry season. For example *Jacquinia pungens* (Myrsinaceae), a shrub from the dry seasonal forests of Costa Rica, loses its leaves during the wet period and produces new ones in the dry season, apparently synchronized to the light conditions; it drops its leaves when the forest canopy closes, growing new ones when exposed to the abundant light penetrating the partly defoliated and relatively open upper canopy.

There is also variation in the beginning of flowering and fruiting. In a single area, some trees may be starting to flower while others of the same species are already fruiting. It has also been observed that many species, especially in the lower levels and understory, flower in the dry season, producing a bright display of colors quite unlike the drab green of the lower levels of the rainforest. Costa Rica's forests show a flowering peak during the dry period and another at the end of the rainy period. In the monsoon forests of Sri Lanka flowering has been recorded when the soil was parched. In Puerto Rico it was observed that only half of the 33 species surveyed produced fruit at the same time. More or less 50% produced fruit at least twice a year, whereas 25% fruited more or less continually. Most species produced fruit at the end of the two wet seasons, whereas fewer than 10% did so in the winter dry period.

272 **The amount of leaf litter of the forest floor** obviously increases during the dry season, when the deciduous trees shed their leaves. The photo shows a large tarantula (*Aphonepelma*) crossing the soil surface of a Mexican monsoon forest, into which it blends perfectly.
[Photo: Adolf de Sostoa & Xavier Ferrer]

In seasonal forests the annual increase in diameter is approximately half that found in rainforests. In dry areas, the trees may even increase in diameter during the rains and shrink during the dry season; this regularity may produce visible growth rings in some species, but generally the growth is so small and the wood so dense that the rings cannot be distinguished, making them very difficult to measure.

The ecological role of fire

Fire's effects on the general character and geographical distribution of the dry forests is not well understood. The effect of fire is complicated by the effects of grazing livestock and other human disturbances, such as selective logging and firewood extraction. There has been much debate whether fire alone can turn dry forest into savannah, but it seems reasonably clear that forests and dry woodlands can be reduced to savannah and other degraded vegetation types by the action of fire combined with other human disturbances.

The experience of British forestry officers in India in the 19th century clearly illustrates the influence of fire in the monsoon forests. At the time, many of India's seasonal forests were being destroyed by fires, normally set by people to clear the surrounding vegetation. In order to conserve the valuable deciduous species, reserves were created where neither grazing or agriculture were permitted, thus avoiding fires as far as possible. It was expected that the forest would regenerate naturally, thus ensuring a constant supply of timber. Although regeneration greatly improved, to everybody's surprise, the trees that grew were not the expected species. In many protected areas, the saplings that grew up were mainly typical rainforest evergreen species, clearly showing that these formations were not true climax monsoon forests. To the contrary, they were the result of fires and other human disturbances that they had suffered. The thick bark of teak (*Tectona grandis*) and other deciduous trees makes them resistant to ground fires, whereas the trees of the evergreen tropical forest have thinner barks and cannot survive repeated fires.

Teak (*Tectona grandis*) is the most economically important of the monsoon forest trees. In addition to being fire-resistant, its saplings can survive repeated fires and grazing. In Myanmar, the forests are completely felled and the area is burned, as the excellent regeneration from seedlings gives rise to large single-species plantations, of even greater value to logging companies. Throughout the seasonally dry tropics large teak plantations have been established.

In the seasonally dry areas of Indonesia, the forests are dominated by cemera (*Casuarina junghuhniana*), as this trees sprouts abundantly even after major fire damage. This is fortunate as an estimated 4,000 ha (1 hectare=2.47 acres) of cemera forest are burned every year. If fire is avoided, a mixed forest of members of the

Fagaceae and Lauraceae appears. The plants adapted to fire include several species of Leguminosae and Myrtaceae that have fruits with tough pods or shells that only open in the heat of a fire; this allows them to disperse and germinate.

In many of these seasonal areas, fires are responsible for the forest structure and composition. Even in the seasonally wetter areas, fires often cause the replacement of evergreen thickets by herbaceous plants, especially if the cover is relatively open. Bamboos are also favored by fires and other disturbances. The often clear absence of seedlings and saplings is also due to fires and sporadic grazing in the forest.

In the African continent fire may have prevented a true deciduous forest, as found on other continents, from ever developing. Outside the African rainforests, open woody formations dominate (see volume 3). Almost all the trees lose their leaves in the five to seven dry months and the herbaceous plants completely dry out, leaving a large amount of inflammable material on the forest floor. The fires that frequently spread through these woodlands destroy most of the saplings and scrub, controlling the density of the forest cover.

Madagascar has the only relatively large area of deciduous dry forest left in Africa, but fires have destroyed most of the forests in the western part of the island, many of them deliberately set. In the western region of Madagascar, where there are most head of cattle, fires are set every year, normally in the dry season when the vegetation is most vulnerable, in order to stimulate the growth of tender new grass as grazing for animals, especially zebu cattle (*Bos taurus* [=*B. indicus*] *indicus*). The deciduous dry forest is more vulnerable to fire than the eastern rainforests, rapidly leading to scrub and tree savannah. Repeated fires aggravated by excessive grazing restricts woody regeneration, and in many sites soil degradation is so bad that natural regeneration would be impossible even if the disturbances ceased. Most of the deciduous dry forests of Madagascar have been burned. The remaining patches are inaccessible to the local population or unsuitable for agriculture.

Studies of the effects of fire on the monsoon forests in northern Australia show they are detrimental. It is generally accepted that relatively intense fires at the end of the dry season damage the patches of monsoon forest, especially on the margins already disturbed by other factors. If these fires occur often, the edges of the forest recede rapidly, and the forest may take decades to reestablish after the fires have ceased. Studies in the Kakadu National Park show that every year more than 50% of the forest and tree savannah communities burn; yet the fires mainly burn the herbaceous undergrowth, only occasionally spreading to the canopy. It seems that fires in forests at the beginning of the dry season are relatively innocuous, and in Australia fire is often used in forest management (see volume 5, pages 344-345). The directors of the national parks use early controlled counterfires to reduce the number and spread of fires late in the dry season and to introduce diversity into the habitats. Farmers also set early fires to stimulate the growth of tender shoots for livestock and to get rid of dry grass.

Species and community diversity

Generally, the number of tree species in the monsoon forest is roughly half that of the rainforest; the lowest values are in the driest areas. Only rainforest growing on marshy soils, at high altitude, or on exceptionally fertile soils has as few species as the seasonal forest. In general, the number of shared tree species is low. For example, in a study carried out in Costa Rica, only 11 of the 298 tree species were found in both rainforest and seasonal dry forest. Likewise, in a study in Puerto Rico, none of the 33 species found in the dry forest also occurred in the neighboring rainforest.

Dry forest is fragmented into a mosaic of hundreds of microhabitats, due to the variety introduced by factors such as the gradient and orientation of the slopes, exposure to light and air, and the temperature and rainfall regime. In contrast the abundance of water in the rainforest blurs many of these differences between habitats. In the areas of monsoon forest, the gallery forests along the watercourses are of great importance, as they offer animals uninterrupted year-round shade, greenery and water. They also provide corridors of evergreen forest that allow them to move from one point to another, as well as refugia from which they can recolonize nearby areas after fires or drought.

2. Animal life in monsoon forests

2.1 Animals and the rhythm of the seasons

Animals in monsoon forests, unlike their counterparts in climatically stable rainforests, have to confront important variations in temperature and humidity throughout the year. During the dry season many trees have shed their leaves, and because the tree canopy is too thin to affect the microclimate of the lower strata, considerable fluctuations in temperature occur. Direct sunlight reaches the lowest strata and dries out the leaf litter, meaning that the soil fauna's environment is very dry. Tree roots have to grow deep into the soil to find horizons with permanent moisture.

The main problem facing animals in seasonal forests is the contrast between the abundant available during one part of the year and the scarce or nonexistent resources available in other periods. For example, the forests of Guanacaste in north-west Costa Rica undergo five windy, sunny months with no rain. This period is highly stressful for the inhabitants of the forest and many have developed adaptive mechanisms to tackle this problem. To illustrate these mechanisms, rather than merely quoting a whole list of examples, it is perhaps more enlightening to look at a number of typical survival strategies employed by animals in monsoon forests.

2.2 Insects in the monsoon forests

The dry season is a time of plenty for seed-eaters and for the insect pollinators, such as bees, because of the numerous woody plants that flower in the dry season. In other words, the dry season conditions are not totally adverse for the fauna of monsoon forests. The insect communities of the seasonal forests in Costa Rica are typical examples of this process.

273 The abundance of insects in the favorable season is one of the typical features of monsoon forests. The entire food web benefits, as does this monsoon forest lizard (*Hemidactylus frenatus*). [Photo: Xavier Ferrer & Adolf de Sostoa]

274 The characteristic arrangement of the nymphs of pentatomid shield bugs, a group of heteropterans, immediately after hatching. They stay around the eggs for a while eating the bacterial layer sown by the female that laid the eggs. These symbiotic bacteria live in the digestive system, allowing the future adults to obtain nourishment from the sap they suck. The nymphs are arranged around the eggs they hatched from, giving the appearance of a poisonous caterpillar, providing them with some protection from predators during this early phase of their life, when they are immobile and easy prey. The photo shows a group of nymphs on the underside of a leaf in the Guanacaste forest (Costa Rica).
[Photo: Adolf de Sostoa & Xavier Ferrer]

Feeding strategies

The insects of the Guanacaste forest in Costa Rica have various ways of surviving the dry season. The first two most common techniques include finding a favorable microhabitat and remaining there until the rains arrive, either first as non-reproductive adults, or second by reproducing very slowly and surviving by exploiting any resources left, however small. A third strategy is to multiply normally in the dry season, increasing their numbers by exploiting a food source that is only available in the dry season.

A fourth strategy is for the adults to migrate, often many miles, in search of a more suitable habitat. Finally, another of the commonest survival strategies is for the insect to survive, immature, in diapause.

In Guanacaste one of the most conspicuous insects that survives by finding an appropriate microhabitat is *Eurema diara*, a small, fragile, black, yellow and white butterfly. It produces several generations of larvae during the rainy season, but the last generation hatches in December and remains inactive through the dry season in groups of up to several hundred adults in riverside or other damp habitats; they do not visit flowers during this period and fly only when disturbed. When the rains return, the insects mate and a new reproductive cycle starts.

Another species that is almost totally inactive in the dry season is *Phelypera distigma*, a weevil that normally feeds on tree leaves. Thousands of individuals of that species gather in caves and hollow trees and wait patiently for the onset of the rainy season.

Those species that manage to reproduce in the dry season generally do so only at low levels and are usually fairly flexible feeders. For example, some *Dysdercus* bugs change their feeding habits: during the wet season they eat the seeds of various species of Bombacaceae (*Bombacopsis*, *Ceiba* and *Pseudobombax*) and Sterculiaceae (*Sterculia*), whereas during the dry season they eat the tender flowers and fruits of herbaceous and bushy members of the Malvaceae, such as *Malvaviscus arboreus* and several species of *Sida* and *Wissadula*.

The insects that find abundant food in the dry season include many solitary and social bees, some species of tiger beetle (cicindellids), ant lions (myrmeliontids), the caterpillars of the seed-boring pyralid moths and weevil larvae. In Guanacaste an enormous range of trees flower in the dry season, and bees have an assured supply of nectar and pollen. Adult carpenter bees (*Xylocopa*) emerge from their pupal cases in May or June having spent the wet season in a state of semi-dormancy. Many other species of solitary bee spend the whole wet season in subterranean cells, emerging as adults at the beginning of the dry season. Some of the tiger beetles that hunt in the sandy, open spaces of the dried-up riverbeds of Guanacaste pass the wet season as dormant adults in their hiding places, emerging in the dry season to hunt and reproduce.

For these species and for ant lions, equally active in the dry season, physical conditions rather than the abundance of food seem to determine seasonal behavior.

Aside from some circumstantial evidence, there is little detailed information on the seasonal migration of lepidopterans away from the lowland deciduous forests of Costa Rica. It appears that certain species migrate to higher ground between 3 and 19 mi (5 and 30 km) away and return when the rains begin. For example, in the Santa Rosa National Park the larvae of *Eunica monima*, a small brown butterfly, uses the incense tree (*Bursera simaruba*) as its food plant. A single abundant generation of adults flies briefly in June and July and then disappears. However, huge numbers of adults are seen in July in the nearby mountains in areas where there is no *Bursera simaruba*. It seems likely that the adults migrate to higher areas to avoid the dry season and then return to the lowlands in the wet season to lay their eggs.

Seasonal diapause

Few insects in deciduous tropical forests undergo the seasonal diapause so common in more temperate latitudes, where the cold winter reduces body metabolism. During the dry tropical "winter" season, temperatures may be as high or even higher than in the wet season. Thus, however efficient the insect is at lowering its metabolic rate, it still has to cope with the difficult problem of storing enough water and food to last throughout its diapause. Yet if the insect remains active, manages to avoid predators, and finds enough food and water to survive, it will also be ready to take advantage of the first fresh shoots or other food source after the rains begin. Even so, some species survive the dry season as chrysalides (pupas). For example, almost all the species of saturniid moths in the Santa Rosa National Park spend the dry season as chrysalides hidden amongst the foliage or on the forest floor, and the humidity of the first rains is the cue for the adults to emerge. *Hylesia lineata*, a minute saturniid, has a different strategy: all the adults emerge from the chrysalids at the end of the wet season (mid-November to the beginning of December) and mate. The females then lay their eggs in a spherical mass and cover this egg-ball with a thick, felty, chestnut-colored layer of hairs taken from their abdomens. The eggs spend six months in diapause, hatching when the first rains arrive.

2.3 Birds in the monsoon forests

In the coastal areas of the north of Australia that are topographically protected from fire or in sites that are relatively humid all year round, scattered patches of semievergreen monsoon forest are found, normally surrounded either by savannah with scattered trees, or by open woody formations dominated by *Eucalyptus* trees. A good example is the monsoon forest near the Kakadu National Park. Like the Costa Rican monsoon forests, the bird life of this national park has been well studied and both areas provide a series of interesting examples.

Habitat distribution

The remaining patches of monsoon forest in Australia share bird species with the neighboring formations—rainforest, open *Eucalyptus* forest, mangrove swamps and tall paperbark (*Melaleuca glomerata*) scrub formations. Also present are a number of generalist bird species that are widespread throughout almost all of northern Australia. This can be interpreted as the result of several different factors: the small size of the patches of monsoon forest and of the area of monsoon forest as a whole, its heterogeneity, and, finally, the dynamic history of these areas, permanently at the mercy of the major fluctuations in size of the other neighboring biomes in the region.

There seem to be more bird species and individual birds in Australian monsoon forests than in comparable areas of open *Eucalyptus* forest; yet, species richness in these monsoon forests is in fact very modest compared with the rainforests of northeast Queensland. The most highly seasonal forests, like the Kakadu National Park, have relatively few rainforest birds. A comparison of the avifauna (bird life) shows that fruit-eating species are more common in semi-evergreen monsoon forests and that seed-eaters and species that glean food from the foliage are more abundant in open *Eucalyptus* formations. Nevertheless, bird species vary greatly from one patch of monsoon forest to another, depending on their floristic composition and location within the relief. The most obvious differences in the composition of the bird communities are between the upland and the lowland monsoon forests. Other factors influence floristic variety and forest structure and therefore the birds that live there. For example, the monsoon forests with a year-round water supply and those near springs are rarely deciduous and have a high canopy. The presence of water and plenty of shade sometimes attracts numerous wild boar (*Sus*

275 The migratory birds that overwinter in Australia's monsoon forests arrive from the colder regions of the continent, including the rufous fantail (*Rhipidura rufifrons*), shown here nesting in Lamington National Park in Queensland.
[Photo: Roger Brown / Auscape International]

scrofa) and water buffaloes (*Bubalus bubalis*), both of them species introduced into Australia whose activities tend to destroy forests, although they reduce the risk of forest fires.

The availability of food

The marked seasonality of monsoon forests causes similarly distinctive changes in the resources available to the birds that live there and even to the birds of the region's other biomes. The lack of water, lasting roughly from March to November, causes many plants to shed their leaves; the leaf litter on the forest floor then dries out, increasing the risk of forest fires. Other important changes affecting bird populations are the reduction in areas of open water and the formation of dense groups of invertebrates that may prevent their access to the water.

Birds in monsoon forests respond to these changes by being far more vagile (free to move) than in rain forests. This is especially noticeable among fruit- and nectar-eaters as their distribution is influenced by the abundance of fruit and flowers. Dispersion is not limited to movements between differing patches of monsoon forest; it seems that at the height of the dry season some species of bird leave the open Eucalyptus formations to take refuge in the monsoon forests.

Migrants and residents

The monsoon forests of the north of Australia are also visited by migratory species escaping from the winter of the temperate regions of Australia, such as the rainbow bee-eater (*Merops ornatus*), the little cuckoo-shrike (*Coracina papuensis*), the rufous fantail (*Rhipidura rufifrons*) and the black-faced cuckoo-shrike (*Coracina novaehollandiae*).

The birds of Costa Rica's seasonal forests also show similar seasonal movements. Some species, including the barred ant-shrike (*Thamnophilus doliatus*), move to the riverside forests in the dry season and return to the deciduous forests when the rains begin, while others migrate to South America as food becomes scarce.

In the Costa Rican seasonal forests, breeding seems to be determined more by climatic conditions than by the availability of any particular resource. Most hole-nesting birds breed in the dry season, probably because there are fewer fungi and molds that could be harmful to nestlings. Crepuscular (twilight) species, such as owls and nightjars, seem to find the clear, cloudless skies of the dry season favorable, as this when they breed. In diurnal birds of prey and large water birds where both parents leave the nest unprotected when they fly off to hunt, and therefore reproduction takes place in the dry season; it makes sense to breed in the dry season, apparently because the young birds are thus reasonably well-grown and feathered by the time the wet season arrives. The increase in the food supply may also satisfy the young birds' increasing food requirements. In areas with an unfavorable wet season, such as Guanacaste, the breeding season of most small birds is shorter and more closely linked to the onset of the rains.

2.4 Mammals in the monsoon forests

The mammals of monsoon and seasonal forests in general have to face the same problems as insects and birds. During the dry season their main concern is simply to survive.

Survival during the dry season

Passing the dry season in dormancy is not a viable option for mammals. Any mammals that fell dormant during the dry season in the monsoon forest would still be available to attack by its predators and parasites that were not estivating (spending to summer in a state of torpor). Snakes and other vertebrates adapted to catching prey underground would find it relatively easy to locate dormant animals in their dens. Moreover, some invertebrates such as army ants and fire ants would quickly devour any dormant rodent or bat they found. As dormant mammals cannot clean and groom their coats, the population of ectoparasites would increase greatly. Dormancy requires a food reserve, and the higher the temperatures, the greater the reserve required, meaning it would be physically impossible for most mammals to survive a period of dormancy at tropical temperatures. This may explain why some bat populations in

temperate zones migrate to cooler places, as is the case of *Myotis velifer*, a bat living in lowland Mexico that migrates to upland areas in the unfavorable dry season.

Another problem making dormancy difficult is the need to accumulate fat, which requires a period of abundant food resources immediately before the critical dry season. Yet in Costa Rica, for example, insect densities are highest at the beginning of the rainy season and lowest at the end, and so there is a food shortage just when insectivorous species most need them to accumulate fats. The same applies generally to fruits, although they are so poor in nutrients that it is physiologically very difficult to accumulate fat through the consumption of fruit. Seed-eaters find most food in the dry season, and herbivores can also generally find sufficient food in the greenest parts of the understory and then amid the verdant vegetation that survives along watercourses.

Examples of seasonal dormancy

Despite these problems, at least one small mammal in monsoon forests the fat-tailed dwarf lemur (*Cheirogaleus medius*) does become dormant in the dry season. This species does not live in Costa Rica or Australia, but in the dry deciduous forests of western Madagascar as well as in the even drier formations in the south of the island. It is probably able to enter dormancy because the temperatures in the dry season (May to October) are relatively low in western Madagascar. Its diet consists of fruit, flowers, nectar and insects, as well as gums, a few grass shoots and even small vertebrates. It eats flowers and nectar in November at the beginning of the rainy season, from December to February it consumes fruit and an increasing number of insects, and then from February to May its main food source is fruit. During the rainy season this lemur accumulates fat under its skin and in its tail, increasing its weight (approximately from 2.6-77 oz [75- 220 g]) and tripling the volume of its tail (from on average 15 cm^3 in November to 42 cm^3 in May). It spends the dry season dormant, alone or in groups of up to five individuals, in hollow tree trunks, and dormancy lasts until November. Adults may enter dormancy as early as March, although the young born that year tend to enter dormancy a little later, thereby avoiding competition for food in the preceding months. Curiously, the greater dwarf lemurs (*C. major*) of eastern Madagascar's rainforests,

276 **The presence of large bovids in the monsoon forest** reveals situations of transition towards subtropical forest formations, as it implies the understory is sparse and abundant grazing is provided by seasonal rains. This leads to the appearance of the banteng (*Bos javanicus*), as in the extremely monsoonal forest in Thailand shown in this photo.
[Photo: Roland Seitre / Bios / Still Pictures]

277 Some animals of the monsoon forest show seasonal lethargy, such as this dwarf lemur (*Cheirogaleus medius*), typical of the dry deciduous forests of Madagascar.
[Photo: Olivier Langrand / Bios / Still Pictures]

where rainfall is almost constant all year round, also accumulate fat in their tails and are lethargic between July and October. Little is known about the metabolism of these two species.

The tambotriky (*Echinops telfairi*), an insectivore from the forests of western Madagascar that resembles the European hedgehog in its feeding habits and defensive mechanisms, also enters dormancy in the dry season. During its seasonal dormancy, this animal can maintain its body temperature approximately 9°F (1°C) higher than the ambient temperature of 66 and 81°F (19 and 27°C). While dormant, it will puff and gnash its teeth if something disturbs it or strikes the tree or hollow log it is sleeping in.

Seasonal changes in feeding habits

Many of the mammals living in Madagascar's seasonal forests have developed dietary adaptations to changes in food resources. For example, the viverrid boky-boky (*Mungotictis decemlineata*), one of only eight carnivores on the island, eats a great variety of small vertebrates, including reptiles, as well as snails, and insect larvae and adults in the wet season. However, in the cool dry season, it feeds on the insect larvae it gleans on the forest floor or in rotting wood. Some lemurs, including the fork-crowned dwarf lemur (*Phaner furcifer*) and Coquerel's sifaka (*Mirza coquereli*) also seem to change their feeding habits according to the season. For example, in the

dry season, Phaner furcifer is apparently more dependent on gums exuded by trees, above all trees of the genus *Terminalia*, whereas during the rainy season *Mirza coquereli* feeds much more on the sweet secretions of homopteran larvae and scale insects (Coccidae).

In contrast to the rainforest, far more herbaceous and bushy species, including plenty of grasses, grow in the lower strata of drier forests. Thus monsoon forests tend to have many large herbivores. For example, the Baluran National Park in eastern Java is a refuge for many herds of ungulates such as bantengs (*Bos javanicus*), water buffaloes (*Bubalus bubalis*) and Sonda sambar (*Cervus timorensis*). In the middle of the rainy season, the Kanha National Park in Madhya Pradesh in India sustains 132-154 lb (60-70 kg)/ha of wild ungulates and 396 lb (180 kg)/ha of domestic cattle. Many of the largest mammals found in the monsoon forests of India, Myanmar and Indochina also occur in the rainforest but at much lower densities; these include Asian elephants (*Elephas maximus*), muntjaks (*Muntiacus muntjak*), sambars (*Cervus unicolor*), wild buffaloes (*Bos*) and wild boars (*Sus*). The high density of herbivores in monsoon forests also attracts many carnivores: the Huai Kha Khaeng Wildlife Sanctuary in Thailand, a rich mosaic of semi-evergreen, deciduous and gallery forests, is home to 22 species of carnivore, or in other words, 75% of the carnivores found in Thailand and 63% of all carnivore species recorded in southeast Asia.

3
Humans in the monsoon forests

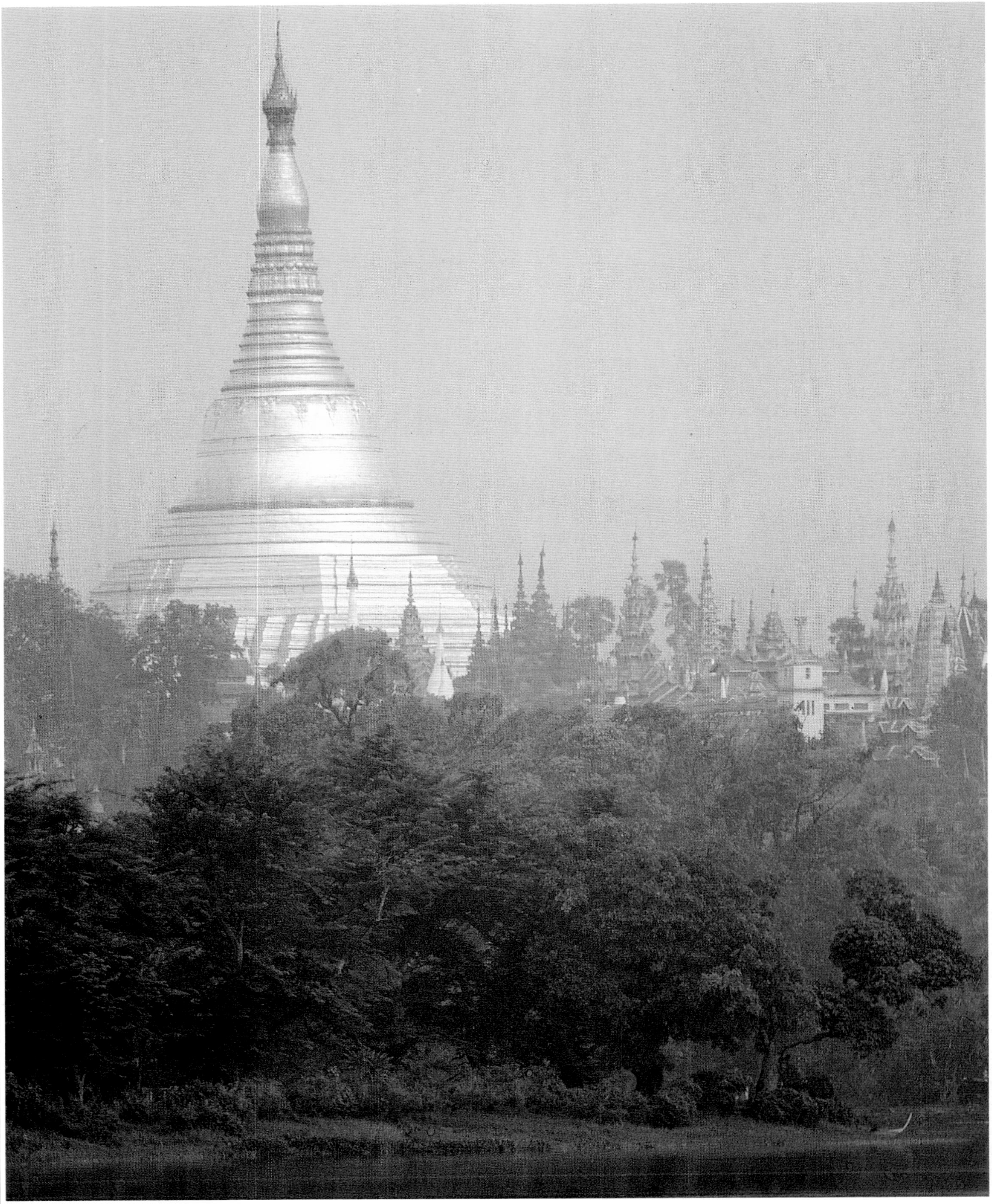

1. The human populations of the monsoon forests

1.1 The humans of southeast Asia

The history of humans in southeast Asia is very long, as was shown by the late 19th century Dutch physician Eugène Dubois' search for the missing link between modern human beings and apes; he in fact found remains almost a million years old, which he placed in the genus *Pithecanthropus*, although they were later assigned to the species *Homo erectus*. Yet the same area contains unmistakable remains of modern humans (*Homo sapiens*) with highly perfected tools. For millennia, the inhabitants of southeast Asia became adapted to the area, giving rise to major civilizations, often intelligently using natural resources, adapting their works to their habitat, and creating landscapes in perfect harmony with their surroundings. Unfortunately, only too often they used up natural resources that could not be renewed, especially in the countries that since ancient times have had high population densities.

Prehistory and history

The oldest anthropological remains (fossil teeth and bones) from the area indicate the arrival of *H. erectus* in southeast Asia. In Java, the Trinil and Sangiran sites contain remains dating from between 1,000,000 and 800,000 years ago, and the Ngandong site —"Solo man"— from about 300,000 years ago, with a later morphology (see the chapter "The expansion of the humans" in volume 1). The oldest remains yet found of modern humans (*H. sapiens sapiens*) in the area are also from Java and are between 60,000 and 100,000 years old. Genetics appears to disprove any possible phyletic link (a single line of descent with no branching) between *H. erectus* and *H. sapiens sapiens* in southeastern Asia, despite the persistence of the working of stone. Although some crossing between the two human types cannot be ruled out, *H. erectus* appears to have been displaced by groups of more modern humans proceeding from Asia Minor.

About 80,000 years, during the last glaciation— the Würm glacial stage—the sea level was much lower, almost 492 ft (150 m) lower than now, meaning the coastline of southeast Asia was very different. Southeast Asia was then 60% larger than it is now; Sundaland included the islands of Sumatra, Java, and Borneo. The current coastline only formed between 9,000 and 7,000 years ago. About 60,000 years ago, when the Würm glaciation spread, modern humans from Asia Minor settled much of the Sunda Peninsula, and when the sea was at its lowest, between 42,000 and 35,000 years ago, they crossed the 44 mi (70 km) wide arm of sea separating the Asian continent from the Sahul (see the chapter on the population of Australia in volume 9 and the section "Expansion and the colonization of new lands" in volume 1). The peoples that performed this feat were the ancestors of the Australian Aborigines as well as the isolated similar populations of the Andaman Islands, northern Sumatra, and probably other islands in Melanesia, although these islands now show the genetic influence of later entry of Polynesian populations with Mongoloid affinities.

The most abundant archaeological remains in southeast Asia date from the period between 12,000 and 40,000 years ago, and include caves, rocky shelters, and stone tools from sites scattered throughout Indonesia, Malaysia, Vietnam, and the Philippines. These remains suggest that the region's first inhabitants hunted a wide range of animals. Little is known about the edible plants that they collected, although some caves in northern Thailand used by humans contain plant remains, including grains of rice that could have been wild. It seems that during prehistoric times small bands of hunter-gatherers used many forest plants and animals, as well as those of the forest margins, such as riversides and lakesides.

Between the end of the Paleolithic and the beginning of the Neolithic, there seem to have been two cultures in southeast Asia. The site in the Niah cave in Borneo, like those at Taban in the Philippines, has superimposed strata showing that remains indicating hunting and gathering were

278 **The ancient and intense human presence in the monsoon area** is shown by its many cities and monuments, such as the marvellous Shwe Dagon Pavilion in Rangoon (Myanmar). The photo shows it rising above the forest through a thin mist over the Irrawaddy River.
[Photo: Michael Freeman / Bruce Coleman Limited]

replaced by the later fragments of pottery and signs of early agriculture. The pre-Neolithic strata date from 13,000 and 22,000 years ago, and correspond to the *Hoa Binh cultural complex* (known after the locality of Hoa Binh, southeast of Hanoi in northern Vietnam, where it was first described). Important sites of this culture on mainland Asia include the Spirit Cave in southwest Thailand, and there are others in northern Sumatra; the remains consist of stone instruments, probably the result of the development of previous local forms. Archeological remains from this time found on the islands of southeast Asia (Java, Borneo and Philippines) that were separated from the mainland between 14,000 and 10,000 years ago are scarce and reveal different stone working industries, presumably due to their isolation. Later deposits show elaborate ceramics, metal knives and axes, clear indicators of the arrival of the Neolithic.

For the last 6,000 years, Mongoloid populations from southeast Asia who spoke languages related to the major linguistic family (Austronesian, formerly known as Malayo-Polynesian), probably originally from the north of the Tropic of Cancer, introduced a Neolithic culture based mainly on rice cultivation (see the section "The Neolithic revolution," volume 1, page 290). Some recently found archeological remains seem to show that the area of origin of these populations lay south of the Yangtse (Chang Jiang), and that their expansion was comparable with the expansion of the Neolithic in Europe. If these cultures practiced slash and burn techniques, it is not surprising that they continually had to seek new land to settle, which they did by moving to the lands to the south. These populations expanded as a result of the Neolithic wave, and eventually dominated southeast Asia below the tropic, colonizing the almost uninhabited areas of Micronesia and Polynesia to the east and even Madagascar to the west (see the chapter "The ancient sea-routes" in volume 10). The few former hunter-gatherer inhabitants of these regions were displaced inland.

In southeast Asia (northeast Thailand) there are archeological deposits dating from 6,500 years ago indicative of rice cultivation and the working of bronze; this is a most surprising find, as it was not expected to find such early working of metal. Between 3,000 and 4,000 years ago, rice cultivation, domestication of the water buffalo to help plowing, and iron tools, such as the plow, allowed human populations to settle in the plains between the Red and Mekong rivers. In mountainous areas, humans still lived as hunter-gatherers, although they occasionally practiced simple agriculture. Thus, two types of culture have coexisted in the area for the last 3,000 years: The agricultural culture in the alluvial plains knew how to work metal, appreciated artistic bronze objects, and developed an urban civilization; the other culture comprised isolated tribes with primitive technology, hunter-gatherers or practitioners of a simple agriculture, probably slash and burn. Some examples of this division still persist in southeast Asia, including the remaining forest hunter-gatherer tribes, such as the Senoi in the Malaysian Peninsula, the Aeta in Luzón, and the Penan in Borneo, who seasonally alternate hunting and gathering with the harvest of previously planted crops. Some of the least technologically developed tribes in southeast Asia and the Philippines (such as the Aeta in Luzón) are members of the *Negrito* local race; the individuals are small, with dark skin and very frizzy hair often have the epicanthic fold so typical of Mongoloid peoples. Like the Pygmies in Africa and other rainforest dwellers, the Negritos have never been totally isolated from the settlements of more sedentary agricultural peoples, with whom they have established permanent trading relationships, more commercial than technological, in a very special regime of serfdom with the neighboring populations. They provide their agriculturist neighbors with bush meat and labor in exchange for rice, cereals, and some cash to buy goods in the coastal markets. There have probably always been trading relations between the two populations, as this dual economy must have been sustained by the rainforest environment.

About 2,500 years ago kingdoms and empires with large urban centers began to develop throughout southeast Asia. The importance of some of them, such as the Gupta dynasty in India, lay in their network of trade links with other civilizations. There is archeological evidence of the export of spices (such as cloves, nutmeg and cinnamon) and later of other forest products (such as some resins) from southeast China and India to Rome. Remains from 2,300 years ago suggest the development of an urban empire with a cereal-based economy, supported by rice cultivation and trade in northern Vietnam, clearly influenced by the Han dynasty in China and then by the Khmer. The empires of Cambodia, Thailand and Burma were occupied by Hindus from 600-800 A.D. and influenced by their culture, as shown by the architecture of the later temples. Between the 9th and 14th centuries A.D., the Khmer empire developed a brilliant Indian-inspired civilization that built the city, temples, and hydraulic complex of Angkor and other

279 The forest's fantastic capacity to regenerate is dramatically revealed by the Angkor hydraulic complex in Cambodia. This is an enormous group of temples and constructions built by the Khmer empire (9th-15th centuries) and totally covered by monsoon forest until its accidental discovery by the French naturalist Henri Mouchot (1826-1861) in 1859. Recovery began in 1907 under the archeologist Bernhard Groslier with the clearing and restoration of the enormous temple of Angkor Wat and is still in progress, despite war-related problems. The photo shows the Ta Prohm temple, one of the many still covered by jungle. *[Photo: The Hutchison Library]*

280 The Akha are one of the most representative tribes of the Indochina monsoon area, and live in northern Thailand. The photo shows an Akha women with child, wearing the headdress characteristic of this group. While the woman carries out her daily chores, this ornament is usually protected with a hood (see figure 293).
[Photo: Michael Freeman / Auscape International]

urban centers such as Phnom Penh and Saigon (now Ho Chi Minh City), formed during the Khmer domination of Cochin China in the 12th and 13th centuries. In Sumatra and Java between the 8th and 13th centuries, the Srivijaya empire established a true trading and maritime empire that has left impressive remains of its culture, such as the Borobudur Temple in central Java, built around 800 A.D.

As has been pointed out, there were more complex migratory movements between the Mongoloids and Melanesian populations living further south, but there is a gradient in the geographical distribution of the epicanthic fold typical of Asiatics and the dark skin color typical of Melanesians. The Melanesian populations are descendants of the first modern humans to reach southeast Asia, Indochina and Melanesia, whereas the Mongoloids are the descendants of Neolithic migration from southern China.

The distribution of the population

The human settlement of eastern and southern Asia was not uniform. Apart from the two most important waves of migration, many others have left their mark. This has led to the formation of genetically, linguistically, ethnically, and culturally different groups. These groups have been affected by common factors, such as the arrival of a powerful empire that took control of the region's production, but they also have also maintained their characteristic features that may have influenced the later formation of different states.

Myanmar

The pre-agricultural societies living in Burma around 4,000 years ago, are thought to have numbered at most about 30,000 individuals. The arrival of the Neolithic around then led to a population boom, and by 2,000 years ago it had reached a million inhabitants. The distribution of these groups was not uniform, but divided into local groups. The Mon-Khmer groups lived to the south, the southern Chinese lived to the north, and close relatives of the Thais lived in the east. About 1,000 years ago the population had probably reached two million while the groups from the north spread to dominate the area, extending Hindu influence and the Buddhist model. The introduction of rice cultivation led to a further increase in population, which reached about five million by 1700 and about 12.5 million by 1900. Burma was a peaceful rice-exporting province of the British empire, and its prosperity brought immigrants from China and India. Burma was conquered by the Japanese during the Second World War, and afterwards it did not remain part of the British empire for long. Since 1948 the population has exceed 30 million inhabitants, with a Chinese community that has grown from 200,000 to more than 500,000 members, and an Indian community that has decreased from a million at independence to half a million.

Thailand

In the times of transition from hunter-gatherers to agricultural producers around 7,000 years ago, it is estimated that Thailand had about 25,000 inhabitants, increasing to about 200,000 people 3,000 years ago, and nearly half a million 2,000 years ago. By the year 1000 A.D., a period for which there are more data, the number of inhabitants seems to have been around a million. The Thai population was then only one half, and the other half was Mon-Khmer, especially in the south where they were in the majority. Population growth, which until recently was not very spectacular (from two million around 1500 to three million around 1800), increased dramatically in the 19th century, when the mainly rice-growing population doubled. The favorable prospects attracted many Chinese who have maintained their identity as a distinct people and now account for 10% of the country's more than 60 million inhabitants.

281 A masticatory-stained mouth is very common among many southeast Asian monsoon forest peoples. This Thai peasant, for example, has teeth, lips and the corners of the mouth stained a purple color by continued chewing of betelnut (*Areca catechu*) mixed with slaked lime, betel leaves (*Piper betle*) and uncaria resin (*Uncaria gambir*).
[Photo: J.M. La Roque / Auscape International]

Eastern Indochina

About 5,000 years ago, the population of the Vietnam, Laos and Cambodia area, about 40,000 people, learned to cultivate plants. They ceased to be hunter-gatherers and adopted agriculture. About 2,000 years ago the number of inhabitants had probably reached a million. The region was ethnically and culturally polarized; groups of Viet lived in the north, socially and politically influenced by China, and to the south were the Khmer whose culture was Hindu-inspired. This mosaic lasted for the next 1,200 years, in a trial of strength between the two communities that was watched by the Lao, relatives of the Thais and settled in the less-developed inland. The Khmer empire initially prevailed, dominating southern Thailand and southern Laos, as well as central and southern Vietnam. The development of irrigation-based rice cultivation led to a major increase in population, and most of the 2.5 million inhabitants were under Khmer influence. The situation then changed: The weakness of the Khmer empire allowed the jungle to reclaim former sacred areas and the Viet created a strong empire. The area had nine million inhabitants in the mid-19th century, and they were governed by the Vietnamese Emperor until French intervention. When decolonization took place in the mid-20th century, the area had 33.5 million inhabitants. Population growth has continued, in spite of the war between the United States and Vietnam, a notable tribute to the human capacity to make love and war at the same time. Clearing and the use of new land for rice paddies allows Indochina to support a population of 91 million people, 76 million of them in Vietnam, 10 million in Cambodia and five million in Laos.

The Malaysian Archipelago

Agriculture did not take root in the area corresponding to Indonesia (except western New Guinea), Malaysia and Singapore until 4,000 years ago, when the region is estimated to have had about 100,000 inhabitants. This innovation is related to the movement of Malay populations from southeast Asia towards the archipelago, displacing the Proto-Melanesians who occupied the area (see section on the settlement of Polynesia, volume 9). Around 2,000 years ago, the Malay population that had settled had grown to a million, concentrated mainly in southern Java. Since 1,900 years ago these populations have been subjected to a strong Hindu influence through the spice trade. The spread of rice cultivation allowed the number of inhabitants to increase to 4 million by 1,000 years ago and to 8 million by 1500. Hindu customs declined with the arrival of Islam, which was brought by spice traders from India. By establishing a base in the Malaysian Peninsula they spread eastward and formed sultanates on the neighboring islands. In the 16th century, Europeans appeared, seeking to take over trade that was dominated by the Arabs, and this was beginning of the disputes between colonial empires to divide the area. They lasted until the early 19th century when the Dutch dominated most of the archipelago and the British dominated the Malaysian Peninsula and northwest Borneo. By 1800 the area's population had reached

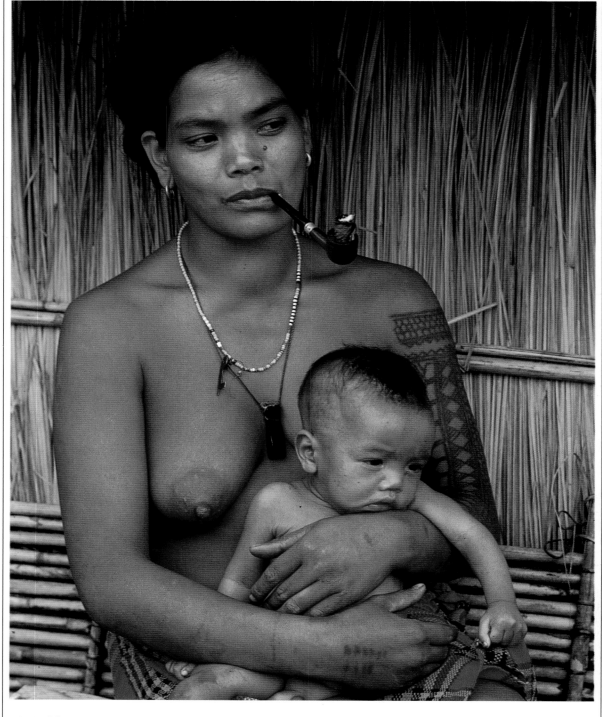

282 **Some places of the monsoon areas of the Philippines** are inhabited by people who maintain ancient cultural practices and lifestyles with little or no western influence, such as the Calinga of northern Luzón, many of whom smoke tobacco leaf in pipes.
[Photo: Heldur Netocny / Still Pictures]

13.5 million people and, perhaps because of successful trade with Europeans, by 1900 it had reached 40 million. In the last century, the Europeans' focus of interest changed from the spice trade to the exploitation of natural resources, and the collection of rubber led to a major immigration of Chinese, mainly to work as rubber tappers. The current population of 145 million is distributed as follows: 2.5 million people, clearly dominated by Chinese in Singapore (where nobody lived in 1800 and only 22,000 people in 1900), a multiethnic nation in Malaysia of more than 20 million people,

(46% Malays, 43% Chinese, and 9% Hindus), and a relatively uniform state in Indonesia with nearly 200 million people—one of the most populated countries on the planet—three quarters of them Muslim and with Christian and Hindu minorities that create serious internal public order problems.

Indonesia has seen the world's largest voluntary migration program. The Indonesian island of Java is one of the world's most densely populated areas, and several times over the last hundred years there have been attempts to resettle part of its inhabitants in some other part of Indonesia (or of the Dutch East Indies before independence). Almost three million people, involved in government development programs, have moved from the islands of Java, Bali, Lombok and Madura, that are densely populated and highly environmentally degraded, to less populated islands like Kalimantan, Sulawesi, and Irian Jaya.

Indonesia's transmigration projects have increased the rate of deforestation in the peripheral islands. Locally, this has caused major problems, for example in the province of Lampung in Sumatra, where soil deterioration has been especially intense. The settlement of areas totally unsuitable for agriculture has caused further environmental problems.

The Philippines

The first modern humans in the Philippines were the ancestors of the Negrito local race, the descendants of the first wave of expansion and of whom only about 10,000 to 20,000 remain today, without much hope of their number increasing. The colonization of the main islands by an Indonesian population around 4,500 years ago and later waves of immigration did not, however, lead to high population densities. Around 3,000 years ago there were only about 100,000 to 200,000 inhabitants. The Filipinos remained unknown to the rest of the world until the 16th century when Spaniards (from Mexico) and Muslims (from Borneo) discovered the islands, which were named after the Spanish king of the time, Philip II. Although the Muslims arrived slightly before, they only colonized the southernmost islands (Mindanao and Jolo) and Spanish missionaries managed to convert the rest of the archipelago to Christianity. In the 16th century, the Philippine population consisted of 750,000 people and high population growth meant it reached 2.5 million by 1800. Since the 19th century the population has been doubling every 50 years, and the rate of growth has increased even further, as in 1950 there were 20 million inhabitants, in 1975 there were 40 million, and by 1995 70 million. As a result of the Spanish colonization, almost 90% of Filipinos are Christians (mostly Catholic), and as a consequence of the Muslim colonizers, about 10% of the population are of the Islamic faith, mainly on the islands of Mindanao and Jolo.

1.2 The human populations of the Indian subcontinent

The Indian subcontinent has long been one of the most densely populated areas on the planet.

Human influence has been so intense that the inhabitants have long been accustomed to the ecological problems raised by overpopulation and over-exploitation.

The first settlers

The arrival of hominids in the Indian subcontinent appears to have been confirmed by archaeological remains: In 1982 the remains of an advanced type of *Homo erectus* of unknown age were found in the terraces of the River Nervada, near Harthnora, in the Indian state of Madhya Pradesh (see the chapter "The expansion of the humans" in volume 1, page 267). When modern humans (*H. sapiens sapiens*) arrived from Asia Minor is uncertain, but there appears to be agreement that it was via Baluchistan, south of the Himalayas, and that it took place between 60,000 and 50,000 years ago. Nothing is known about the lifestyles of the first settlers of the Indian subcontinent, but archaeological remains suggest that about 12,000 years ago the people were mesolithic hunter-gatherers.

The relict populations from these arrivals include the Andamanese, more or less distant relatives of the Negrito local race in the Philippines and of the first settlers of Australia and Indonesia, who all speak pre-Dravidian languages that are mutually unintelligible despite belonging to the Austric language superfamily. Groups sharing intermediate characteristics include the Jarawa and Onge, whose women may show steatopygia (excess fat on the buttocks), have very dark frizzy hair, and speak languages of the Austronesian family. The Andaman Islanders live in the most forested areas and have maintained their genetic isolation from the subcontinent's other inhabitants by ferociously rejecting any attempt at colonization. Only one of the four groups of Andamanese accepted peaceful contacts with foreigners, the Ariostos of the large island of Andaman. The result was that their population declined sharply due to alcoholism, and of the 3,500 inhabitants, only 29 were left in 1858. Another group related to the first modern settlers of the region are the Veddas who originally included the Veddas of Sri Lanka and other now marginal Veddoid populations from the south of the Indian subcontinent, the Nicobar Islands, Sumatra and Malaysia, lower Laos and Sulawesi. The Veddas are short, but not as short as the Negrito local race. They are not related to the Mongoloid populations that descended from the northern part of Asia or with the recent migratory waves from Asia Minor, but they have adopted their culture and speak Indo-European languages.

283 The Vedda people, such as this family in Sri Lanka, are descendants of the first modern human settlers of the Indian and Ceylon monsoon region and speak the Dravidian languages that still survive in the region.
[Photo: Xavier Ferrer & Adolf de Sostoa]

These first inhabitants to settle India were displaced to inland areas, often mountainous, by tribes with more developed Neolithic technology who seemingly spoke Dravidian languages. The new arrivals probably also came from the west, from Iran, where a language of the same family was spoken (until it was replaced by Indo-European) and it seems they spread the use of Dravidian throughout the subcontinent. The Dravidian family, the like Indo-European family, belongs to the Nostratic superfamily, which according to some authors was spoken in Asia Minor more than 12,000 years ago.

The arrival of the Neolithic

Little is known about the beginning of agriculture in India, although it is known that about 7,500 years ago, animals had been domesticated but not plants. Wheat, barley, and millet entered India from the west and a flourishing civilization arose in the valley of the Indus, the Harrapan civilization. The silt deposited in the alluvial plains by the surges of the river Indus allowed the cultivation of wheat and barley without the need for irrigation or plowing—although the Harrapans must have known the plow. An urban culture developed in the valley of the Indus almost as long ago as that in Mesopotamia, with which it traded although both civilizations maintained their distinctive features. Between 4,200 and 3,700 years ago the most important cities were Mohenjo-Daro (which at its peak must have had 40,000 or more inhabitants) and Harappa, which gave its name to the civilization. The Harappans of the Indus Valley showed great cultural uniformity. Not only were the cities laid out on a grid plan and had a large drainage system, but the bricks, houses, weights and measures, ceramics and the parts of looms were also standardized, as were toys. The designs of their hairstyles and of copper jewels were the forerunners of later typical Indian art. They also cultivated cotton, legumes, and other vegetable crops and reared cows, goats, sheep, buffalo, Indian pigs, camels and asses as well as dogs and cats. It is also possible that they invented chess and the windmill. Rice cultivation entered the Indian subcontinent through the plains of the Ganges, and there are no traces of rice cultivation in Maharashtra (western India) until 3,500 years ago and in Tamil Nadu and Karnataka (southern India) until 3,000 years ago. The Harrapan civilization emerged from the pre-Harrapan groups of the area, but did not last long; archaeological remains suggested it lasted no longer than 200 years. Anyway, the disappearance of the Harrapans between 3,500 and 3,750 years ago years ago is not related to signs of violence; some authors believe it was due to the arrival of nomadic shepherds from the northwest, migrants rather than conquerors, while other authors attribute the disappearance to a natural catastrophe, such as a flood or a change in the course of the Indus River.

It is worth pointing out that the Harrapan civilization used a script that has not yet been deciphered, that the script was nonsyllabic, unlike Sanskrit, and not based on ideograms, as is Chinese. Anyway, despite borrowing from neighboring languages, some authors consider it to be Dravidian. One of the difficulties of deciphering this writing is that almost all the written texts are seals or fragments of pottery items.

The Indo-Europeans and the caste system

The peoples responsible for the next population displacement spoke an Indo-European language, *Indiranic*. Indo-European, with its subgroups, might have evolved from Nostratic among the tribes that remained in Asia Minor or Iran. The new tribes that entered the Indian subcontinent around 3,500 years ago, from an area of Iran, probably introduced ironwork and the domesticated horse to India, and displaced the speakers of Dravidian languages to the south of the subcontinent. These immigrant groups, also known as "Aryans" (a term corrupted by incorrect use in the 20th century, as it in fact means "noble" or "foreigner"), installed the caste system in India. The nobles naturally occupied the upper classes, while the former Harrapans and the most ancient settlers of the continent formed the lower castes. The *Rig Veda* (the ancient collection of hymns dedicated to the gods of the Veddan pantheon, compilation of which began more than 3,000 years ago) was written in Sanskrit, and already implied the fixed nature of the castes in the Hindu religion. In India, the castes became the basis of religious, social and political life almost as soon as the Indo-Iranians arrived, as they sought to keep themselves apart from the existing population. The *Brahmins* made use of the caste system to monopolize religion and teaching and established the upper caste, the priestly caste. Below them was the warrior caste, then the merchants, peasants and stockraisers. Below them were the craftsmen and below them were the *Harijan*, also known as *untouchables*), the caste that did the dirty tasks. Within this great division, castes have subdivided, multiplied and fragmented into very many groups. Twenty-three hundred years ago there were seven inbreeding castes separated by professions and with their complex internal hierarchies. The maximum number of castes reached was 75,000 while now

284 A Harrapan seal with a unicorn and nonsyllabic writing from the excavations at Mohenjo-Daro. The Harrapean script has still not been deciphered, limiting understanding of the development of civilization of the Indus.
[Photo: AGE Fotostock]

3. HUMANS IN THE MONSOON FORESTS

there are about 43,000. Membership in a caste is by birth and can only be changed on rebirth. Marriage between individuals of different caste degrades both spouses to the category of *pariah*, still considered to be despicable and to forfeit social rights, and so have to do the most disagreeable jobs. Hindus are forbidden to eat with persons of a lower caste or eat food prepared by them. In India the system is so deeply rooted that government attempts to abolish it have caused great social protest, but the system was legally abolished by the 1947 constitution. This social structure has conditioned the success of the waves of immigrants over the history of the Indian subcontinent, as it has been difficult for isolated foreigners to assimilate into Indian society, while assimilation has been easier if the group was large enough to establish an inbreeding caste of its own. Furthermore, studies of mitochondrial DNA seem to suggest a gene distribution in keeping with the castes. Yet the Muslims have never entered this hierarchical system, nor have the technologically primitive tribal groups living in the mountains, often unaware of even the Neolithic advances that have occurred on the subcontinent.

Recent events

The arrival of Alexander the Great 2,300 years ago did not lead to major demographic changes. The first Muslims arrived in 712 A.D. The generalized implantation of Islam did not take place until the 13th century, when four Turkish dynasties governed India. In the 16th century, these sultanates fell apart, and the Mongols took advantage of this to carry out some incursions, and then the Portuguese arrived. The Portuguese were present in the region from the

285 Human population densities in the monsoon area are among the highest on the planet, especially in the Indian subcontinent. This street in Dhaka, Bangladesh, jammed with city dwellers with their small vehicles, is a good example.
[Photo: Mark Edwards / Still Pictures]

16th century onwards, the British and Dutch from the early 17th century, and the French from the second half of the 17th century. In the 18th century the area was occupied by the British, who tried to change some traditional customs, such as suttee, the ritual suicide of widows, but popular antagonism led to a halt in these interventions in Indian life. In the second half of the 19th century an independence movement started that began in the highest castes and wished to emphasize India's Hindu character. This movement gradually changed with the appearance of terrorism and boycotts of British products in the early 20th century. After the First World War a person appeared who became very popular for his spiritual conception of political action, Mohandas Karamchand Gandhi. The Mahatma, or enlightened one, preached civil disobedience and the nationalist movement became a mass movement behind the slogan "Quit India." Antagonism between Hindus and Muslims worsened until, after the crisis of the Second World War, India achieved independence from the British empire in 1947. It was divided into two states, India and Pakistan. Pakistan consisted of two separated halves, Eastern Pakistan and Western Pakistan, but the eastern half became the independent state of Bangladesh in 1971. These measures have not brought social peace, due to the existence of enclaves of minority religions and the existence of other groups with different beliefs, such as the Sikhs (followers of a religion that is a hybrid between the mystic Sufi branch of Islam and Vishnuism, followed mainly in the Punjab), and the Tamils (speakers of Dravidian languages and the descendants of the Neolithic settlers preceding the Indo-Iranians, who mainly live in southern India and Sri Lanka).

Population movements

To understand the history of the population of the Indian subcontinent it is necessary to take account of the three states into which the subcontinent is divided India, Pakistan, and Bangladesh.

About 12,000 years ago, in the Mesolithic and before the arrival of agriculture, the entire Indian subcontinent is thought to have had no more than 100,000 inhabitants. After the arrival of the Neolithic and the Dravidian languages, about 7,000 years ago, from what is now Afghanistan through the Indus Valley, the population grew to an estimated one million inhabitants about 6,000 years ago. This spectacular population growth continued and it is estimated that by 4,000 years ago around 5 million people lived in the valley of the Indus, while the Mesolithic settlers of the rest of the subcontinent numbered no more than one million. After the fall of the Harrapan civilization, between 3,750 and 3,500 years ago, the area went through a dark age lasting a thousand years, making it very difficult to estimate populations during this period. During this time when the Dravidian languages were replaced by Indo-European ones. The arrival of rice cultivation and use of metals led to such a population boom that it is calculated that about 2,500 years ago around 25 million people lived in the subcontinent, 15 million of them in the Ganges Valley, where rice cultivation had first arrived. In the period of development of the Mauryan empire, about 2,200 years ago, around 30 million people probably lived in the subcontinent, 20 million of them in the Ganges Basin. In the 6th century, when the empire of the Gupta dynasty stopped the entry of the Huns, 50 million people lived in the subcontinent. The population had reached 50 million by the 12th century, and 100 million by the 15th century. There are populations of Hindu origin in other parts of the planet, such as Sri Lanka, Malaysia, South Africa, Mauritius, Myanmar, Trinidad, Guyana, Fiji, parts of east Africa, and many areas of the United Kingdom and the Commonwealth.

The languages spoken in the Indian subcontinent are divided into four main families: the Indo-Pacific, spoken mainly by the descendants of the first modern human settlers, such as the Negrito local race; the Dravidian languages, including Telegu, Tamil, Malayalam, and Kanarese, mostly spoken by the descendants of the probable introducers of the Neolithic into India; the Indo-European, including Hindu, Bengali, Marathi, Urdu and Gujarati, introduced by the descendants of the Indo-Iranians and also spoken by the Veddas, although they are descended from the first settlers of the region (an example of linguistic substitution); and the fourth linguistic family is the Sino-Tibetan, spoken by populations in the north of the country. The most widely spoken languages belong to the Indo-European family, spoken by 74% of Hindus, followed by Dravidian, spoken by 24% of the population, then the Indo-Pacific languages, which are spoken by 1.5% of India's population, and finally the Sino-Tibetan languages, which are spoken by 0.5% of the subcontinent's population. The Mongols promoted Hindi as a common language for the whole of India—it was mainly spoken in the north, and could be written in both Devanagari script or Arabic script—but they also respected regional languages.

In terms of religious beliefs, the dominant religion in modern India is Hinduism (80% of the population), after the two mainly Muslim regions were split off to form Pakistan, but there are still some Muslims (10%). Independence from the British empire led to the movement of 6-7 million

286 **The distribution of linguistic families in southeastern Asia, the Indian subcontinent and Oceania**. The unfolding of history has meant that this area of the planet is one of the most varied in terms of linguistic families, and interestingly also shows a correspondingly high level of genetic diversity. In the Indian subcontinent, the Indoiranian peoples displaced the Dravidian populations, who had displaced the former inhabitants. Sino-Tibetan and Austric languages are also spoken in southeast Asia. These were the languages of the descendants of the Neolithic rice center, and developed into the Dayak languages (the former Thai-Kadai languages), Miao-yao and Austro-Asiatic languages (with Mon Khmer and Munda). Austronesian languages are thought to have developed in or near Taiwan from Austric, and these are thought to have been spoken by the humans who colonized Polynesia as far as Easter Island and Madagascar. Two additional families, Australian and Indo-Pacific (or Papuan), are older than Austronesia and include the languages spoken on the Australian continent, in New Guinea and the other islands of Melanesia. The Australian and Indo-Pacific groups of languages are probably derived from the languages spoken by the first pre-Neolithic settlers of Melanesia, and are extraordinarily diverse. New Guinea has one of the highest indexes of linguistic diversity known. Note that the language spoken by the former Tasmanians (extinct since the 19th century) belonged to the Indo-Pacific group, and not to the Australian groups. The Polynesians partly interbred with the Melanesians, but mainly occupied uninhabited islands. This successive chain of human expansion resulted in a curious mosaic in which the oldest languages were left as islands among speakers of more recently arrived languages. There are also two isolated languages, Nahali and Buruichaski, that have not been classified.
[Drawing: Editrònica, from data provided by the authors]

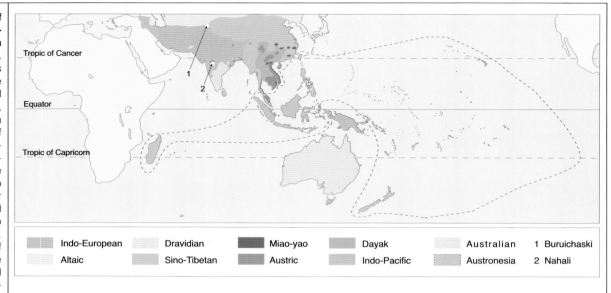

Tropic of Cancer

Equator

Tropic of Capricorn

1 Buruichaski
2 Nahali

Indo-European	Dravidian	Miao-yao
Altaic	Sino-Tibetan	Austric

Dayak | Australian
Indo-Pacific | Austronesia

Muslims to Pakistan and 6 million Hindus to India. This migration was especially conflictive in Pakistan, as the immigrants settled in the cities. Other religious minorities in India include Christians (3% of the population), Sikhs (2%, concentrated in the Punjab), Jainism, and Buddhism (five million believers).

1.3 Health and illness in the monsoon forest

Health problems in the monsoon forest are not very different from those of the rainforest in general. Cholera, however, has long been endemic in some regions of southern Asia, especially northern India. Cholera is discussed in the appropriate section in volume 3.

Malaria

The incidence of malaria (and of diseases with a mosquito vector in general, such as dengue fever) is very high, and there are genetic anomalies related to malaria resistance, such as sickle-cell anemia, which is not as frequent as in western and eastern Africa but does occur in India and Bangladesh, and thalassemia, which also occurs in India. Hemoglobin E, which provides some protection against malaria, is most frequent among the Thais (13%).

Kala-azar

Kala-azar, although its distribution is more widespread, has its highest incidence around the Bay of Bengal, mainly in Bihar, West Bengal, Bangla Desh and the states of northeast India. The name by which the illness is internationally known, *kala-azar*, means "black fever" in Hindi.

Kala-azar, or visceral leishmaniasis, is caused by the presence in the blood and some organs, such as liver, spleen, and bone marrow, of the parasitic kinetoplastid protoctist *Leishmania donovani*, which is transmitted by the bite of a sandfly *Phlebotomus*. *Leishmania donovani*, like most species of *Leishmania*, has a relatively simple life cycle, with two distinct phases. One phase occurs in the human body, and is known as the amastigote phase because the parasite loses its flagellum and becomes almost spherical. The other phase, the promastigote phase, develops in the stomach and lower intestine of the mosquito, and consists of elongated cells, 10-25 mm long, slightly thicker at the middle, and with a single apical flagellum. The promastigote phase of *L. donovani* lives and multiplies in the stomach and the intestines of different species of *Phlebotomus*. The illness takes the form of irregular prolonged fever and swelling of the spleen and liver, followed by muscle and joint pains, anemia, weight loss, pallid appearance and weakness of the immune defenses to other infections.

Dengue fever

Dengue fever is an illness caused by a flavivirus, a virus with RNA that is transmitted by arthropods and is similar to yellow fever; it was first identified in Manila in 1953. The vectors are also mosquitoes of the genus *Aedes* that may also act as vectors of yellow fever. It occurs in

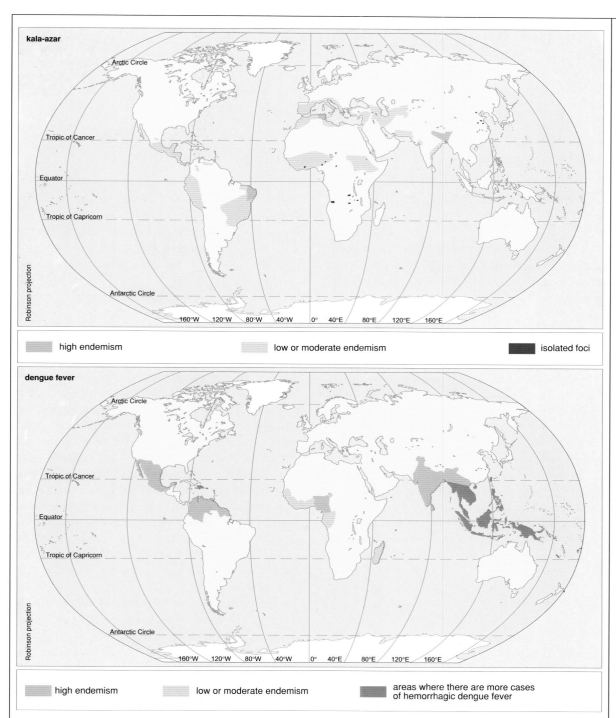

287 **Global distribution of visceral leishmaniasis, or *kala-azar*, and of dengue fever**. Tropical forests show high levels of infectious illnesses, mostly produced by pathogens that survive in the warm wet environment or those transmitted by a vector (illness) such as visceral leishmaniasis and dengue fever. Dengue fever is an illness caused by an arbovirus and transmitted by mosquitoes of the genus *Aedes*, whereas visceral leishmaniasis is caused by a protist (*Leishmania*) and transmitted by sand flies of the genus *Phlebotomus*. These diseases are very frequent in some areas of the planet, and so it is possible to consider areas of high endemism. [*Drawing: Editrònica, from several sources*]

kala-azar

Robinson projection

Arctic Circle
Tropic of Cancer
Equator
Tropic of Capricorn
Antarctic Circle

160°W 120°W 80°W 40°W 0° 40°E 80°E 120°E 160°E

| | high endemism | | low or moderate endemism | | isolated foci |

dengue fever

Robinson projection

Arctic Circle
Tropic of Cancer
Equator
Tropic of Capricorn
Antarctic Circle

160°W 120°W 80°W 40°W 0° 40°E 80°E 120°E 160°E

| | high endemism | | low or moderate endemism | | areas where there are more cases of hemorrhagic dengue fever |

Madagascar, the tropical Pacific islands and in the Antilles, but it is more frequent in the urban areas of southern Asia from India to the Philippines and Indonesia.

It usually takes a mild flu-like form, with a very high temperature and widespread severe muscle and joint pains, often accompanied by photophobia and pains behind the eyes. After an apparent improvement within 24 to 36 hours of appearance, the fever rises again, and a distinctive rash appears over the entire body, especially the thorax, that gives the impression of small burns in the affected area. These symptoms disappear after four or five days, leaving the patient weakened for three to six months. The hemorrhagic form is more serious, leading to death in 15% of cases: instead of the apparent improvement within two or three days of the syndromes appearing, hemorrhaging occurs which may lead to coma and death or to recovery after a week of high fever and hemorrhaging of the mucous membranes.

2. The use of plant resources

2.1 Harvesting without planting

The useful plant resources provided by the monsoon forests include hardwoods, food plants, medicinal plants, spices, and a wide range of other plants used locally to satisfy everyday needs.

Food plants

The fruit trees and food plants that occur in the monsoon forests of Sri Lanka include the longan (*Dimocarpus* [=*Euphoria*] *longan*, Sapindaceae), whose fruit have an edible aril with a taste similar to the lychee, *Dialium ovalifolia* (Leguminosae), whose fruit is similar to the tamarind, and *Drypetes sepiaria* (Euphorbiaceae). The edible seeds of the mowra tree (*Madhuca indica* [=*M. latifolia*], Sapotaceae), an evergreen from Sri Lanka and the monsoon forests of southern India, yield an oil used to produce cooking oil and to make soap.

Medicinal plants

The inhabitants of the monsoon forest regions depend almost entirely on plants as a source of medicinal products. Of India's 2,000 marketable drugs, about 1,500 are of plant origin from the country's different vegetation types. Some important medicinal plants are cultivated commercially, but many are still collected from the wild. In Thailand, most plants used in rural medicine are collected from the forest. Many of the raw materials are of commercial value in the manufacture of traditional drugs, for modern pharmaceutical production, or as export commodities.

The medicinal plants of Sri Lanka include the chaste-tree (*Vitex negundo*, Verbenaceae), used to treat rheumatism and colds and also possessing insecticidal properties; *Croton aromaticus*

(Euphorbiaceae) and *C. laccifer*; *Cissus quadrangularis* (Vitaceae), thought to speed up healing, especially of fractured bones; *Cassia fistula* (Leguminosae), a mild laxative; *Micromelum zeylanicum* (Rutaceae); and *Murraya koenigii* (Rutaceae), known as the curry-leaf plant, which is used to treat dysentery and nausea.

The importance of plants in Indonesian traditional medicine is especially great in Java. The traditional preparations known as *jamu* are believed to have health-giving properties and increase resistance to disease. Shops sell elegantly packaged products and prepared drinks, and jamu gendong sellers hawk their products from door to door. Most plants used in traditional jamu preparations are forest species. In central and eastern Java there are still remnant patches of monsoon forest, although most of the island's original vegetation was cleared long ago. The species traditionally used in jamu are becoming harder and harder to find. Some are cultivated in small quantities for family use, but others are scarcely cultivated.

Two medicinal species found in the Javanese teak forests (*Tectona grandis*) are *Cassia tora* (Leguminosae) and *Parameria laevigata* (Apocynaceae). The leaves of *Cassia tora* are put in jamu to relieve constipation, and the seed is used to protect the eyes. The bark of *Parameria laevigata* is used to restore and stimulate the hormonal system after childbirth. Both species are now very scarce in Java. A further medicinal species that has become rare is *Parkia roxburghii* (Leguminosae); excessive harvesting of its fruits has led to its decline.

Ornamental plants

Monsoon forest orchids (like other rainforest plants) are highly sought after for their attractive flowers and exotic appeal. Thailand is the main source of orchids on the international market.

288 A workshop in Gantesari (Java) preparing *jamu*, the traditional mixture of wild medicinal herbs in Java. Jamu preparation has led to the development of great local trade.
[Photo: Alain Compost / WWF / Still Pictures]

289 The cultivation of **ornamental orchids**, such as these monopodial specimens, is an important agronomic activity. Starting from a few wild species, varieties have been bred that are especially interesting for their beauty, resistance, etc. They are vegetatively propagated and cultivated intensively in adapted greenhouses, such as this one in Thailand.
[Photo: David Vilasis]

290 **Burning joss sticks of sandalwood (*Santalum album*)** as an offering at religious ceremonies is a widespread practice throughout the Indian subcontinent, as shown by this photo taken in a Buddhist temple in Nepal. [Photo: Jaume Altadill]

Some plants are propagated in modern nurseries and others collected from the wild. Wild orchids collected in Myanmar and Laos are also exported through Thailand.

Wild species of *Dendrobium* and *Paphiopedilum* have been collected in large quantities for sale in local markets and export, threatening the survival of some species, even in Thailand's national parks, where collection is banned. As new populations are discovered, they are uprooted for sale on the international market, as has happened recently with *Dendrobium harveyanum*, an attractive species from Thailand and Myanmar that had not been seen on the market for about a century. Rare species of *Paphiopedilum* have suffered a similar fate.

2.2 Forestry uses

Sandalwood (*Santalum album*) and teak (*Tectona grandis*) are two of the most internationally appreciated woods from Asiatic monsoon forests. The different species of ebony (*Diospyros*) are also among the most sought-after tropical hardwoods, and some of the most valuable species of the genus, mainly the ebony of commerce (*D. ebenum*), are found in monsoon forests. Other timbers, such as sal (*Shorea robusta*), although less well known, are highly appreciated in their region of origin.

Sandalwood

The use of sandalwood, *Santalum album*, has formed part of India's culture and heritage for thousands of years. Sandalwood was one the first items traded in India, along with spices and silk. The tree's heartwood yields an aromatic oil that is of great value in perfumery and has medicinal uses. Sandalwood is also used for carvings and boxes and for burning as incense in thin sticks.

In India, sandalwood generally grows in the dry deciduous forests of the Deccan Peninsula, at the base of the western Ghats, and is most abundant in the states of Karnataka and Tamil Nadu. India's production of heartwood is about 2,000 tons per year. The price has increased dramatically in the last few years partly due to the reduction of sup-

291 **Large plantations of teak** (*Tectona grandis*) account for most of southeast Asia's timber production. The domesticated Indian elephant (*Elephas maximus*), native to the region, provides much of the brute strength needed to manipulate the trunks. [Photo: Peter Stevensson / Planet Earth Pictures]

plies, made worse by smuggling, and partly due to fire, animals that eat the young shoots and a disease spread by sap-sucking insects.

Teak

Teak (*Tectona grandis*) is one of the most appreciated and versatile hardwoods. It is widely used in shipbuilding, bridges, flooring, furniture, carvings and sculptures. It is native to Cambodia, India, Laos, Myanmar, Thailand, and Vietnam and has been widely planted outside its natural range since the 14th century. It remains uncertain if the "natural" teak forests in Indonesia are truly spontaneous or were first planted by Hindu colonists centuries ago. Teak plantations are now found in many tropical countries in Africa, the Caribbean, and Central America. Teak is remarkable because it is one of the few tropical hardwood species that has been successfully cultivated in plantations.

International trade in teak began in the 19th century. The wood was supplied from India, Myanmar, Java, and later Thailand. Teak exploitation formed the basis for early forest management in India; in 1800 a commission was appointed to investigate the availability in Kerala and minimum girth limits for felling were introduced: The first teak plantation in India was established in Kerala in 1842. The State Forests Department and Forestry Development Corporation extract wood in accordance with approved management plans, but no teak is exported.

For a long time, teak has been very important in Thailand as timber, and it is a major source of for-

eign exchange. Foreign trading companies began commercial exploitation of the northern teak forests in the mid-19th century. By the end of the century excessive timber extraction was already degrading Thailand's monsoon forests. In 1889, property and control of all Thailand's forests were transferred to the Thai government, and the first legislation was introduced to regulate the excessive exploitation of teak. In 1977 Thailand banned the export of teak, although the ban was later revised, allowing export of some worked timber. Generally, government permission is needed to fell teak. All commercial logging was banned in Thailand in 1989, after flooding thought to have been caused by deforestation, but illegal logging still continues. Felling is permitted for domestic use, and this has led to abuse, such as the rapid construction of dwellings from teak, which are then equally rapidly dismantled and the timber sold. Enormous elephants carved from teak have also been exported, for later production of sawn timber, as a way of evading export controls.

The ban on logging teak in Thailand and Laos has led to increased demand in Myanmar, leading to concern about the rate of logging within the country. Immediately after the Thai ban came into force in January 1989, 20 logging concessions were set up along the Thai border and they were allowed to export more than 200,000 t to Thai timber mills. The number of concessions is thought to have doubled by the end of 1989. Teak is one of Myanmar's main sources of foreign exchange, and its exploitation is the monopoly of the State Timber Corporation. Conservation of intact patches of natural teak forest is now one of Myanmar's main conservation priorities. This

292 The progressive loss of the monsoon forest and international efforts to protect it have stimulated forestry activities to the detriment of the classic exploitation of wild forests. The photo shows a plantation in Mae Suai in northern Thailand.
[Photo: J. Hobday / Natural Science Photos]

will ensure the future supply of selected seed for commercial plantations.

Indonesia is now a main supplier of teak on the international market. Java produces about 17,700,000 ft³ (500,000 m³) of teak, almost 10% of it exported. The island's long established teak forests are now rapidly shrinking because of agricultural pressure to make more land available for growing crops.

Other countries with teak plantations only supply a small amount to the international market. It is very important to promote plantations and protect the valuable remaining wild populations. Logging, illegal logging, deliberate burning and grazing are exerting increasing pressure on the natural populations of teak.

Sal

Another quality hardwood from the monsoon forest is sal (*Shorea robusta*, Dipterocarpaceae). This grows mainly in northeastern India, especially Bihar, and also in Bangladesh and Nepal. Every part of the tree has its uses: The trunk has a valuable hardwood timber, greatly appreciated in building, and its bark has medicinal applications and is used to tan hides.

Sal also produces the resin (or dammar) known as *ral*, and oil is pressed from the seeds. Sal dammar has been used in India since time immemorial; it is burned as incense and is an ingredient in the samagri for cremations. Sal oil is used in the conversion of fat into a substitute for cocoa butter. Locally, it is also used in cooking, for lighting and to make soap. In India, export of sal timber, like all other timbers, is banned, but the oil pressed from sal seeds is a major export commodity.

Ebonies and other hardwoods

Four hundred and seventy-five species of the genus *Diospyros* (Ebenaceae) are distributed throughout the tropics, but only 20 are important commercial sources of timber. The main species now exploited is the ebony of commerce (*D. ebenum*), a tree native to India and Sri Lanka, long used as a raw material by European luxury furniture manufacturers. It is now scarce in Sri Lanka, as is coromandel (*D. quaesita*), now virtually extinct after centuries of exploitation.

In Sri Lanka, another valuable hardwood of the monsoon forest and dry zones is satinwood (*Chloroxylon swietenia*), which like *Diospyros ebenum* has long been exploited for its valuable wood. Satinwood has been exported for about a century, and within Sri Lanka it was used for railway sleepers, but it is now scarce there.

Bamboos

Bamboos are fistular (hollow) grasses with a tree-like growth form and are, essentially, giant grass stems. They are of great use to humans and show many unusual biological features related to their structure, growth and ecological requirements. They are not strictly speaking a botanical group, but a group of 700 fistular species that prefer areas subject to disturbances and whose shoot or cane is long, resistant, and fast-growing.

Bamboos are typical of monsoonal Asia, but are also found in any tropical or even temperate location between 40°N and 40°S. There are about 400 species in Asia, half of them in India, Myanmar and Thailand (species of the genera *Arundinaria, Bambusa, Cephalostachyum, Dendrocalamus, Dinochloa, Gigantochloa, Guadua, Melocalamus, Melocanna, Ochlandra, Oxytenanthera, Phyllostachys, Schizostachyum, Teinostachyum, Thyrsostachys*, etc.), two hundred species in America (*Arthrostylidium, Arundinaria, Chusquea, Guadua*, etc.); there are just a dozen in Africa (*Arundinaria, Oxytenanthera*, etc.) but in Madagascar there are 25 species (*Cephalostachyum, Ochlandra, Schizostachyum*, etc.). Its monsoon-influenced climate means Thailand has many bamboos, with about 50 native species, while India has 136 native species.

Bamboos need temperatures of 68-86°F (20-30°C) and annual rainfall of 39-79 in (1,000-2,000 mm) but there are other species that grow in more extreme conditions. The African species of bamboo *Oxytenanthera abyssinica* can survive temperatures of 104-122°F (40-50°C), while the Chinese species *Phyllostachys* can resist snow. Similarly, there are also relatively xerophyllous species, such as *Dendrocalamus strictus* which grows in sites with rainfall of 30-39 in (750-1,000 mm), or like *O. abyssinica* which needs less than 30 in (750 mm). Most bamboos grow at altitudes below 800 m, but there are exceptions. The Himalayan species *Arundinaria racemosa* and *Thammocalamus aristata*, and the Andean species *Chusquea andina* and *C. aristata* grow high in the mountains up to altitudes of 10,000 ft (3,000 m).

Bamboos have two basic types of morphology. Leptomorphic (slender) bamboos (*Phyllostachys, Melocanna*) have long rhizomes that bear aerial stems, so that they generate large but transparent bamboo "groves." Pachymorphic (thick) bamboos *Dendrocalamus, Gigantochloa*), however, have very short rhizomes that produce a single aerial shoot at their tip, and this then produces another rhizome that behaves in the same way, so that they eventually form dense clumps of canes that do not however, cover a very large area. Leptomorphic bamboos are typical of tropical or sub-temperate zones, such as certain parts of Japan, whereas pachymorphic bamboos are typically tropical.

Bamboos have many diverse uses, from making all sorts of vessels to paper production, and they are also eaten (see "The enchanted cane," pages 468-471). So it is not surprising that bamboo plantations, together with the areas where it grows wild, cover a very large area. The bamboo jungles of India cover an area of about 25 million acres (10 million hectares), 13% of the total area of forest, and produce more than 3 million tons of cane a year. Thailand has a million hectares of bamboo groves, Myanmar more than two million hectares and China has almost three million.

2.3 Agricultural activity

As in the equatorial rainforests, one of the main forms of traditional agricultural activity in monsoon forests is shifting agriculture. This is still widely practiced and shows many local and regional variations.

Shifting cultivation in monsoonal India

In India, shifting cultivation is known as *jhum*, many different forms of which are practiced in the northeast of the country. In the Khasi Hills in Meghalaya, the local farmers of the Garo tribe cultivate up to 35 plants together. Important cereals include rice and maize, together with leaf- and fruit-producing plants and tuber crops, such as cassava (*Manihot esculenta*), sweet potato (*Ipomoea batatas*), yam (*Dioscorea*) and eddoes (*Colocasia antiquorum*). Castor oil plant (*Ricinus communis* is also cultivated to raise silkworms.

In the months of winter, the men of several families work together under the direction of the village chief to clear the vegetation of a patch of monsoon forest; they leave the larger trees in place, cutting the smaller ones and the bamboos. At the end of March or the beginning of April they burn the debris before the start of the monsoon, and sowing of crops takes place after the first rains. Harvesting takes place throughout the year as the different crops mature. Normally, the women are responsible for weeding.

The enchanted cane

Stereotyped western literature has often attributed to Asian people the doubtful honor of being masters of torture. The refined cruelty of Chinese torture, for example, is commonplace in western adventure novels. Despite such biased attitudes, some ancient Asian tortures do inflict dreadful progressive and lasting suffering. For example, tying the victim to a young bamboo cane and leaving the victim to hang or be torn apart by the growing bamboo canes. One might think that the unfortunate victim would in fact die of hunger or thirst, as would happen if they were tied to a beech or an oak. In fact they would not live long enough to starve.

Detail of bamboo cane [M. Claye / Gamma]

Bamboo plant (Phyllostachys edulis) [Flore / Jacana]

In fact, no other plant grows as quickly as the bamboo. The growth of each cane from the rhizomes is incredibly quick, about 12 in (30 cm) a day, and some grow unbelievably fast. *Bambusa gigantea* can grow 20 in (50 cm) a day, but *Phyllostachys edulis* holds the record, as it can grow up to 47 in (120 cm) a day, almost 0.04 in (1 mm) per minute. These figures show the extreme cruelty of the torture described above... The results of this runaway growth can easily be imagined: within a few weeks, the new bamboo canes easily dominate the site where they are growing. When the shoots cease growing, within two or three months of the new shoot sprouting, the canes reach heights of 33-49 ft (10-15 m), or even greater in some species. *Dendrocalamus giganteus* reaches the greatest height, around 114-125 ft (35-38 m), although there are species that do not exceed 16-33 ft (5-10 m).

The stem does not, however, increase in thickness as it grows, as bamboos are grasses and do not show secondary thickening. Bamboo canes are effectively smooth, uniform cylinders (although some are prismatic in cross section, such as *Chimonobambusa quadrangularis*) between 3 and 6 in (8 and 15 cm) in diameter, with alternating nodes and internodes, like all other canes. The remarkable *D. giganteus* in addition to being the tallest bamboo is also the thickest, with canes up to 12 in (30 cm) in diameter. Bamboo canes are usually green, but there are other colors, such as the golden yellow *Phyllostachys aurea* and the completely black *Gigantochloa atter*, which is greatly appreciated for ornamental uses. In gardening, the term bamboo is often incorrectly applied to dwarf species called sasas (*Sasa*), which are also fistular grasses but much smaller and extratropical, mainly from Japan.

Bamboos flower only at long intervals and then the canes that have flowered usually die, but not the entire clump. This occurs every 30-35 years, although there are species like *Phyllostachys bambusoides* and *Melocanna bambusoides* that only flower every 40-60 years. This means they are longer living than those of any other herbaceous plant, another of their records.

Detail of bamboo cane (*Bambusa*) [A. Manoni / Gamma]

The bamboo cane is a marvelous structure. The arrangement of the cells, arranged axially at the internodes and radially in the nodes, the layout of the vessels, the sclerenchyma fibers 1.5-3.5 mm long running along the stem and holding it together, and the alternation of hollow internodes with solid nodes, all make bamboo cane surprisingly resistant and light. However, this usual structure, popularly known as a "female cane" is duly complemented by the "male cane" of species like *Arundinaria prainii* and *Dendrocalamus strictus*, which have canes with very short internodes. When compared with wood, bamboo cane is three times more resistant and, for a given thickness, is half as resistant as a steel bar but is of course much, much lighter. This lightness and strength combined with its natural shape like a long cylindrical beam has made it an unbeatable construction material throughout the monsoon area, and this usefulness is increased by local people's skill at doing more practical things than torturing people...

Bamboo grove (*Dendrocalamus giganteus*) [Michel Viard / Gamma]

Bamboos can be used for almost every purpose imaginable, making furniture, containers and baskets, fences, agricultural tools, poultry cages, ladders, blinds, irrigation piping, fans, umbrellas, toys, and other culturally important artifacts, such as some musical instruments, (for example the Madagascar zither, the *valiha*). Bamboo leaves provide valuable fodder for livestock, bamboo sheaths are used to line caps and sandals, the seeds are eaten in many parts of India in times of famine, the edible shoots of some species are genuine culinary delicacies, and a wine is made from the African species *Oxytenanthera braunii*). *Dendrocalamus hamiltonii* even has shoots that resemble rhinoceros horns, and are sold fraudulently as such in Asian markets. In addition to these domestic uses, bamboos have many architectural and industrial uses.

Bamboo scaffolding in Shanghai [Heather Angel / Biofotos]

The main industrial use of bamboo is in making paper. In India it is the most important source of pulp for paper, ordinary paper today but also simple forms of paper in antiquity, when expert miniaturists drew delicate images, often with the bamboo itself as the main motif, the distinctive emblem of oriental art. Bamboo is for many reasons the enchanted cane.

Detail of bamboo cane (Phyllostachys aurea) [Michel Viard / Jacana]

Bamboos are of great importance in the construction of rural dwellings and are used for scaffolding and to build bridges. In some areas of Thailand there are houses entirely built of the bamboos *Phyllostachys pubescens*, *Bambusa vulgaris*, etc. The main framework and the supports use long culms (stems), and smaller ones are used for windows and door frames. Woven strips of bamboo matting cover the walls and small sections of culm of the appropriate size and shape are used as tiles to cover and waterproof roofs. In the coffee-growing areas of Colombia, *Guadua angustifolia* is used for exactly the same purposes.

Bamboo pram [Heather Angel / Biofotos]

293 Shifting agriculture is practiced in the monsoon forest, even though sedentary agriculture is much more developed than in the rainforest. These Lua' women of the Akha group in Thailand are preparing to plant after hoeing the site.
[Photo: Mark Edwards / Still Pictures]

Traditionally, in northeast India a jhum cycle lasted at least 20 years, a reasonable period to allow the forest and its soil to recover, as well as meeting the farmer's needs. Recently, population pressure and the decline in forest cover mean that jhum cycles have shortened to only four or five years. Such intense shifting agriculture makes natural forest regeneration impossible. Nepalese alder (*Alnus nepalensis*) is being widely planted as part of plans to redevelop shifting agriculture, as it grows rapidly and improves soil fertility by fixing nitrogen. It is a useful timber species, its wood is good for furniture, and its leaves can be used as cattle fodder.

Shifting agriculture in monsoonal Thailand

In Thailand, most of the inhabitants of the highland forest practice various forms of shifting agriculture. The Lua' farmers of northwest Thailand cultivate rice (*Oryza*) as their staple food crop, following a special cultivation system they have used for centuries. Traditionally, the Lua' use different forest areas in different ways. Outside their cultivated plots the mature forest was reserved as a home for spirits and for burials. Patches of forest were also conserved to prevent soil erosion, protect watercourses, provide shelter for wild animals, and produce seeds for forest regeneration.

Plots of cleared forest around the Lua' villages are still cultivated in a 10-year rotation sequence.

The fields are cut in January or February, without felling the large trees, although branches are pruned so they do not shade the crops. The debris is burned in late March. The first crops planted are cotton and maize, followed in mid April by upland rice. Tall-growing sorghum is planted to mark the limits of the plots. The plots closest to the field shelters are planted with peppers, beans and other vegetables.

The Lua' complete their diet with wild fruit and tubers, especially in times of food shortage. They also use some wild plants for construction, for basket making and as dyes and medicines. More than 200 wild plants are used as sources of foods and more than 70 are used as traditional medicines. Some medicinal herbs and lianas usually used to make shampoo are traded in the lowland markets to supplement income from the sale of livestock.

The Lua' system of agriculture is less productive than permanent irrigated rice cultivation, but it has been proved to be sustainable and allows rapid forest regeneration. The system is now declining as a result of population pressure, deforestation, and changes in the Lua' people's beliefs and customs.

Traditionally clearing the forest, burning the debris, and sowing crops were controlled by the chief priests, but their authority has declined. According to Thai law, shifting agriculture is illegal in the highland forests and the Lua' have no legal title to the land they were granted hundreds of years ago.

Rice cultivation

Shifting agriculture, as still practiced by some southeast Asian and Indian tribal populations, is clearly marginal when compared with intensive rice cultivation. This occupies much of the region's population, producing food for themselves and for extratropical regions in eastern Asia and elsewhere.

The basic food of one third of humanity

Rice (*Oryza sativa*) is one of humanity's basic food crops. Rice is the staple foodstuff for many millions of people, especially in eastern and southern Asia, which account for almost one third of the planet's population. More than 1,600 million people, most of them subsistence farmers, obtain half or more of their food intake from rice.

Oryza is a grass genus widely distributed throughout the planet's wet tropical areas. The most important cultivated species are *O. sativa*, native to a wide area from eastern India to southern China, including the islands of the Indo-Malayan region, and *O. glaberrima*, red rice, native to west Africa, but there are more than 20 wild species. There are thousands of varieties of cultivated rice, but they can be divided into three main groups or subspecies: *indica*, *japonica* and *javanica*. The *indica* varieties are essentially tropical, short-day plants, producing long thin grains (at least three times as long as wide), although they may vary greatly in plant height, size of panicle (pyramid flower structure), hairiness, and grain color, etc. The *japonica* group of varieties are subtropical rather than tropical, with a short round grain borne on low plants and with rather small panicles that are almost entirely unaffected by day length. The *javanica* varieties of rice are tropical and native to Indonesia, and there are awned (bulu) and awnless (gundil) varieties.

There is disagreement about the origin of rice cultivation and the site or sites where it was first domesticated. Generally accepted data show rice cultivation goes back 5,500 years in the eastern slopes of the Khorat plateau in Thailand (see volume 1, pages 295-296), in the lower River Chang Jiang (Yangtze) and the Ganges Valley. There are also unconfirmed finds suggesting rice was domesticated as long ago as wheat and other cereals in the Fertile Crescent. In any case, the last 3,000 years yield abundant archaeological proof of rice cultivation in the Ganges Valley, and other sites in India.

294 **Terraced rice paddies on mountainsides** like those shown in this photo are typical images of Bali, but are frequent in many mountainous areas of monsoonal southeast Asia. The sheets of water in these beautiful landscapes all follow the contours.
[Photo: Josep M. Barres]

295 Rice is still harvested manually in many monsoon areas, such as in these fields in Sulawesi. Paddling through the water, the women gather armfuls of spikes (upper photo) and then arrange them in sheaves before threshing (lower photo).
[Photos: Teresa Franquesa]

There are written records from 2,300 years ago, in the times of the Han dynasty, showing intensive rice cultivation was practiced in southern China.

Rice needs high temperatures during its growing season, with average monthly temperatures over 68°F (20°C) for at least four or five months. The vast majority of varieties need to grow in a 4-6 in (10-15 cm) layer of water for three-quarters of their growing period. Only a few varieties, dry farming upland varieties, can grow in unflooded fields under conditions of very high rainfall, and they are cultivated by different tribal groups that practice subsistence agriculture. At the other extreme, there are some varieties of rice from Bangladesh and the south of Indochina, known as floating varieties, that are adapted to growing as quickly as the water level in the major surges and can reach heights of up to 20 ft (6 m). The need to keep the rice paddies flooded for part of the year means that regions with steep slopes must be elaborately terraced and irrigation channels built.

The typical rice cultivator of the monsoon regions (and of the rest of southern and eastern Asia) has only a few acres of land, rarely more, except in regions recently brought into cultivation or in more developed regions. Most rice paddies are family plots, producing for family consumption. Only 12 million t out of a world production of 500 million t is sold, and most of this is produced outside Asia, mainly in the United States, Italy, and Australia.

Rice cultivation is a form of agriculture that is intensive in land use and labor force. At the beginning of the growing season it is necessary to check and repair the dykes, edges and channels and to carefully flatten, the plots, which must be quite horizontal to maintain the water level uniform throughout. It is also necessary to work the earth to give it the right consistency, apply silt and fertilizer. The small size of most plots makes mechanization difficult, but this would only be within the reach of very few of the peasants in monsoon regions anyway. It also requires draught animals (water buffalo or zebu cattle) and even human traction in all tasks. The paddies are traditionally fertilized with animal and human excrement and other organic fertilizers. The introduction of more productive, but more demanding, new varieties of rice of the "green revolution" has made fertilizer use necessary in some places. Seedlings are also sown and transplanted to their final site by hand, as seed is not usually sown directly by scattering. The complexity of all these techniques impregnates everyday life and religion, social structures, beliefs, rites, art and literature of all the rice-growing regions of Asia (as well as Madagascar, where rice cultivation was taken by Indonesian settlers). Rice cultivation is a culture that depends on intimate knowledge of the land, requiring careful and detailed work, attention to the smallest detail, the use and recycling of everything that can be recycled; even the main events of the year are tied to the demands of rice growing.

Where it is practiced, rice cultivation is in reality a monoculture. It rarely forms part of a crop rotation, although some legumes are interspersed, such as Chinese astragalus (*Astragalus sinicus*), as a green manure. In many regions of Vietnam, the small aquatic fern azolla, mainly *Azolla pinnata*, is cultivated as green manure. The azolla have symbiotic cyanobacteria of the genus *Anabaena* in their leaves, and these fix atmospheric nitrogen. When the rice is harvested and the paddy drained, the layer of azolla covering the surface of 2.5 ac (1 ha) of paddy, provides an input of two tons fresh weigh, containing about 57 lb (26 kg) of nitrogen.

India is the country with the largest area under rice, with 40 million hectares, most of them in the country's monsoon regions. The next largest area is in China, with 85 million ac (35 million ha), many of them far to the north of the areas where rice was first cultivated. Bangladesh and Thailand hold third place, with 25 million ac (10 million ha) each. The low yields of many Indian rice fields mean that India's harvest of 102 million tons makes it the second largest producer after China, with 172 million tons, followed by Indonesia with 42 million tons.

296 The symbiosis between the cyanobacteria *Anabaena* and the floating fern *Azolla pinnata* is used by Vietnamese rice growers as a natural fertilizer for their fields, as the bacterial symbiont can fix atmospheric nitrogen. The illustration is a scanning electron micrograph showing *Anabaena* filaments in the fern's leaf cavities. [Photo: David Hall / Science Photo Library / AGE Fotostock]

The culture of rice

Like dry farming of cereals in southwest Asia and the Mediterranean region, thousands of years of rice cultivation have profoundly influenced the culture and lifestyles of the inhabitants of the monsoon areas of southern and eastern Asia and the other areas it has spread to. Since the remote past, rice-growers have had to invest great effort to protect their crops from excessive surges by channeling and controlling the riverbeds, and to carry water to their rice paddies and to take it away. In many south Asian languages there is a clear distinction between rice paddies and other types of cultivated land, and paddies and fields are often distinguished from the family vegetable plot, considered to be part of the house's garden. For example, in Vietnamese, the rice paddy (*ruông*) is distinguished from the unleveled field (*nüöng*), and in fact to term used for fields in general is *ruông nüöng*. For some peoples in southeast Asia, the word rice signifies food in general, as does bread in many European cultures.

In the mythology of many of these peoples, rice has its own spirit, the rice spirit, whose worship and rites often influence cultivation techniques. The rice spirit may flee, rendering useless all efforts to obtain a good harvest, so it is necessary to follow more or less complex rituals to protect it and make it stay. In most cases, the rice spirit is given anthropomorphic features. According to a Malay legend, rice did not have to be harvested from the fields, but every morning a single grain went to the pot to be boiled; a taboo banned uncovering the pot until the afternoon, when it was full of rice ready to be eaten. One day, a little girl from a peasant family opened the pot

297 **World distribution of rice cultivation** (showing *Oryza sativa*, the most widely cultivated species, and *O. glaberrima*, grown in western Africa). The Asian continent produces about 89% of the world's total production, and the rest is distributed between Latin America (6%) and Africa, Europe and Oceania (the remaining 5%). Rice grows in a wide range of environmental conditions; its distribution stretches from 50°N to 40°S and from sea level to altitudes of 8,202 ft (2,500 m) or more, and includes widely varying temperature conditions.
[Drawing: Editrònica, from several sources]

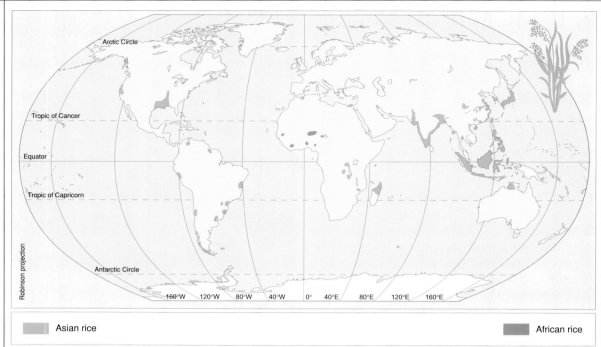

Asian rice — African rice

before time, and saw within it a very small girl who suddenly disappeared, leaving in her place a tiny grain. It was the rice spirit, and since then the descendants of the peasant family have had to work hard planting and harvesting the rice to make the rice spirit return and obtain food.

The Tamils, a week after the winter solstice, coinciding with the rice harvest, celebrate the Pongal festival; the Tamil word *pongal* means to boil a liquid and also for a pan or casserole to boil over. Performing pongal requires milk to be boiled on a hot fire until it froths, when pukkai rice is added, the rice used in the typical Tamil dish of sweetened rice with milk. The white foam that forms is a good omen, and even better if it is prepared in the right time and place with the appropriate instruments. The right place is always an open air fireplace, which may be in front of a temple, (an offering to the gods, a collective pongal), before a domestic shrine to ancestors (family pongal, an offering to the ancestors and a ritual present to the neighbors), in a rice paddy, in the threshing yard or in any other place to bring it health, wealth, and good luck. The best time is dawn, so that if the person performing the ritual is skilled enough, they can regulate the heat so that the milk boils over at exactly the moment the first rays of light hit the pot. This time is reserved for the higher castes, while lower castes have to make do with performing their pongal in the afternoon. The pot has to be new (custom demands that old pots are broken during this festival) and is often decorated with the ash of dung from sacred cows, sandalwood paste and red ochre.

Pukkai is considered a very suitable offering to the gods because it is made of white substances (rice and milk), traditionally considered noble and pure. They are not the only ingredients; apart from the cane sugar, or jaggery (brown palm sugar) needed to sweeten it, the ingredients may include coconut, raisins, or fried lentils or beans, and almost always a flavoring such as cardamom, camphor, or saffron. The portion offered to the gods is especially aromatic; it is prepared in front of temples and placed at the base of the idols, together with fruit, flowers and leaves so that the gods may consume the invisible parts as it cools. Once it is cold, when it is assumed that the gods have finished eating, the rice is distributed among those present.

Other crops

Compared with rice almost all other crops seem secondary, although some are of great economic importance. In several regions a second crop is obtained from the rice paddies in the winter. In the valley of the Ganges, for example, it may be barley, sugarcane, legumes, or forage crops, and in family vegetable plots fruit trees and leaf vegetables are grown. In other sites, coconut, sugarcane, citrus fruit, coffee or tobacco plantations share with rice part of the area exploited or part of the annual cycle.

As a heritage of the colonial epoch, there are plantations of several of the tropical crops that can withstand the periods of drought typical of monsoon forests, such as sugar cane, coffee, tea, and tobacco.

3. Using animal resources

3.1 Hunting

It would be misleading to talk about a fauna found exclusively in monsoon forests. Many of the species that are found only in monsoon forests are small and relatively immobile and are not especially sought after by hunters. The wild species that are hunted for subsistence or by professional hunters tend also to be exploited in lowland rain forests and are generally large birds and animals that move freely between rain forests and other biomes.

Hunting in the monsoon forests of Central America

The seasonal forests of Central America stretch along the Pacific side of the long chain of volcanoes separating the Pacific and the Atlantic basins. The soils are alluvial and volcanic, although in southern Mexico this habitat extends into the poor soils of the calcareous Yucatán Peninsula. For centuries before the arrival of Europeans, these areas were inhabited by societies such as the Mayas and related groups that practiced highly developed forms of agriculture. Hunting rituals were likewise already well defined many centuries ago and are still practiced today.

Nevertheless, since colonization by Europeans traditional hunting methods have disappeared and bows and arrows, blowpipes and spear launchers have been superseded by firearms. The game species hunted now are no different from those listed by the first Europeans, though all are less abundant and have had their habitats drastically reduced.

The commonest large game species are peccaries (*Tayassu*), deer (*Odocoileus, Mazama*), tapirs (*Tapirus*), and a number of hystricid rodents such as tree porcupines with prehensile tails (*Coendou*), pacas (*Cuniculus*) and agoutis (*Dasyprocta*). In areas with anthills and termite mounds anteaters (*Myrmecophaga tridactyla* and *Tamandua*) and armadillos (Dasypodoidea) are found. Opossums (*Didelphis*), squirrels (*Sciurus*) and rabbits (*Sylvilagus*), as well as various species of monkey, are hunted for food. The only carnivores that are consumed are the coati (*Nasua nasua*), raccoon (*Procyon*), kinkajou (*Potos flavus*), and hog-nosed skunk (*Conepatus*).

Other carnivores, such as felines with spotted coats, are hunted for their skins. Game species are found in various environments, although the semideciduous dry forests are today poor in game owing to the destruction of much of this habitat.

The most hunted of the many wild game bird species are tinamous (Tinamidae), guans (*Penelope*), curassows (*Crax*), chachalacas (*Ortalis*), and several species of doves and quails, as well as the common turkey (*Meleagris gallopavo*). Game meat supplements protein intake obtained from domesticated animals.

Hunting in the Southeast Asian monsoon forests

In southeast Asia's monsoon forests, game species have been seriously affected by the deforestation and forest fires. Fires are set by stockraisers to create new pastures and in the dry season even hunters resort to fire to induce game to flee from their hiding places into the guns of waiting hunters. This is a common hunting technique in many parts of the Philippines and is practiced, for example, in the vicinity of the Iglit-Baco National Park in Mindoro.

Similar tactics are employed in the foothills of the southern slopes of the Himalayas, from Nepal to northern Assam in India. The forests, already highly degraded, are set ablaze largely to preserve pastures and meadows, although at the same time pygmy boars (*Sus salvanius*) are forced to seek refuge in the few remaining areas of intact vegetation. These areas are then beaten by hunters and boar and other animals are shot as they are driven out of their hiding places.

Bengal tigers, Gujarat lions

For decades the Bengal tiger has embodied the stereotype of a ferocious wild animal. Exotic films, often more fiction than fact and designed only to entertain the public, and circuses attempting "the impossible" have both contributed decisively to shaping this image of the tiger. The tiger has come to be seen as the man-eating animal par excellence, often receiving the same bad press as sharks, which are sometimes referred to as "sea tigers." Today, although documentary evidence shows that aggressive tigers ate human flesh, these splendid felines are the real victims: victims of human depredation.

Asian lion (*Panthera leo subsp. persica*) in the Gir Lion Sanctuary [John Cancalosi / Bruce Coleman Limited]

The natural range of the tiger (*Panthera tigris*) stretches from Bali to Siberia, though today the most important population of these felines is in the Indian subcontinent, especially all in the monsoon areas. In fact, this wide range including biomes as different as rain forest, monsoon forests and the Siberian taiga, harbors a variety of different subspecies of tiger. They are separable by their ecological needs and by the wide variety of background coloration of their fur, ranging from almost white through a variety of yellows and ochres to orange, but all with black stripes.

The most imposing subspecies are the typical Bengal tiger (*P. tigris tigris*), found in India, Nepal and Bangladesh, and the largest of all, the long-haired Siberian tiger (*P. tigris altaica*), the males of which can weigh up to 772 lb (350 kg). Today barely a couple of hundred survive in Manchuria and the Amur Basin in Siberia. There are other relatively small tigers in Sumatra (*P. tigris sumatrae*), some may still survive in Java (*P. tigris sondaica*), and until it became extinct, there was a subspecies in Bali (*P. tigris balica*). There is a third and last group in Indochina and China, consisting of *P. tigris corbetti* and *P. tigris amoyensis*), but *P. tigris amoyensis*) is probably now extinct, and the Caspian tiger (*P. tigris virgata*) seems to be extinct, too, though it was once quite common in the north of Persia and Afghanistan, as well as in Turkmenistan, Tadzhikistan and Sinkiang. All subspecies, nevertheless, show the same preferences for wooded areas with rivers and shallow lakes.

Throughout its vast range, the tiger has stirred people's imagination, giving rise to myths and legends and

A pair of Bengal tigers (*Panthera tigris tigris*) in Ranthambhor, India [A. & M. Shah / Planet Earth Pictures]

inspiring poets. British colonialists in India adopted the long-established custom of maharajahs and other local dignitaries of hunting tigers from the safety of a saddle, high up on the back of an elephant. These hunting expeditions were welcomed by the local population who saw them as a way of eliminating a potential danger from their lives. If necessary, a village would independently

organize a less extravagant, but probably more risky, hunting expedition designed to deal with a particular tiger overfond of domestic cattle or of the locals themselves.

Yet this species, feared but also highly symbolic, is today fast becoming reduced to memory and legend. Former ritual hunting expeditions and simple punitive hunting drives, and the current proliferation of safaris and professional trophy hunters, together with a reduction of suitable habitats, have all drastically reduced tiger populations. At the beginning of the 20th century, the many different habitats in India as a whole contained more than 40,000 tigers, but only 1,800 were recorded in a census carried out in 1970. As a result, the Indian government banned hunting and launched Project Tiger in 1973, acting together with the World Wildlife Fund (WWF).

The first step was to create nine reserves, occupying 5,300 sq mi (13,723 sq km) of which 1,638 sq mi (4,242 sq km) were core areas. Forestry and grazing were restricted to the surrounding buffer zones, while villages in the core areas, and sometimes even in the buffer zones, were relocated outside the reserve. The number of reserves has now increased to 18, covering a total area of 10,817 sq mi (28,017 sq km). As a result, by the beginning of the 1990s, the tiger population had grown to 4,300 individuals, a somewhat less worrying figure.

Problems still remain, however. Outside protected areas, the destruction of forests continues apparently unchecked, while the need for even more firewood and grazing forces people to enter reserves illegally. In some areas, the increase in tiger numbers has led to individuals straying outside reserve boundaries (a female tiger needs a territory of between 16 and 19 sq mi (25 and 30 sq km) and a male needs between 19 and 31 sq mi (50 and 80 sq km), if not more, that normally coincides with the territories of the three or four females in his harem). Inevitably this leads to conflicts occur with local people, demonstrating that efficient protection of a country's natural heritage can never be

Illustration from *Le Petit Journal*, Paris (1914) [Archiv für Kunst und Geschichte]

separated from the needs of local inhabitants, as much as for reasons of social justice as for those of ecological expediency. Nevertheless, Project Tiger has managed to halt the decline in tiger numbers in India and has also given valuable protection to important forest areas. In Nepal too, in the Chitawan Park, tigers are being especially protected and studied.

Inspired by the success of Project Tiger, a similar project has been launched to save the last remaining population of Asian lions (*Panthera leo persica*), restricted to the Gir Forest. This has led to the creation of the Gir Reserve in Gujarat, one of the largest forest masses in India. Towards the end of the last century, hunting had reduced the population of Indian lions to a mere 15 individuals, but since hunting was banned, numbers have gradually risen, only to be threatened once again by increasing deforestation. After independence, large areas of forest in Gujarat were cut down for agriculture, reducing even further the availability of pastures. Grazing pressure increased in the Gir Forest. During the monsoons, more than 48,000 head of cattle from the surrounding areas were regularly driven into the Gir Forest, and the resulting overgrazing drastically reduced wild ungulate (hoofed animals) populations, the lions' main prey. The lions of Gir were first protected in 1965, and in 1972 a management project was set up on the reserve to improve the living standards of its inhabitants, the Maldhari people. The lion population has subsequently increased to 200 animals, showing that perhaps after all, there is hope for Asia's lions and tigers.

Tiger hunting, in an illustration from an 1860 German textbook [Mary Evans Picture Library]

3.2 Domesticated fauna

Since time immemorial wild animals of the monsoon forest have been domesticated. One of the most affected groups has been the bovids, although a number of birds have also been domesticated. The ocellated turkey (*Agriocharis* [=*Meleagris*] *ocellata*) and Muscovy duck (*Cairina moschata*) are the only neotropical birds which have been domesticated; the ocellated turkey reached northern Peru with the European settlers and was bred, in part, for its feathers.

The wild banteng (*Bos javanicus*) resembles European cattle more than any other bovid, and it is the ancestor of the domestic banteng found over much of Indonesia (Java, Bali, Nusa Tenggara, Sulawesi, Maluku and the Kalimantan area). Domestication of the bantengs has potential, because they provide a lot of tender, lean meat, survive on little forage, and are resistant to parasites, especially trypanosomes. Yet they produce little milk and revert to the wild if not constantly tended. There are three subspecies that reflect the species' wide but discontinuous natural distribution: *B. javanicus javanicus*, in the grassy plains and cut forests of Java, *B. javanicus lowi*; in eastern and central Borneo; and *B. javanicus birmanicus* in the patchwork habitats of Myanmar, Thailand, and Indochina. This last subspecies lives in the bamboo and meadows at high altitudes along the drier side of the region's mountains.

On the Indonesian island of Madura near Java, a population of hybrids between the banteng and zebu cattle (*Bos taurus indicus* [=*B. indicus*]) arose 1,500 years ago. These animals are hardy and very productive even in extremely high temperatures and despite poor nutrition. Traditionally

stud animals are chosen from the winners of competitions and give the animals their characteristic strength, speed and endurance (and bad temper). Their skin and meat are said to be of a better quality than any other known race of bovid.

The gaur (*Bos gaurus*) is probably the ancestor of the gayal (*Bos gaurus frontalis*), the main domesticated animal of the mountain tribes of northeast India, of the Chittagong in Bangladesh and of the Arakan and the Chin in Myanmar. It is a large, well-muscled animal that, given it grows well and remains healthy on little forage, is ideal for meat production. The gaur, a grazer of grass and a nibbler of trees, lives in the clearings of many seasonal and mountain forests and is, therefore, well adapted to patchwork habitats in monsoon forests. There are two subspecies: *B. gaurus gaurus* from India and Nepal and *B. gaurus laosiensis* from Myanmar, Thailand, Indochina and the Malayan Peninsula, where it is known as the seladang. It was once very common and widespread but today only a few scattered herds remain. In most of its natural refugia, it is in danger of extinction.

The kouprey (*Bos sauveli*) has a lot in common with some of the bovids that were alive during the Pleistocene and it is thought to be the most primitive of all living bovines. It is a close relative of *B. namandicus*, an ancestor of the zebu. Nevertheless, it is almost extinct and is found only in a limited area of eastern Cambodia near the border with Thailand. It lives in forest clearings kept open by fire as well as in dense and open monsoon forests. It is known to be resistant to cattle plague (rinderpest), though its potential as a domestic animal or as a source of improvements in cattle breeding is as yet unknown.

4. Environmental management and problems

4.1 The retreat of the forests

The monsoon forests suffer the same problems of deforestation as the equatorial rainforests. In general, they have always been easier to clear for agriculture and nowadays there are few unmodified areas left. Increasing population pressure and demand for forest resources are now causing rapid deforestation in the monsoon regions.

The ancient colonization of the monsoon area

Most of the monsoon forests in India, Indochina, and Java, if not all, are the results of old secondary succession. Originally, the forests of Myanmar, Thailand, Cambodia, Laos, Vietnam, and China were a mixture of rainforest and monsoon forest. Over the centuries these have been modified throughout the region, and it is doubtful whether any true original monsoon forest remains. The first inhabitants of this area of tropical Asia were hunter-gatherers, but they soon adopted shifting agriculture and the use of fire. It was easy to burn the monsoon vegetation in the long dry season, and these fires changed the forest's composition by favoring the growth of some tree species, such as teak, and bamboos.

The site of one of the oldest human settlements is in Java, and its highly fertile volcanic soils have always supported the highest populations in Indonesia. The clearing of the lowland forests began centuries ago, and virtually all Java's monsoon forest has been destroyed, above all by fire. The spread of agriculture to mountain regions has occurred recently. Colonization by the Dutch in the mid-18th century promoted cash crop production on the most fertile soils, with slaves imported from Sulawesi to work on coffee, sugarcane, tea and tobacco plantations. Teak plantations were also established on the island. When they lost their lands, the local farmers moved to the hill country and began to clear the forest.

299 Deforestation, fires, and erosion all occur in the monsoon forest. The combined action of the three factors ravages large areas, such as these slopes in Insulindia. [Photo: J. Hobday / Natural Science Photos]

In America, especially in Central America, the vast majority of seasonal forests growing on good soils are now croplands. Many of them have been cultivated since the remote past, and the rest have been deforested more recently, mainly for grazing for cattle. There are few areas that are still covered by forest and often they only survive thanks to some form of protection.

The effects of repeated fires

Monsoon forests are intensely affected by fires in most of the areas they occur, as the dry season makes them especially vulnerable to fires. Repeated fires turn them into simple communities consisting of fire-resistant trees or into grasslands. In fact it is probable that all tropical grasslands, except those in marshy areas, are the result of repeated fires in seasonal tropical forests, and are probably maintained as such by the fires set to stimulate growth of forage for cattle. These fires burn the seedlings and prevent colonization by woody vegetation.

Although there are fewer and fewer forests near these grasslands, the trees still survive in some regions along watercourses, from where animals disperse the seeds. In northwest Costa Rica experience has shown that if meadows are protected from fires and hunting, reforestation rapidly begins, and after five years saplings rise above the grasses. This gives some hope for the ecological rehabilitation of the upland areas that have a seasonal climate that used to be forested and that still have at least some remains of forest nearby.

4.2 The impact of European colonization and the postcolonial period

The colonization of the areas of monsoon forest in Asia by Europeans caused a general and spectacular increase in deforestation. The main factors were logging (mainly teak), the spread of plantations of commercial crops, and the introduction of a new attitude to nature. Changes in forest use under British rule in India are a good and illustrative example of the increase in deforestation during the colonial period.

Forest management in monsoon India

India contains about 40 million ac (16 million hectares) of monsoon forest, over twice that of its area of rainforest. Monsoon forest is the natural vegetation cover of most of the Indian peninsula and the Ganges Basin. Depending on rainfall and humidity, variations include tropical moist deciduous forest, tropical dry deciduous forest and scrub vegetation. In the northern and eastern India, the dominant tree species is sal (*Shorea robusta*), whereas the southern plateau's vegetation is dominated by teak (*Tectona grandis*). Fire and grazing have been the main agents leading to the replacement of monsoon forest by more open savanna vegetation.

Traditional models of forest use varied greatly throughout India and were generally developed on the basis of religious or quasi-religious respect for natural resources. Mountain forests and those on slopes, for example, have traditionally been held sacred and protected from exploitation. British colonial rule imposed a completely new system of forest use, mainly based on the extraction of valuable hardwoods. Teak production increased greatly to satisfy the needs of the expanding British empire, with the consequent impact on the monsoon forests. It should be borne in mind that the tonnage of the British merchant fleet increased from 1,270,000-4,937,000 tons between 1798 and 1860, and the Royal Navy increased at a similar rate. Teak replaced the white or Weymouth pine (*Pinus strobus*) and oak, used until then by the British fleet in naval construction, and Indian timber became a monopoly of the British administration. After 1853, the need for sleepers and fuel for the new railways were added to those of naval construction, in which iron was beginning to replace timber. Around 1844 concern was first expressed over the rapid reduction of teak supplies, and in 1850 the British Association for the Advancement of Science set up a special committee to review the economic and physical consequences of tropical deforestation, in India in particular. The committee's recommendations gave rise to the creation in 1864 of the Imperial Forest Department. In subsequent years, the Forestry Reserve Act and colonially imposed control over the use made by the people of India's forests led to a total appropriation of forest resources by the colonial government, which formally annulled the common law rights of rural communities and tribal peoples.

Soon after independence in 1947, private property rights to forests were abolished as a land reform measure, and now 97% of India's forests are under public ownership. After independence, the Indian government assumed forest ownership without developing a rational land use policy. Forests were used for the wood derivatives industry (especially paper and synthetic fibers). In hilly areas, the forests were cleared for cultivation without taking appropriate soil conservation measures. As a result, large areas were eroded and turned into bare and sterile wastelands. Little attention was paid to the needs of peasant communities, such as communal grazing and village forests required to satisfy the villagers' most basic needs. Clearing forests for agriculture was a main cause of deforestation, especially between 1950 and 1980, when more than 370,000 ac (150,000 ha) of forest were felled legally every year. A much larger area was illegally changed into permanent agricultural land or

plantations of fast-growing, nonnative trees (eucalypts or tropical pines) for the cellulose derivatives industry (paper and artificial fibers).

During the 20th century India's population has increased spectacularly, from 234 million people in 1911 to almost 685 million in 1981, reaching almost 845 million in 1991 and more than 950 million in 1996. The country's rural population has more than doubled, while the urban population has increased sixfold since 1911. Gathering firewood and provision of pasture are still two of the basic needs of many of India's rural inhabitants. India has an estimated 400 million cows, 90 million of them dependent on forests for grazing. Forest conversion for development programs, such as irrigation, mining and road projects, has also been an important factor in the loss of India's monsoon forests. Hydroelectric projects have

300 Firewood collection and shifting agriculture exert great pressure on the monsoon forests. This photo shows a woman of the Garo people, shifting agriculturalists of northeastern India, crossing a field or *jhum* in Modhupur, with a bundle of firewood, and brings out the seriousness of the situation. The Garo are victims rather than the cause, because their population is small.
[Photo: Gilles Saussier / Gamma]

301 Illegal logging of the monsoon forest is an everyday occurrence on the Thai frontier with Myanmar. The trees are felled rapidly before the authorities can react, and the trunks are smuggled or mixed with legally obtained wood. The use of elephants is traditional in the area, and as they are very effective and silent this makes the operation easier (see photo 291).
[Photo: David Hoffman / Still Pictures]

been responsible for major forest losses, amounting to several million acres by the decade of 1980s.

In the 1980s, the Indian government adopted major new policies to tackle the ecological degradation caused by rapid and widespread deforestation.

The National Wildlife Action Plan was approved in 1983 with directives for the expansion and rehabilitation of protected areas. A new National Forestry Policy came into force in 1988 and stated explicitly that the basic aim of forest management was the achievement of ecological stability. Many practical problems remain in the implementation of the government's forestry and conservation policy, but India is now committed to reversing the trend of national deforestation.

The effects of deforestation in monsoonal southeast Asia

In Thailand, deforestation has also caused serious environmental problems, forcing major changes in government forest management policies. Floods in 1988 caused by the deforestation of the highlands, led to hundreds of deaths and a ban on commercial logging. Thailand was formerly one of the main exporters of teak, is now one of the world's major importers of tropical sawnwood. Logging is only one of the factors contributing to loss of Thailand's seasonal forests. In the highlands, another major cause of deforestation has been shifting agriculture, and forest clearance for cash crops has also caused ecological damage. Cassava (*Manihot esculenta*) is now widely cultivated in northeast Thailand, and the area cultivated has increased from 247,000 ac (100,000 ha) in 1965 to more than 2,500,000 ac (1,000,000 ha), mostly for the tapioca export market. Tapioca is produced from cassava's dried pelleted roots and is widely used as pig feed in several countries of the European Union, such as the Netherlands.

Vietnam was originally covered by forest, mostly monsoon evergreen forests. Most of the forest vegetation has now been destroyed, and an estimated further 247,000 ac (100,000 ha) are lost every year. 30 years of modern warfare not only took a heavy toll of Vietnam's human population but also of its forests. The rate of deforestation has even increased since the war ended in 1975. Post-war reconstruction may explain the increase in logging for timber, but shifting agriculture, logging for export, firewood gathering, and forest fires have caused major deforestation and the consequent decline of several plant and animal species. A recent list of rare and threatened species includes more than 50 animals (not including birds), such as the kouprey (*Bos sauveli*), the thamin (*Cervus eldi siamensis*), the musk deer (*Moschus berezovskii*), black gibbon (*Hylobates concolor*), the Tonkin langur (*Trachypithecus* [=*Presbytis*] *francoisi*), the green peacock (*Pavo muticus*), the Annamite pheasant (*Lophura edwardsi*) and the Siamese crocodile (*Crocodylus siamensis*). The list includes 60 birds and 100 plants—including valuable hardwood species, such as Cochinchina tamarind (*Dialium cochinchinensis*), the rosewood *Dalbergia cochinchinensis*, and the ebony *Diospyros mun*—that are in danger of extinction. Vietnam has taken great steps to reverse deforestation and the loss of species. In 1986, The National Conservation Strategy recognized that "forest loss is the most serious factor threatening the sustainable production of the country." This strategy has included the development of new laws and extension of the network of protected areas. It is also improving the management of forest reserves and it has been proposed that buffer zones should be created around the parks to satisfy the needs of the people living close to the reserve.

Sri Lanka has a long history of deforestation, and it remains one of the country's main environmental problems. The areas of monsoon, or dry zone, forests have been greatly modified and are generally now occupied by different stages of secondary succession. These forests have developed over the last 500-800 years since the abandonment of ancient irrigation systems. In the northern lowlands this was as a consequence of invasions from southern India and internecine strife between different rulers. This led to the displacement of the population to the lowland evergreen forests in the south of the island, a process that had begun when the first Portuguese trading stations were established in the 16th century. The dry zone forests now suffer increasing deforestation, with large areas under irrigated crops. Sri Lanka has a well-developed system of protected areas, but urgent action is needed to preserve the deciduous forests of the north of the island, now once more the scene of violent strife.

The decline of Madagascar's monsoon forests

The first people to arrive in Madagascar came from Indonesia around 1,500 years ago. They seem to have practiced hunting, fishing, and shifting agriculture, and these were the small-scale beginnings of deforestation. Shortly afterwards, African livestock raisers arrived. Between them they had probably destroyed most of Madagascar's seasonal forest before the second main wave of immigration from Indonesia between the 9th and 11th centuries A.D., which led to the establishment of rice cultivation in permanently irrigated terraces on the island's central plateau.

Most of Madagascar's monsoon seasonal forests have been destroyed and the main threat to the remaining ones is undeniably fire, often deliberately started. Every year more than a third of the entire land area of Madagascar is burned. This burning is mainly to provide grazing for herds of zebu cattle (*Bos taurus indicus*) and grazing restricts regeneration of woody vegetation. Zebu cattle are very important in the life of the peoples of western and southern Madagascar, especially in their religious rites. The possession of a large zebu herd is a sign of wealth. The tombs of rich men are paid for with zebu and the burial ceremony is a major festival when hundreds of zebu are slaughtered and eaten. The tombs are decorated with zebu horns and woodcarvings decorated with reliefs or drawings of the cattle. There are estimated to be more than 10 million zebu in Madagascar.

4
Protected areas
and biosphere reserves
in the monsoon forests

1. The world's protected monsoon forests

1.1 General considerations

Monsoon forests are legally protected in a variety of ways. These include forest reserves, national parks, and nature reserves on the western coast of Central America, in India, in Sri Lanka and in southeast Asia, including the islands of Insulindia.

In fact, many protected areas in this geographical area include both monsoon forest and rainforest. Depending on altitude and other factors, monsoon forest replaces rainforest in space, so that some of the large protected areas in, for example, southeast Asia affect both. The same sometimes occurs in relation to biomes with longer dry periods than the monsoon forest can stand, which are dealt with in volume 3. The areas discussed in this section contain different climatic conditions and vegetation, but special reference is paid to the most typically monsoon areas. Their general problems are often comparable with those discussed in the section on protected areas of rainforest.

1.2 Protected parks and areas

In Central America, the areas of monsoon forest (although it would be better to call them dense seasonal forest) are scattered in small coastal patches from Costa Rica to Mexico. On many of these coasts, mangroves occupy the coastline and seasonal forest occurs inland.

The protected areas containing seasonal forest include: the Cosiguina Volcano (30,677 ac [12,420 ha]), that of Estero Real (98,121 ac [39,725 ha]) and that of the Indio and Maíz rivers, all three of them in Nicaragua; the Barra de Santiago National Park in El Salvador is the smallest, with an area of only 5,681 ac (2,300 ha). The Santa Rosa National Park covers 91,926 ac (37,217 ha) of forest and is the oldest protected area in the region.

In southeast Asia, the largest protected areas of monsoon forest are in Thailand, Cambodia and in Myanmar, where a large part is still relatively intact. This region contains the largest areas of monsoon forest, and the largest protected spaces are Preah Vihear in Cambodia, with 3,624,000 ac (1,467,000 ha) of monsoon forest and scattered rainforest, the 634,800 ac (257,000 ha) Huai Kha Nature Reserve in Thailand, and the 395,200 ac (160,000 ha) Alaungdaw Kathapa in Myanmar.

The Wasur National Park

The Wasur National Park (1,018,329 ac [412,279 ha]), in Irian Jaya, in the southern part of New Guinea, is in one of the driest areas in the island. The park and the nearby transfrontier reserve, the Tonda Wildlife Reserve, in Papua New Guinea, are mostly covered by monsoon forest and savannah vegetation.

Natural characteristics and values
The canopy of the evergreen dry monsoon forests is dominated by two myrtaceous (myrtle-like) genera, *Tristania* and *Syzygium*, and *Maranthes* (Chrysobalanaceae). These forests have three distinct strata and include, depending on local soil and drainage conditions, scattered lower open woody formations with several species of *Eucalyptus* and another myrtaceous genus, paperbark (*Melaleuca cajuputi*), a fire-resistant species that produces a valuable essential oil. Human activity, fires, and floods have all modeled the landscape, and the open woody formations form a mosaic with the large areas of savannah. Every year in the cooler dry season (from June to November), fires sweep through the dry herbaceous vegetation and the edges of the monsoon forest. These fires often spread from stubble lit by hunters, as these open grasslands are important habitats for the park's large herbivores, wallabies, and deer. In December, the wet monsoon season starts, when the area receives 75% of its entire annual rainfall, and the many resulting shallow pools attract many migratory birds that come to feed and overwinter. Hundreds of herons perform

302 The beautiful and valuable monsoon forests have to be conserved. In addition to correct overall management of the monsoon area, it is necessary to consolidate the areas that are totally protected, such as the Lamington National Park in Queensland (Australia), shown in the photo.
[Photo: Jean-Paul Ferrero / Auscape International]

303 Young specimen of the wallaby (*Macropus agilis*), feeding in the Wasur National Park in Irian Jaya (New Guinea). This Indonesian kangaroo is one of the park's most notable animals. *[Photo: Gerald Cubitt / Bruce Coleman Limited]*

their ritual courtship displays, and pelicans, ducks, storks, egrets and ibis congregate in the extensive flooded areas.

Wasur is one of Indonesia's most recent national parks and contains an estimated 400 species of birds (65% of New Guinea's bird fauna) and at least 80 mammals (many of them nocturnal). The native mammals are all marsupials, including the wallaby (*Macropus agilis*), New Guinea's largest marsupial. The Rusa deer (*Cervus timorensis*), originally introduced as a game species, lives in the open meadows. When the rains start, the grass grows rapidly in the burned areas, providing good grazing for the wallabies and the herds of deer. They are both heavily hunted for their meat, for local consumption and for sale in the neighboring town of Merauke. Deer represents 80% of Merauke's meat supply and generates income estimated at $20,000. Until recently, almost none of these profits went back to the park's traditional

residents, the 2,000 members of the Kanum, Marind, Marori, and Yei tribes who live within the park's limits.

Management and problems

The greatest threat to the long-term survival of Wasur National Park is the poverty of the human populations that depend on it. In addition to the 2,000 members of the 13 tribal peoples that live in the park, there are a further 65,000 people living near it, many of them subsistence farmers. The need to buy essential domestic items is often the incentive for logging and hunting and the sale of small plots of land. The Irian Jaya Program of the World Wide Fund for Nature (WWF, formerly the World Wildlife Fund) works with local community groups and government agencies for the park to be recognized as an area for traditional usage, allowing the indigenous peoples and former residents to cultivate and hunt on a sustainable basis. The management strategy is partly based on a ban on hunting with firearms, while permitting the indigenous population to continue hunting with bows and arrows. Each clan and family has a traditional and fixed area where they hunt, cultivate and perform their rituals. By protecting wildlife from over-exploitation by outsiders and ensuring that the benefits reach the indigenous residents, the WWF and authorities are ensuring good local support for the park. Now that poachers are prevented from entering the park, local hunters are more successful. For example in 1992 the villagers earned the equivalent of $3,750 in three months from the sale of meat obtained by traditional methods. Local communities are increasingly seeing that they may benefit from living in a conservation area and now play a more active and constructive role in its administration. Other options to mitigate rural poverty and improve the socioeconomic benefits are being explored, such as ecotourism and the sale of essential oils extracted from the bark of some of the reserve's trees.

The essential oils extracted by distillation of the paperbark (*Melaleuca cajuputi*) can be obtained from leaves and twigs, without needing to fell the trees, using a simple technology that involves the indigenous peoples at all levels of production from collection to sale. Their participation in the protection, administration, and controlled exploitation of the natural resources is really the best contribution to conservation. The sales of oil may significantly increase income and the self-sufficiency of the villages within the park.

The wildlife sanctuaries of Huai Kha Khaeng and Thung Yai Naresuan

The Huai Kha Khaeng wildlife sanctuary (994 sq mi [2,575 sq km]) and Thung Yai Naresuan Wildlife Sanctuary (1,418.5 sq mi [3,674 sq km]) protect a forest area covering 2,402 sq mi (6,222 sq km) on Thailand's frontier with Myanmar, 218 mi (350 km) west of Bangkok. The sanctuaries are located on the two sides of the Shan-Thai Mountains, in a complex meeting of the Dawna Range and Tenasserim Range with a mosaic of habitats ranging from lowland monsoon forests to montane forest at an altitude of 5,900 ft (1,800 m). They form part of a much larger complex of national parks and other protected areas that cover a total of more than 2.5 million acres (1 million ha).

Together, these two sanctuaries form the area with the greatest biodiversity in Thailand, which has led to their being designated World Heritage Sites. They are at the junction of four different biogeographical zones and contain 2,500 plant species, with at least 11 endemic species, with floristic and faunistic elements from the west, east, and north (the Himalayas) and the south (the Sunda strait region). The area's biological richness can be attributed, in addition to its special location at the biological crossroads of southeast Asia, to the fact that the vegetation is a mosaic of evergreen and deciduous forest formations. About 50% of the area, almost the entire area below 2,625 ft (800 m), is covered by deciduous forest, while the higher and wetter slopes

304 **The splendor of the semideciduous monsoon forest** is clear in this photo of the Huai Kha Khaeng Reserve (Thailand). It shows the gentle relief covered by dipterocarp forest, the trees that dominate the reserve.
[Photo: Hartmut Jungius / WWF / Still Pictures]

305 The large bovids typical of the monsoon forest are well represented in the Huai Kha Khaeng Reserve (Thailand). The photo shows a guar (*Bos gaurus laosiensis*), locally known as *seladang*, a powerful herbivore that grazes on grass and browses on tender shoots. The reserve also contains banteng and buffalo (see photos 276 and 298). [*Photo: Konrad Wolfe / Bruce Coleman Limited*]

are colonized by evergreen or semievergreen seasonal forests. There are also open woody formations in the sanctuary, that are distinct from the deciduous dry forest but restricted to Thung Hai, and everywhere there are patches of savanna that are of great importance for the survival of the large ungulates; the thung yai (which means "big meadow") that gave its name to the sanctuary consists of several large grasslands surrounded by dry open woody formations. Evergreen gallery forests also run along the sanctuary's permanent watercourses, and these provide temporary shelter for many animals during the dry season and when fires break out.

The mixed deciduous forest, or monsoon forest, is dominated by the purple-flowered *Lagerstroemia calyculata* (Lythraceae), by several species of dipterocarp and by *Xylia xylocarpa* (Leguminosae), a hardwood species that is now scarce in the rest of Thailand. On the drier soils and on ridges a mosaic forms with dry forests of dipterocarps. In the understory, often as an integral part of succession after fire, there are communities of cycads (*Cycas siamensis*), palms (*Phoenix acaulis*), and sometimes oaks (*Quercus*).

The fauna, like the flora, is a mixture of northern species from the Himalayas, southern species from the Sunda region, and eastern ones from Indochina. There are at least 120 mammals, 45% of all the land

mammals occurring in Thailand, and 1 in 35 of all the world's species. The sanctuaries are perhaps one of the few protected areas in Thailand large enough to support species of large mammal. These include: 10 primates (including the five species of macaque known from the region); three species of bovids, the banteng (*Bos javanicus*), the gaur (*B. gaurus*) and the water buffalo (*Bubalus bubalis*); the Indian elephant, (*Elephas maximus*); the tapir (*Tapirus indicus*); four of the five known species of deer from Thailand; and the mouse deer (*Tragulus javanicus*). The grass in the undergrowth of the monsoon forest provides grazing for the ungulates that form the food supply of a remarkable set of carnivores. The 27 species of carnivore living in the sanctuaries represent 75% of all the carnivores in Thailand and 63% of all those found in mainland southeast Asia.

The bird fauna of the sanctuaries, with more than 400 species, includes approximately one third of the birds in mainland southeast Asia and 57% of those living in Thailand's forests. Some of these species are in danger of extinction or are rare in Thailand, including some lowland forest species, such as the dusky broadbill (*Corydon sumatranus*) and the black-and-red broadbill (*Cymbirhynchus macrorhynchos*). Riverine species that probably no longer survive in viable populations anywhere else in Thailand—such as the green peacock (*Pavo muticus*), the

306 **There are many notable species of birds** in the Huai Kha Khaeng Reserve (Thailand), including the hornbill *Aceros nipalensis*. The photo shows a male passing food to a female on the nest inside a hollow tree. *[Photo: Morten Strange / NHPA]*

Indian black vulture (*Sarcogyps calvus*), the greater pied kingfisher (*Ceryle lugubris*) and the hornbill (*Rhyticeros subruficolis*), exploit the habitats both of the monsoon forest and of the more open savannah. In the sanctuaries there are 22 species of woodpecker, almost twice as many as in any other tropical forest, and they occupy the many ecological niches created by repeated fires in deadwood or dying trees.

The sanctuaries are inhabited by 96 species of reptile from 56 genera, including four of the rarest reptiles in Asia. Limited inventories have recorded 41 species of amphibian and 107 species of freshwater fish, including one that appears to eat nothing but elephant feces. This small freshwater fish's apparent dependence on the largest land animal in Asia and the dependence of the elephant on the monsoon forest illustrate the complex nature of the food web and show the need to protect entire ecosystems in order to conserve the species that live in them.

Management and problems

In addition to its ecological value, the sanctuaries protect the basins of the Khwae Yai and Huai Kha Kaeng Rivers and their tributaries, and part of three other rivers. The Huai Kha Kaeng sanctuary is very unusual as it includes the basin's entire forested area. The park's two main rivers are unique in Thailand as their lowland stretches have not been logged, dammed, or turned into farmland. It is estimated that the sanctuary's protection of these basins, in 1987 alone, represented a value of 344 million baht (13.8 million U.S. dollars) to neighboring areas in terms of water conservation and soil protection.

Almost every year fires are set in the sanctuaries by shifting agriculturists and hunters of the tribes living in them, the Karen, and the Hmong. These fires represent a long-term threat to their biodiversity, preventing natural regeneration and causing changes in the natural vegetation. Fires have probably formed part of the ecosystem's dynamics for a long time, contributing to the shaping of the biological landscape. Now that the human population is increasing and closing in on the conservation area, the frequency and intensity of the fires threatens to destroy the area's high biodiversity. Regular fires modify the forest because they bring forward seedfall, kill shoots, slow down regeneration, and eliminate the less adapted species (the non-evergreen ones). Although large trees may appear to survive fires, many of these forest giants are "living dead" whose trunks are weakened by the fires and fall easily in later storms. Without effective control, fire, the most efficient and pitiless of all predators, will erode and simplify the habitats within the sanctuary and eventually lead to the loss of the species of animals and plants they were created to protect.

2. The UNESCO biosphere reserves in the monsoon forests

2.1 The biosphere reserves in the monsoon forest

The 15 biosphere reserves in the monsoon or seasonal forests cover an area of more than 10 million acres (4 million ha), although in many of them monsoon forest occupies only a small part of the forested area. The size of the protected areas varies greatly: Dinghu Nature Reserve in China has 2,964 ac (1,200 ha), the Maya National Park in Guatemala covers almost 3.7 million ac (1.5 million ha), although only a small part of this is seasonal forest.

2.2 The biosphere reserves in the Central American monsoon forests

Central America has two biosphere reserves covering a total of two million hectares, while the 10 reserves in Asia cover 1.2 million hectares.

The Maya Biosphere Reserve in Petén (Yucatán, Guatemala) is a good example of the Central American monsoon forest. The reserve is on the frontier with Mexico and covers a total of 3,500,000 ac (1,400,000 ha), rising from sea level to 2,000 ft (600 m) in the reserve's center. After initially being declared a national monument, it became a national park in 1955. To the north, on the other side of the frontier with Mexico, it is prolonged in the Calakmul Biosphere Reserve, with similar characteristics.

Interpenetrated by the monsoon forest, the park contains the largest area of tropical rainforest in Central America, with about 2,000 species of plant, some as important as breadnut *Brosimum alicastrum*) and Honduran mahogany (*Swietenia macrophylla*). The park is home to 54 species of mammal, most of them globally threatened, including the giant anteater (*Myrmecophaga tridactyla*) and the jaguar (*Panthera onca*). The bird fauna consists of 333 species representing 63 of the 74 families of birds present in Guatemala, including the ocellated turkey (*Agriocharis ocellata*), which is in danger of extinction.
The reserve's main attraction, however, is the archeological remains of the former Mayan cities of Tikal and Uaxactún. The marvelous remains at Tikal, still largely unexcavated, consist of about 3,000 constructions between 2,400 and 1,100 years old, such as temples, dwellings, religious monuments decorated with inscriptions, and tombs.

The annual burning of pastures affects the breeding of some birds, especially the ocellated turkey. Habitat destruction continues to occur within the reserve, as do hunting and trapping, urban development and theft of archeological remains, but their frequency is unknown.

2.3 The biosphere reserves in the Indomalaysian monsoon forests

In the Indomalaysian region is the Komodo National Park, or Taman Nasional Komodo, on the island of Komodo, which is in the Sunda Strait and forms part of Indonesia. The park was first established in 1965 as a nature reserve, and in 1980 it was made a national park to protect the Komodo dragon (*Varanus komodoensis*), the largest living saurian and endemic to the island of Komodo.

The reserve is in one of the driest regions of Indonesia, with relief dominated by hills rising to about 2,000 ft (600 m), and is located on the active volcanic belt running from Australia along the Sunda Platform. Monsoon forest grows at the base of the hills and in the valley bottoms. This remarkable forest is characterized by trees such as *Sterculia foetida* (Sterculiaceae), *Oroxylum indicum* (Bignoniaceae), *Tamarindus indica* (Leguminosae), and *Zizyphus horsfeldi* (Rhamnaceae), and by the almost total absence of the Australian tree flora, which is found farther to the east. The remaining 70% of the reserve consist of open herbaceous savannah. The Komodo dragon's favorite prey are introduced species such as the Rusa deer (*Cervus timorensis*), and feral domesticates, such as horses and water buffalo.
The island's original native fauna includes pri-

307 **The star of the Komodo Reserve** is the large and well-known Komodo dragon (*Varanus komodoensis*), the largest living saurian (lower photo). It can reach a length of 10 ft (3 m) and a weight of 331 lb (150 kg), and moves quite fast on dry land, and is also able to swim. The adults can capture large prey, such as wild boar and small deer, such as the Rusa deer (*Cervus timorensis*), an animal occurring naturally on several islands in the Strait (Java, Bali, Moluccas, Celebes, etc.) but introduced to Komodo (upper photo). [Photos: Gerald Cubitt / Bruce Coleman Limited and John B. Ratcliffe / WWF / Still Pictures]

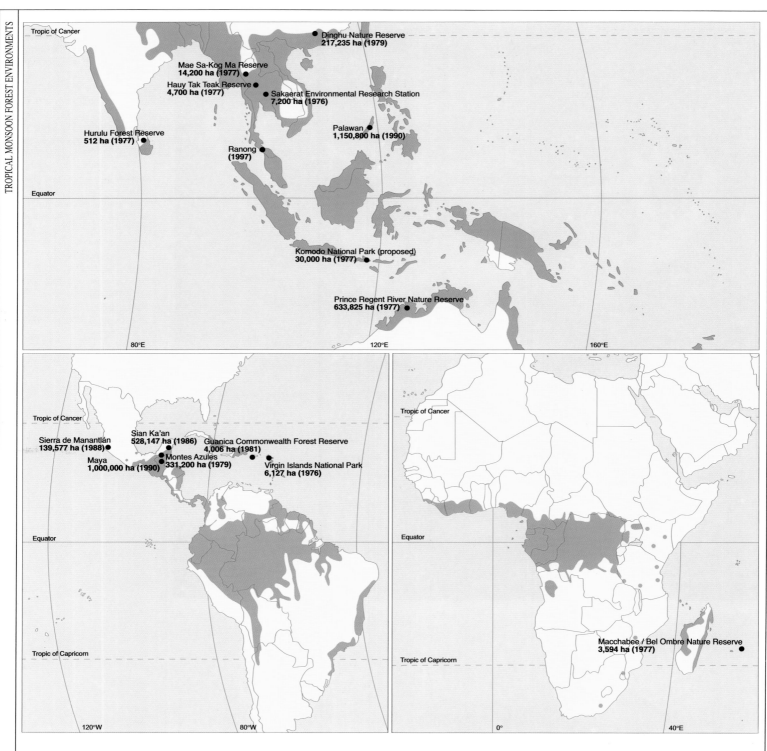

308 **Biosphere reserves (1998)**, indicating the year it was declared a biosphere reserve and its size (in hectares), corresponding to the total area of the reserve, although it may include other types of formation, especially monsoon forest.
[Drawing: Editrònica, from several sources]

mates such as the long-tailed macaque (*Macaca fascicularis*) and the Komodo rat (*Komodomys rintjanus*) as well as 72 species of bird.

The reserve's main management problem is the reduction in availability of prey for the Komodo dragon, such as the Timor deer (*Cervus timorensis*), due to

predation and poaching. The Komodo dragon is an important tourist attraction, but it is feared that tourism will interfere with the natural development of the predator-prey relationship and is also making humans more trusting, which may have fatal consequences for them. The dragons have a powerful venom.

Bibliography

This bibliography includes general works used for basic reference. It includes general works on geography, climate, soils, wildlife, plantlife and anthropology, as well as more specific works on the rainforests, cloud forests and monsoon forests, either as a whole or separately.

AGRAWAL, D.P. 1992. *Man and environment in India through the ages.* New Delhi: Books & Books.

ALDERTON, D. 1991. *Crocodiles & alligators of the world.* London: Blandford.

AYENSU, E.S. 1981. *Selvas. Las últimas reservas de vida.* Barcelona: Ed. Folio.

BADA, J.L. 1991. *Atles mèdic de les malalties tropicals.* Bellaterra: Universitat Autònoma de Barcelona.

BEADLE, N.C.W. 1981. *The vegetation of Australia.* Stuttgart: Gustav Fischer Verlag.

BELOUSOVA, L.S., AND L.V. DENISOVA. 1992). *Rare plants of the world.* Rotterdam: Balkema Publishers.

BEHRENSMEYER, A.K., J.D. DAMUTH, W.A. DiMICHELE, R. POTTS, H.D. SUES, AND S.L. WING. 1992. *Terrestrial ecosystems through time.* Chicago: The University of Chicago Press.

BENZING, D.H. 1990). *Vascular epiphytes.* Cambridge: Cambridge University Press.

BLOCKHUS, J.M., ed. 1992. *Conserving biological diversity in managed tropical forests.* Cambridge: The IUCN forest conservation programme, IUCN/ITTO.

BLOMBERY, A., AND T. RODD. 1982. *Palms of the world.* Auckland: Angus & Robertson Publishers.

BOO, E. 1990. *Ecotourism: the potentials and pitfalls.* Washington, DC: World Wildlife Fund.

BRADY, N.C. 1990. *The nature and properties of soils.* New York: Macmillan Publishing Company.

BRAMWELL, D. 1979. *Plants and islands.* London: Academic Press.

BRIGGS, J.C. 1987. *Developments in palaeontology and stratigraphy.* Cambridge: Elsevier Scientific Publishing Company.

BRÜCHER, H. 1989. *Useful plants of neotropical origin and their wild relatives.* Berlin: Springer Verlag.

BUOL, S.W., F.D. HOLE, AND R.J.McCRACKEN. 1980. *Soil genesis and classification.* Iowa: Iowa University Press.

BURGESS, P.F. 1969. *Ecological factors in hill and mountain forests of the states of Malaya.* Malay Nature Journal 22:119-128.

CAMPBELL, B., AND E. LACK, eds. 1985. *A dictionary of birds.* Carlton: T. & A. D. Poyser.

CAMPBELL, D.C., AND H.D. HAMMOND. 1989. *Floristic inventory of plant systematics, collections and vegetation, plus recommendations for the future.* New York: New York Botanical Garden.

CAVALLI-SFORZA, L.L., P. MENOZZI, AND A. PIAZZA. 1994. *History and geography of human genes.* Princeton: Princeton University Press.

CHAUDHURI, K.N. 1990. *Asia before Europe.* Cambridge: Cambridge University Press.

CLAY, J.W. 1988. *Indigenous peoples and tropical forests.* Cultural Survival Report 27.

COLLINS, N.M. 1990. *The last rain forests: a world conservation atlas.* New York: Oxford University Press.

COLLINS, N.M., J.A. SAYER, AND T.C. WHITMORE, eds. 1991. *The conservation atlas of tropical forests:* Asia and the Pacific. London: MacMillan.

CORTESÃO, J. 1991. *Mata atlântica.* Rio de Janeiro: Editora Index & Fundação S. O. S. Mata Atlântica.

CRANBROOK, EARL of. 1988. *Malaysia. Key environments.* Oxford: Pergamon Press.

DAVIES, B.R., AND K.F. WALKER. 1986. *The ecology of river systems.* Dordrecht: Dr. W. Junk Publishers.

DEFOLIART, G.R. 1989. "The human use of insects as food and animal feed." *Entomological Society of America* 35(1):22-35.

DENSLOW, J.S., AND C. PADOCH. 1988. *People of the tropical rain forest.* Berkeley: University of California Press.

DOWNING, T.E., ed. 1992. *Development and destruction: the conversion of tropical forests to pasture in Latin America.* Westview Press.

DUELLMAN, W.E. 1979. "The South American herpetofauna: its origin, evolution and dispersal." *Monograph. Mus. Nat. Hist. Univ. Kansas* 7:1-485.

DUELLMAN, W.E. 1988. "Patterns of species diversity in anuran amphibians in the American tropics." *Annals of the Missouri Botanical Garden* 75:79-104.

EMMONS, L.H. 1990. *Neotropical rainforest mammals. A field guide.* Chicago: University of Chicago Press.

EVANS SCHULTES, R., AND R.F. RAFFAUF. 1990. *The healing forest.* Dioscorides Press, Portland. 484 p.

FAO. 1993. *Forest resources assessment 1990: tropical countries.* FAO Forestry Paper, 112. Rome: FAO.

FAO/UNESCO. 1971. *Soil Map of the world. South America.* Paris : FAO/UNESCO.

FAO/UNESCO. 1973. *Soil Map of the world. Africa.* Paris: FAO/UNESCO.

FAO/UNESCO. 1974. *Soil Map of the world. Legend.* Paris: FAO/UNESCO.

FAO/UNESCO. 1988. *Soil Map of the world. Revised Legend.* Paris: FAO/UNESCO.

FITTER, A.H., AND R.K.N. HAY. 1987. *Environmental physiology of plants.* Academic Press, London.

GADGIL, M., AND R. GUHA. 1993. *This fissured land. An ecological history of India.* Oxford: Oxford University Press.

GENTRY, A.H. 1989. *Four neotropical forests.* New Haven: Yale University Press.

GÓMEZ-POMPA. 1991. *The rain forest regeneration and management.* The Biosphere, series 6. Paris: UNESCO/MAB.

GOODALL, D.W., ed. 1983. *Ecosystems of the world: tropical rain forest ecosystems.* Amsterdam: Elsevier Scientific Publishing Company.

GOULDING, M. 1979. *Ecologia da pesca do rio Madeira.* Manaus: Instituto Nacional de Pesquisa da Amazônia.

GOULDING, M. 1980. *The fishes and the forest.* Berkeley: University of California Press.

GRIGG, D.B. 1974. *The agricultural systems of the world. An evolutionary approach.* Cambridge: Cambridge University Press.

GROOMBRIDGE, B. 1992. *Global biodiversity: status of the Earth's living resources.* London: WCMC, Chapman & Hall.

HALFFTER, G. 1992. *La diversidad biológica de Iberoamérica.* Xalapa: CYTED-D.

HARDY, R. 1982. *The weather book.* London: Harrow House Editions.

HERNÁNDEZ, J.E., AND J. LEÓN, eds. 1992. *Cultivos marginados. Otra perspectiva de 1492.* Producción y Protección Vegetal 26. Rome: FAO.

HILL, F. 1951. *Economic botany.* New York: McGraw Hill.

HLADIK, C.M., ed. 1994. *Food and nutrition in the tropical forest: biological interactions.* Paris: UNESCO/MAB.

HOWARD, R.A. 1970. "The 'alpine' plants of the Antilles." *Biotropica* 2:24-28.

HUBINGER, C., J. DÖBEREINER, AND M. FREITAS. 1979. *Plantas tóxicas da Amazônia a bovinos e outros herbívoros.* Manaus: INPA.

HUECK, K. 1978. *Los bosques de Sudamérica.* Georg-August-Universität-Göttingen: Sociedad Alemana de Cooperación Técnica.

JACOBS, M. 1988. *The tropical rainforests: a first encounter.* Berlin: Springer-Verlag.

JOLLY, A.P. OBERLE, AND R. ALBIGNAC, eds. 1984. *Key environments. Madagascar.* Oxford: Pergamon Press.

JUNYENT, M.C. 1989. *Les llengües del món.* Barcelona: Empúries.

KISS, A., ed. 1990. *Living with wildlife: wildlife resource management with local participation in Africa.* Washington, DC: The World Bank.

KIPLE, K.F., ed. 1993. *The Cambridge world history of human disease.* Cambridge: Cambridge University Press.

LEE, P.C., J. THORNBACK, AND E.L. BENNET. 1988. *Threatened primates of Africa: the IUCN Red Data Book.* Gland: IUCN.

LEONARD, J.H. 1987. *Natural resources and economic development in Central America.* Washington, DC: International Institute for Environment and Development.

LEWINGTON, A. 1990. *Plants for people.* New York: Natural History Museum Publications.

LOWE-McCONNELL, R.H. 1975. *Fish communities in tropical freshwaters.* London: Ed. Longman.

LUGO, A.E., M.M. BRINSON, AND S. BROWN, eds. 1990. *Ecosystems of the world: tropical rain forest ecosystems.* Amsterdam: Elsevier Scientific Publishing Company.

LUGO, A.E., AND F.N. SCATENA. 1992. *Epiphytes and climate change research in the Caribbean: a proposal.* Selbyana, 13:123-130.

MAB/UNESCO. 1983. *Swidden cultivation in Asia.* Bangkok: UNESCO Regional Office.

MABBERLEY, D.J. 1983. *Tropical rain forest ecology.* Oxford: Blackwell.

MARTIN, C. 1991. *The rainforests of West Africa.* Berlin: Birkhäuser.

MATTISON, C. 1990. *Snakes of the world.* London: Blandford.

MATTISON, C. 1992. *Frogs and toads of the world.* London: Blandford.

MCEVEDY, C., AND R. JONES. 1978. *Atlas of world population history.* Middlesex: Penguin Books.

MCNEELY, J.A. 1990. *Conserving the world's biological diversity.* IUCN, WRI, CI, WWF-US, The world bank.

MOHR, E.C.J., F.A. VAN BAREN, AND J. VAN SCHUYLENBORG. 1972. *Tropical soils. A comprehensive study of their genesis.* The Hague: Mouton-Ichtiar Baru-Van Hoeve.

MORÁN, E.F. 1982. *Human adaptability.* Boulder, CO: Westview Press.

MORÁN, E.F. 1990. *A ecologia humana das populações da Amazônia.* Petrópolis: Editora Vozes.

NADKARNI, N.M., AND T.J. MATELSON 1989. "Bird use of epiphyte resources in neotropical trees." *The Condor,* 91:891-907.

NEIMAN, Z. 1989. *Era verde? Ecosistemas brasileiros ameaçados.* São Paulo: Atual Editora.

NELSON, J.S. 1984. *Fishes of the world.* New York: John Wiley and sons.

NIGHTINGALE, N. 1992. *New Guinea: an island apart*. London: BBC Books.

NOWAK, R.M. 1991. *Walker's mammals of the world*. Baltimore: The John Hopkins University Press.

PETTER, J.J., ALBIGNAC, R., AND RUMPLER, Y. 1977. *Faune de Madagascar*. Paris.

PHILLIPS, K., AND M. DAHLEN 1985. *A guide to market fruits of Southeast Asia*. Hong Kong: South China Morning Post.

PODOLSKY, R.D. 1992. "Strange floral attractors: pollinator attraction and the evolution of plant sexual systems." *Science* 258:791-793.

POLUNIN, I. 1987. *Plants and flowers of Singapore*. Singapore: Times Editions.

POSEY, D.A., AND W. BALEÉ. 1989. *Resource management in Amazonia: indigenous and folk strategies. Vol. 7, Advances in economic botany*.

PRANCE G.T., AND T.E. LOVEJOY. 1985. *Amazonia. Key environments*. Oxford: Pergamon Press.

PROCEEDINGS OF AN INTERNATIONAL CONSULTATION, HELD AT CHIANG MAI, THAILAND. 1991. *The conservation of medicinal plants*. Cambridge: Cambridge University Press.

REHM, S., AND G. ESPIG. 1991. *The cultivated plants of the tropics and subtropics*. Berlin: Verlag Josef Margraf.

ROBINSON, J.R., AND K.H. REDFORD, eds. 1991. *Neotropical wildlife use in Latin America*. Chicago: University of Chicago Press.

SALE, J.B. 1981. *The importance and values of wild plants and animals in Africa*. Gland: IUCN.

SÁNCHEZ, P.A. 1976. *Properties and management of soils in the tropics*. New York: John Wiley & Sons.

SÁNCHEZ-MONGE Y PARELLADA, E. 1980. *Diccionario de plantas agrícolas*. Madrid: Ministerio de Agricultura.

SAYER, J.A., C.S. HARCOURT, AND N.M. COLLINS. 1992. *The conservation atlas of tropical forests*: Africa. London: Macmillan.

SCHNELL, R. 1987. *La flore et la végétation d'Amérique tropicale*. Paris: Masson.

SELL, J., AND F. KROPFT. 1990. *Propriétés et caractéristiques des essences de bois*. Zurich: Lignum.

SIBLEY, C.G. 1990. *Distribution and taxonomy of the birds of the world*. New Haven: Yale University Press.

SING, U., A.M. WADHWANI, AND B.M. JOHRI. 1990. *Dictionary of economic plants in India*. New Dehli: Indian Council of Agricultural Research.

SIOLI, H. 1984. *The Amazon: limnology and landscape ecology of a mighty tropical river and its basin*. Dordrecht: W. Junk.

SLOAN DENSLOW, J., AND C. PADOCH, eds. 1988. *People of the tropical rain forest*. Berkeley: University of California Press.

SMITH, A. J.E., ed. 1982. *Bryophyte ecology*. London: Chapman & Hall.

SMITH, N.J.H. 1979. *A pesca no rio Amazonas*. Manaus: Instituto Nacional de Pesquisa da Amazônia.

SMITH, N.J.H. 1981. "Man, fishes and the Amazon." *Biol. Conservation* 19:177-187.

SMITH, N.J.H. 1981. *Caimans, capibara, otters, manatees and man in the Amazon*. New York: Columbia University Press.

SOMBROECK, W.G. 1966. *Amazonian soils*. Wageningen: Centre for Agricultural Publications and Documentation (PUDOC).

STEWARD, J.H. 1963. *Handbook of South American Indians*. New York: Cooper Square Publications.

TAKHTAJAN, A. 1986. *Floristic regions of the world*. Berkeley: University of California Press.

TINDALE, N.B. 1974. *Aboriginal tribes of Australia*. Berkeley: University of California Press.

TOLEDO, C., A.F. COIMBRA, AND A. HOUAISS. 1991. *Ecosistemas brasileiros*. Rio de Janeiro: Index Editora.

VEEVERS-CARTER, W. 1984. *Richess of the rain forest. An Introduction to the trees and fruits of the Indonesian and Malaysian rain forests*. Singapore: Oxford University Press.

WALTER, H., AND S.W. BRECKLE. 1985. *Ecological systems of the geobiosphere*. Berlin: Springer-Verlag.

WAYNE, R.P. 1985. *Chemistry of atmospheres*. Oxford: Clarendon Press.

WEST, R.C., ed. *Handbook of Middle American Indians. Natural environment and early cultures*. Austin: University of Texas Press.

WHITMORE, T. C. 1989. *Tropical forest of the Far East*. Oxford: Clarendon Press.

WHITMORE, T.C. 1990. *An introduction to tropical forests*. Clarendon Press, Oxford.

WHITMORE, T. C., AND J.A. SAYER, eds. 1992. *Tropical deforestation and species extinction*. Cambridge: IUCN/ITTO.

WILSON, E.O., ed. 1990. *Biodiversity*. Washington, DC: National Academy Press.

WOLFE, J.A. 1985. "Distribution of major vegetation types during the Tertiary." In "The carbon cycle and atmospheric CO_2". *Geophysical Monographs* 32:233-256.

Indexes

Species' index

This index contains the scientific and common names of the species mentioned in the text. The number refers to the page or pages where the name appears in the main text. Page numbers in italics refer to illustrations.

abeokuta, 390
Abies, *338*, 409
abiuarana, *155*
abura, 152, *206*
Abuta, 201
Acacia aulacocarpa, *89*
A. catechu, 217
A. farnessiana, 430
A. koa, *338*, 365
A. mangium, *89*
Acanthophrynus, *435*
acapà, *270*
acarí, *270*
Aceros [=Rhyticeros] cassidix, 137
A. nipalensis, *495*
Achatina, 275
A. achatina, 257
Achraszapota, 217, 219
Achrosticum aureum, 196
acras, 219
Acrobates, 126
acrocomia, 238
Acrocomia, *198*, 238, 239
Adansonia, 429
A. za, 429
Adenia lobata, 202, 272
Adinandra dumosa, *89*
Aechmea, 71
Aedes, 191, 460, *461*
Aeranthes, 401
afara, *206*
Aframomum melegueta, 252
African blackwood, *206*
African juniper, 361
African mahogany, *206*
African mahogany, 208, 323
African oak, *206*, 214, 284, 474
African otter, 163
African river martin, 325
African rosewood, *206*
African walnut, *206*
Afropavo congensis, 113
afrormosia, *206*, 211, 288
afzelia, *206*
Afzelia, *206*
Agathis, 62, 283, 364
A. alba, 215, 287
A. montana, 365
A. philipinensis, 215, 286
Agave, 382, 410
agba, *206*
Agouti paca, 165
A. taczanowskii, 393
agouti, 154, 165, 259, 267, 477
Agouti, 259, 477
Agraecum sesquipedale, 47
Agriocharis ocellata, 179, *179*, 496
Ahaetulla prasina, 120
"ahuejote", *227*
ají de Nueva Granada, 362
Albizia falcataria, 74
Alcedo, 165
Alchemilla, *338*
Alchornea triplinervia, *89*
alder, 289, 472
álep, 324
Alestes, 157
Alligator, *161*
allocebus, *48*

Allocebus, 131
A. trichotis, *48*, 327
allspice, 252
Alnus, *338*
A. nepalensis, 289, 472
Alocasia, 233
Alouatta, 75, 155, *317*
A. palliata, 317
A. pigra, 179
A. seniculus, 156, *317*, 320
Alphitonia petrei, *89*
Alpinia, 252
Altingia excelsa, 412
Amaracarpus caeruleus, 365
amaranth, 82, *206*, 381, 382
Amaranthus, 382
Amaurornis, 165
Amazona finschi, *408*, 410
ambarella, 235
Amboyina, *206*, 213, *213*, 286
American alligator, *161*
American mahogany, *206*, 208
Ammomum, 300
Amorphophallus, 97, 108, *109*
amphihuasca, 200
Anabaena, 148, 474, *474*
anaconda, 163, 165, *165*
anagre, *206*
anahaw, 204
Ananas bracteatus, 243
A. comosus, 194, *195*, 223, 225, 242, *244*
A. guaraniticus, 243
A. microcephalus, 243
A. sativus, 242
Anaphalis, *338*
A. javanica, *338*
Anaxagorea, 201
Ancylostoma duodenale, 187
Andaman redwood, *206*, 213, *213*, 286
Andean cat, 320
angelica, *206*
Angiostrongylus, 187
Angraecum, 401
anhima, 321
Anhima cornuta, 321
anhinga, 165, 321
Anhinga anhinga, 165, 321
Aniba rosaeodora, 214, 287
aninga, *148*
aningeria, *206*
Aningeria, *206*
aningre, *206*
Anisoptera, *206*
Anisoscelis flavolineata, *114*
Annamite pheasant, 487
Annona, 235, *237*
anoa, 274
Anoa depressicornis, *482*
A. mindorensis, 274
A. quarlesi, *482*
Anodorhynchus hyacinthinus, *268*
Anomma, 138
Anopheles, 188, *188*, 189, 191
Anorrhinus, 137
Anthocephalus, *89*
Anthocleista nobilis, *89*
Anthracoceros, 137
Antiaris toxicaria, 202
ant-thrush, 121

anuran, 354, 355
Aonix congica, 163
Aotus, 131, 268
A. trivirgatus, 320
aphelandra, *18*
Aphelandra, *18*, *99*
Aphonepelma, *438*
Apinagia, 154
apitong, *206*
Aponogeton, 327
aquatic bug, 257
aquatic fern, 153
Aquila chrysaetos, 410
Aquilaria malaccensis, 216
Ara, 259
A. ararauna, *105*, 321
A. chloroptera, 321
A. macao, 259, 275
A. manilata, 321
A. militaris, 410
aracari, 136
Arachis hipogaea, *195*
aracu, *270*
Aramides, 165
arapaima, 271, *271*
Arapaima gigas, 158, *270*, 271, *271*
arapari, *144*, 154
Araucaria, 62, 364, 365
Archaeopteryx, 132
Archontophoenix cunninghamii, 428
Areca catechu, 226, 238, 332, *453*
Arenga, 196
A. obtusifolia, 204
A. pinnata, 300
argus pheasant, 261
Argusianus argus, 261
Argyroxiphium sandroicense, *338*
armadillo, 259, *30*, 320, 477
Arrabidaea, 292
arrow-poison frog, 355
Artabotrys odoratissimus, *215*
Arthrostylidium, 467
Artocarpus, *195*
A. altilis, 199, 238, *238*
A. heterophyllus, 238, 300
A.pus integer, 238
"aruanä", *270*
Arundinaria, 467
A. alpina, 362, 397
A. prainii, 470
A. racemosa, 467
Ascaris lumbricoides, 187
Asian golden cat, 130
Asplenium, 363
A. australasicum, *417*
A. nidus, 412
A. schnelli, 411
assai palm, 149, *150*, 154, 197, 300
Astragalus sinensis, 474
Astrapia, 135
astrocarya, 244
Astrocaryum, 202, 238, 244, 319
Astronium, *206*
Astronotus ocellatus, 155, *270*
Atalantia rotundifolia, 330
Ateles, 155
A. geoffroyi, *124*, 179, 317
A. paniscus, 319
Atelocynus microtis, 321

Thematic index

The montane equatorial cloud forests   333

Authorship and source of the illustrations

Pictures and maps:

- Albert Martínez (Barcelona), 33
- Editrònica (Barcelona), 20, 23, 26, 31, 43, 55, 72, 89, 99, 125, 146, 160, 161, 184, 185, 188, 190, 278, 279, 291, 315, 339, 360, 383, 407, 418, 420, 460, 461, 476, 498
- Jordi Corbera (Barcelona), 24, 25, 41, 50, 51, 70, 118, 147, 227, 338, 349
- Jordi & Josep Oriol Sabater (Barcelona), 254
- Jordi Sabater i Pi (Barcelona), 90, 394, 395, 396

Photographs:

- Adalberto Ríos & Maria Lourdes Alonso (Barcelona), 268
- Adolf de Sostoa (Barcelona), 205, 340, 365
- Adolf de Sostoa & Xavier Ferrer (Barcelona),19, 34, 39, 52, 53, 54, 66, 92, 94, 95, 116 119, 123, 129, 133, 139, 158, 165, 198, 200, 209, 235, 321, 351, 353, 370, 431, 434, 438, 441
- AGE Fotostock (Barcelona), 29, 210, 307, 457
- Aisa (Barcelona), 142, 212
- Alain Compost / Bios / Still Pictures (London), 108
- Alain Compost / Bruce Coleman Limited (Uxbridge), 137, 246, 469
- Alain Compost / Visage / Bios / Still Pictures (London), 107
- Alain Compost / WWF / Still Pictures (London), 412, 463
- Alain Rainon / Jacana (Paris), 59
- Alan Colclough / Planet Earth Pictures (London), 304
- Alex Kerstitch / Planet Earth Pictures (London), 299, 356, 357
- A. Manoni / Gamma (Paris), 470
- A. & M. Shah / Planet Earth Pictures (London), 480
- Ancient Art and Architecture Collection (London), 177
- André Bärtschi / Planet Earth Pictures (London), 236, 266, 283, 302, 319, 359, 363
- André Bärtschi / WWF / Still Pictures (London), 49, 159, 322
- Andy Smith / WWF / Still Pictures (London), 372
- Anna Motis (Barcelona), 106
- Antonio Ribeiro / Gamma (Paris), 181
- Archiv für Kunst und Geschichte (Berlin), 31, 140, 143, 219, 220, 247, 387, 389, 481
- Arkell Katie / Gamma (Paris), 193
- Biblioteca de Catalunya (Barcelona), 140, 170, 241
- Bibliothèque Nationale (Paris), 141
- Bill Leimbach / South American Pictures (Woodbridge), 203, 272
- B.N.S. Deo / Planet Earth Pictures (London), 220
- Brian J. Coates / Bruce Coleman Limited (Uxbridge), 102
- Brian Moser / The Hutchison Library (London), 183, 371
- Bridgeman / Giraudon (Paris), 389
- British Library (London), 176
- Carlos Roquero (Lleida), 33, 36
- Carol Farneti / Natural Science Photos (Watford), 119, 301, 408, 409
- Carolus Sys (Gant), 34
- Christer Fredriksson / Bruce Coleman Limited (Uxbridge), 388
- Christian Errath / Jacana (Paris), 237
- Christiane D'Hotel / Jacana (Paris), 251
- Christie's Images (London), 211, 213
- Christine & Myriam Masson (Lilla), 331
- C. Jones / Natural Science Photos (Watford), 350, 362
- C. Mattison / Natural Science Photos (Watford), 163
- Compton Tucker, Biospheric Science Branch, Laboratory for Terrestrial Physics, NASA Goddard Space Flight Center (Greenbelt, MD), 145
- Dave Brinicombe / The Hutchison Library (London), 290
- David E. Rowley / Planet Earth Pictures (London), 136
- David Hall / Science Photo Library / AGE Fotostock (Barcelona), 475
- David Hoffman / Still Pictures (London), 486
- David Vilasis / Jaume Sañé (Taradell), 463
- Deni Bown / Oxford Scientific Films / Firo Foto (Barcelona), 109
- Departamento de Farmacología / Facultad de Farmacia / UCM (Madrid), 376, 377
- Dominique Halleux / Bios / Still Pictures (London), 59, 61, 135, 244, 390
- Edward Parker / Still Pictures (London), 150, 219, 228, 229, 271, 295, 308
- Eric Sander / Gamma (Paris), 249
- E.T. Archive (London), 135
- Fiore / Jacana (Paris), 468
- Francesc Serrat & Àngela de Dalmau (Palafrugell), 197, 358, 394, 395, 396, 397, 400, 402
- François Gohier / Auscape International (Redfern Hill, NSW), 124
- François Gohier / Jacana (Paris), 44
- Fritz Prenzel / Bruce Coleman Limited (Uxbridge), 244
- George Gainsburgh / NHPA (Ardingly), 117
- Georges Merillon / Gamma (Paris), 260, 285
- Gerald Cubitt / Bruce Coleman Limited (Uxbridge), 482, 492, 497
- Gerard Lacz / NHPA (Ardingly), 162
- G.I. Bernard / NHPA (Ardingly), 80
- Gilles Saussier / Gamma (Paris), 485
- Greenwood / Liaison / Gamma (Paris), 28
- Gunter Ziesler / Bruce Coleman Limited (Uxbridge), 345

- Gunter Ziesler / Jacana (Paris), 274
- Hamilton / Index (Barcelona), 218
- Hans C. Heap / Planet Earth Pictures (London), 95
- Hans Reinhard / Bruce Coleman Limited (Uxbridge), 137
- Harriet Logan / The Hutchison Library (London), 230
- Hartmut Jungius / WWF / Still Pictures (London), 493
- Heather Angel / Biofotos (Farnham), 471
- Heldur Netocny / Still Pictures (London), 454
- Herbert Giradet / Still Pictures (London), 294
- Index Editora / South American Pictures (Woodbridge), 201
- Jacques Jangoux / Auscape International (Redfern Hill, NSW), 150, 364
- Jany Sauvanet / Auscape International (Redfern Hill, NSW), 119, 121, 312, 357
- Jany Sauvanet / Bios / Still Pictures (London), 122
- Jaume Altadill (Barcelona), 405, 464
- Javier Andrada (Sevilla), 66
- J.C. Muñoz / Incafo (Madrid), 69
- Jean-Michel Labat / Auscape International (Redfern Hill, NSW), 137, 157
- Jean-Paul Ferrero / Auscape International (Redfern Hill, NSW), 110, 114, 127, 128, 134, 226, 233, 256, 345, 416, 427, 490
- Jean-Paul Ferrero / Jacana (Paris), 127
- Jean-Paul Ferrero & Jean-Michel Labat / Auscape International (Redfern Hill, NSW), 22
- Jean-Pierre Champroux / Jacana (Paris), 234
- Jeff Foott / Auscape International (Redfern Hill, NSW), 17
- Jesco von Puttkamer / The Hutchison Library (London), 261, 267
- J. Hobday / Natural Science Photos (Watford), 466, 483
- J.M. La Roque / Auscape International (Redfern Hill, NSW), 453
- Joan Biosca (Barcelona), 382
- John B. Free / NHPA (Ardingly), 238
- John B. Ratcliffe / WWF / Still Pictures (London), 429, 497
- John Cancalosi / Bruce Coleman Limited (Uxbridge), 268, 479
- John Downer / Planet Earth Pictures (London), 225
- John Newby / WWF / Still Pictures (London), 122
- Jon & Alison Moran / Planet Earth Pictures (London), 44
- Jordi Vidal (Barcelona), 324
- Josep M. Barres (Barcelona), 239, 473
- J. Zwaendepoel / Bruce Coleman Limited (Uxbridge), 436
- Ken Lucas / Planet Earth Pictures (London), 166
- Kevin Rushby / Bruce Coleman Limited (Uxbridge), 64, 469
- Kevin Schafer / NHPA (Ardingly), 358
- Kimball Morrison / South American Pictures (Woodbridge), 307
- Kjell B. Sandved / Oxford Scientific Films / Firo Foto (Barcelona), 109
- Konrad Wothe / Bruce Coleman Limited (Uxbridge), 494
- Laboratori• Natural de Las Joyas / WWF / Still Pictures (London), 384
- Laboureur Mathieu / Bios / Still Pictures (London), 265
- Liaison / Gamma (Paris), 379
- Lucas Abreu / Incafo (Madrid), 331
- Luiz Claudio Marigo / Bruce Coleman Limited (Uxbridge), 154, 198, 222, 230, 239
- Manuel de Sostoa (Barcelona), 391
- Manuel de Sostoa & Adolf de Sostoa (Barcelona), 204, 304
- Marcel Astruc / Gamma (Paris), 30
- Mark Edwards / Still Pictures (London), 32, 168, 217, 240, 275, 276, 277, 285, 309, 380, 458, 472
- Martin Breese / Retrograph Archive (London), 374, 389
- Martin Gilles / Bios / Still Pictures (London), 62
- Mary Evans Picture Library (London), 106, 134, 140, 142, 143, 248, 249, 481
- Mauri Rautkari / WWF / Still Pictures (London), 232
- M. & C. Denis-Huot / Bios / Still Pictures (London), 478
- M. Claye / Gamma (Paris), 468
- M. Daniel / Gamma (Paris), 386
- Michael & Patricia Fogden (Dunblane), 27, 69, 80, 114, 336, 354, 404
- Michael & Patricia Fogden / Bruce Coleman Limited (Uxbridge), 18, 100, 102, 346, 355
- Michael Freeman / Auscape International (Redfern Hill, NSW), 452
- Michael Freeman / Bruce Coleman Limited (Uxbridge), 448
- Michel Gunther / Bios / Still Pictures (London), 58, 263, 296
- Michel Loup / Jacana (Paris), 326
- Michel Viard / Bruce Coleman Limited (Uxbridge), 250
- Michel Viard / Jacana (Paris), 215, 247, 248, 251, 388, 470, 471
- Montserrat Ferrer (Barcelona), 237, 422, 423
- Morten Strange / NHPA (Ardingly), 131, 495
- Museo de América / Scala (Florence), 178
- Museo de la Farmacia Hispánica / Facultad de Farmacia / UCM (Madrid), 376, 377
- Nat Quansah / WWF / Still Pictures (London), 174
- Nick Garbutt / Planet Earth Pictures (London), 130, 328
- Nigel Dickinson / Still Pictures (London), 175, 194, 261, 286
- Nigel Smith / The Hutchison Library (London), 214
- Olivier Langrand / Bios / Still Pictures (London), 48, 446
- Oriol Alamany (Barcelona), 103
- Paco Luque / Biblioteca del Real Jardín Botánico (Madrid), 374, 375
- Paul Harrison / Still Pictures (London), 281
- P. Burton / Natural Science Photos (Watford), 97
- Peter Davey / Bruce Coleman Limited (Uxbridge), 411
- Peter Stevensson / Planet Earth Pictures (London), 465

- Peter Ward / Bruce Coleman Limited (Uxbridge), 103
- Philip Perry / FLPA (Wetheringsett), 29
- Philip Wolmuth / The Hutchison Library (London), 289
- Pillitz / Network / AGE Fotostock (Barcelona), 419
- Ramon Folch (Barcelona), 216, 239, 243, 388
- Raphael Gaillarde / Gamma (Paris), 73
- Rick Weyerhaeuser / WWF / Still Pictures (London), 206
- Richard Chesher / Planet Earth Pictures (London), 243
- Richard Mattews / Planet Earth Pictures (London), 223
- Rod Williams / Bruce Coleman Limited (Uxbridge), 60, 328
- Roger Brown / Auscape International (Redfern Hill, NSW), 443
- Roland Seitre / Bios / Still Pictures (London), 79, 112, 132, 166, 445
- Ron Petocz / WWF / Still Pictures (London), 368, 392
- Rosa Carvajal (Barcelona), 237
- Royal Anthropological Institute (London), 186
- Rudolf König / Jacana (Paris), 228, 302, 357
- Sandra Mbanefo / WWF / Still Pictures (London), 208
- Setsu / NASA / Gamma (Paris), 78
- Staatsbibliothek zu Berlin - Preußischer Kulturbesitz, Musikabteilung mit Mendelssohn-Archiv (Berlin), 387
- Stephen Dalton / NHPA (Ardingly), 164
- Sylvain Cordier / Jacana (Paris), 47, 209
- Teresa Franquesa (Barcelona), 474
- The Hutchison Library (London), 179, 258, 273, 378, 451
- The Ronald Grant Archive (London), 478
- Thierry Falise / Gamma (Paris), 222
- Tony Morrison / South American Pictures (Woodbridge), 71, 85, 145, 151, 153, 228, 230, 231, 234, 269, 287, 363, 385
- VCL / TCL / Index (Barcelona), 171
- Wayne Lawler / Auscape International (Redfern Hill, NSW), 56, 84, 87, 156, 205
- Xavier Ferrer (Barcelona), 66, 232, 399
- Xavier Ferrer & Adolf de Sostoa (Barcelona), 53, 74, 76, 77, 79, 81, 83, 98, 105, 144, 173, 225, 316, 317, 320, 330, 341, 342, 343, 401, 408, 425, 430, 440, 456
- Yves Lefevre / Bios / Still Pictures (London), 179